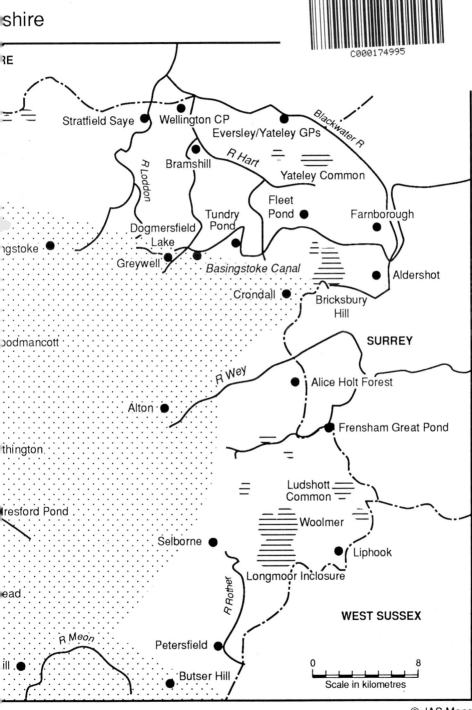

shire

RE

C000174995

Stratfield Saye ● Wellington CP
Eversley/Yateley GPs

Bramshill ●

R Loddon

R Hart

Yateley Common

Fleet
Pond ●

Farnborough ●

Tundry
Pond
Dogmersfield
Lake
Greywell ●

Basingstoke Canal

ngstoke ●

Aldershot ●

Crondall ●

Bricksbury
Hill

SURREY

R Wey

Alice Holt Forest ●

oodmancott

Alton ●

Frensham Great Pond ●

thington

Ludshott
Common

resford Pond

Woolmer

Selborne ●

Liphook ●

R Rother

Longmoor Inclosure

ead

WEST SUSSEX

Petersfield ●

ill ●

Butser Hill ●

0 ———————— 8
Scale in kilometres

# Birds of
# Hampshire

*Edited by*
J M Clark & J A Eyre

Hampshire Ornithological Society

Published in December 1993 by the Hampshire Ornithological Society

SUPPORTED BY

Publication of this book has been aided by financial assistance from British Gas Southern, East Hampshire District Council, Eastleigh Borough Council, Exxon Chemical Ltd, Grocers' Charity, Hampshire County Council, Hart District Council, Havant Borough Council, John Spedan Lewis Trust for the Advancement of the Natural Sciences, Monsanto PLC, New Forest District Council, TV South, Shell UK Ltd, Southampton City Council and Winchester City Council.

ISBN 0 9509805 1 X

British Library Cataloguing-in-Publication Data. A catalogue record for this book is available from the British Library.

Camera ready copy prepared by Dilmun Secretarial Services, Hartley Wintney, Hampshire

Printed by BAS Printers Limited, Over Wallop, Hampshire

# Contents

# Foreword

The years following World War II were times of unrivalled opportunity for Hampshire's ornithologists. Prior to that, a dedicated handful of pioneers, from Gilbert White to Edwin Cohen, had set out to discover the county's avifauna, but observer coverage was so sparse that the picture they obtained was of necessity piecemeal.

The ornithological "revolution" of the 1950s brought unprecedented numbers of observers into the field, with a degree of expertise and enthusiasm that was quite remarkable. Every venture into the countryside was a voyage of real discovery. Equipped with powerful optics that had not long been available, this observer force built up a much fuller picture of Hampshire's bird-life. This was first recorded in Edwin Cohen's *Birds of Hampshire and the Isle of Wight* and then in the "Revised List" by Edwin and myself.

Our skilled body of observers has continued to multiply and as a result of their studies, a wealth of data has accumulated, providing a comprehensive picture of Hampshire's avifauna. This new *Birds of Hampshire*, which in my judgement is a model for county bird-books, is the result of that knowledge. It is the product not only of the team that has put it together, but also of the small army of observers and their countless thousands of hours studying birds in every corner of Hampshire.

Organised national projects such as the Breeding Atlases of 1968-72 and 1988-91, the Winter Atlas, Wildfowl Counts, the Birds of Estuaries Enquiry and the Common Bird Census have led to a depth of knowledge in most English counties that is unequalled in *any* sphere of natural history *anywhere* in the world. These projects have been supplemented by comprehensive local projects such as the recent HOS Tetrad Atlas Survey which means that Hampshire can be claimed amongst the group of English counties where coverage has been most complete.

Such a volume as this performs two main functions. It is of immediate interest to people today, but much more importantly in my view, it is a benchmark for ornithologists in the future. Here, towards the close of the twentieth century, is a detailed catalogue of every bird species seen in Hampshire. Future ornithologists will be able to judge exactly how the fortunes of species have waxed or waned and since conservation depends on knowledge, they will be better equipped to make appropriate decisions.

Fittingly, it appears just two hundred years after the death of Gilbert White, whose pioneering work is known to all. What strides have been made since his time. One wonders what he would think of this volume's contents. This is a book of which Hampshire should be proud and I consider it an honour to be asked to write a Foreword to such an erudite work. It will be indispensable to all who are interested in Hampshire's birds for many years to come.

John Taverner
Winchester

September 1993

# Introduction and Acknowledgements

The idea to produce this book was first considered by the Hampshire Ornithological Society in 1984 – about a decade ago. The previous county avifauna, *A Revised List of Hampshire and Isle of Wight Birds* by Edwin Cohen and John Taverner, had been published in 1972, just 12 years earlier, and yet the need for a completely new, up-to-date work was already apparent. The volume of data about Hampshire's birds was expanding rapidly; knowledge of scarce migrants was much improved and some breeding species had undergone major changes in status. For example, the Red-backed Shrike and Cirl Bunting had become extinct while Gadwall and Cetti's Warbler had colonised the county. However, at that time, information on distribution and numbers of most of our commoner breeding species was limited. In 1985, it was decided to initiate a Hampshire Tetrad Atlas Breeding Bird Survey and to delay the production of the new book so that the results could be incorporated. The fieldwork for the Tetrad Atlas lasted from 1986-91; once finished, preparation of the book began at once and it has taken over two years to complete.

A great many people have contributed their expertise and enthusiasm to its production. We are most grateful to Colin Tubbs for writing the opening chapter, "An Introduction to Hampshire", in which he describes the county's geology, the history of its land use and the resultant impact on birds and their habitats; also to Norman Pratt and Richard Leach, who have collaborated on "Twentieth Century Ornithology in Hampshire", presenting for the first time a detailed review of the development of birdwatching in the county. Particular thanks go to fellow members of the HOS Book Committee – Dennis Bright, Glynne Evans, David Gumn, Richard Leach, Gilbert Rowland, David Thelwell, Eddie Wiseman and John Wood – who, in addition to providing particular skills, have guided its course from inception to publication. We are grateful to John Taverner for writing the Foreword, to Eddie Wiseman for compiling the Gazetteer and to those who drafted some species accounts: Keith Betton (Nightjar), Charles Cuthbert (Sand Martin, Cetti's Warbler and Reed Bunting), Glynne Evans (breeding warblers), Peter Puckering (Grey Heron and Rook), Jess Pain (Barn Owl and Stone Curlew) and Eddie Wiseman (breeding raptors and sea birds).

We would like to thank Dennis Bright, the photographic editor, and the following photographers who have given so generously of their highly professional work: Jimmy Baldwin, Jason Groves, David Kjaer, Charles Moult, Norman Orr, John Taverner, Craig Vincer and Roger Wilmshurst. Similarly, David Thelwell must be congratulated, not only for his superb painting of a Dartford Warbler which is reproduced on the book's cover, but also for bringing together the collection of excellent line drawings. In addition to David himself, our grateful thanks go to Andrew Birch, Robert Gillmor, Stephen Message, Richard Millington and Dan Powell.

We have been particularly fortunate to have David Gumn as a member of the Book Committee. A professional printer, David's input has been invaluable and our special thanks go to him and BAS printers for their expert advice and printing skills. We would also like to thank Anne Hallowes for her typesetting and word processing services – as well as for her forbearance. Gilbert Rowland has taken care of processing all the pre-publication orders, and Richard Leach has striven successfully to raise sponsorship during a particularly difficult economic period. In this regard we acknowledge the valued help of the following companies and organisations in generously funding either the Tetrad Atlas Breeding Bird Survey and/or the book: British Gas Southern, East Hampshire District Council, Eastleigh Borough Council, Exxon Chemical Ltd, Grocers' Charity, Hampshire County Council, Hart District Council, Havant Borough Council, John Spedan Lewis Trust for the Advancement of the Natural Sciences, Monsanto PLC, New Forest District Council, TV South, Shell UK Ltd, Southampton City Council and Winchester City Council.

Thanks are also due to the British Trust for Ornithology for access to ringing data, Common Bird Census and Waterways Bird Survey results and population estimates from *The New Atlas of Breeding Birds*; to the Sussex Ornithological Society for Chichester Harbour count data; and to Peter Bircham (Cambridgeshire), S T Buckland (North-east Scotland), Ian Castle (Kent), Graham Harrison (West Midlands), Ken Smith (Hertfordshire) and Humphrey Sitters (Devon) for sharing their experiences on publishing county avifaunas.

In addition, many individuals have helped with information relating to particular species, locations or events, with special skills, or by reading and commenting on the draft text. The following list is as complete as possible, but we must apologise for any omissions:

Keith Betton, David Billett, Paul Bowman, Dave Burges, Richard Carpenter, Bob Chapman, Dave Christie, Mike Clarke, Norman Clayden, Rob Clements, John Cloyne, John Collman, Peter Combridge, Mike Combridge, Ron Cooke, Chris Corrigan, Humphrey Crick, Barry Duffin, Brian Dudley, Glynne Evans, Philip Fawkes, David Gibbons, Graham Giddens, David Glue, John Grafton, Pete Jennings, Eric Jones, Ron King, Peter Le Brocq, Richard Levett, Lew Lewis, John Lucas, Peter Mann, Keith Maycock, Peter Maynard, Tony Miller, Tim Norriss, Norman Orr, Chris Packham, Andrew Page, Stephen Parr, Pete Potts, Norman Pratt, Graham Rees, Bryan Renyard, Mike Rogers, John Rowe, Gilbert Rowland, Jim Rushen, Mick Scott, John Simms, Alf Smallbone, Alan Snook, Graham Stephenson, Denis Summers-Smith, George Sweet, John Taverner, Martin Terry, Phil Toye, Paul Toynton, Colin and Jenni Tubbs, Dave Unsworth, Brian Warren, Mike Wearing, Eddie Wiseman, Bert Woods.

Thanks are also due to the hundreds of observers who have submitted their observations over the years, for without them, the preparation of the Systematic Species Accounts, which form the bulk of this book, would have been impossible. They are listed in full on pages 493-498.

Finally, one of us (JAE) would like to take this opportunity to thank his wife Sue for the tolerance and understanding that she has unfailingly demonstrated as a result of birds, birdwatching, bird meetings and latterly bird books.

John Clark and John Eyre

# An Introduction to Hampshire

## *Colin R Tubbs*

Those who consult this book will, quite reasonably, be looking for information about the birds of Hampshire. In this introduction to the county, however, I would like to turn their minds first to the environmental context of the birds – to the origins, development and destruction of the habitat fabric on which the birds depend. Much of this introductory chapter is about the ecological history of Hampshire, a story which I have chosen to tell in three parts. First, I describe the main long term trends in habitat development. Second, I reflect on the Hampshire landscape of the 18th century, a time when habitat diversity may have been at a maximum. Third, I sketch the events of the ensuing era of biological impoverishment caused by population growth and the intensification of agriculture and forestry. Arriving in the present, I summarise the status of the main bird habitats and their conservation in Hampshire today and focus on features which are of national ornithological importance.

Considering the abuses to which the Hampshire landscape has been subjected by urban and industrial development and, perhaps more significantly, by the scramble for agricultural self-sufficiency which propelled farmers into overproduction and gross habitat destruction, Hampshire remains a biologically very rich county. The climate is mild. Winters, especially on the coastal fringe, are usually very mild. Consequently, many species of plants and animals occur in the county as outlying populations of southerly or continental distributions – the wild gladiolus *Gladiolus illyricus*, Dartford Warbler and sand lizard *Lacerta agilis* are well-known examples. At the same time, many species, especially of plants with respectively eastern and western distributions, overlap in Hampshire. For example, both of the dwarf gorses occur here – *Ulex galii* at its eastern limits and *Ulex minor* at the western edge of its range. In addition to these natural distributional factors, the county is still relatively richly endowed with habitats which are now scarce in lowland Britain, indeed in the lowlands of western Europe – heaths, valley mires, ancient woodland, chalk grasslands, fen meadows, reed fen and undamaged estuaries. Familiarity is prone to obscure the limited north European distribution of these natural resources.

7

**Origins and Physical Transformations**

The geological structure and land forms of Hampshire were largely determined by folding of Cretaceous and Tertiary rocks in the Miocene era, roughly 25 million years ago (Chatwin 1960). The folds are ripples from the collision of tectonic plates in the Mediterranean region, an event which also gave rise to the elevation of the alpine regions of central Europe. The dominant structural feature is a broad uplifted, or anticlinal, area extending west-east across the county and continuing westward as Salisbury Plain and eastward across the Weald where the crest has been removed by denudation. To the north and south of the anticline lie downfolds, or synclinal regions, the Thames Basin to the north and the Hampshire Basin to the south. There the Tertiary sands and clays survive, but over the central anticline they have been eroded away to expose the underlying Cretaceous chalk. The anticline is now an undulating plateau, the surface of which is traversed by west-east trending ridges and escarpments marking minor anticlines.

Similarly, the chalk outlier of Portsdown derives from a strong underlying anticline in the Hampshire Basin. Beneath the Hampshire Basin the chalk dips steeply to a maximum of 518 m beneath The Solent, reappearing again as the long backbone ridge of the Isle of Wight, which today forms the backdrop to The Solent estuaries.

On the surface of the chalk plateau there are discontinuous but extensive spreads of residual Tertiary material, while at footslopes deposits of soliflucted chalk, Tertiary material and clay ("Coombe Rock") occur. The spreads vary widely in composition but are mostly clay and loam in texture, often with flint gravel. The chalk plateau increases generally in height from south to north, achieving a maximum elevation of somewhat less than 300 m and terminating in a steep, north-facing escarpment overlooking the Thames Basin.

Eastern Hampshire includes the western extremity of the Weald. Here, the continuation of the Miocene anticline was denuded of chalk to expose the Lower Cretaceous sands and clays, which have themselves been eroded further so that the margins of the Miocene dome survive as chalk ridges (the North and South Downs). In Hampshire the chalk terminates in a steep escarpment extending for 25 km from Binsted to Old Butser. The sinuous line of the east-facing chalk escarpment, now mostly wooded, is matched faithfully a little to its east, by a smaller escarpment marking the junction of the Upper Greensand rock and the Gault Clay.

This escarpment appears to derive from comparatively recent slipping of the Gault, the latest significant episode being that recorded by Gilbert White on 8 March 1774 when "a considerable part of the woody hanger at Hawkley was torn from its place", an event resulting from the water-loading of the clay by seepage through the Upper Greensand escarpment against which it rested. Eastward of the clay belt, the Wealden beds are mostly sandy and comparable in texture to the sands which outcrop in the Tertiary basins.

Geological history has left a legacy of contrasting ecological determinants. Ecologically, the age and origin of a deposit are of less importance than its chemical composition and texture. Chalk is a soft, white calcite (calcium carbonate), very fine-grained and composed largely of the skeletons of microscopic marine animals. It is rich in calcium and phosphorus but poor in potassium and nitrogen. It is highly porous and water collects in large aquifers. The rivers which drain the chalk plateau – the Avon, Test, Itchen and Meon – are spring-fed and have few tributaries. Their waters are calcareous, hard and low in nitrates. In contrast, the Tertiary and Lower Cretaceous rocks of the Hampshire and Thames Basins and of the Weald are mostly acid or neutral in reaction and generally only slowly permeable. They yield a high volume of surface water run-off and are drained by dense networks of mostly small streams subject to wide variation in seasonal flow and to flash-flooding after heavy rain. Their waters are soft and relatively poor in exchangeable bases. These contrasts are reflected in fig. 1, which shows the drainage networks in relation to Hampshire's main structural features.

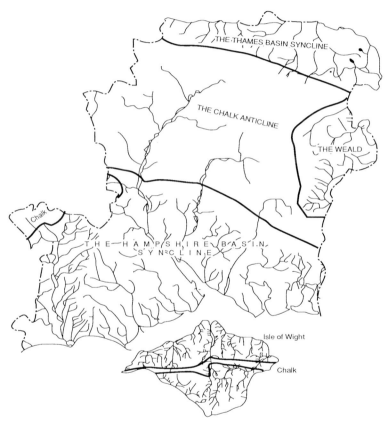

*Figure 1. The drainage networks and main structural features of Hampshire.*

Hampshire was spared the direct effects of glaciation during the Pleistocene period (the "Ice Age") of the Quaternary era. However, the Pleistocene has left characteristic relics in the landscape, the most important and extensive of which are terraces of gravel ("Plateau Gravel") and brick-earth (mostly brown loams of partly loessic, or wind-blown, origin), and the extensive raised beach which now forms the coastal plain of south-east Hampshire and West Sussex. In the

Hampshire Basin the terraces are thought to be the flood plain deposits of the ancient Solent River (Keen 1980). They descend in a sequence of steps towards The Solent and are arranged in conformity with it, reflecting the progressive down-cutting of the river and its migration southward in response to falling sea levels during successive glaciations. The terraces have themselves been dissected by erosion, the higher in the series providing much of the material for those at lower elevations. Their relics dominate the topography of the Tertiary Basins and especially that of the New Forest, where they descend in a flight from a maximum elevation of 120-130 m to sea level, with intervening valleys and wide, eroded hollows drained by dense networks of small streams (Tubbs 1986a). The terrace flight continues below modern sea level, the lowest (and most recent) terraces having been drowned by rising sea level since the end of the last glacial period.

The Solent is the flooded heartland of the Hampshire Basin. As The Solent evolved, the soft, easily eroded sands and clays have yielded abundant material for redistribution as mud and sand flats and bottom deposits. Rising sea level in post-glacial times flooded an ancient river system which once flowed across the Hampshire Basin. The Pleistocene was not a time of uniformly cold climate but comprised a succession of glacial episodes with intervening warmer periods when the ice sheets withdrew, sea level rose and temperatures were comparable with, or warmer than, those of today. During glaciations, when sea level was 100 m or more below that of today, the great river flowed eastward across the Hampshire Basin, its tributaries following approximately the courses of the present rivers draining the area. This Solent River drained a vast tundra and had its source near, or beyond, the headwaters of the modern River Frome in Dorset. It flowed through today's Poole Harbour, across Poole and Christchurch Bays, and through The Solent before turning southward, probably to join forerunners of the Seine and Somme, and flowing westward to the contemporary coast in what is now the western Channel (Dyer 1975; West 1980).

During interglacial periods, the ice withdrew northward and the sea level rose usually to above the present level, flooding The Solent River and the lower parts of its tributaries to form a series of estuaries around a central inlet opening eastward to the sea. The modern Solent is the outcome of the most recent withdrawal of the ice and the invasion of The Solent River valley by the sea. The chalk ridge which connected the Isle of Wight with Purbeck in Dorset was overwhelmed and The Solent River system was consequently dismembered more completely than hitherto, this time forming not so much an estuarine system as a marine waterway (fig. 2). These events have taken place within as short a time as the past 12,000 years. By about 7500 BP (Before Present) the chalk ridge had been breached and the main body of The Solent had been drowned. About this time or shortly thereafter, the lower part of the river valley, which later became Southampton Water, was penetrated by the sea (Hodson and West 1972). By about 5000 BP the estuaries and harbours of The Solent had probably begun to take their present form.

Since then, sea level has continued to rise in a succession of pulses, though at a generally much slower rate than previously. An extensive low-lying region of islands and intertidal areas, seaward of the present coastline of south-east Hampshire and the Selsey region of West Sussex, appears to have been drowned between the 10th and 14th centuries and there are various manifestations of a more recent pulse of rising sea level which probably began early in the 19th century. These pulses (transgressions) and the intervening standstills or retreats (regressions) of the sea are probably associated with global oscillations in temperature which result in short-lived glacial advances and retreats. The present transgression is marked in The Solent region by a sea level rise of about 5.0 mm per year, which is among the highest recorded around the British coastline (Tubbs 1991a; Tubbs in press).

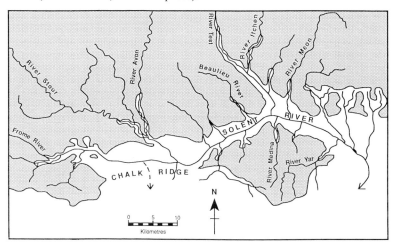

*Figure 2. The Solent River and its tributaries*

Terrestrial denudation has continued throughout the post-glacial period although the erosion potential of the climate has, for most of the time, been limited. The amount of water in the terrestrial environment has been relatively small. The present climate of Hampshire is comparatively dry and temperate and, despite oscillations of rainfall and temperature, it has probably remained essentially unchanged for two millennia or more. Average annual rainfall is about 90 cm. Precipitation is lowest in April - August and highest in December - January. Very severe winters are rare and in most winters snowfalls are brief and light. Frosts are common and, although night temperatures do not usually fall below -10°C, they have a discernible fracturing effect on exposed soil surfaces.

Despite the limited denudation potential of the climate for much of the post-glacial period, substantial volumes of material have been eroded and re-deposited as flood-plains of alluvium and gravel in the river valleys. There is circumstantial evidence that denudation and re-deposition were initiated by early forest clearance and primitive agriculture, starting in Neolithic times (4000 - 5000 BP) on the chalk and in the succeeding Bronze Age in the Tertiary Basins (Tubbs 1986a; Moffat and Cope 1984).

Forest clearance and consequential increased surface water run-off in the Tertiary Basins has also been linked with the inception of peat, and hence bog formation in valley bottoms. Various other causal mechanisms have been suggested by different researchers – beaver dams, the impediment of drainage by soliflucted clay plugs, and the development of impermeable iron pans in soils

11

which have been degraded through leaching after the removal of forest. Probably all these mechanisms have triggered mire formation but the ultimate causes are likely to be a combination of a poor hydraulic gradient with impermeable, soliflucted fill in valley bottoms. Peat occurs extensively in the chalk stream valleys and formerly supported a rich fen vegetation, mostly now converted to pasture. In the New Forest, bogs are numerous, both in valleys and as peat accumulations immediately downslope of hillside seepages which occur below the junction of permeable and impermeable strata. Most of these New Forest bogs appear to date from the Neolithic or subsequent cultural periods, but some are known, from the analysis of pollen preserved in their profiles, to be of very early post-glacial origin and began to form 10,000 - 13,000 years BP (Tubbs 1986a; Clarke 1987).

**The Transformations of Man**
The Solent may be the work of nature, but it is man who has transformed the terrestrial landscape, first by clearing the forests which it is generally believed came to dominate the land after the retreat of the ice and tundra. Much of our information about this process derives from the convenient fact that the walls of pollen grains decay only very slowly under anaerobic or acid conditions. Thus the pollen rain, which falls on the surface of peat mires and is preserved in their growing profiles, provides a stratified record of the surrounding vegetation. Lake and pond sediment can preserve a similar record. Plant remains, of which peat mire is composed, also provide information about the vegetation history of the mire itself. Archaeological and other evidence and the physical and chemical structure of soils yield supplementary evidence of change  (Dimbleby 1967). Fig. 3 portrays the main events revealed by these sources in Hampshire and gives an approximate time scale.

Early in the post-glacial period, first birch then pine spread northward in the wake of the retreating ice and tundra. As the climate ameliorated yet further in the Boreal period, hazel, elm, oak, ash and other trees invaded the woodland. Pollen analyses suggest that, for perhaps 4000 years from sometime in the Boreal until the close of the succeeding Atlantic period, the landscape of southern England – indeed, of most of Europe – was forested. What is generally regarded as the climatic optimum was achieved in the Atlantic period (5000 - 7000 BP) when the climate was warmer and wetter than now, the tree and shrub flora achieved its maximum diversity and the forest its maximum extent. The Atlantic woodland was dominated by oak, with abundant lime, elm, ash, alder and hazel. Interestingly, lime and elm were common in areas such as the New Forest where the soils are now too impoverished to support these species, thus pointing to a significant decline in fertility (Tubbs 1986a).

Post-Atlantic vegetation history is a record of soil impoverishment and the spread of open habitats at the expense of woodland. Man was the principal cause of these events. The earliest clearances of woodland probably occurred in Mesolithic times, but in Hampshire the archaeological and pollen analytical evidence suggests that man's impact on his forest environment was first extensive in the Neolithic period and that it occurred then on the chalklands. It is commonly supposed that a combination of light, well-drained soils and low density woodland cover made the chalkland relatively more attractive for settled agriculture and pastoral farming than heavier soils or denser woodland elsewhere, though the evidence is ambiguous and conflicting (Waton 1982). Forest clearance and farming began on the sands and clays of the Tertiary Basins and Weald rather later, in the Bronze Age. The twin processes of woodland clearance and the establishment of farming settlements advanced progressively through successive cultural periods to medieval times. Progressively too, the density of settlements and the transfer of man's mental agility from farming to other economic activities increased with rising population. The forest diminished. To portray the story of nature's interaction with human endeavour in all its wealth of detail demands a larger canvas than is given to me here. In any event it is more important from the point of view of the distribution and density of the different habitats left to us, and to birds, to understand something of the kinds of ecological transformations which have taken place.

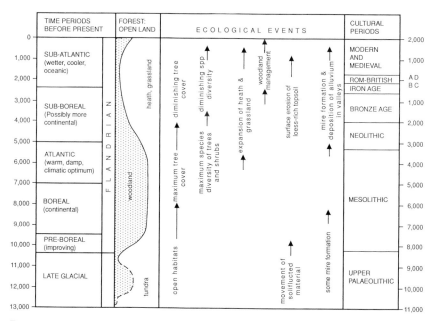

*Figure 3. Post-glacial chronology and main ecological changes in Hampshire*

Forest was cleared for arable, pasture and living space. Early cultivation resulted in the removal of more nutrients from the soil than were replaced in dung or marl, so that farming generally left a legacy of soil impoverishment which affected the composition of the succeeding natural plant communities. This was especially so on the acid rocks of the Thames and Hampshire Basins and in the Weald, where the acidification of already base-poor sands and clays encouraged the widespread establishment of dwarf shrub heath dominated by ling *Culluna vulgaris*, cross-leaved heath *Erica tetralix*, bell heather *Erica cinerea* and purple moor-grass *Molinia caerulea*. On less impoverished soils, various kinds of

13

grasslands developed in response to forest clearance. On the chalk, these grasslands came to be composed of a species-rich profusion of herbs and grasses, the latter mainly being species of fescue. Where they survive today, these chalk grasslands are often colourful islands in a desert of modern, intensive arable. On more acidic soils, the grasslands are generally less rich in species and tend to be dominated by bent rather than fescue. In their more impoverished form they are dominated by purple moor-grass and bristle bent *Agrostis curtisii*, a community which grades into dwarf shrub heath and often has a canopy of bracken *Pteridium aquilinum*. Bristle bent is a western, oceanic species, and is replaced in the east of Hampshire by wavy hair-grass *Deschampsia flexuosa*. Most "heathlands" are in fact a mosaic of heather-dominated dwarf shrub heath and acidic grassland, usually with bracken; they usually also have a scrub component of gorse *Ulex europeaus* (Tubbs 1986a, 1986b; Webb 1986; Pennington 1969; Roberts 1989; Rackham 1986).

Woodland clearance and farming also affected the environment by encouraging erosion. It is probable that the chalkland had a cover of fine, fertile, wind-blown soil deposited in Pleistocene glacial periods and that, with the advent of Neolithic and Bronze Age farming, this was lost. Similarly, there is evidence of considerable soil erosion coinciding with farming episodes in the New Forest, the eroded material infilling hollows and valleys and probably helping to induce peat and mire formation. Both on the chalk and on the more acidic rocks, early farming undoubtedly impoverished the soil (Tubbs 1986a; Catt 1977).

Relatively infertile the soils may have become, but the secondary heaths and grasslands became valuable open-range grazing lands. By late Saxon times, many areas were the recognised common grazings of specific communities and possessed a definite economic value. In the Norman feudal system they became the common lands of the manor over which the inhabitants had specific rights, which included grazing and the removal of fuel, bedding and other essentials. Areas unencumbered with common rights, or where the legal interest of the commoners could be circumvented, saw an ebb and flow of cultivation over the centuries. In times of economic prosperity and population growth the natural vegetation was reduced to provide more arable. In times of economic stress or declining population, the farmland was abandoned to grassland and heath. Indeed at times, farmland and settlements returned to the woodland from which they had been carved. On the downland in particular, many woods preserve the relics of pre-Saxon settlements and field systems and probably arose in the centuries after the Roman withdrawal.

The transition from forest to open habitats poses a problem which will be readily understood by ornithologists. Most pollen analysts picture the Boreal and Atlantic vegetation of Europe as a continuous forest. Today's heaths and grasslands are seen as nature's response to forest clearance by man. However, such a scenario omits to account for the persistence during the forest phase, which is thought to have lasted several thousand years, of the large proportion of the European flora and fauna which is adapted to open habitats. Very many species are morphologically or physiologically ill-equipped to live in a woodland environment. Of 139 species of birds which either breed today in Hampshire or which certainly or probably bred there in medieval times (in fact the total may be much larger), 44 are marsh, coastal or riverine species; 48 are woodland species, though many have adapted to scrub, gardens, hedges and other modern habitats; and 47 (34%) are physiologically or behaviourally adapted to open habitats of various kinds. Comparable proportions of other taxonomic groups are also adapted to open habitats, in some cases having developed complex symbiotic relationships which must have taken long periods to evolve and which required open land in which to do so, as for example those between certain species of ants and some of the blue butterflies.

This sort of evidence is usually countered by proposing refugia such as transient glades (the result perhaps of intensive herbivore grazing, lightning strikes or fire-clearance by Mesolithic man), coastal fringes and islands from which trees were excluded by exposure to salt-laden winds and mountain tops beyond the tree-line. It seems unlikely, however, that large numbers of open-ground species of birds, mammals, plants and invertebrates persisted for millenia with the fragmented distributions required by such an explanation. More likely, the primeval forest was less continuous than the pollen analyses suggest. Indeed, a few pollen analysts have begun to think on these lines. It follows that the avian fauna, along with other groups, may have changed less in composition than the prevalent view of the continuous forest would imply.

In parallel with the progressive expansion of a secondary heathland and grassland in the wake of the forests, there is a second thread in the ecological history of southern England. Woodland was both an impediment to settlement and farming, and a vital natural resource. Human communities demanded wood for fuel, construction timber, fencing, wattle, furniture and a multitude of other essential goods. Hence, as the woodland area diminished so the surviving areas acquired an economic value and came to be managed to give a sustained yield (Tubbs 1974b; Peterken 1981; Rackham 1986; Marren 1990).

In Hampshire, as elsewhere in the lowlands, the usual form of management which evolved was coppice-with-standards, in which a shrub layer (in Hampshire usually dominated by hazel) was cut on a relatively short rotation to give material for produce such as hurdles, wattle panels and domestic and industrial fuel, while timber trees, mostly oaks, were grown at a lower density for construction timber. The coppices, so-called, were enclosed against stock at least in the early stages of regeneration after cutting. In the 17th, 18th and 19th centuries the coppices of southern Hampshire helped sustain a major shipbuilding industry centred on Portsmouth, Southampton, Redbridge, Hamble and Buckler's Hard. Despite clearance for cultivation and grazing, woodland remained extensive in Hampshire, even during late medieval and early modern times when it came to its lowest ebb in England as a whole. Most Hampshire woods at that time were ancient in the sense that they had survived many hundreds of years and were probably the structurally modified descendants of the primeval forest of Atlantic times. There were also many secondary woods which had arisen spontaneously on grassland and heath at times when grazing had been withdrawn. Most of the escarpment beech woods of Hampshire arose in this way, although some were planted in the 18th and 19th centuries when it was fashionable to "improve" on nature (Tubbs 1974b; Colebourn 1983).

Not all woodland was managed for its timber or planted for its contribution to the landscape. Much woodland survived on common lands, in deer parks and in the royal forests, and in all these places it was grazed by domestic stock. Both parks and forests were medieval phenomena. The former were embanked areas of woodland, scrub, heath and grassland where deer were kept as a convenient source of meat and hides, and incidentally for hunting. Forests were conceived for similar purposes, although they rapidly acquired political connotations. They were mostly large tracts of country on poor soils with low human populations, where pre-existing land uses became subservient to deer conservation. Woodland was generally extensive, but not necessarily dominant. Most forests included some coppices, though they were generally supposed to be managed under peculiar constraints which favoured the deer. In many forests, farmland was extensive and in most the land remained in private ownership, though subject to the forest law. At their maximum extent in the 13th century, forests covered most of Hampshire. Only the largest and best known, the New Forest, survived subsequent legal disafforestation and partition between the crown, the landowners and the commoners. Rather unusually too, most of the New Forest was, and is, crown land (Colebourn 1983; Tubbs 1986a).

The structure of the woods on commons and in parks and forests was greatly modified by centuries of herbivore grazing. The absence of sustained timber harvesting left many trees to grow to their natural life span and thus to afford a habitat rich in timber-dwelling insects, epiphytic lichens and mosses, and hole-and crevice-nesting birds. On the other hand, the ground flora and shrub layer of the woodland became impoverished by grazing and browsing. Pollarding was often employed as a means of providing browse for the deer and fuel for the commoners, and has left an inheritance of ancient, multiple-stemmed beeches and oaks such as those of the New Forest woods. Few of these pasture woodlands survive in Hampshire outside the New Forest, where there are about 3700 ha, but there are fragments elsewhere and a major survival from the medieval Wolmer Forest, Binswood, is now thankfully owned by the Woodland Trust and still grazed by commoners' cattle.

The chalk stream valleys provide a third thread in the ecological history of Hampshire. Before man began to manipulate them, the rivers flowed in shifting, bifurcating channels through flood plains of carr and fen vegetation, probably with extensive reed beds. Rivers and their flood plains receive a constant supply of nutrients and mineral particles from their catchments. Once cleared and sufficiently drained, the flood plains provided rich grazing and hay meadows. In this, they contrast with the more base-deficient secondary heaths and grasslands on the higher ground but have an affinity with estuaries, which also are the recipients of a continuous supply of nutrients (and organic matter).

Although the evidence is slight, the first clearance and thus the first meadows are at least as old as Romano-British times. Most of these earliest reclamations probably returned to fen after the Roman withdrawal, to be reclaimed again in Saxon times. Upstream and downstream of Winchester there is evidence of extensive Romano-British drainage systems in the Itchen valley. These subsequently reverted to fen. The valley was more systematically drained for meadow around the 7th and 8th centuries (Biddle 1975).

From early in the 17th century, the flood plains of the Hampshire chalk streams were gradually transformed again by the construction of floated water meadows (Williamson 1861; Vancouver 1810; Green 1940; Sheail 1971).

Concurrently, and indeed beginning in medieval times, the rivers were much modified by diversion and training to provide water-heads for mills. The water meadows were irrigation systems in which the meadow was formed into successive ridges and furrows. Water was led into carriers along the crests of the ridges and permitted to overflow down their sides into drains (or drawns) which carried the water into a main drawn and off the meadow, sometimes into the next to be watered. The purpose was to irrigate with nutrient-enriched water without flooding. The ridge-and-furrow layout served to ensure a steady flow of water across the meadow. Watering was a skilled job. The systems were often complex, with intricate patterns of interdependent meadows. The periodicity of watering, mowing and grazing varied but a vital function of the meadows was to provide an early bite for stock, one or more hay crops, and a late bite before maintenance and winter watering. The constant and relatively high temperature of the chalk stream water, derived from the deep aquifers, ensured that the meadows remained frost-free. I vividly recall this phenomenon in the winter of 1962/63, when the surviving water-meadows in the Avon valley stood out as bright green frost-free patches in a frozen, snowy landscape. They were, I remember, populated by large numbers of very tame Water Rails and were visited by abundant thrushes, finches and other passerines.

**Hampshire and its Habitats in the Eighteenth Century**
Let us pause in the middle of the 18th century and survey the Hampshire scene. The time was something of an ecological watershed. Although man had destroyed most of the primeval woodland, he had inadvertently created a complex mosaic of habitats suitable for a diversity of birds, invertebrates and plants. Habitat diversity was at a maximum even though the area of woodland was minimal. In Hampshire, the habitat mosaic included arable and meadow, farmed without the benefit of modern fertilisers and herbicides, hedges, droveways, green lanes, extensive heaths and chalk grasslands, coppice woodlands, commons, forests and village greens and a multitude of small corners left aside to nature alone. After the mid-18th century there began an era

of habitat impoverishment, heralded towards the end of the century and the beginning of the next by the large scale enclosure of common lands, the disafforestation of many of the remaining forests, and a surge in arable cultivation at the expense, in Hampshire, mainly of chalk grassland. The French wars, industrialisation and rising population gave the first impetus to these trends. Later, biological impoverishment came to be sustained by a combination of agricultural intensification (and, in particular, the use of inorganic fertilisers and synthetic herbicides and pesticides), blanket afforestation (in Hampshire and neighbouring counties) mainly of heathland, the conversion of broadleaved woods to conifers, and urban and industrial development, joined in recent decades by leisure developments such as golf courses and marinas. From the ornithological point of view, the invention of the percussion cap in the early 19th century, and the subsequent development of the "sport" of driving game over the guns, led to intensive game rearing and predator control which grossly impoverished raptor populations and brought some species close to extinction in England. Such was the case in Hampshire, a county which was, by the 19th century, dominated by large landed estates.

A reconstruction of the Hampshire landscape in the mid-18th century is aided by Isaac Taylor's map of Hampshire, published in 1759 at a scale of one inch to one mile. The Old Series Ordnance Surveys, from late in the 18th century, also help to show what the county was like before the era of impoverishment was far advanced.

For centuries the downlands of Hampshire, in common with those of the rest of Wessex, were sheep country. After the 16th century a tide of arable farming began to consume the ancient turf but, even at the end of the 18th century, there still remained great tracts of natural grassland cropped by sheep. "The vast flocks of sheep, which one everywhere sees upon these Downs, and the great number of these flocks, is a sight truly worth observation", commented Daniel Defoe of his journey from Winchester to Salisbury in the 1740s. From the evidence (admittedly sometimes ambiguous) of Isaac Taylor's map, I estimate that there were still at least 20,000 ha of pristine downland turf in Hampshire at that time. Each chalkland parish had its sheep down and they were often large, sometimes contiguous with the downs of other parishes, and sometimes identified by "warren" place names signifying a use to which many such places were put in medieval and early modern times. The great tracts of cropped downland might have held prodigious numbers of birds such as Stone Curlews, Wheatears and Woodlarks, besides the last Great Bustards.

Most chalkland parishes also had their coppice woodlands on the clay-with-flints, and most had their water meadows in the chalk stream valleys. The parishes today often remain long and narrow so that they stretch from the high downs to the alluvial valleys. The economy of the chalkland largely depended on four interactive elements – the arable and enclosed pasture, the open downland (often common land), the water meadows and the woodland (Vancouver 1810; Naish 1960). All were necessary to the community and to individual farmers. In the 18th century huge tracts of the Tertiary Basins and the Weald were heathland, their drainage networks marked by mires, woodlands and ribbons of alluvial grassland. In some districts (e.g. the New Forest and the Forest of Bere in the Hampshire Basin), there was a mosaic of heath, pasture woodland, mire and an abundance of transitional habitats. These wildernesses were of a sufficient scale to be regarded with some degree of apprehension by such celebrated travellers as Daniel Defoe, William Cobbett, John Byng, Celia Fiennes and the brothers A W and D Driver (who claimed to have lost their notes for a government report on the New Forest when robbed by footpads on the Surrey heaths). To the agricultural writers of the late 18th and early 19th centuries – Charles Vancouver, Arthur Young and others – they were wastes to be made fertile and productive.

I estimate that in the Hampshire and Thames Basins and the Weald 97,700 ha of heathland remained at the end of the 18th century, of which about 50,000 ha were in Hampshire. The 9000 ha of heath in north-east Hampshire continued east over much of Surrey. In the Weald, the heath of Woolmer Forest was the western segment of a larger area of heathland extending into Surrey and Sussex. In the south-west of Hampshire, the New Forest was the core of a greater heathland district which extended widely around the present Forest and westward to Poole and Purbeck, broken only by the valleys of the Avon and Stour. Bournemouth (until 1974 in Hampshire) was built on what was once Bourne Heath (Tubbs 1986b).

The surviving royal forests were all on the poorer soils of the Weald and Tertiary basins. Gilbert White (letter VI to Thomas Pennant) described Woolmer Forest, on the Wealden sands, as "a tract of land about seven miles in length and two and a half miles in breadth" consisting "entirely of sand covered with heath and fern .... somewhat diversified with hills and dales, without having one standing tree in the whole extent". He adds that "in the bottoms, where the waters stagnate, are many bogs". Alice Holt, just to the north but on clays, was mostly pasture woodland. In southern Hampshire the Forest of Bere and the New Forest covered much of the Tertiary sands and clays, both of them mosaics of unenclosed heathland, mires, acid grasslands and pasture woodlands, studded with enclosed oak plantations. In the Thames Basin, the Forest of Pamber survived as a tract of pasture woodland adjoining Silchester Common. A tract of heathland was most of what remained of the medieval Forest of Eversley.

Pamber Forest later became an oak plantation – now a Local Nature Reserve – and most of the Forest of Eversley was eventually planted with conifers by the Forestry Commission. In the 18th century the Forests of Hampshire were set in a habitat-diverse countryside of small farms, commons, greens and woods.

It is necessary to emphasise that, though much of Hampshire in the 18th century remained relatively remote and wild, the wild places were common lands which formed essential elements in local economies. Even the most superficially impoverished heathland sustained a population of cottagers and smallholders living around its margin and exploiting the heath for grazing, turf fuel, kiln faggots, honey, material for cob building and other natural products. The still-extensive pasture woods on the forests and commons were grazed by cattle year-round and in the autumn the pigs were turned out on the mast. It was the enclosure of the commons, mainly in the 18th and 19th centuries, which enabled individual entrepreneurs to tame the wilderness.

**Post-Eighteenth Century Changes**
Between the end of the 18th century and 1985, the lowland heaths of southern England were reduced from about 190,000 ha to about 48,000 ha, which is a 75% loss. The 98,000 ha of heath in the Thames Basin, Hampshire Basin and Weald were reduced to about 32,000 ha, a 67% loss. Taking Hampshire alone, the loss has been somewhat smaller because of the remarkable survival of the New Forest. There were about 40,000 ha of heathland at the end of the 18th century. There are now 18,560 ha (53.6% loss), of which 16,100 ha are in the New Forest. The remainder is distributed in 34 heaths ranging in size from 10 ha to 380 ha. This is all that remains of the great heathland wilderness of the 18th century (Tubbs 1986b; Hazel 1983).

Cheap artificial fertiliser and improved reclamation techniques permitted heathland to be converted to farmland. In the present century large tracts were afforested with conifers, mainly by the Forestry Commission – even the New Forest suffered something of this indignity. After enclosure, which involved the effective dispossession of the commoners whose animals had grazed the heaths and suppressed tree invasion, many of the heaths of the Thames Basin and Weald became military training grounds. Though this has conferred upon them a degree of protection, the absence of grazing and management has led to widespread succession to secondary woodland, at first mainly birch. Now, in the 1990s the value of heathlands as part of our natural and cultural inheritance is sufficiently recognised for a start to be made on retrieving some of these lost heaths. In March 1992, Hampshire County Council (HCC), the District Councils, Ministry of Defence, Forestry Commission and Nature Conservancy Council (NCC)[1] came together to initiate a North East Hampshire Heathlands Project, the purpose of which is to restore and manage as many of the heaths as possible. Good progress has been made but sadly, no amount of determination and goodwill will re-create the 18th century heathland landscape. We can only hope to save and manage enough heathland to hint at what it was like.

---

[1]Since 1 April 1991, The Nature Conservancy Council has been split into regional authorities of which The Nature Conservancy Council for England, also called English Nature, is one. For convenience, I have continued to use NCC in this account.

The natural chalk grasslands of 18th century Hampshire suffered an even greater percentage decline than the heaths between about 1800 and the 1980s. A survey in 1966 found 2115 ha remaining in Hampshire, distributed in 119 fragments of which only three were over 150 ha. This represented at least an 80% loss (Blackwood and Tubbs 1970). A repeat survey in 1980 showed that in the intervening 24 years, the area had been further reduced to 1822 ha (NCC, unpublished). Unfortunately, these surveys omitted areas of less than 2 ha. A Hampshire County Council survey during 1980 - 1982, which included these smaller sites, found 2052 ha in 155 fragments of which 67, totalling 57 ha, were less than 2 ha (Prescott 1983). Small though these places are, they collectively comprise an important reservoir of chalk grassland plants and insects and a habitat for scrub and grassland birds.

Most heaths and chalk grasslands fell victim to agricultural intensification. This was progressive rather than continuous and, during agricultural depressions based mainly on tumbling cereal prices, the arable tide receded. I suppose, however, that in Hampshire it still more or less laps its highest ever shoreline. Much of the chalkland is little less than a biological desert, however aesthetically attractive it may seem. The loss of heaths and downs was only one manifestation of agrarian intensification. The common and large scale, routine use of artificial fertilisers and synthetic herbicides and pesticides, mainly in the post-1940 era of soaring farm production driven by public funds, has had an even more profoundly impoverishing effect on the flora and fauna of the Hampshire countryside. It is still strangely difficult to convince farmers that chemical fertilisers applied to grassland will eliminate the rich meadow flora by giving a gross competitive advantage to a few grasses, and to convey the truth that herbicides and pesticides – not to mention straw burning, now mercifully nearly a thing of the past – reduce the density and diversity of plants and animals in the countryside. During the second half of the 20th century, unimproved, plant-rich meadowland, once an everyday feature of Hampshire farmland, has been reduced to relative scarcity. Except in the chalk stream valleys, most surviving meadows are small and isolated and it is doubtful if they exceed 1000 ha in total area. The arable fields, themselves once rich in weeds of cultivation, are now deprived of all but the monospecific crop species. The drive to intensify destroyed countless small, uncultivated corners of plant and animal habitat which, among other things, were the hunting sites of Kestrels, Barn Owls and other predators. It destroyed innumerable ponds and small wetlands, a huge mileage of hedges and numerous woods.

In the chalk stream valleys, the water meadow system survived more or less intact into the 1930s, though meadows had been going out of use for many decades before then. They were expensive to maintain, their operation demanding skills which were dying with a passing generation. Conventional drainage schemes and fertilisers were a more convenient and (it is said) cost-effective substitute. The last working meadows in Hampshire survived on the Avon below Fordingbridge into the 1960s. Drainage and fertilisers transformed the water meadows as well as many other wetlands in the chalk stream valleys. Remarkably, however, much remains. There are sections of the Test and upper Itchen valleys, rich in fen and wet, unimproved meadows, which must somewhat resemble the valleys a thousand years ago or more.

21

I estimate that in the late 18th century there were about 50,000 ha of coppice woodland and wood pasture, besides some extensive oak plantations and other secondary woodlands, in Hampshire. It was then, and remains, one of the most extensively wooded counties in England. In 1885, the Board of Agriculture recorded 51,000 ha of woodland in the county, which probably excluded 11,000 ha of oak plantations in the New Forest, Forest of Bere and Alice Holt, planted as Navy timber earlier in the century. During the 20th century most of the coppice industries, the best known of which was probably hurdle making, failed through a combination of falling demand, scarcity of skilled craftsmen and other factors, so that most of the ancient coppice woodland left to us is overstood and unmanaged. Nonetheless, Hampshire remains relatively well endowed with working coppices. Today, there is no lack of demand for produce like hurdles, but there are few skilled craftsmen and few coppices now in a condition to produce material of the right age without preliminary unproductive cutting, some replanting, and a long wait for the regrowth. In many cases it is only their importance as game coverts which has saved coppice woods on the chalk from conversion to arable in the past three or four decades.

The best estimate is that, since about 1940, roughly 17,000 ha of ancient coppice woodland and wood pasture (34% of the estimated total) have been grubbed up for arable or converted to conifers. What remains, however, represents about 10% of the national resource of ancient woodland. The total woodland area of Hampshire has, of course, greatly increased since the 18th century – to about 74,000 ha – through afforestation of forests, commons and downland turf, at first by oak for shipbuilding, latterly by conifers. Where the oak plantations remain unconverted to conifers they have evolved into splendid woodland habitats. I cannot dwell so lovingly on the conifers and beech which the Forestry Commission imposed on such formerly exquisite places as some of the New Forest heaths, the Micheldever coppices and War Down. This last name is now practically lost in the search for grace which has given it the alternative name of Queen Elizabeth Forest. When I first saw War Down in the early 1950s, Stone Curlews, Wheatears, Woodlarks and rabbits bred on the old down among the recently planted trees. I doubt if they will breed there again.

22

I need to touch briefly on game conservation, for it has had a pervading influence on the Hampshire countryside. It saved – and saves – many habitats from destruction, but there has been a price to pay. This is no place to review the effects of gamekeeping on raptor populations in Hampshire, but perhaps I can at least permit one witness to tell us what it was like in much of the county at the end of the 19th century. At that time the Meinertzhagen family leased the Mottisfont estate, south of Stockbridge on the west side of the Test valley. Richard Meinertzhagen wrote thus about it in *The Diary of a Black Sheep:*

> "Most gamekeepers and a few landowners are ignorant and prejudiced about vermin and are inclined to class everything which is not game as vermin. Things are better now, but when we were at Mottisfont no kestrel or owl was ever allowed to live; keepers would loaf about with a gun shooting everything big, including woodpeckers. Many estates had exterminated hawks, owls, rooks, jackdaws, herons, little grebe, moorhen, coot, water-voles, badgers, squirrels and hedgehogs under the impression that game birds alone should be allowed to live."

There may have been some exaggeration in this account, written years later, but there is no doubt that gamekeeping was a grossly impoverishing influence until the latter half of this century. It would give me pleasure to record that its influence is now wholly benign. However, there remain significant areas of Hampshire, dominated by large estates, which predators like Buzzards do not seem able to recolonise and in which other predators are few. It is not difficult to find those among the keepering community who will explain why.

Finally, in this sketch of the post-18th century habitat history of Hampshire, let me return to the estuaries and harbours of The Solent. Here, nature as well as man (to adopt the customary but arbitrary distinction) has been a major force for change. In medieval and early modern times, a long pause in sea level rise permitted a period of saltmarsh growth and the reclamation of many marshes and creeks for embanked grazing marshes and salterns. The era of intertidal reclamation came to an end early in the 19th century. Farlington Marshes, among the best known coastal nature reserves in England, was embanked from Langstone Harbour in the 1770s. There were few subsequent Hampshire reclamations, despite the economic incentives of the French wars. Normandy Marsh, on the north-west shore of The Solent, was one of the last, and was embanked in the 1820s.

By mid-century a pulse in sea level rise had commenced which continues today. This period has been marked by saltmarsh erosion and a steady narrowing of the intertidal zone – and hence a considerable loss of potential feeding area for waders and wildfowl. This phenomenon has been most dramatic in the west Solent where the width of the intertidal zone has more than halved. From the evidence of successive Ordnance Survey maps, the area of mudflat has been reduced by more than 30% since 1870 in The Solent as a whole. Given the present rate at which the sea level is rising and the lack of compensatory sedimentation, most of the mudflats outside the sheltered estuaries and harbours will be gone by about 2030 and the area of flats exposed in the more sheltered places will have been considerably reduced. The consequences for the internationally important assemblages of waterfowl, which congregate in these places, have yet to be evaluated (Tubbs 1991a; Tubbs in press).

The *Spartina* story is no less dramatic (Gray and Benham 1990; Gray *et al* 1991). Though elucidated only in the 1950s, the story began in the late 19th century when the native saltmarsh grass *Spartina maritima* hybridised with the introduced North American species *S. alterniflora* in Southampton Water. The resulting male sterile hybrid, named *S. townsendii*, spread widely by vegetative reproduction. Sometime towards the end of the century a doubling of the chromosomes occurred, giving rise to a "new", fertile form now called *S. anglica*. This plant proved to possess a remarkable capacity to colonise open mudflats. It spread widely around the European coastline. In many estuaries, including some in The Solent, it was planted to aid coast protection and as a precursor to the embankment of intertidal areas for farmland.

Since the 1920s, the *Spartina* marshes have been in retreat, partly because of wave attack at their cliffed edges, and partly through the die-back of the plants themselves through causes which are still imperfectly understood. The loss of sediment from the intertidal zone has itself probably exacerbated cliffing at the edges of the marshes and increased their susceptibility to erosion. Today, of the 9060 ha of intertidal sediment in The Solent, 430 ha are occupied by what remains of the medieval saltmarshes and 1710 ha by *Spartina* marshes, of which 650 ha are in an advanced stage of degeneration. Probably The Solent *Spartina* marshes will be gone by the middle of the next century (Haynes and Coulson 1982; Tubbs 1991a; Tubbs in press).

Superimposed on these natural events have been the losses of intertidal habitat to development. Industrial reclamation began at Southampton in the 1830s, when 80 ha of saltmarsh and mudflat were infilled, later to become the Old Docks. This was followed by the loss of 160 ha for the New Docks between 1927 and 1933 and about 100 ha for the Container Port in the 1960s. About 350 ha were lost to the disposal of dredgings on what was formerly Dibden Bay and to the construction of the refinery and power station at Fawley. Southampton Water is among the British estuaries which have come closest to destruction. Further east, in Portsmouth Harbour, 240 ha (25% of the harbour) were lost to the construction of the M27, to refuse tipping and, latterly, to the development of Port Solent marina and its associated housing. In Langstone Harbour, 80 ha were lost to tipping between 1960 and 1975. Of the 24 marinas in The Solent, half were excavated at the expense of the intertidal zone. In The Solent as a whole, 1090 ha, or 11% of the intertidal area, were destroyed by development between 1930 and 1980 (Tubbs 1991a; Tubbs in press).

### Hampshire Today
Remarkably, in view of its recent history, Hampshire remains a biologically-rich county, which itself is a comment on its former condition. It must once have been a naturalists' paradise. The surviving area of each of the principal habitats is given in Table 1.

Hampshire has nationally important resources of ancient woodland, lowland heath, valley mire and probably unimproved species-rich meadow, although surveys remain incomplete. The chalk streams, with their extensive unimproved flood-plain meadows and fens, have ecological parallels in Europe only in the remainder of Wessex. Hampshire's heathlands and valley mires represent significant proportions of the European resource. In the New Forest they form an integral part of a complex ecological system, the other main habitat components of which are ancient pasture woods, acid grasslands, nutrient-enriched lawns and a wide range of wetlands and riverine plant communities.

| Habitat | Area (ha) |
|---|---|
| Ancient woodland | 33,000 |
| Chalk grassland | 2,053 |
| Lowland heathland | 18,560* |
| Unimproved neutral meadow | c2,500 |
| Peat fen (excluding reed beds) | c500 |
| Reed beds | c370 |
| Coastal grazing marsh | 510 |
| Intertidal flats and saltmarshes | 9,060 |
| Total | 66,553 |
| Total area of Hampshire | 377,900 |
| % of Hampshire "unsown" | 17.6 |

\* Including 95 valley and seepage mires

*Table 1. The principal natural ("unsown") habitats in Hampshire in 1990.*

The New Forest is Hampshire's brightest gem. It is widely recognised as being of international importance to nature conservation and biological science. It embraces the largest tract of "unsown" vegetation in lowland Britain. Its heathlands, valley and seepage mires and pasture woods are on a scale now unparalleled in Europe, whilst nowhere else do they occur as major components in a cohesive ecological system. There are about 3800 ha of oak/beech/holly pasture woodland, about 12,500 ha of heath and acid grassland, 2900 ha of wet heath and mire, and 8400 ha of plantations dating from various periods since the early 18th century, including many of oak of 18th and 19th century origin. The New Forest is probably large enough to ensure the long term survival of the widest possible spectrum of its characteristic flora and fauna. The smaller and more isolated examples of its major habitat components, which survive elsewhere, are highly vulnerable to biological impoverishment. The Forest is intrinsically rich in species, relatively undisturbed and positively managed in such a way as to ensure maximum species-survival. A key element in the Forest ecosystem is the persistence of a pastoral economy based on the exercise of common rights of grazing and of mast (the right to turn out pigs in the autumn), which inhibits natural succession to uniform forest whilst perpetuating great local diversity in plant and thus animal communities. This pastoral economy in turn depends on the continued existence of a community of part-time farmers. The Forest is an exceptional combination of natural and cultural elements which has seldom survived elsewhere in the lowlands of Europe (Tubbs 1986a).

Geomorphologically, the New Forest comprises a series of eroded Pleistocene terraces capped with flint gravel, brick-earth and other superficial material. The terraces are highest and most fragmented in the north, and lowest and most complete in the south, where they form extensive level plains. Erosion has exposed the underlying Tertiary sands and clays in wide valleys and hollows. The Forest soils are mainly acid, poor in nutrients and susceptible to leaching, though, mainly because of the occurrence of nutrient-enriched clay marls in the Headon Beds exposed in places in the south, some enriched environments occur locally. The Forest is drained by a fine network of small streams and there are abundant wet flushes along slope springlines, and around 300 ponds. Soils are mostly only slowly permeable. In consequence of these conditions, the Forest, and the woodlands in particular, has a humid microclimate which is important in supporting its rich lichen, bryophyte and fern flora, besides giving rise to muddy, stock-poached places which possess their own distinctive flora and fauna, now largely vanished from southern Britain because of the demise of grazed commons. Such conditions, indeed, probably prevailed widely in the primeval woodland matrix of prehistory but have now largely been lost in lowland Europe. In more than a cultural sense, the New Forest is a survival of medieval England (Tubbs 1986a).

Geographical location and the scale on which the principal habitats still occur confers on Hampshire a wealth of plants and animal species. It has a vascular flora of about 1400 species, which is larger than that of any other county. The flora of mosses, liverwort and epiphytic lichens in the New Forest is among the most species-rich in Britain. Measured in numbers of species and the numbers of localities supporting assemblages of nationally rare species, Hampshire is the most important British county for several groups of insects – *Orthoptera* (grasshoppers, crickets and allied groups); *Odonata* (dragonflies); *Diptera* (two-winged flies); the *Coleoptera* (beetles) of dead wood; and the *Lepidoptera* (butterflies and moths) of woodland and heathland. For many species of insects, Hampshire, and the New Forest in particular, is either the only or the main centre of their British distribution. In the New Forest alone, there occur at least 1234 (55%) of the 2250 species of *Lepidoptera* known from Britain; 1539 (46%) of the 3240 species of *Coleoptera*; 27 (64%) of the 42 British *Odonata*, and 22 (67%) of the 33 British *Orthoptera* (Tubbs 1986a). The heathland areas of Hampshire have important populations of all 12 native species of reptiles and amphibians (Tubbs 1986b).

In my perception, Hampshire can claim seven features of outstanding ornithological importance.

- The large colonies of Black-headed Gulls, Common Terns, Sandwich Terns and Little Terns breeding on the saltmarshes, shingle and shell islands and spits of the Hampshire coast. The Black-headed Gull colonies of the west Solent (14,000 pairs in 1991) represent approximately 9% of the British breeding population and are among the largest in Britain. Between 8% and 10% of the British breeding population of Little Terns are on the Hampshire coast, around 2% of the Sandwich Terns and 4% of the Common Terns.
- The concentrations of breeding waders on the coastal saltmarshes and embanked grazing marshes, in the New Forest and in the chalk stream valleys, especially the Avon valley. Although these regions have not been surveyed simultaneously, the data suggest total populations of about 550 pairs of Redshank, 750 pairs of Lapwing, 200 pairs of Snipe, 130 pairs of Curlew, 160 pairs of Oystercatcher and 140 pairs of Ringed Plover. These concentrations of waders are dense and important, although only in the case of the Ringed Plover do the absolute numbers exceed 1% of the British total. The Avon valley on the Hampshire/Dorset border is among the eight most important places in England for meadow-breeding waders.
- The breeding bird community of the Hampshire heathlands. Of special importance, this includes high percentages of the national breeding

26

populations of Dartford Warblers (about 75% in 1989 and 1990), Woodlarks (31% in 1986 according to the BTO survey of that year, probably nearer 25% in subsequent years), Nightjars (18% in 1992) and Stonechats (up to 5%). Hobbies are also strongly associated with heathland districts, where they achieve high densities, but they occur in all the other Hampshire biotypes. The Hampshire population represents about 10% of the national breeding total.

- The breeding bird community of the New Forest pasture woodlands. These include about 3% of the national population of Wood Warblers, up to 1% of the Redstarts and an exceptionally rich fauna of hole and crevice-nesting birds including notably large numbers of Lesser Spotted Woodpeckers and Hawfinches.

- The migratory and over-wintering waders and wildfowl which occur in the estuaries and harbours of The Solent[2]. The average winter peak of waders during 1983/4 to 1987/8 was 103,000, which was about 8% of the national total, placing The Solent among the "top" six estuarine systems in Britain for this group of birds. During the same period, the average winter wildfowl peak was about 40,000. The Brent Goose, Shelduck, Wigeon, Teal and seven species of waders occur in numbers which meet criteria of international importance. The combined wader and wildfowl peaks represent a density of about 20 birds per hectare of mud and sand flat, which would appear to be higher than in any other major UK estuarine system. Among The Solent's component estuaries, Langstone and Chichester Harbours support the highest numbers of wintering birds, each ranking among the top 15 UK estuaries for their wader numbers. Despite the extent of fringing urban and industrial development, The Solent remains of great ornithological significance.

- The overwintering populations of wildfowl inhabiting the Avon valley between Christchurch and Fordingbridge and the adjacent Blashford Lakes. The valley regularly holds in excess of 5000 wintering wildfowl and, when extensively flooded, considerably more may be present. Two species, Bewick's Swan and Gadwall, occur in numbers which meet criteria of international importance, while a further eight species, Mute Swan, White-fronted Goose, Wigeon, Teal, Shoveler, Pochard, Tufted Duck and Coot, occur in numbers of national importance.

---

[2]The Solent here refers to the whole estuarine system, including the small estuaries of the north shore of the Isle of Wight, and the large part of Chichester Harbour which is in West Sussex.

- The breeding population of Stone Curlews on the chalklands. In recent years 21 - 23 pairs, or 14% of the British total, have been reported as breeding in Hampshire. This population is a relic, not only of much larger numbers of this species, but of a chalkland avifauna now largely lost to agricultural intensification. The surviving Stone Curlews are in a precarious position and depend heavily on the protection of individual nests from farming operations.

During the late 1980s and early 1990s, Hampshire has held 10% or more of the national breeding populations of a number of other species including Pochard, Honey Buzzard, Nightingale, Cetti's Warbler and Firecrest.

**The Protection of Hampshire's Natural Heritage**

The nearest to a guarantee of protection which can be achieved is the ownership of land by an organisation irrevocably committed to nature conservation. The Hampshire and Isle of Wight Wildlife Trust (HIWWT) owns, or in some cases leases, 1470 ha of prime meadow, woodland, fen and coastal habitats. The NCC has five National Nature Reserves (1189 ha) comprising three of the most important remaining chalk grasslands (Martin Down, Beacon Hill (Warnford) and Old Winchester Hill), a meadow (Ashford Hill Meadows) and, through an agreement with the Beaulieu and Cadland Estates, the North Solent NNR based on the Beaulieu Estuary. There are 13 Local Nature Reserves (LNRs) owned and declared by HCC or the District Councils, totalling 1045 ha and including many of the most important chalk grasslands, woodlands and coastal areas in the county. Five more areas totalling about 440 ha await declaration.

The protection of the Hampshire coast through nature reserve purchases began about 1970, when Portsmouth City Council purchased Farlington Marshes as an LNR, subsequently leasing it to the HIWWT. In 1972, Titchfield Haven, an 85 ha freshwater marsh created by the exclusion of the tide from the estuary of the River Meon, originally in the early 17th century, came on the market and HCC was persuaded to purchase and declare as an LNR. The following year, first Normandy Farm, a 32 ha sea-walled marsh, and then The Salterns, another 12 ha of grazing marsh and lagoons, both near Lymington, went to auction and were purchased by the County and District Councils. The succession of purchases was the foundation of a policy of coastal acquisitions for conservation by the County Council which have included Oxey and Pennington Marshes and Keyhaven Marshes on the north-west shore of The Solent west of Lymington; large parts of the Hamble Estuary; an intertidal area at Calshot Spit in Southampton Water; The Kench in Langstone Harbour; Sandy Point at the mouth of Chichester Harbour and a large area of saltmarsh within Chichester Harbour. In addition to the County Council reserves are those of the RSPB in Langstone Harbour, the HIWWT reserve covering the intertidal area between Hurst Spit and the Lymington River and the NCC's reserve at the Beaulieu Estuary. In 1992, 1630 ha of intertidal flats and saltmarshes (18% of the total) and 435 ha of embanked grazing marsh (65% of the total) on the Hampshire coast were protected as nature reserves.

Hampshire owes much to the late David Pumfrett who, as Chairman of HCC's Recreation Committee, was the motivating force behind the start of the County Council's policy of protective coastal acquisitions. Equally too, conservation owes a great debt to Freddie Emery-Wallis, latterly Leader of HCC, and to many of his colleagues, for nurturing and developing this policy which has led to the protection of a large part of Hampshire's remaining unspoilt coastline.

A second level of protection is afforded by the notification (by the NCC) of Sites of Special Scientific Interest (SSSIs) under the Wildlife and Countryside Act 1981. Local planning authorities are required to consult the NCC over relevant planning issues and to pay special regard to SSSIs but there is no mandatory protection against development. Owners and occupiers, however, are required to seek the NCC's consent to carry out any of a list of potentially damaging operations which forms part of the notification. The NCC can recompense for profits lost by foregoing the operation, the vehicle for compensation being a management agreement. SSSIs are not a magic solution to conservation problems but they are a helpful protective device. In Hampshire in 1992, 122 SSSIs have been notified, totalling 50,100 ha or 13.3% of the county. They include almost àll the heaths and ancient pasture woods, most of the larger areas of chalk grassland, large sections of the chalk stream valleys, most of the richest unimproved meadows, most of the intertidal area and grazing marshes of The Solent, and the whole of the New Forest. The New Forest also receives protection against both development and major land use changes by the New Forest Acts 1877 - 1970, which in effect define what may take place there. The NCC is closely involved in the management of the Forest by the Forestry Commission and other owners including the National Trust.

In parallel with the notification of SSSIs, HCC has a policy of identifying Countryside Heritage Sites which it is committed to protect through offering financial incentives enshrined in management agreements. At the time of writing in March 1992, there are 285 sites covering about 5000 ha.

Large areas of Hampshire qualify for two international designations, both of which, in effect, commit government to their protection.

The Convention on Wetlands of International Importance was adopted at Ramsar, Iran, in 1971 (The Ramsar Convention) and was designed to check the loss and damage to wetlands. The UK government signed the Convention in 1973 and ratified it in 1976. In so doing it entered into a commitment to promote wetland conservation generally and to undertake the protection of particular places of international importance which the Convention required each Contracting State to designate ('Ramsar Sites'). Criteria were subsequently agreed for identifying Wetlands of International Importance for inclusion in the national Ramsar lists.

The European Community's Directive on the Conservation of Wild Birds, made in 1979, requires Member States to conserve the habitat of listed rare and vulnerable species and regularly-occurring, migratory species. It requires that particular attention should be paid to wetland conservation. Member States are required to designate the most suitable areas for both classes of birds as Special Protection Areas (SPAs).

A list of places which meet the criteria for designation in the UK was agreed by Ministers in 1990, but the rate at which sites have been designated has been slow, evidently because of the brake on economic development which designation can involve. In Hampshire (and West Sussex), Langstone and

Chichester Harbours were designated as both a Ramsar site and SPA in 1987. Portsmouth Harbour, the surviving intertidal parts of The Solent and Southampton Water, the Avon valley from the estuary to Fordingbridge, the New Forest and the heathlands of north-east Hampshire (and west Surrey) all qualify for designation under the Ramsar Convention, the EC Directive, or both. At the time of writing there is a real hope that the New Forest will be designated in 1993 and that the other sites will follow, though this requires a process of consultation with owners and government departments which inevitably involves lengthy delays.

Designations, whether as SSSIs, Ramsar sites or SPAs, deter but do not preclude, threats. Hampshire has a population of 1,528,000 people. Until recently, south Hampshire between Southampton and Portsmouth, and north-east Hampshire were designated as growth areas into which urban and industrial growth was directed by government policy. In both parts of the county, habitat destruction took place on a grand scale from the 1940s to the 1980s. Only now in the 1990s, has growth area status been dropped but nonetheless, Hampshire generally remains under intense pressure for development. The protection of the natural places, whose history I have tried to sketch in this introductory chapter, depends on the deployment of evidence. The strong leaning towards quantification in the ornithology of the past three decades has provided an important part of the evidence used by conservation bodies to oppose – with, it has to be said, increasing success – development proposals affecting important wildlife habitats. One of the intentions of this book is to consolidate that tradition and help to underpin the conservation of the remaining bird habitats in the county. Despite abuse, Hampshire remains habitat-rich and worth the fight to keep it so.

**Editors' Note**
As anticipated above, the New Forest was designated as a SPA and Ramsar site on September 22nd 1993.

# Twentieth Century Ornithology in Hampshire

*Richard A Leach and Norman H Pratt*

"It is a great pity so little is written about the history of ornithology and the people involved in it, especially at grass roots and county level." (Everett and Prytherch 1991)

## Introduction

The primary purpose of this chapter is to present an outline history of the evolution of ornithology in Hampshire in the 20th century. In common with other counties during this period, Hampshire experienced what may be caricatured as the transition from "shooting and collecting specimens" to "collecting data primarily for conservation purposes". We begin with a brief sketch of the situation prior to the publication of Kelsall and Munn's *Birds of Hampshire and the Isle of Wight* in 1905. The approach is then essentially, but not rigidly, chronological, providing short biographies of those who have contributed much to the development of Hampshire's ornithology. Evaluation of contributions is principally restricted to those no longer holding office in Hampshire ornithological organisations.

Whether concerning people or events, the choice of material is subjective but with, hopefully, sufficient background and detail for the reader to form a realistic overview. As the account approaches the end of the 20th century, it becomes increasingly concerned with collaborative ornithology and its interface with conservation.

## Setting the Scene

Hampshire is particularly fortunate in its ornithological riches. The context and characterisation of this richness have been addressed in the previous chapter. The present chapter is concerned with the people involved and the manner in which they have developed knowledge of Hampshire's avifauna in the 20th century.

Although an earlier origin can be demonstrated, it may be claimed that British amateur ornithology effectively began in Hampshire in and around the village of Selborne due to the great naturalist Gilbert White (1720-1793). White's *Natural History and Antiquities of Selborne* runs to more than 150 editions.

Knowledge of birds in Hampshire before 1900 depended, principally, on four different source types: "shotgun ornithology", which gave rise to a number of significant skin collections; personal diaries, of which examples are noted later; the work of a few naturalists, often of national repute; and the incidental content of the writings of several famous literary authors and poets.

One of the best and most significant of the skin collections, which survives in part to this day, is the Hart collection. Edward Hart (1847-1928) was a taxidermist who lived at Christchurch and built up his collection, including many locally taken specimens, until 1897. At the time, it was considered by many to be one of the finest in private hands. The collection remained in Christchurch at the Bow House until 1930, when it passed to a Mrs. Hall, whose executors donated it to Stowe School. In 1950, the Director of the Leicester Museum was asked by the School to inspect the, by then, decaying collection. Conservation work at Leicester saved some 290 out of the original 400-plus cases. In 1980, the collection was split and sold. Hampshire County Council (HCC) was given first choice and 22 cases are now housed safely in the "Red House" Museum, Christchurch, still run by the HCC; 17 cases remain at the Leicester Museum and the rest are in the Horniman Museum, London. The Winchester College skin collection is another worthy of mention. Supervised by Kelsall, it originally belonged to Chalkley and, incidentally, contains a Honey Buzzard dated 1874 from the New Forest (Chalkley 1900).

The diaries include those of Colonel Peter Hawker (1786-1853), a prominent wildfowling sportsman. They provide a rich source of information, especially on the wildfowl and waders of The Solent. A particular version of his shooting diaries is *The diary of Colonel Peter Hawker 1802-1853* (Payne-Gallwey 1893). The original diaries are now in Yale University library. Hawker also wrote a book *Instructions to young sportsmen in all that relates to guns and shooting* which appeared in numerous editions from 1814 onwards. This is quite different from the diaries but also contains several references to Hampshire birds.

Several naturalists of national repute may be mentioned. John R Wise wrote *The New Forest: its History and Scenery* (1862), containing a list of birds of the New Forest, which he regarded as the area bounded by Southampton Water, the coast and the Avon; Dr P L Sclater, who lived at Odiham Priory and contributed the section on Hampshire ornithology in *Hants and Dorset Court Guide and Blue Book* (1897); and E G B Meade-Waldo, who lived at Boldre for a time, introduced the Little Owl into the New Forest in the 1870s and produced a list of birds (almost confined to the New Forest) in the *Victoria History of Hampshire* (1900). Others of national fame who contributed to our knowledge of Hampshire's birds include the poet-naturalist W H Hudson (1841-1922), who wrote a number of books, of which *Hampshire Days* (1903a) and *Adventures among Birds* (1913) allude to birds. The former incorporates an article entitled "A Summer's End on the Itchen" which originally appeared in *Longman's Magazine* in 1901. Another article described what were then thought to be the last Hampshire breeding Ravens (1903b). George Dewar was another prolific natural history and field sports writer at the turn of the century. He spent his early years in north-west Hampshire and mentions Hampshire birds in several books including *Wildlife in Hampshire Highlands* (1899) and, referring to Doles Wood, *The Birds in our Wood* (1903).

Some great 18th and 19th century literary authors residing in Hampshire also mention local birds in their books, among them Jane Austen (1775-1817), when living at Chawton; Charles Kingsley (1819-1875), who lived at Eversley as curate and rector from 1842 until his death and wrote *Charm of Birds* (1867); Charlotte Yonge, who lived at Otterbourne for the whole of her life, writing *An Old Woman's Outlook in a Hampshire Village* (1892) and *John Keble's Parishes* (1898), which contain lists of birds for the parishes of Hursley and Otterbourne. Keble was vicar of Hursley from 1836 till his death in 1866. Lord Tennyson (1809-1892) was also a keen observer and lived on the Isle of Wight from 1853 onwards.

**The First Half-century**
At the beginning of the 20th century, the Rev. John E Kelsall and Philip W Munn published the first avifauna for Hampshire and the Isle of Wight (Kelsall and Munn 1905). They used material from Gilbert White's writings, the responses to an appeal for records first made by Kelsall in 1883, which had previously been used to produce county lists (Kelsall 1890, 1898), other casual records (by late 20th century standards) and the "collections" noted above. Some of the account in the previous section is an elaboration of material in the Introduction to Kelsall and Munn's book, to which the reader is referred for a more extensive list of the earlier literature.

Kelsall was born at Fareham in 1864. He was rector of New Milton from 1897 until his death in 1924 and, unusually for that period, never collected birds or their eggs. He was a pillar of the Hampshire Field Club (HFC), being a founder member, appointed Vice-President in 1898 and Ornithological Secretary from 1922-24 (see later), the latter jointly with Munn. Among several publications, additional to those noted previously, was one on the birds of Milford (Kelsall and Coles 1913). He had collected a large amount of material for a revision of the Kelsall and Munn book at the time of his death.

Munn (1865-*c*.1946), who became a Bank manager at Laverstoke and served in the First World War, was also heavily involved with the HFC, being Ornithological Secretary from 1922-1928. He remained a member of the HFC until 1946, but he appears to have moved to Majorca in about 1928.

The years 1905 to 1950 may be described as the second historical period in Hampshire ornithology. Shooting and stuffing of birds declined but the activities of oologists continued strongly, at least until the Second World War and, to a lesser extent, to the present day. Bird recording, however, remained casual and disorganised throughout this period. For the early part of the century we have to rely, therefore, on other sources, especially diaries, to flesh out the picture. Fortunately a number of ornithologists of international repute, whose contributions overlap the 19th and 20th centuries, provide some information on Hampshire's birds.

Colonel Richard Meinertzhagen (1878-1967) was one of the more colourful, some would say culpable, characters of late-19th and 20th century ornithology. His father rented the 2000-acre Mottisfont Abbey estate in 1884, and the young Meinertzhagen quickly showed an interest in the estate's wildlife, his ornithological observations appearing in his later writings (Meinertzhagen 1959, 1964). Although he left Mottisfont in 1900, his biographer mentions a return there in 1942 (Cocker 1989). In his early years he met, and was influenced by, many of the illustrious figures of the late 19th century, including Darwin, Thomas Huxley, Herbert Spencer, Gatke, Rothschild, Bowdler-Sharpe, Hartert, Thorburn – who visited Mottisfont – and others. Meinertzhagen's military, political and later full-time ornithological activities took him to many parts of the globe, and he wrote on the birds of many areas, particularly those on the southern rim of Asia.

He established a large skin collection, of which those collected in his Mottisfont days are of particular interest here, with a catalogue plus notes running to 42 volumes in the Natural History Museum Library at Tring. He kept a diary from boyhood, the leather bound volumes of which fill a bookcase in the Rhodes House Library at Oxford. The information that these contain about the birds of the Mottisfont area in the late 19th century was not known to Kelsall and Munn, but became available to Cohen in time for the second county avifauna in 1963 (see later). Unfortunately rumours and suspicions of malpractice have long surrounded Meinertzhagen and recent work suggests that some of them may have been well founded. To quote Knox (1993) "Like other aspects of Meinertzhagen's life .... it seems that much that he has left us cannot be taken at face value". Against this must be balanced Lawrence's (1935) oft-quoted pen portrait of him in his prime ".... a student of migratory birds drifted into soldiering .... possessed of an immensely powerful body and savage brain".

Two other notables of Western Palearctic, particularly European, ornithology with Hampshire connections, must be mentioned. The first, Harry Forbes Witherby (1873-1943), lived at Burley from an early age until he married Lilian Gillson from Itchen Abbas in 1904. It is reputed that, having an interest in birds, she was taught to skin them by her husband while on honeymoon in Algeria! At the age of 18, Witherby had entered the family firm of Witherby & Co, of which the publishing branch became H F & G Witherby. From this stemmed his prodigous publishing contributions to ornithology. At 21, he published a book mentioning birds of the New Forest, *Forest birds, their haunts and habits* (1894); he contributed to and helped in the production of Kelsall and Munn's 1905 book; he founded the magazine *British Birds* in 1907, remaining as editor-in-chief all his life, and through it started the National Ringing Scheme in 1909. He was a co-author of *A Handlist of British Birds* in 1912; he edited *The Practical Handbook of British Birds* (1919-24) and its five volume successor *The Handbook of British Birds* (1938-41). He was also a founder member of the British Trust for Ornithology in 1933. One of numerous honours bestowed upon him was the Godman-Salvin gold medal, the British Ornithologists' Union's highest award, in 1938. His contributions to Hampshire records include notes on breeding Crossbills in 1910 and 1931; he was also responsible for the identification of the county's first Western Mediterranean Shearwater from a bird taken in Christchurch Harbour (now in Dorset) in 1859 (Witherby 1922).

The second of the duo, a close associate of Witherby, was the Rev. Francis Charles Robert Jourdain (1865-1940), who had retired to Southbourne, then in Hampshire, in 1926. A noted oologist, Jourdain was a joint author of the 1938-41 Handbook. He was recognised as a leading authority on the breeding biology of the birds of the Palearctic region and was very much more than a mere egg collector. His contribution to Hampshire ornithology came through his

Ornithological Secretaryship of the HFC (1936-1937) and his initiation and editing of the first annual Bird Report (as distinct from papers or occasional summaries of bird records) for the county (1936), published as part of the Proceedings of the HFC.

The great politician and ornithologist Edward, Lord Grey of Falloden (1862-1933), who was educated at Winchester College, escaped from the affairs of state (Foreign Secretary 1905-1916) to his fishing cottage at Itchen Abbas (1890-1923). He and his wife kept a notebook, chiefly concerning birds observed at the cottage and in the vicinity of Itchen Abbas. This was published privately in 1909 with the title *Cottage Book, Itchen Abbas 1894-1905*. His book, *The Charm of Birds* (1927), also describes instances of bird life in the county. *The Falloden Papers* (1926) mentions his walk with Theodore Roosevelt in 1910, down the Itchen Valley from Tichborne to Martyr Worthy, then, after a car journey, from Stoney Cross through the New Forest to Brockenhurst. This walk of ornithological and political significance led to the signing in 1916 of the Migratory Birds Treaty. The walk was repeated in the early 1920s by Grey with the famous American ornithologist Frank Chapman and described in *Autobiography of a Bird Lover* (Chapman 1933). In commemoration of the original event, 51 birds typical of the New Forest are mounted as a group in the American Museum of Natural History in New York, depicted at a site in the New Forest selected by Lord Grey in 1932. In celebration of its 50th anniversary, on June 19th 1960, part of the walk, from Stoney Cross to Brockenhurst, was retraced by the Presidents of the Audubon Societies of the USA and Canada, accompanied by Sir Julian Huxley, Sir Peter Scott, James Fisher, Dr David Lack, E M Nicholson and, among others, W A Cadman, Deputy Surveyor of the New Forest, Edwin Cohen, Chairman of the Ornithological Section of the HFC and Colin Tubbs, then at the beginning of his professional career with the Nature Conservancy.

Another contribution overlapping the centuries comes from the wildfowling diaries of William Mudge (*c.*1880-1964). These have been analysed recently (Tubbs 1991b, 1992). The diaries contain records of waders and wildfowl in The Solent and Southampton Water and include data on Mudge's seasonal bags and other observations, including some counts, covering the period 1897-1952, undoubtedly one of the longest, near-continuous periods of personal records available. He notes large bags in both World Wars, when wildfowling pressure was low, and small bags in the 1930s, when such activity was high.

There is considerable further material on Hampshire's wildfowl in the ornithological (e.g. Taverner 1962) and the wildfowling literature, including the writings of J E H Kelso, a local doctor who watched and shot off Hayling Island in the early years of the century (Kelso 1912). A particular feature of Kelso's contribution was the value he placed on accurate observation. More information can be gleaned from other wildfowling sources (see Tubbs in press).

For game birds, there is also a long-running national record of annual bags from the sporting estates, going back to the 19th century. This information, some key parts of which relate to Hampshire, has been collated and reviewed recently (Tapper 1992).

Papers written by (now Captain) Munn (1919, 1920), report on ornithological information obtained since the Kelsall and Munn book. He mentioned that Stone Curlews were still common and described their courtship display. Corncrakes were declining by then, but Redshanks, nesting in the river valleys, showed an increase. Red-backed Shrikes were plentiful and Cirl Buntings occurred throughout Hampshire. He mentions two specimens of note collected before the First World War: in 1905 a Great Snipe at Newton Stacey and in 1910 a Great Bustard at St Mary Bourne. He also reported that Bitterns appeared regularly in winter but were ruthlessly killed.

A study of changes in the species nesting in a small area of the New Forest near Ringwood, for the period 1913-24, is of interest as one of the first attempts at a breeding survey in the modern sense (Longstaff 1926). The Wryneck was evidently a regular breeder in the survey area throughout this period.

B J Ringrose kept a record of his bird observations in the New Forest for the period 1922-39. His notebook, arranged in species order, came into the hands of Tubbs by a somewhat circuitous route, having been found in the attic of the house in which Ringrose had previously lived on the western edge of the New Forest. It includes extensive information, some of which appeared in the HFC Proceedings at the time, about such species as Dartford Warbler and Buzzard.

The diaries of Lt Gen E F Norton, of Everest fame, include lists of species seen along the coast in the Titchfield area in the 1920s and 1930s. Although no quantitative information is given, it is interesting to note the regular presence of Hooded Crows in the 1920s, compared with their apparent scarcity in the 1930s and complete absence from two lists for the 1940s.

Information on birds around Farnborough and Winchester in the late 1930s appears in Bruce Campbell's autobiographical *A Birdwatcher at Large* (1979); the author also relates his introduction to ringing at Winchester College in 1930 and his meetings with Cohen in the 1940s. Campbell (1912-1993) was born in Southsea and did much of his early birdwatching in Hampshire, especially on the heathlands. After a spell at the British Trust for Ornithology, where, for ten years from 1948, he was the first full-time secretary funded by a generous covenant set up by Cohen, he went on to become a senior producer with the BBC in Bristol. He wrote several books on birds and contributed the prefaces to this book's immediate predecessors (Cohen 1963; Cohen and Taverner 1972).

Another well-known author and broadcaster, also associated with Winchester, is Brian Vesey-Fitzgerald. He was editor of *The Field* magazine (1938-46) which had its offices in Winchester during the Second World War. He wrote a number of books containing references to Hampshire birds including *A Country Chronicle* (1942) and was a contributor to the county Bird Report.

We have previously referred to Winchester College and its Natural History Society, and to the Hampshire Field Club. These, the first societies involved in natural history in Hampshire, came into being late in the 19th century.

The Winchester College NHS was formed in 1870. At the turn of the century, besides Chalkley's stuffed birds (collected 1863-1900), the College possessed an extensive egg collection (Davies 1904). A report on the birds around Winchester for the years 1927-31 was produced (Campbell *et al* 1931). In 1935 the 2.5 acre Falloden Reserve was set up in the Itchen water meadows on College land. Bird ringing was actively pursued from the 1930s onwards, with J A L Myers producing a Bird Ringing Report 1936-1949 (4820 birds ringed). A study of Swallows and martins was undertaken in 1936. The account of birds around Winchester was brought up to date (Heycock 1939). In 1949 detailed observations were made at Warren Shore, Beaulieu, in support of a campaign against the setting up of an RAF bombing range there. The arrival of W H "Bunny" Dowdeswell as Master-in-Charge of the Science Department (1953-1968) boosted ornithological activity, which now included wildfowl counts in the upper Itchen Valley, a ringing study of Blue Tits (1954-57), and further intensive watching around Winchester. This culminated in the publication of *Birds of the Winchester District* with a preface by Dowdeswell (Cheke 1962) containing the previous ten years' records of the NHS. Later in the post-war period, the names of Giles Pepler and Tim Jorgenson appeared as participants in the British Trust for Ornithology's Sand Martin and *Acrocephalus* warbler ringing programmes. Dowdeswell himself took on the dual roles of President of the College NHS and first Chairman of the Ornithological Section of the HFC formed in 1954. Not unnaturally, these two organisations were closely linked at this time (1958-62) and organised joint meetings.

We note, in passing, the formation during the 20th century of several other "local" natural history societies with ornithological interests, such as those at Alton, Portsmouth and Southampton.

The HFC was the only county-wide organisation contributing to Hampshire ornithology prior to the formation of the separate Ornithological Section in 1954. Formed in 1885, it had a Natural History Section from its early days, but it was not until 1922 that the Club appointed subject Secretaries, of whom Kelsall and Munn were the first for Ornithology (table 1).

Beginning with the arrival of a local doctor, Frederick Haines, as Ornithological Secretary in 1931 and later Jourdain, the HFC published brief county Bird Reports as part of its Proceedings from 1932. The first separate report, emanating from the new Ornithological Section, appeared in 1957. Haines is noteworthy for maintaining the HFC's ornithological activities for some 15 years up to his death in 1946. Additionally, from 1934-46 the *South Eastern Bird Report*, covering Kent, Sussex, Surrey and Hampshire, edited by Ralph Whitlock, contained Hampshire sightings. Initially these were not necessarily the same as those appearing in the HFC Bird Report but, in later years, the Hampshire report was simply reprinted in the regional publication. A low ebb was reached in 1947 when there were only 25 contributors to the Hampshire report. In 1949, Whitlock appealed to Hampshire observers to send their bird records to Cohen, newly appointed as County Recorder (1949-56) by the HFC.

| Year | Name | Role/Event |
|---|---|---|
| 1885 | Kelsall | Founder Member |
| 1898-1924 | Kelsall | Vice-President |
| 1922-24 | Kelsall and Munn | Ornithological Secretaries |
| 1926-28 | Munn | Ornithological Secretary |
| 1931-34 | Haines | Ornithological Secretary |
| 1936-37 | Jourdain | Ornithological Secretary * |
| 1939-44 | Haines | Ornithological Secretary |
| 1946-52 | Whitlock | Ornithological Secretary |
| 1949-56 | Cohen | Bird Recorder |
| 1953-54 | Cohen | Ornithological Secretary |
| 1954 | | Ornithological Section formed |

* Jourdain produced the first annual Bird Report in 1936

*Table 1. Notable names and events relating to ornithology within the Hampshire Field Club 1885-1954*

## The Second Half-century: the Development of Collaborative Ornithology

### *Groups*
The early 1950s were probably the most critical few years of the century for the progress of Hampshire ornithology. A number of teenagers began to watch birds around Langstone Harbour with an intensity and recording rigour not seen previously in the county. They became known as the Portsmouth Group. Members of the Group soon began to extend their studies and influence to other parts of the county, visiting the remainder of The Solent, the New Forest, the chalk downland, the Avon valley and the Isle of Wight. Other groups followed, notably at Christchurch, then still in Hampshire. The records accumulated by these groups in the 1950s provided the basis and major impetus for the next book on Hampshire's avifauna (Cohen 1963).

These groups were not particularly well organised, at least not in their early days. They were loose associations of observers, including small groups of friends, who agreed to pool their records and submit them to the County Recorder as a single entity rather than as a number of overlapping and duplicating solo efforts.

While nationally there was a rapid growth of interest in birdwatching at this time, the Portsmouth example is exceptional for its longevity and integrity. There are a number of general and particular reasons for this development in Hampshire, including the start of the Wildfowl Trust National Wildfowl Counts, the dawning recognition of the need for some coordination in counting birds in estuarine and other coastal habitats and, not least, the competitive human trait of one-upmanship, or, to quote one of the founder members of the Portsmouth Group: "to put one over on everyone else by doing something new"! Interactions with Canning Suffern also probably contributed. In 1921, Suffern, affectionately known as "Doc", first visited and recognised the importance of Titchfield Haven as a sanctuary for wildlife. He also began to appreciate the need to collect observations on a systematic and cooperative basis. In the years after the Second World War, Suffern actively encouraged the young enthusiasts with whom he came into contact at Titchfield to organise themselves in this way.

Suffern (1892-1978) spent much of his early life in Rubery, Worcs., where he showed significant interest in the natural history of his "home patch", as his manuscript records, from age ten onwards, testify. He began reading medicine at Cambridge in 1911, but did not complete his studies (at St Thomas's, London) until after he had served in the Royal Naval Volunteer Reserve, as a Surgeon-Probationer, during the First World War. He recorded his experiences at this time in *The log of a loblolly boy at sea, 1915-17* (Suffern *c*.1920). After several hospital posts, he entered medical journalism and in due course joined the staff of *The Lancet*. He developed a wide range of interests, of which those involving aspects of natural history, besides ornithology, included entomology; he was a good all round naturalist, with additional interests in archaeology – especially human artifacts. He was a Fellow of the Royal Anthropological Institute and in his manuscript notes he alludes to the discovery of a metal "ring" on a bird's leg (probably a guinea fowl) from the Roman occupation level at Silchester (Suffern collected papers), rather pre-dating our modern interest in these devices! The family took up residence at Hill Head in 1921 and Suffern eventually moved to Hook Cottage, Warsash. Shortly after the Second World War he started the enduring practice of conducting parties of birdwatchers around the Haven on Sunday mornings. Among his papers, deposited in the University of Southampton library, are 53 manuscript files with notes in species order intended to form the basis of a comprehensive account of the birds of Titchfield Haven. In fact, it reads like a review of the birds of Britain, a feature reflected in the proposed title: *The birds of Titchfield Haven in relation to those of Hampshire and of Great Britain historically considered.*

Birdwatchers under his guidance established the database which enabled the Haven to be declared an SSSI in 1959. When the HCC purchased the major part of the area in 1972, one of Suffern's "enthusiasts", Barry Duffin, was appointed warden. The full story of this successful conservation project is told in *The Birds of Tichfield Haven* (Duffin 1991), based partly on Suffern's manuscript material, with a Foreword by Roy Dennis, then RSPB Regional Officer for North Scotland, who had been one of Suffern's early "pupils". Suffern is commemorated by the birdwatching hide carrying his name at the Haven.

Our account of the Portsmouth Group now continues. In March 1951, David Billett and Tubbs met for the first time, at Farlington Marshes. Prior to that time both had been making regular independent visits and Tubbs had been contributing to the National Wildfowl Count scheme. A chance meeting later that year with Suffern at Titchfield Haven, encouraged Billett in August 1951, to begin recording the numbers and distribution of all species around Langstone Harbour.

In 1952, George Clay, Cliff Henty, Graham Rees and Bryan Renyard, all contemporaries, also "discovered" Farlington Marshes. With the increased manpower, it was agreed to pool efforts to conduct a comprehensive survey of the Langstone Harbour area and submit an annual report to the County

Recorder, at that time Cohen. Billett collected the records and he and Rees edited the first report which was sent to Cohen at the end of 1952. It was the latter who coined the term "Portsmouth Group". The comprehensive counting, begun in Langstone Harbour in 1952, continues to this day and constitutes the longest-running continuous series of such data in Europe. It is proving invaluable in constructing a picture of long term changes in populations of many wader and some wildfowl species. In 1954 new names, including Michael Bryant, Eddie Wiseman, Johnny Bowers and Billy Truckle, appeared in the Portsmouth Group and counts began to cover heathland birds and raptors in the New Forest, together with regular sea-watches at St Catherine's Point on the Isle of Wight. It is important to remember the background against which these developments were occurring. Not only was knowledge of Hampshire's birds rather sketchy, but travel was significantly less easy than it is today. There are innumerable stories of travel from Portsmouth to distant parts of the county, involving bicycles, ferries, much walking, and sleeping under groundsheets. It was at the end of the time of petrol rationing and comparatively few people owned cars.

Billett, one of the Group's founders, has remained continuously and actively involved as a key member in its affairs to date. Of particular importance has been his association with the Farlington Marshes LNR from its inception. As well as his contributions to the establishment of the reserve, he has been successively honorary warden and then warden until 1992, during which service he was once hospitalised by a chestful of shotgun pellets from a "marsh cowboy". Two statements made by his contemporaries reflect the significance of his efforts: "Farlington (i.e. the reserve) would not have happened without him" and "the Marshes would not be the place they are today without the habitat management regime he has helped design and has so successfully implemented". Nor has he neglected to contribute to the written record (Billett 1966). He has also been a member of the Editorial and Records panel for the *Hampshire Bird Report* and was County Recorder from 1979-84.

Other groups in the county were developing recording work in the 1950s and later. The New Forest Ornithological Club, originating in the early 1950s and based on the New Forest and Southampton Water, published an annual report called *Argus* for a time in the mid-1950s.

In the south-west of the county, the Christchurch Harbour Ornithological Group (now part of the Christchurch Ornithological Society) was founded in 1956 by Frank Clafton and played an important part in developing knowledge of Hampshire's birds in that area. Better known by its acronym, CHOG was the first group in the county to become involved in ringing, concentrating on migrants at Hengistbury Head and Stanpit Marsh. It produces reports annually.

The Gilkicker Point Group, involving Martin Terry, Richard Carpenter and others, who had been influenced by Suffern, was particularly active in coastal migration studies in the east Solent during the 1960s and early 1970s. It also produced annual reports on its activities.

Another informal coastal group, which is still active, has contributed records for the Hurst/Keyhaven stretch of the west Solent – compiled by Wiseman.

In the north-east of the county in the late 1960s and early 1970s several young birders were developing under the influence of Ewart Jones, head of Biology at Farnborough Grammar School, aided by Gilbert Rowland, a teaching colleague. This north-east Group included, at that time, Richard Millington and Steve Gantlett (who later jointly founded the Bird Information Service), Stephen Millington and John Clark. Emanating from this Group, from 1971 onwards, were the annual *Hants/Surrey Border Bird Reports* which culminated in the book *Birds of the Hants/Surrey Border* (Clark 1984). The Group continued the work of Jones in systematic recording of the area, including counts of heathland breeding species.

### Organisational Aspects and some of the Individuals Involved
By 1954, as indicated earlier, Cohen and Dowdeswell (with the help of others, such as P L Day) had set up the "Ornithological Section" of the HFC. With Dowdeswell as Chairman and Cohen as Honorary Secretary, the Section produced annual Bird Reports as parts of the Proceedings of the HFC until 1965. For 1966-77, the Bird Reports were published by the Ornithological Section independently of the HFC, thereafter becoming the responsibility of the Hampshire Ornithological Society (HOS). Table 2 contains a list of honorary officers of the Ornithological Section from 1954-1978.

| Year | Chairman | Secretary | Bird Report Editorial and Records Committee Personnel* |
|---|---|---|---|
| 1954-56 | Dowdeswell | Cohen | |
| 1957 | Dowdeswell | Cohen | Cohen/Taverner/Palmer/Bryant/ |
| 1958-63 | Cohen | Grove | Stafford/Wiseman/Adams/Billett/ |
| 1964-65 | Pierce | Grove | Wooldridge/Rees/Truckle/Husband/ |
| 1966-70 | Pierce | Puckering | Elms/Clark/S. Millington/Steventon |
| 1971-78 | Bryant | Weatherly | |

\* In order of first appearance

*Table 2. Honorary Officers of the Hampshire Field Club Ornithological Section 1954-1978.*

Edwin Cohen (1894-1970) had arrived in Sway in 1940 from Cheshire. After education at Rugby, he had entered his father's shipping business, for which he often travelled abroad, especially to South America. In the 1914-18 war he served as a Captain in the Royal Marines, at Gallipoli and in France, where he was severely wounded. He gained a Private Pilot's Licence between the wars, piloting his own Avro Avian around the country, and served in the RAF at the beginning of the Second World War. He was invalided out and helped James Fisher to organise the 1944-46 national Rook Investigation at the Ministry of Agriculture. He had started ringing in about 1926, an activity which was to result in the study of birds in and around his garden at Sway, the subject of a TV film "Birds of a Hampshire Garden". A noted ornithologist, he served on the Councils of the RSPB, BTO and the International Council for the Protection of Birds (ICPB - now Bird Life International). He was made a Verderer of the New Forest in 1969. Part of his extensive library is now with the Hampshire Wildlife Trust as the "Edwin Cohen Memorial Library".

By 1957 Cohen was both HFC Ornithological Section Chairman, a post he held until 1964, and again, briefly, the Bird Report Editor, having taken over from Day, who had reorganised the layout but died suddenly shortly thereafter. (Day's birdwatching diaries (1942-57) have recently come to light and contain daily entries for the New Forest and north shore of the west Solent. Earlier diaries appear to have been lost.) (Tubbs pers comm.) Cohen's influence in the 1950s and 1960s was extremely important; he acted as a focus for the growing recording effort in the county. Whereas before the World Wars birdwatching had been for those of ample means and leisure, now many more began to take part. From all the records he was receiving, Cohen was able to write *Birds of Hampshire and the Isle of Wight* (Cohen 1963) which, nearly a decade later, was brought up to date with *A Revised list of Hampshire and Isle of Wight Birds* (Cohen and Taverner 1972). Cohen had been working on the latter when he died in 1970 and it was completed by John Taverner.

The 1960s also saw the beginnings of the move towards a totally independent ornithological organisation – what was eventually to become the Hampshire Ornithological Society. In 1966, a number of Hampshire's leading ornithologists set up a small group, known unimaginatively as the "Ginger Group", with the twin objectives of achieving independence from the HFC and of revitalising the organisation of ornithological activities in Hampshire. An interim report of the Group advocated the setting up of a register of observers/fieldworkers in the county, an improved Bird Report format, and the formation of an Executive Committee and of a Field Studies Committee. The Group's final report, accepted at the Ornithological Section AGM in 1968, contained recommendations, including those just listed, which remain the basis of HOS's operation today. It took another decade of negotiation between the Ornithological Section and the HFC before an amicable secession on terms satisfactory to both parties was finally agreed.

On March 17th 1978, the Hampshire Ornithological Society was launched under the Presidency of Guy Mountfort, noted international conservationist and field guide author, with Bryant as Chairman. James Hancock, then President of the British Trust for Ornithology, took over as President of HOS in 1986. A list of these and other HOS officers appears in table 3.

"Doc" Suffern at home in Hill Head, summer 1960. *W H Truckle*

The Portsmouth Group "in action" at Farlington Marshes, August 1959. From left: Tubbs, Bryant, Walker, Burnop, Simonds, Searle, Billett and Wiseman. *W H Truckle*

Edwin Cohen, Chairman of the
Hampshire Field Club
Ornithological Section,
1958–63.          *RSPB*

Peter Le Brocq using his "Lebrocqulars" at North Binness Island, Langstone
Harbour, June 1957.                                              *W H Truckle*

Bryant served as Chairman until 1982. A solicitor by profession, a respected botanist and ornithologist, he was one of the prime movers behind the scenes from 1959 onwards, working through the Portsmouth NHS, in the formation of the Hampshire and Isle of Wight Naturalists' (now Wildlife) Trust in 1961 and becoming its first Honorary Secretary. Similar behind the scenes work enabled him, as Chairman of the Ornithological Section of HFC, to lead the Section's negotiations for secession. He served for a number of years as a member of the Editorial and Records Panel which produced the annual Bird Report. For these and many other services to county ornithology, he was made a Life Member of HOS in 1988.

| Year | President | Chairman | Secretary | Bird Report Editor | Recorder |
|------|-----------|----------|-----------|--------------------|----------|
| 1978 | Mountfort | Bryant | Weatherly | Taverner | Billett |
| 1979-82 | Mountfort | Bryant | Weatherly | Panel | |
| 1983-85 | Mountfort | Evans | Wood | Panel | Wiseman |
| 1986 | Hancock | Evans | Wood | Clark | Wiseman |
| 1987-90 | Hancock | Leach | Wood | Clark | Wiseman |
| 1991 | Hancock | Leach | Morrison | Wood | Wiseman |
| 1992 | Hancock | Eyre | Morrison | Wood | Wiseman |
| 1993 | Hancock | Eyre | Morrison | Wood | Clark |

*Table 3. Honorary Officers of the Hampshire Ornithological Society, 1978-1993.*

In the 1980s, HOS progressed through a period of consolidation and membership growth (*c.*400 in 1978 to *c.*1000 in 1991). Flesh was added to many of the embryo activities instituted in the late 1960s and early 1970s, such as the setting up of the Publicity, Recruitment and Programme Committee, the beginnings of a computerised county ornithological database and formulation of a data release policy, stronger conservation liaison and better services to members.

Before proceeding further, a few words are necessary concerning the production of the annual Bird Report. From 1958 the report was produced by a panel, which included Cohen until his death in 1970, and Taverner. Throughout this period Taverner was the only ever-present member, increasingly undertaking the role of editor-in-chief until relinquishing the post in 1980. The panel format continued into the mid-1980s. In 1974, the county boundaries changed and thereafter no records for Christchurch Harbour and part of the Avon valley below Sopley were included in the records, because that part of the county was transferred to Dorset. Isle of Wight records continued to be included until 1979.

Taverner has been a principal contributor to much of the written record on Hampshire's birds for the latter part of the century. By profession a geographer, he worked as a teacher for 35 years at Peter Symonds' School, Winchester. He admits a significant debt to the example of founder members of the Portsmouth Group: "....they changed my whole outlook on ornithology; for me they changed birdwatching from an interest into a study to be pursued with discipline". How productive has been that change! Mention has been made previously of his work on wildfowl, but this interest was not confined to the county, for he analysed data on the distribution of wintering Eider on a national basis (Taverner 1959,

1963, 1967). On his favourite patch at Needs Ore, which he visited regularly from 1958-85, he was able to confirm the first successful nesting of the Mediterranean Gull in Britain in 1968 (Taverner 1970) – a just reward for discipline. As well as his more specialist interests, which also include butterflies, orchids and a passion for photography, he has been an excellent publicist and popularist, writing regular articles in the *Hampshire Magazine* and the *Southern Evening Echo*. His outstanding contribution to Hampshire ornithology was recognised in 1988 when, on the occasion of HOS's tenth anniversary, he was made a Life Member of the society.

### *Field Studies Committee and Related Activities*

The Field Studies Committee (FSC) held its first meeting in 1968, with a remit to "concern itself with organised field work of all kinds, liaison with the Ornithological Section Editorial and Records Panel, conservation interests, etc." The committee was comprised of members with interest in breeding, migration, ringing, wildfowl and wader counts, conservation liaison and Records Committee liaison. This is still its essential *modus operandi* in the 1990s. Its activity was, and remains, a mixture of scientific planning, organisation and liaison in order to satisfy the growing aspirations of the increasing number of members who wish to see the results of their fieldwork put to good use for conservation purposes.

It set up the framework which focused and permitted the development of ornithological teamwork on a county-wide basis and provided a mechanism for county cooperation in both local and national surveys. This need had first become evident with the 1968-72 BTO Breeding Atlas (although, in the event, Taverner had carried the organisation of this virtually unaided). In its conservation role, it provided guidance for the gathering and analysis of ornithological data necessary to enable credible information to be supplied to the primary conservation bodies, principally the Royal Society for the Protection of Birds, the Hampshire Wildlife Trust and English Nature.

In addition to its involvement with long-running national studies, including estuaries and wildfowl counts, Common Bird Census and Waterways Bird Survey work, the FSC and its members have helped in the organisation in Hampshire of other national surveys, such as the BTO Winter Atlas, the second Breeding Atlas 1988-92 and, among many single species surveys, those concerning Nightjar, Nightingale and Lapwing. This is additional to planning county-wide and other local surveys, among which may be mentioned roosting gulls, nesting House Martins, wintering Water Pipits and Green Sandpipers and, in 1986, the Tetrad Atlas Survey of breeding birds, which was to last for the next five years and provide a major input to the species accounts of this book. The FSC has also been responsible for initiating and organising the annual HOS Fieldworkers' Meetings, at which progress with the survey work is presented and discussed.

The FSC in particular, and county birdwatchers as a whole, have been particularly fortunate to have had Peter Puckering as the first FSC Secretary (1968-86). It can be said with some authority, by one of the writers of this chapter, that the likelihood is that the FSC would have collapsed without his characteristically thorough contributions. Puckering was Secretary of the

Ornithological Section of HFC for several years (1966-71), taking over from Edward Grove. From Cohen and Grove he also inherited the BTO Regional Representative mantle (1972-86), which brought with it responsibility for overseeing the BTO's annual Heronries census in the county (1972-90). He also acted as coordinator for the HOS Tetrad Atlas Survey (1986-91) and was actively involved in the 1975 and 1980 national Rook censuses. In recognition of these contributions and much else he was made a Life Member of HOS in 1991.

## Ringing Groups

One of the activities which the FSC encouraged, in order to improve quantitative knowledge of Hampshire's birds, was ringing. From the 1960s onwards several specialised ringing groups emerged in the county, often as parts of broader-based groups. They were stimulated by activities like the BTO Sand Martin ringing enquiry and the investigation of the Bearded Tit annual immigration to Farlington Marshes. A few examples are mentioned below, not forgetting CHOG's ringing efforts noted earlier.

An outgrowth of the Portsmouth Group, the Farlington Ringing Group, which continues to the present day, was initiated by Billett and Rees and joined later by John Oakshatt. It was particularly active in ringing waders, the results for Greenshank leading to national recognition. This work was maintained through the 1970s and early 1980s by Keith Grant and David Steventon, the latter introducing cannon-netting to the Group.

At Fleet Pond, the Group led by Tony Miller and Noel Elms was formed in 1976 initially to study its Reed Warbler colony. This Group also undertook the first large-scale ringing of Canada Geese in the county. The Group flourished until the early 1980s when members moving out of the area and changes in habitat led to the cessation of its activities.

The Lower Test Ringing Group was started in 1975 by Hugh Insley and Roger Jackson, largely to study migrant *Acrocephalus* warblers using the extensive reed beds of the Lower Test Marshes (Insley and Jackson 1976; Insley and Boswell 1978). This Group, which has regularly ringed the moulting Mute Swans on Eling Great Marsh, continues today with different personnel and produces an annual report.

The first Ringing Report for the county, covering 1967-68 and written by Oakshatt, the ringing representative on the FSC, appeared in the 1968 *Hampshire Bird Report*. Ringing Reports have appeared annually since 1972, produced by Keith Grant (1972-76), Glynne Evans (1977-82), Brian Dudley (1984-88) and Peter Potts (1989-to date). For a short period in the heyday of county ringing, in the late 1970s and early 1980s, the ringers held annual one-day "conferences".

## Examples of Individual Contributions to Hampshire Ornithology

We begin by noting the work of two professionals, John Ash and Tubbs.

Ash, who worked in the county for the Game Research Association (now Game Conservancy) at Fordingbridge, was among the first biologists to draw attention to the widespread deaths of farmland birds through toxic seed dressings in the early 1960s. He contributed to a number of reports on the subject (Cramp *et al* 1960-65). From his other work we select his extensive studies on game birds and birds of prey on the chalkland of western Hampshire (Ash 1960) and his long term study (1954-66) of Red-backed Shrikes in the New Forest (Ash 1970).

Tubbs undertook similar long term studies. He started his survey of the Buzzard in 1961, and published the results in *The Buzzard* (Tubbs 1974a) and elsewhere (Tubbs and Tubbs 1985). He also studied the Dartford Warbler in the New Forest (e.g. Tubbs 1967b) and the wildfowl and waders in The Solent and its harbours (e.g. Tubbs 1980).

From the contributions of the "amateur" ranks, we select the "rediscovery" of the Honey Buzzard in the county in the early 1950s by Peter Le Brocq, noteworthy from the mid-1950s onwards for sporting a huge pair (15x60) of Barr and Stroud binoculars (the so-called Lebrocqulars); Mike Adams' evidence for the first successful breeding of the Firecrest in Britain in the New Forest in 1962 (Adams 1966) and Steventon's work, organising wader counts and analysing the results (Steventon 1977), which helped to show the great importance that the Hampshire coastline plays in the life-cycles of large numbers of waders. As a final example, out of the many who should receive mention, we choose Clark for the combination of his Hampshire fieldwork and his important inputs to HOS. His contributions to knowledge of the birds of the north-east of the county have been mentioned. He has also provided extensive data on wildfowl and waders in the Avon valley and was one of the pioneers of the Tetrad Atlas Survey (1986-91). Besides his editorial role for the county Bird Report (1981-89), he is co-editor of this book.

**The Conservation Interface**

As the century has progressed, emphasis has increasingly focused on collecting records and undertaking studies primarily for conservation purposes. One of the aims of HOS is to use the results to encourage and support the conservation of birds and their habitat in the county. The requirement is for data on birds and their populations at specified sites, the trends in their numbers, their use of the habitat and any special needs of particular species. Acquiring such quantitative data involves much diligent, often collaborative, effort from a large body of observers. Once the data has been collected and collated, it can be analysed and disseminated. It is then available for use by, among others, local planners and it may be deployed as evidence by the primary conservation bodies.

Estuaries work in the county is a good example of amateur collaborative study with a strong conservation application. The Birds of Estuaries Enquiry (BoEE) is often held up as a model of effective cooperative data gathering. It is gratifying to note that the activities of Hampshire ornithologists provided a strong stimulus to its establishment. The need for facts about the use made of estuaries by shore birds had been evident for a significant time when the first attempt at coordinated north-European estuaries counts was made in 1966. The project was coordinated by the Wader Working Group of the International Waterfowl Reseach Bureau and followed similar work in Denmark earlier that decade. In Hampshire, counts in Langstone Harbour had been undertaken by the Portsmouth Group since 1952, in Christchurch Harbour by CHOG since 1956, to a lesser extent at Dibden Bay by the New Forest Ornithological Club and others since 1950, and by Taverner, who started regular counts on the Beaulieu river estuary in 1958. All had accumulated relevant count series.

When the BTO established the estuaries counts pilot survey in 1969/70, David Glue, from Hampshire, was appointed organiser. This was soon after he had helped to write up an account of the use made of Dibden Bay by waders (Pratt and Glue 1968). The results of estuaries counts for the county have subsequently been detailed annually in the Bird Report. The designation of significant parts of the county's intertidal coastline as protected areas, as noted in the previous chapter, has been one noteworthy development to which these cooperative activities have contributed.

A different view of the relationship between data gathering and conservation is exemplified by the recent history of the Sand Martin. After the major Sand Martin ringing studies of the 1960s and 1970s, there was evidence of a significant decline and then some partial recovery in the national population, which was reflected in Hampshire. In 1987, inspired by Charles Cuthbert, HOS surveyed all known breeding colonies in the county, repeating it in 1988, but with the emphasis that year shifting towards conservation measures in association with the Naturalists' (now Wildlife) Trust, the County Council and the (now defunct) Farmers and Wildlife Advisory Group. To what extent the near 70% increase in breeding pairs between the two years could be attributed to the conservation measures is a matter for conjecture but it certainly helped locally.

It is self-evident from these examples that if HOS fails to have adequate, comprehensive, collated ornithological data available, both on a species and on a site basis, it will not be in a position properly to assist the conservation organisations. Ornithological data gathering is still largely dependent on a large body of amateur fieldworkers. Its collation, analysis and dissemination, however, is dependent on a remarkable few. Achievement of habitat and species protection is not just a product of good data gathering, analysis and availability; it is also in large measure a result of dedication by particular individuals. We conclude this section by offering tribute to two very different contributors, one a professional who we have already mentioned, the other an amateur.

In his introductory chapter, Tubbs points to the efforts of people like David Pumfrett and Freddie Emery-Wallis in progressing the acquisition of Titchfield Haven as a Reserve within the coastal protection policy of the County Council. What was omitted was mention of Tubbs' own role in these and other similar developments. Careful, sustained and informed persuasion of many individuals, particularly in local government, over long periods lies behind these conservation successes. It is not the place here to list the particulars of his many contributions, at planning enquiries, at innumerable meetings, in a host of important ornithological and other publications (of which some were noted earlier), or in many other ways. However, at the time of his "retirement" in 1993, after 33 years with the Nature Conservancy, Nature Conservancy Council and English Nature, it is opportune that we acknowledge the enormous debt owed to Tubbs for his efforts in the cause of wildlife conservation in the county. Nor will it be out of place to salute his wife Jenni for her assistance in many of his studies, as well as her important role in the administration of the Lyndhurst office.

As a contrast, Norman Orr's contributions provide a role model for the best in amateur involvement. Based in Sussex, where he won a prize for a conservation study on Peregrines, Orr made birdwatching trips to Hampshire in the 1930s and paid further visits in the 1940s while on leave from the RAF. He took up residence in the south-west of the county, now in Dorset, in 1958 and has remained there ever since. He was involved in the founding of the Naturalists' Trust, of which he became the first Chairman. He concerned himself with the protection of Little Terns nesting on Hurst Beach, was involved in the Forestry Commission modifying their felling policy in the New Forest during the breeding season and initiated, with Lord Normanton's assistance, ten years of wardening, conducted by the Trust, of the wintering White-fronted Geese in the Avon valley. He undertook the "marking" of Stone Curlew nests on the chalk downland in the west of the county where, for a number of years, he carried out independent survey work of this and other scarce species. He was actively involved in the acquisition of Farlington Marshes as a Reserve and served for five years on the RSPB Council. In his own view, bird photography has produced some of his major achievements. This is very well illustrated by several of his superb photographs which are reproduced in this book.

## Concluding Remarks
The reader will have noticed how ornithology in Hampshire has progressed from the "shooting and stuffing" era, with only casual sight records, at the end of the 19th century, to the "collection" of large quantities of data by observation, which is increasingly being applied for conservation purposes, in the second half of the 20th century.

For 21st century Hampshire, we see a need to improve the quantification of knowledge still further for both sites and species, with good quality data which will admit adequate historical comparisons so that population trends and changes in habitat extent, quality and usage may be discerned.

## Editors' note
Any account of twentieth century ornithology in Hampshire would be incomplete without mention of the co-authors of this chapter. Richard Leach was Chairman of HOS from 1987-1991. He devoted his abundant energy and enthusiasm to the society during a period of expansion in both membership and activities. Norman Pratt has been an active ornithologist in the county for over 30 years. He was a founder member of HOS and has served on its Management Committee since its inception. He was first Chairman of the Field Studies Committee and has been particularly active liaising with local and national conservation bodies to ensure that information gathered by HOS members is utilised to good effect.

# The Birdwatching Year

*John A Eyre*

The previous chapter describes how ornithology in Hampshire has evolved and how ornithologists have brought the knowledge of birds in the county to its current state. The interest in birds and birdwatching has grown dramatically over the past four decades. In the early 1950s, only 30-40 people contributed records to the *Hampshire Bird Report*; today there are about 350. Over the same period there have been more than 2100 individual contributors and it is thanks to all of them and their predecessors that this book can be written. It is their information, gathered as individual observations or as part of organised surveys, that combines to paint an overall picture of birds in Hampshire.

In recognition of these many individual contributions, this chapter, as a forerunner to the species accounts which follow, is intended to give a flavour of birdwatching in the county as it is today – where birds can be found, in what numbers and how they are influenced by the seasons and the weather. The aim is not to provide a site by site guide – Green and Cade (1989) have already satisfied that need – but rather to describe in more general terms, Hampshire's special habitats and the birds that can be found in them throughout the birdwatching year. It is to be hoped that in future still more people will grow to appreciate and seek to preserve the diversity of birds and habitats which Hampshire has to offer.

## Winter

A birdwatcher beginning a year in the county may well choose, in January, to visit one of many localities on the coast. The Hampshire shoreline is broken and lengthened by a series of estuaries, extending from Chichester Harbour in the east, through Langstone Harbour, Portsmouth Harbour and Southampton Water to the Beaulieu and Lymington estuaries in the west. It is these tidal inlets that make The Solent of international importance for birds. In winter, they provide food and shelter for vast numbers of wildfowl, waders and gulls. A visit to any one of them can easily fill a short winter day but the best time for watching birds on the coast is around the time of high tide.

As the water rises to cover the mudflats, waders are forced to feed closer to the shore and finally to congregate in densely packed roosts. An excellent place to watch this happen is in Langstone Harbour, where birds gather on the islands and at favoured sites around the shore such as The Kench on Hayling Island and on the fields and lagoon at Farlington Marshes. As the tide ebbs, birds leave their roosts and can be watched flying back to feed on the freshly exposed mud. High tide is also a good time to search for divers, grebes and sea ducks in the harbours and to watch for the sudden panic brought to roosting birds by a hunting raptor. Sparrowhawk and Kestrel are the species most frequently encountered but Merlin, Peregrine, Hen Harrier and Short-eared Owl also occur.

During the winter some species are ubiquitous along the Hampshire coast. The Brent Goose is one of the most conspicuous. Numbers have increased dramatically over the past 20 years and some 25,000 now winter regularly in

The Solent. They occur in all the estuaries and also feed on the adjacent pastures and arable land. Gulls are also numerous, particularly Black-headed Gulls; Common Gull numbers peak in February and March, while Herring and Great Black-backed Gulls increase after storms or during cold weather. Lesser Black-backed Gulls occur in very small numbers except in Southampton Water, where a pre-roost gathering now regularly exceeds 200 birds.

Of the wildfowl, Shelduck, Wigeon, Teal and Mallard are common and Pintail and Shoveler occur in reasonable numbers. Common waders include Oystercatcher, Ringed Plover, Grey Plover, Lapwing, Dunlin, Curlew and Redshank. Other waders, such as Knot and Black-tailed and Bar-tailed Godwits, favour Chichester and Langstone Harbours, as do wintering Great Crested and Little Grebes and sea ducks such as Goldeneye and Red-breasted Merganser. These species are easily found although changes in local conditions can cause changes in numbers and distribution of some of them. For example, Black-tailed Godwits tend to concentrate at Titchfield Haven when the area is flooded; during such periods, numbers in Langstone Harbour are much reduced.

Species such as Black-necked and Slavonian Grebes and Eiders are regular but less widespread. They favour particular areas and can be viewed best from one or two locations. For example, the most reliable place to find Black-necked, Slavonian and, occasionally, Red-necked Grebes in Langstone Harbour is in the Langstone Channel off Hayling Oyster Beds. A walk around the embankment that surrounds the Oyster Beds between November and February usually guarantees Black-necked Grebe and, with a more careful search, one or two Slavonian Grebes as well.

Many other species winter regularly around The Solent in small numbers and can often be found by visiting specific sites. At the time of writing, Southsea Castle is reliable for Purple Sandpiper, Lee-on-the-Solent for Mediterranean Gull, The Hardway in Gosport for Glaucous Gull and Eling, Needs Ore and Pennington and Keyhaven Marshes for Peregrine.

Severe weather can bring increased numbers and a greater variety of birds to the coast. Divers, Red-necked Grebes, ducks such as Scaup and Smew, and gulls such as Little and Iceland are all more likely to be found during, or immediately following, such conditions. Sheltered spots, like the Eling/Redbridge area at the head of Southampton Water, are well worth checking at such times. Freezing conditions can also result in spectacular coastal movements of Lapwings, Skylarks, thrushes and other ground-feeding birds.

Hampshire's river valleys provide another important habitat in winter. The county is fortunate to have several rivers that rise on the chalk and flow south to the sea – the Avon, Test, Itchen and Meon. All are rich in nutrients and hence in water plants and fish. The flanking grasslands are fertile and lush and subject to flooding. Where gravel has been extracted, there are water-filled pits and these, together with watercress beds, fish farms, sewage farms and reed beds, add to the variety of habitats that make the valleys so attractive to birds.

The westernmost river, the Avon, is the best. More than 100 Bewick's Swans winter in the valley. They may be found almost anywhere from Christchurch north to the Wiltshire border but the meadows at Ibsley are the most reliable spot. The valley also regularly supports a flock of White-fronted Geese which, unfortunately, has been getting smaller in recent years. Many other wildfowl, including Mute Swan, Wigeon, Gadwall, Teal, Shoveler, Pochard and Tufted Duck, winter in the valley and on the adjacent Blashford Lakes; they are joined by occasional Smew, Goosander and Scaup in cold weather. Gadwall numbers there have been increasing for some years and the Avon valley wintering population is now of international importance. Waders such as Lapwing, Golden Plover and Snipe also occur in large numbers. Following heavy flooding, numbers increase and additional species such as Dunlin, Black-tailed Godwit, Redshank and Ruff can sometimes be found. Winter rarities in the valley have included Red-breasted Goose, Night Heron and Little Bustard.

The gravel pits in the Avon valley are particularly productive as are many others elsewhere in the county, for example in the Test valley at Timsbury, on Hayling Island at Sinah and in the north-east, in the Blackwater valley at Eversley and Yateley (partly in Berkshire). There are also several large ponds and ornamental lakes such as Fleet Pond, Frensham Pond (mainly in Surrey), Alresford Pond and Sowley Pond and wetland areas such as Titchfield Haven, which is situated at the mouth of the river Meon. All these sites hold high numbers of the regular waterfowl and less common species are often recorded, particularly after bad weather. Goosanders winter regularly at Eversley, a Ring-necked Duck has occurred at Timsbury for several years and Bitterns are seen almost annually at Fleet Pond and Titchfield Haven. The waterside sallows and alders are attractive to wintering Chiffchaffs, as well as flocks of Siskins and Redpolls.

Of the more specialised river valley habitats, the watercress beds on the Test and Itchen remain unfrozen in winter and Water Pipits, Grey Wagtails, Kingfishers and Green Sandpipers are attracted to them. Green Sandpiper and Water Pipit numbers have declined in recent years, probably as a result of reduced food availability caused by changes in watercress growing and harvesting practices. The latter species can still be found at some sewage farms such as Camp Farm and, most reliably, on the Lower Test Marshes and at Titchfield Haven. The reed beds at Lower Test and the Haven, and also at Farlington Marshes and Fleet and Alresford Ponds, are good places to find Water Rails and Bearded Tits, especially during cold weather.

The open heathlands of the New Forest and the north-east can appear almost birdless in winter. Of the Hampshire specialities, Dartford Warblers remain but can be inconspicuous. Woodlarks and some Stonechats leave the heaths, although a few of the latter persist through all but the harshest winters, as do some Meadow Pipits and Reed Buntings. The larger heaths are visited by Hen Harriers, Merlins and Great Grey Shrikes, while the surrounding woods hold flocks of Siskins, Redpolls and, in some years, Crossbills. The latter are found in Scots pine and larch throughout the winter, whereas Siskins and Redpolls favour alder early in the season, moving to birch as the alder seeds are depleted.

The chalk too is quiet at this time of year. Flocks of Lapwings, Golden Plovers, Skylarks and finches, including Bramblings, can be found, but the most exciting feature of the high downs, at sites such as Cheesefoot Head, Great Lichfield Down and Old Winchester Hill, is undoubtedly the variety of raptors that winter there. Buzzards are resident while Hen Harriers, Short-eared Owls, Merlins and Peregrines are winter visitors. Red Kites are also being seen more frequently in the county following their re-introduction elsewhere in England. Areas of unimproved grassland and young conifer plantations are usually most rewarding for raptor watching.

**Spring**
Throughout the county, spring is signalled by the break-up of the winter tit and finch flocks and the return of the summer visitors. Woodlarks and Skylarks can be heard singing in February and the first migrant Sand Martins, Wheatears and Chiffchaffs have arrived by mid-March. Several other species, including Garganey, Little Ringed Plover, Stone Curlew, Blackcap, Willow Warbler and Swallow, have usually put in an appearance before the month is out. The first Redstarts and Tree Pipits generally arrive in early April, to be followed later in the month by the remaining warblers, Nightingales, Hobbies and Turtle Doves, and by Nightjars and Spotted Flycatchers in May. Many of these species, including Hobby, Nightingale and Turtle Dove, are widespread and can be found in a variety of habitats including the heathlands, downlands and river valleys. Others, like Nightjar, Woodlark, Redstart and Tree Pipit, are decidely scarce away from the acid soils of the south-west and the north-east, and Stone Curlews are restricted to just a few locations on the chalk.

Spring passage is most noticeable on the coast, although there are few classic migrant traps or ideal places to sea-watch in the county. Hampshire lacks the open sea with protruding headlands and promentaries so prized as vantage points in neighbouring counties. From almost anywhere along the entire coast, the five-kilometre width of The Solent is viewed against the backcloth of the Isle of Wight. Furthermore, some of the birds moving east along the south coast undoubtedly bypass The Solent to the south of the island. This means that Hurst Beach at the western entrance to The Solent and Sandy Point, Hayling Island, at the eastern entrance are the best sea-watching sites. Both tend to be most productive early in the day, particularly when there is a south-easterly wind to drift birds on to the coast. At both sites, Sandwich Terns are amongst the earliest arrivals in late March but the main passage occurs between mid-April and mid-May.

Sea-watches are seldom spectacular. Common Terns and Bar-tailed Godwits are usually the dominant species, and a good day sees in addition a steady but thin stream of Fulmars, Gannets, Common Scoters, Sandwich and Little Terns, a wide selection of waders including Grey Plovers, Knots, Sanderlings and Whimbrels, plus occasional divers and skuas. Little Gulls and Black Terns are also seen regularly.

The coastal marshes, for example at Farlington, Titchfield Haven, Lower Test, Needs Ore and Keyhaven, are attractive to migrant waders. Species such as Little Ringed Plover, Ruff, Spotted Redshank, Greenshank and Common Sandpiper are regular, while Avocet, Little Stint, Curlew Sandpiper and Wood Sandpiper pass through in small numbers. Less common species, such as Temminck's Stint occur almost annually and, in most springs, an occasional vagrant is recorded. 1990 was an exceptional spring with Black-winged Stilt and Terek Sandpiper both recorded at Farlington Marshes. Waders are also seen on passage at inland sites where there are suitable mud or gravel edges. Indeed, some species, such as Green Sandpiper and Common Sandpiper, are as or more common inland than on the coast. In recent years Mockbeggar Lake, one of the Blashford complex of gravel pits, and Eversley Gravel Pits have been productive with Temminck's Stint, Knot, Avocet, Spotted Redshank and Wood Sandpiper recorded in addition to the commoner species.

Almost any patch of woodland or scrub along the coast is worth checking for migrant land birds. Well-watched areas include Sinah Common and Sandy Point on Hayling Island, the scrub on Farlington Marshes and the woodland surrounding Titchfield Haven. In addition to the usual summer visitors, spring migrants include occasional Black Redstarts, Ring Ouzels and Pied Flycatchers. Inland, these species can occur anywhere but are seen most frequently at well-watched sites such as Old Winchester Hill, Beacon Hill and Fleet Pond.

## Summer

Despite Hampshire's many attractions for birds in winter and during migration periods, it is unarguably its breeding birds that make the county really special. Blessed with mild winters and warm summers, proximity to the European mainland and specialised habitats, it is not surprising that some species, close to the northerly edge of their range, retain a foothold in this fortunate county. Regrettably some have been lost. The Red-backed Shrike is one of the saddest and, in some ways, the most surprising, because much of the habitat that it once occupied remains and is seemingly unchanged. Corncrakes, Wrynecks and Cirl Buntings have also gone but other specialities survive and some even flourish. There have also been some recent colonists to compensate, in part, for the losses.

On the coast, there are colonies of Black-headed Gulls, and Sandwich, Common and Little Terns. Britain's first record of breeding Mediterranean Gull was from Needs Ore in 1968 and one or two pairs have bred irregularly since then. Roseate Terns have also bred occasionally in recent years.

The New Forest preserves a unique patchwork of heath and woodland habitats that is undoubtedly Hampshire's greatest wildlife treasure. There are many different and distinct habitats in the Forest each with its own bird community. In some places the open heathland is dry and thickly carpeted with heather and gorse; in others, where it is heavily grazed, it is short-cropped sward; in yet others, it is sodden mire characterised by purple moor grass, cotton grass and sphagnum moss. There are also several types of woodland including ancient groves of oak and other broadleaved species which are particularly attractive to birds. Large areas of heath have been planted with conifers, while invasion by pine and birch scrub increases the habitat diversity.

Characteristic breeding birds of the dry, heather and gorse-covered heathland include Skylark, Woodlark, Meadow Pipit, Stonechat, Dartford Warbler and Linnet. A few pairs of Whinchats and Wheatears breed successfully most years. Tree Pipits, Nightjars and Yellowhammers are found around the woodland edges and where trees are invading the heath, and Woodcock can be watched roding in similar areas at dawn and dusk.

The bogs hold Shelduck, Teal, Snipe, Redshank and Curlew, while Grey Wagtails and Kingfishers occur on the forest streams.

In the broadleaved woodlands, Wood Warblers and Redstarts are relatively common, as are several species of hole-nesting birds such as Tawny Owl, Stock Dove, all three woodpeckers, Nuthatch and Marsh Tit. Mandarin numbers are also increasing. Hawfinches are one of the New Forest specialities but they can be elusive. Their sharp, distinct "tsick" calls, once recognised, are the best aid to locating them.

In the conifer plantations, Coal Tits and Goldcrests are numerous and Siskins, Crossbills and Firecrests also occur. Like the Hawfinch, the latter three species are most easily detected by their calls. The population of Crossbills fluctuates and is boosted occasionally by post-breeding influxes, as in 1990 when a large invasion began in mid-June and continued through the autumn.

Of the raptors breeding in the Forest, the Hobby is one of the most attractive. It can be seen almost anywhere, hunting over the bogs or heath, or displaying over woodland, but one of the most reliable places to look for it is from the Lyndhurst-Beaulieu Road over Bishop's Dyke and Denny Wood. The Forest also supports good populations of Buzzards, Sparrowhawks and Kestrels and a few pairs of Honey Buzzards breed each year. Goshawks occur erratically while Red-footed Falcons are occasionally recorded in early summer.

The heathlands in the north-east of the county are similar in some respects to the New Forest, but markedly different in others. The once-extensive heathland has been fragmented so that only small and isolated pockets remain. In many cases, these continue to be under intense pressure from encroaching urbanisation. Furthermore, the lack of grazing means that pine and birch invasion is a more serious problem. Huge areas have been lost in this way while others have been "improved" for agriculture or building land, or planted with conifers by the Forestry Commission. If it was not for occasional fires and deliberate scrub clearance in a few places, little open heathland would remain. Thanks in part to the Ministry of Defence, which uses them as military training grounds, some areas of open heathland survive and here, as in the New Forest, Hobbies, Nightjars, Woodlarks and Dartford Warblers occur. In fact the north-east Hampshire heaths, in combination with the neighbouring ones in Surrey and Berkshire, represent an important remnant of Britain's lowland heathland and merit far greater recognition and protection than they presently enjoy.

Characteristic birds of the Hampshire downlands in summer include Red-legged and Grey Partridges, Turtle Dove, Skylark, Yellowhammer and Corn Bunting. Apart from the first, which is replenished by continual restocking, the populations of these species are declining, many under the pressure of modern agricultural practices. Another chalkland species, the Stone Curlew, is under even greater threat. Its call, for those fortunate enough to hear it, is one of the most evocative sounds of the downlands in early summer. The species retains a tentative foothold in the county with 20-25 pairs breeding annually thanks to the protection afforded by local farmers under guidance from the RSPB. One of the best places to watch them is on the Hampshire-Wiltshire border on MOD land at Porton Down, although permission is required to enter this restricted area. Another scarce and secretive downland species, far more likely to be heard than seen, is the Quail. Numbers vary from year to year with occasional influxes, such as that in 1989 when an unprecedented 73 calling males were recorded. Of the downland raptors, Kestrels and Sparrowhawks are relatively common while Buzzards and Hobbies are widely, though thinly, spread. The status of Long-eared Owl remains uncertain; a few pairs nest each year but sites occupied in one season are often abandoned the next for no obvious reason. Montagu's

Harrier is seen most years, particularly in the west of the county, but has not been proved to breed since 1978.

Breeding birds of the river valleys and gravel pits include several species of waterfowl. Mute Swan, Mallard, Tufted Duck, Coot and Moorhen are common; Pochard have established a firm foothold in the Test and upper Itchen valleys, while Gadwall now breed in several parts of the county. The introduced Ruddy Duck is established at Blashford Lakes in the Avon valley. Feral Greylags occur in four areas, Barnacle Geese have recently started breeding in the north-east and Canada Geese reach almost pest proportions. Little and Great Crested Grebes breed where the habitat is suitable with notable concentrations in the gravel pit complexes at Blashford and Eversley/Yateley.

The river valleys are also important for many other breeding birds, including several species of waders. The Avon in particular holds high concentrations of Lapwing and Redshank. Snipe also breed regularly but unfortunately numbers have declined markedly over the past few years. Both Little Ringed and Ringed Plovers breed around the gravel pits, favouring the working ones where freshly exposed gravel provides the best nesting opportunities. Other riparian species such as Kingfisher, Grey and Yellow Wagtails, Sand Martin, Dipper and Cetti's Warbler also occur. Dippers are rare and unlikely to become common because the rivers are generally too slow-running and deep, providing little suitable habitat; Yellow Wagtail numbers have fallen dramatically in recent years, but the Cetti's Warbler is one of Hampshire's success stories. After the first record for Britain at Titchfield Haven in 1961, breeding was not proved in the county until 1979. Since then, it has been quick to establish a healthy population, spreading rapidly along the coast and up the main river valleys. Today, there are more Cetti's Warblers in Hampshire than in any other county.

**Autumn**
On the coast, some non-breeding waders such as Grey Plover, Dunlin, Black-tailed and Bar-tailed Godwits and Curlew remain in small numbers throughout the breeding season but numbers begin to build up from late June. Spring passage is barely over before returning autumn migrants start to appear and by the end of July, many waders have arrived, attracted to the coastal lagoons at Farlington, Titchfield, Pennington, Needs Ore and elsewhere. Wader passage peaks in August and September and continues through October. Regular migrants, in addition to those mentioned above, include Ruff, Whimbrel, Spotted Redshank, Greenshank, Green Sandpiper and Common Sandpiper, and usually scarcer species such as Little Stint, Curlew Sandpiper and Wood Sandpiper. This is the time to be alert for rare waders. Hampshire gets its fair share of both Palearctic and Nearctic vagrants which, in recent autumns, have included Pacific Golden Plover, Sociable Plover, Buff-breasted, White-rumped and Baird's Sandpipers, Long-billed Dowitcher, Lesser Yellowlegs and Wilson's Phalarope.

Another one-time rarity that is now being seen regularly on the coast in late summer and early autumn is the Little Egret. Until recently, this species was an occasional passage migrant, but an unprecedented influx took place in the autumn of 1989 with 17 present in the Keyhaven area in late August. Similar, through smaller arrivals took place in subsequent years with some birds remaining throughout the winter. At the time of writing, in late summer 1993, another major influx is occurring and it would seem that we may be witnessing a significant change in status of this attractive species.

D. Thelwell.

Throughout the county the end of the breeding season is marked by birds gathering into roosting and pre-migration flocks. Hirundines mass over the ponds and form reed bed roosts. On the downs, parties of Stone Curlews gather at traditional sites and family groups of Woodlarks come together on the heaths. In late summer at Titchfield Haven, flocks of terns can be seen offshore and inside the reserve at high tide; this is a good time to look for Roseate, Arctic and Black Terns among the much more numerous Common Terns.

Visible migration is more obvious in autumn than in spring, particularly on the coast. Swifts and Sand Martins begin to leave in July and, by early August Yellow Wagtail numbers are building up at Farlington and elsewhere. For many species, passage peaks in late August or September. At this time, counts of migrating Swallows and House Martins can reach four figures at both coastal and inland sites such as Fleet Pond. Meadow Pipits, warblers, including Lesser Whitethroat, Whitethroat, Chiffchaff and Willow Warbler, Whinchats and Wheatears are conspicuous. Thrushes and finches continue to move through later in the season and less frequent species such as Black Redstart, Ring Ouzel and Firecrest appear fairly regularly. Recent autumn rarities have included Red-rumped Swallow, Richards and Tawny Pipits, Barred, Icterine, Melodious, Pallas's and Yellow-browed Warblers, Red-breasted Flycatcher and Penduline Tit. Migrant raptors are also a feature of the autumn particularly at well-watched sites such as Farlington Marshes and Titchfield Haven, with a few records each year of Marsh Harrier, Osprey and Merlin.

In contrast, sea-watching in autumn is generally less productive than in spring. Sandwich and Common Terns are the most obvious migrants and there is a trickle of Common Scoters, Black Terns and Arctic and Great Skuas. Gales at this time of year increase both the numbers and variety of species seen with the possibility of storm-driven rarities such as Storm and Leach's Petrels, Grey Phalarope and Sabine's Gull. One of the most spectacular storms of recent years occurred during the night of October 15th and 16th 1987. This will long be remembered in birdwatching circles, not only for the changes that it brought to the Hampshire landscape, but also for the birds that it brought to the county. Unprecedented numbers of Sabine's Gulls – over 120 – were recorded, mostly on the coast but some as far inland as Eversley and Aldershot. Prior to this, there had been only nine other records. There were also about 130 Little Gulls and smaller numbers of Grey Phalaropes, Leach's and Storm Petrels and Mediterranean Gulls.

By mid-October, most of the summer visitors have left and the winter visitors are arriving. Diurnal movements of Wood Pigeons, Skylarks, thrushes, Starlings and finches are recorded on the coast and at well-watched inland sites such as Fleet Pond and Old Winchester Hill. The conditions under which such movements occur are difficult to predict but the birds are often seen flying into head-winds, presumably because they are forced to fly lower and are thus more easily seen. This is most noticeable on the coast where easterly movements of Linnets and other finches are often associated with easterly winds.

With the onset of winter, Hampshire's harbours and estuaries are once again teeming with waders and wildfowl, the White-fronted Geese and Bewick's Swans are back in the Avon Valley, Hen Harriers and Great Grey Shrikes have returned to the heaths and Short-eared Owls to the downs.

## A New Birdwatching Year

As each annual cycle is completed a new one begins which, in many ways, will be similar to the one before, but there will always be differences. It is these changes that make birdwatching so fascinating to so many people. Some, caused for example by the weather, are obvious, but others are more subtle and almost imperceptible on an annual basis. Decreases in bird populations may be hard to spot from year to year but can, over a period, eventually lead to the extinction of species – a fate that has befallen Red-backed Shrike and Cirl Bunting as breeding birds in Hampshire. Continued, systematic recording of our birds is essential if such negative trends are to be identified and, where possible, timely action taken to counteract them. In the following section of this book, we have attempted to bring together what is known about Hampshire's birds today in the hope that it will provide a baseline against which the information collected by future birdwatchers can be assessed.

# Systematic Accounts of the Birds of Hampshire

## John M Clark

*J A Eyre, E J Wiseman, G C Evans,*
*C R Cuthbert, P J Puckering, J W C Pain and K F Betton*

## Introduction

In the following species accounts, an attempt has been made to provide an accurate picture of the pattern of occurrence of every species which has been recorded in Hampshire in the 19th and 20th centuries. In most cases, this involves a review of the available records for 1951-92, or, for winter visitors, for 1950/51-91/92. The extensive count data available for wintering wildfowl and waders has been analysed for the 35 winters from 1955/56-89/90 (see Tables and Histograms below), but relevant records for the next two winters are also included. The main source of breeding information is the Tetrad Atlas Breeding Bird Survey, carried out from 1986-91 (see Tetrad Atlas below), but earlier information has also been reviewed for all but the most numerous species. Several other phenomena, e.g. the arrival and departure dates of migrants, and the spring passage of seabirds, waders and waterfowl eastwards along the coast, have been analysed for the period from 1971-92, since earlier data are sparse and probably unrepresentative. To make the book as up to date as possible, a few 1993 records have been included, mostly of vagrants; these include two species seen for the first time in the county.

The main source of information has been the files of the Hampshire Ornithological Society, which contain data back to 1951. It is from these records that the annual *Hampshire Bird Reports* have been compiled. However, the research for this book has been based, not on the reports, but on the archived source data; as a result, many previously unpublished records are included. Several local publications have provided additional information: the annual reports of Southampton NHS (1960-78), Alton NHS (1969-90), Newbury District Ornithological Society (1959-90), Reading Ornithological Club (1960-73) and the Gilkicker Point Group (1964-73), and bird reports for the Calshot/Fawley area (1969-76 and 1982-84), the Hants/Surrey Border (1971-90), Titchfield Haven (1974-87) and Hayling Island (1981-85). A large volume of invaluable, unpublished records has also been received from a number of correspondents; they are acknowledged on page 6 and in the species accounts as appropriate.

In many cases, the available records suggest a change in status of a species through the period reviewed. Often this can be attributed to variations in the level of observer coverage, which has increased steadily since the early 1950s. A crude measure of this change is given by comparing the number of observers submitting records to *Hampshire Bird Reports*. The average number of contributors in each five-year period from 1951-90 is shown below.

| 1951-55 | 1956-60 | 1961-65 | 1966-70 | 1971-75 | 1976-80 | 1981-85 | 1986-90 |
|---------|---------|---------|---------|---------|---------|---------|---------|
| 50 | 125 | 115 | 156 | 182 | 226 | 299 | 318 |

With some species, however, the status change is almost certainly real; in such cases, possible explanations are discussed in the text.

Records for the period prior to 1950 are limited to Kelsall and Munn's *Birds of Hampshire and the Isle of Wight* (1905), Ralph Whitlock's *South Eastern Bird Reports* (1933-46) and various other papers and reports published in the first half of this century. These are described in the chapter Twentieth Century Ornithology in Hampshire. Reference may be made to pre-1950 records for one of four reasons: (i) if the records indicate a definite change of status when compared with subsequent data; (ii) where the species only occurs in Hampshire as a vagrant; (iii) if a migratory species has occurred on an earlier or later date than those recorded since 1951; and (iv) if the species is considered a Hampshire "speciality" and thus it is considered worthwhile to trace the history of its status in the county back to the 19th century.

In all the species accounts, statements are supported wherever possible by quoting actual records. The accounts review the status in Hampshire, but also put the species in a wider context. Hampshire and/or national ringing data are used to elucidate the origins and destinations of birds moving to or from the county. Where this is not possible, e.g. for infrequently-ringed species or for rare visitors and vagrants, a statement of the breeding and wintering range is given. For each breeding species, an estimate of the county population is calculated, based either on the results of the Tetrad Atlas Survey or, for the more numerous species, national CBC data for 1989. The latter, termed the New Atlas method, is basically the same as that used to calculate national populations in *The New Atlas of Breeding Birds of Britain and Ireland: 1988-91* (Gibbons *et al* 1993). The estimates of the county population are quoted along with the most-recently available figures for the British total, which have generally been taken from the New Atlas. For wildfowl and waders, concentrations at individual sites which are of national or international importance are highlighted, while the importance of Hampshire as a whole is indicated, for the more numerous species, by giving the average proportion of the total British wintering population found in the county over the period 1985/86-89/90.

### Area covered

The species accounts include records for the present day administrative county of Hampshire. Certain well-watched localities straddle the county boundary; in general, records for Frensham Great Pond, Eversley and Yateley Gravel Pits and the Avon valley between Sopley and Ringwood are given in full. Birds of Estuaries Enquiry data are given for Chichester Harbour (which is largely in West Sussex), but counts for the Hampshire part (East Hayling) are also shown separately. Historic records for the Isle of Wight and that part of south-west Hampshire transferred to Dorset in 1974 are excluded. Grid references of all localities mentioned in the text are listed in the Gazetteer on pages 486-492.

### Explanation of Status Terms

The account for each species begins with a brief statement of its status in the county. These use certain terms which have an approximate numerical range attached to them, as shown below.

|  | Breeding pairs | Winter/Passage |
| --- | --- | --- |
| Rare | Less than annual | Less than annual |
| Very scarce | 1-10 per year | 1-20 per year |
| Scarce | 11-100 | 21-200 |
| Moderately Common | 101-1000 | 201-2000 |
| Common | 1001-5000 | 2001-10,000 |
| Numerous | 5001-30,000 | 10,001-60,000 |
| Abundant | 30,000+ | 60,000+ |

## Tables and Histograms

For those species which occur in Hampshire in significant numbers and are monitored by the National Wildfowl Counts and Birds of Estuaries Enquiry, the available counts have been analysed for the 35 winters from 1955/56-89/90. This has been divided into seven periods covering five winters each, i.e. 1955/56-59/60, 1960/61-64/65 etc. For each five-winter period, the mean of the maximum counts recorded in each winter is shown, together with the peak count made during the 35 winters. Part of a typical table is shown below.

|  | 75-80 [1] | 80-85 | 85-90 | Peak counts |
| --- | --- | --- | --- | --- |
| Chichester Harbour | 760 | *1240* [2] | **1518** [3] | 2010, Dec. 1988 |
| East Hayling[4] | - [5] | 892^[6] | 718 | 1240, Feb. 1983 |
| Langstone Harbour | 775*[7] | 610 | 811 | 1150, Jan. 1987 |

1   This shows the five winters covered, i.e. 1975/76-79/80.
2   *Italics* = a nationally important concentration, i.e. greater than 1% of the British wintering population of that species.
3   **Bold** = an internationally important concentration, i.e. greater than 1% of the north-west European wintering population of that species.
4   An indented site name indicates a sub-site. The data given are also incorporated in the figures for the main site above, in this case Chichester Harbour.
5   - = No counts available.
6   ^ = Datum based on three or four maxima, not five.
7   * = Datum based on 1 or 2 maxima, not five.

For details of the qualifying levels of national and international importance, introduced in 1969/70, see Prater (1981) and Kirby *et al* (1990).

Records of scarce species may be displayed using histograms. These are of two main types, one showing annual or winter totals (i.e. the total number of individuals recorded in each year or winter during a specified period). In some cases, the annual totals are split into spring (up to June 30th) and autumn (from July 1st). The other uses cumulative weekly totals to illustrate the pattern of occurrence over the course of a year. Birds are included for all the weeks they were present. For the purpose of the analysis, the year is divided into 50 seven-day periods, plus the week of Feb. 26th-Mar. 4th (which includes Feb. 29th every fourth year) and the eight day period from Dec. 24th-31st. The histograms have not been corrected to take account of the two longer periods. Cumulative weekly totals have only been used for migrant species which generally pass through the county quickly. Patterns of occurrence of other species which are present for longer periods are shown by tabulating the cumulative monthly totals. Birds are included for all the months they are present, not just the one in which they arrived.

## The Tetrad Atlas Breeding Bird Survey

This survey ran from 1986-91. It was planned and overseen by a Steering Committee consisting of Peter Puckering (who acted as survey coordinator), Glynne Evans, Norman Pratt, Eddie Wiseman, John Wood, John Eyre and John Clark. The aim was to map the distribution of all Hampshire birds on a tetrad basis, i.e. a 2 x 2 km grid. The methodology employed was the same as that used for *The Atlas of Breeding Birds of Britain and Ireland* (Sharrock 1976). Evidence of breeding was divided into three categories: Confirmed Breeding, Probably Breeding and Possibly Breeding.

Every tetrad in the county, a total of 1031, was visited at least once during the survey. The total included a considerable number of boundary tetrads which had varying amounts of the county in them, although a few with less than 33% Hampshire were omitted. All parts of a boundary tetrad were surveyed, but in the final analysis, registrations of scarce species were excluded if it was known that they were not found in Hampshire. In all, a total of 57,750 records was collected – an average of 56 species per tetrad. The map below gives an indication of the number of species recorded in each tetrad. 12 tetrads held 80 or more species and a further 117 held 70-79. Coverage was generally considered to be excellent – only in a few tetrads in Portsmouth and the centre and north-west of the county could it have been significantly improved. In all, a total of 134 species was confirmed breeding in at least one year during the survey, with a further ten probably breeding.

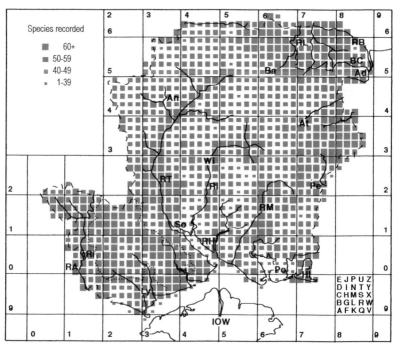

Most of the maps generated by the Atlas Survey have been included in the species accounts. Those for species which were found in 90% or more of the tetrads have mostly been excluded; the number of registrations recorded at each level and a description of the areas from which the species were not recorded are included in the texts. Maps for species with a restricted distribution (e.g. exclusively coastal) or for which there were very few registrations, have also been omitted.

In a few cases, the information displayed on the maps has been modified for security reasons. This has been achieved in three ways: (i) by plotting all registrations at level 2; (ii) by moving some registrations by up to two tetrads; or (iii) by plotting some or all registrations on a 10 km grid instead of by tetrads.

Where species have significantly declined, changed their distribution or were considerably under-recorded during the Atlas Survey, the available older records have been incorporated into the maps. Usually, these have been divided into those for 1971-85 (indicated by an open red-tinted square) and those for 1951-70 (indicated by a red-tinted cross). On the maps, Atlas Survey records take precedence over records for 1971-85, which in turn take precedence over those for 1951-70. The mapping of historical records is intended only to give an indication of the extent of earlier distributions. Coverage during those periods was random and incomplete when compared with the intensive fieldwork carried out in 1986-91.

The following abbreviations for various features have been used on the maps.

| Ad | Aldershot | Ly | Lymington | RI | River Itchen |
|-----|-----------|-----|-----------|-----|-----------|
| An | Andover | Pe | Petersfield | RL | River Loddon |
| At | Alton | Po | Portsmouth | RM | River Meon |
| Ba | Basingstoke | RA | River Avon | RT | River Test |
| BC | Basingstoke Canal | RB | River Blackwater | So | Southampton |
| HI | Hayling Island | RH | River Hamble | Wi | Winchester |
| IOW | Isle of Wight | Ri | Ringwood | | |

### Records of Rare and Scarce Species

All records accepted by the *British Birds Rarities Committee* (*BBRC*) and a number of others, still under consideration by the *BBRC* or not yet submitted to it, have been included. The latter are all considered acceptable by the *Hampshire Ornithological Society Records Panel* (*HOSRP*), and are indicated by † in the text. Records not accepted by the *BBRC* are excluded.

The *HOSRP* has reviewed previously accepted records of a variety of species, e.g. Rough-legged Buzzard, Melodious and Icterine Warblers and Red-breasted Flycatcher. Records of these and other species published in *Hampshire Bird Reports* but not included here are now considered to be inadequately documented.

### Nomenclature and Sequence

The scientific names and sequence used follow Voous (1973, 1977), apart from certain "splits", i.e. Rock and Water Pipits, American and Pacific Golden Plovers, Manx and Mediterranean Shearwaters. English names follow the *British Birds List of Birds of the Western Palearctic* (1984). All species that have occurred in Hampshire in a wild (or feral) state are included, provided that they are in categories A, B or C of the British and Irish List. Two appendices give details of records of (i) ship-assisted birds and (ii) category D and other exotic species.

## Standard References and Abbreviations Used

The following regularly-quoted references are abbreviated in the text as follows:

BWP — Cramp, S (Ed) 1977, 1980, 1983, 1985, 1988, 1992, 1993. *The Handbook of Birds of Europe, The Middle East and North Africa: The Birds of the Western Palearctic* Vols. 1-7. Oxford University Press. Oxford.

Cohen — Cohen, E 1963. *Birds of Hampshire and the Isle of Wight*. Oliver & Boyd. Edinburgh.

C & T — Cohen, E and Taverner, J H 1972. *A Revised List of Hampshire and Isle of Wight Birds*. Oxford Illustrated Press. Oxford.

K & M — Kelsall, J E and Munn, P W 1905. *The Birds of Hampshire and the Isle of Wight*. Witherby. London.

New Atlas — Gibbons, D W, Reid, J B and Chapman, R A 1993. *The New Atlas of Breeding Birds in Britain and Ireland: 1988-91*. Poyser. London.

Winter Atlas — Lack, D 1986. *The Atlas of Wintering Birds in Britain and Ireland*. Poyser. Calton.

68-72 Atlas — Sharrock, J T R 1976. *The Atlas of Breeding Birds in Britain and Ireland*. British Trust for Ornithology. Tring.

Other abbreviations used are as follows:

Atlas Survey — HOS Tetrad Atlas Breeding Bird Survey, 1986-91
*BBRC* — *British Birds Rarities Committee*
BoEE — Birds of Estuaries Enquiry
*BOURC* — *British Ornithologists' Union Records Committee*
BTO — British Trust for Ornithology
CBC — Common Birds Census
GRA — Game Research Association
*HOSRP* — *Hampshire Ornithological Society Records Panel*
IWRB — International Waterfowl and Wetlands Research Bureau
RSPB — Royal Society for the Protection of Birds
WWT — Wildfowl and Wetlands Trust

# Red-throated Diver                    *Gavia stellata*

A scarce winter visitor and passage migrant.

K & M described the Red-throated Diver as "a common winter visitor to the coast". Few were seen during the first half of this century, but since the 1950s it has been recorded in variable, but generally low, numbers each winter. The wintering population was at its highest level in the 1950s and early 1960s, lower until the early 1980s, but recovered slightly thereafter (fig. 1). At Langstone Harbour, which has been consistently watched since the early 1950s, the species was regularly present from 1951/52-1962/63, with up to six recorded each winter and a total of some 42 during that period. Since then, in the 29 winters up to 1991/92, only 31 have been recorded. Four winters produced none at all, while in most a single bird was seen on one date only.

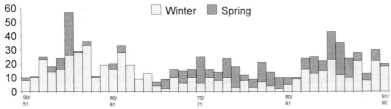

*Figure 1. Winter and spring totals of Red-throated Divers, 1950/51-91/92.*

Several factors may have contributed to the fluctuating numbers. Oiled birds tend to seek shelter close inshore, in harbours or on inland waters, where they are more likely to be observed. During the 1950s and early 1960s, when oiling incidents were not uncommon, almost 30% of those reported were dead and/or oiled. In recent years, such pollution has been much reduced and the proportion of affected birds has declined. This may account for their current scarcity in Langstone Harbour, healthy individuals apparently preferring the open sea. Red-throated Divers often appear after storms or during periods of hard winter weather. In the late 1960s and 1970s, when most winters were mild, no more than ten were recorded each winter, but since then numbers have been higher. This may be connected with the increased frequency of colder than average winters during the 1980s, although improved observer coverage along some parts of the coast, e.g. off Hayling Island, may also have contributed.

In autumn, the first Red-throated Divers usually appear in late October or early November, but the earliest ever was one which stayed off Pennington and

Keyhaven Marshes from July 16th-Sep. 18th 1988. There has been one other July record, three for August and eight for September. A small peak is apparent between mid-November and early December, e.g. six were off Hill Head on Nov. 15th 1957 and Dec. 1st 1991 and six were off Hurst Beach on Dec. 1st 1973.

In mid-winter, most occur on the open sea, where sightings typically involve one or two birds. They rarely remain in the same area for long; this, combined with the large proportion of records relating to birds in flight, suggests that the wintering population is fairly mobile. Numbers are highest off Hurst Beach, where counts have occasionally reached five and at least nine were present on Feb. 1st 1958. Elsewhere, the largest number recorded was eight off Browndown on Jan. 4th 1986. Storm-driven birds, or those weakened by hard weather or oiling, may seek shelter in the eastern harbours and especially the upper reaches of Southampton Water. These often stay for several weeks, e.g. up to five were between Weston Shore and Eling from Feb. 4th-Apr. 12th 1986.

Apart from 1956, few were seen in spring until the mid-1960s. Regular sea-watching since then has shown that there is a small eastward passage through The Solent annually (fig. 1). Movement is observed between late March and mid-May and usually peaks in the first week of May. High day totals include 23, of which nine flew east, between Stokes Bay and Lee-on-the-Solent on Apr. 2nd 1956, seven flying south-east off Hurst Beach on May 5th 1971, eight flying east at Gilkicker Point on May 3rd 1986 and 17 in Hayling Bay after gales on Apr. 4th 1987. A few have been seen in late May and there are eight records for June, the latest being of one in the Lymington Estuary on June 26th 1989. The total recorded each spring has rarely exceeded 15; considerably higher numbers are seen from St. Catherine's Point, which shows that the main migration route is to the south of the Isle of Wight rather than through The Solent.

Storms, severe frosts or oiling episodes seem to account for most inland records. Since 1952, 50 have been recorded, with 29 up to 1965, seven between 1972 and 1978 and 14 between 1983 and 1991. Most were on waters close to the coast, at Hatchet Pond (16, but only one since 1965), Sowley Pond (9) and Broadlands Lake (7). Others occurred at Frensham Great Pond (5), Fleet Pond (3), Heath Pond (2), Avon Causeway, Sopley and the River Itchen at Winchester (1 each), while a further five were picked up dead or dying at other sites. Of the fit birds, 19 were recorded on one date only but stays of a week or more were not infrequent. Long-stayers included those at Hatchet Pond from May 11th-June 1st 1955 and Feb. 1st-Apr. 6th 1957, Heath Pond from Jan. 28th-Feb. 20th 1957, Frensham Great Pond from Feb. 28th-Mar. 27th 1960 and Sowley Pond from Jan. 3rd-28th 1989. Exceptionally, at Broadlands Lake there were two to four from Feb. 25th-Apr. 2nd 1983 with five on Mar. 31st, one remaining until Apr. 22nd. All other records were of single birds apart from those of two at Hatchet Pond on Mar. 16th 1956 and Jan. 23rd 1962 and Fleet Pond on Feb. 10th 1972.

The cumulative monthly totals of all records for 1950/51-91/92 are shown below.

|  | Jul | Aug | Sep | Oct | Nov | Dec | Jan | Feb | Mar | Apr | May | Jun |
|---|---|---|---|---|---|---|---|---|---|---|---|---|
| Coast | 2 | 4 | 8 | 19 | 81 | 130 | 190 | 150 | 123 | 170 | 130 | 7 |
| Inland | 0 | 0 | 0 | 1 | 1 | 0 | 16 | 17 | 18 | 7 | 1 | 1 |

The Red-throated Diver has a circumpolar breeding distribution. The limited national ringing data suggest that those occurring in southern England originate from Greenland, Scotland and Fenno-Scandia (BWP).

## Black-throated Diver                                    *Gavia arctica*

A very scarce winter visitor and passage migrant.

K & M described the Black-throated Diver as "an occasional winter visitor to the coast .... much less common than either the Great Northern or Red-throated species". Among the few records for the first half of this century are those of two at Hatchet Pond on Mar. 4th 1933 and one caught on a trimmer baited with dace for pike on the River Enborne on Mar. 5th 1935. Since the mid-1950s, it has occurred in winter in variable numbers but appears to have been most numerous between 1955/56 and 1962/63 and from 1976/77 onwards. Up to five have been recorded on spring passage in most years but above average numbers were seen between 1984 and 1987 (fig. 2).

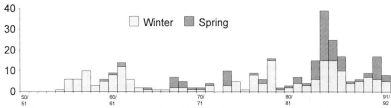

*Figure 2. Winter and spring totals of Black-throated Divers, 1950/51-91/92.*

The species' pattern of occurrence is similar to the Red-throated Diver's but in lower numbers. The earliest ever was one off Sandy Point on Sep. 21st 1985, but otherwise none has been recorded before Oct. 13th. Many of those occurring in autumn are moving west, e.g. a flock of five off Eastney on Oct. 14th 1976. In mid-winter, most are recorded on one date only but in very cold weather longer stays occur. In the sheltered upper reaches of Southampton Water, a favoured area, one or two were seen regularly in the first quarter of each of the years 1983-86, while off Southsea Castle one was present from Jan. 29th-Feb. 20th 1985. Severe weather may also induce movements offshore, such as six east off Gilkicker Point on Dec. 29th 1961, seven east through Hurst Narrows on Jan. 6th 1979 and five east off Sandy Point on Feb. 5th 1985. Most wintering birds depart by late March. Spring passage peaks in the first week of May, although the highest day total has been of five east off Gilkicker Point on Apr. 8th 1968. Occasional birds are seen after mid-May and the latest ever was one off Hill Head on June 2nd 1987.

Inland, a total of 14 has been recorded in nine years since 1957. Sightings were made at Frensham Great Pond and Sowley Pond (3 each), Blashford Lakes and Hatchet Pond (2 each) and Eversley/Yateley Gravel Pits, Heath Pond, Middle Wallop Airfield and Timsbury Gravel Pit (1 each). Eight were seen on one date only but longer stays included those at Frensham Great Pond from Jan. 15th-27th 1970 and Sowley Pond from Feb. 11th-24th 1984.

The cumulative monthly totals of all records for 1950/51-91/92 are shown below.

| | Sep | Oct | Nov | Dec | Jan | Feb | Mar | Apr | May | Jun |
|---|---|---|---|---|---|---|---|---|---|---|
| Coast | 1 | 11 | 26 | 52 | 56 | 55 | 30 | 43 | 58 | 1 |
| Inland | 0 | 1 | 1 | 1 | 2 | 6 | 3 | 0 | 0 | 0 |

The Black-throated Diver breeds from Scotland to eastern Siberia. Most occurring in southern England probably originate from Scandinavia.

## Great Northern Diver                                          *Gavia immer*

A very scarce winter visitor and passage migrant.

K & M described the Great Northern Diver as "a winter visitor to the coast". This century, few were recorded until the upsurge in birdwatching after the Second World War. Between the mid-1950s and early 1960s, small numbers were present each winter. Subsequently, the species was recorded infrequently until the 1980s, when a recovery occurred (fig. 3). In spring, this is the least numerous of the three divers, no more than seven being recorded in any one year.

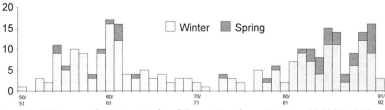

*Figure 3. Winter and spring totals of Great Northern Divers, 1950/51-91/92.*

The first normally arrive in November, but there have been five October birds, including one off Gilkicker Point on Oct. 4th 1960. The earliest ever was one in summer plumage flying west off Lepe on Aug. 4th 1978. The favoured stretches of coast for wintering birds are from Black Point to Eastney and Hill Head to Warsash. In the former area, early records included four on Jan. 19th 1957 and five on Nov. 20th 1960. Between 1981/82 and 1989/90, one or two were recorded each winter with peaks of four from Jan. 26th to Feb. 1st 1986 and three on Mar. 11th 1989. In the Hill Head area, five were present on Nov. 16th 1957 and counts reached four in three other winters around that time. Since 1977/78, one or two have been recorded in every winter but two; three were off Warsash on Dec. 12th 1981 and at Hill Head on Jan. 19th 1987 and Mar. 2nd 1990. As with the other divers, severe weather attracts birds to the Hythe/Eling area of Southampton Water, where individuals have often remained for several weeks. Most wintering birds depart by late March or early April; sightings after this are mostly of birds moving east offshore, a small peak being noted in early May. Late records were of birds flying east in Hayling Bay on May 16th 1986 and off Hurst Beach on May 21st 1961.

There have been seven inland records, the most recent in 1964. At Hatchet Pond, single birds were present on Feb. 2nd 1957, Jan. 14th 1958 and from Feb. 1st-Apr. 20th 1959. Another was at Frensham Great Pond from Jan. 5th-Feb. 21st 1964. The other records were of storm-driven birds: one picked up alive at

Woodlands (Southampton) on Feb. 11th 1951 and singles found dead at Blashford Lakes on Jan. 3rd 1954 and in the New Forest near Beaulieu on Dec. 9th 1954.

The cumulative monthly totals of all records for 1950/51-91/92 are shown below.

|        | Aug | Sep | Oct | Nov | Dec | Jan | Feb | Mar | Apr | May |
|--------|-----|-----|-----|-----|-----|-----|-----|-----|-----|-----|
| Coast  | 1   | 0   | 5   | 43  | 76  | 89  | 73  | 36  | 27  | 25  |
| Inland | 0   | 0   | 0   | 0   | 1   | 3   | 4   | 1   | 1   | 0   |

Great Northern Divers wintering in England probably originate from Iceland or Greenland, although the breeding range extends west into Canada.

# Divers                                                    *Gavia sp.*

Some divers, especially those seen in flight far out to sea, are difficult to assign to a particular species. The three highest counts of divers on record all involved flocks which were not specifically identified: 18 flying south-east off Hurst Beach on Apr. 17th 1978, 16 flying west off Sandy Point on Nov. 16th 1985 and 12 off Hurst Beach on May 19th 1990. The records of unidentified divers all fell within the period September to May except for single birds seen at Lymington on June 1st 1957, off Needs Ore on June 16th 1962 and off Brownwich on Aug. 26th 1987.

# Little Grebe                                    *Tachybaptus ruficollis*

A moderately common resident, passage migrant and winter visitor.

The Little Grebe breeds on still and slow-moving waters where there is sufficient emergent vegetation to enable it to anchor its nest structure. As the Atlas Map shows, it is widely distributed in the county, breeding on rivers, canals, gravel pits, lakes, ponds and coastal lagoons.

A partial survey of the county in 1978 located 226 pairs, from which the total population was estimated at 500+ pairs (Clark 1979). Counts from selected areas during and since that survey are shown in Table 1.

| Area surveyed | Year | Pairs |
|---|---|---|
| River Test, Lower Test Marshes-Fullerton (28 km) | 1978 | 102* |
| Basingstoke Canal, Greywell-Ash Vale (25 km) | 1978 | 34 |
| | 1980 | 34 |
| | 1984 | 16 |
| | 1991 | 9 |
| Eversley Gravel Pit | 1981 | 12 |
| River Loddon, Sherfield-Stratfield Saye (14 km) | 1981 | 17 |
| Blashford Lakes | 1986 | 16 |

\* partial coverage; 146 pairs estimated in whole stretch (Evans 1981).

*Table 1. Selected counts of breeding Little Grebes.*

The decline along the Basingstoke Canal has been attributed to the dredging and subsequent use by motorised craft of all but the Greywell-North Warnborough section (Rowland 1993). Other data are too fragmentary to indicate any overall trend, although gravel extraction continues to create new habitat, especially in the Avon and Blackwater valleys. Nationally, WBS data suggest a slight decline in the early and mid-1980s, perhaps due to the series of harsh winters during that period (Marchant *et al* 1990). Although some tetrads held five or more pairs during the Atlas Survey, assuming an average of two pairs in those squares where breeding was confirmed or probable indicates a county population of around 400 pairs in 1991. The most recent estimate of the British population is 5000-10,000 pairs (New Atlas).

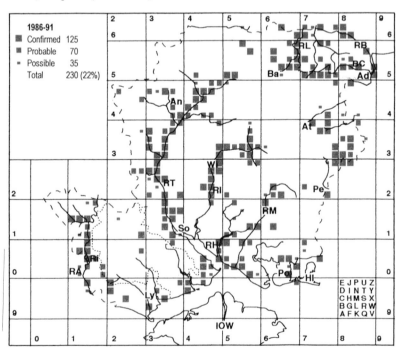

After the breeding season, large gatherings occur on the main gravel pit complexes, e.g. 72 at Blashford Lakes on Aug. 16th 1985 and 41 at Eversley/

Yateley Gravel Pits on Sep. 20th 1987 and Oct. 8th 1988. However, few remain on still water throughout the winter, most moving to the main rivers or sheltered estuaries. Regular counts have been made on the River Test between Longstock and Leckford, where the largest gathering was of 88 on Nov. 14th 1983. A survey of the River Itchen between Bishopstoke and Itchen Abbas on Jan. 1st and 2nd 1983 located 110.

On brackish water, the highest numbers are found in the Lower Test/Eling area. A maximum of 50-70 is recorded in most winters, with the peak count normally occurring in November or December. Exceptional numbers were present in the mild winter of 1988/89, with a maximum of 110 on Nov. 22nd. The largest regular gathering elsewhere is at Ports Creek (Langstone/Portsmouth Harbours), where up to 30 are usually present and the highest count was of 49 on Dec. 3rd 1988. The only other counts above 30 have been off East Hayling, where there were 64 on Dec. 20th 1975 and 54 on Nov. 14th 1981. In mild winters, numbers decline from February onwards and there is a corresponding increase on inland waters, but during severe weather high numbers are maintained well into March.

There is little evidence to indicate whether our wintering population comprises exclusively local birds or includes immigrants from elsewhere. Passage is suggested by a record of five at Titchfield Haven which left eastwards over the sea on the evening of Apr. 12th 1984 and by the only ringing recovery, which was of a bird ringed at Farlington Marshes on Sep. 11th 1971 and found dead at Somme, France, 302 km ESE, on Nov. 21st 1972.

## Great Crested Grebe                    *Podiceps cristatus*

A moderately common resident, passage migrant and winter visitor. Both breeding and wintering numbers have increased considerably in the last 30 years.

K & M gave details of breeding at Fleet and Tundry Ponds in the 1890s, but otherwise described the Great Crested Grebe as a winter visitor, especially to the coast. In Britain, a marked increase in breeding numbers took place from the latter part of the 19th century onwards (Parslow 1973). This was probably due to a combination of reduced hunting and egg-collecting following the passing of four Bird Protection Acts between 1870 and 1880, and a north-westerly expansion of range across Europe (68-72 Atlas). In Hampshire, this was shown by the national survey in 1931, when 26 pairs were found on 15 waters (Harrison & Hollom 1932). Details of this and subsequent surveys are shown in table 2.

| Year | Lakes | Rivers | Blashford Lakes | Blackwater valley GPs | Other GPs | Total |
|------|-------|--------|-----------------|-----------------------|-----------|-------|
| 1931 | 24 | - | - | 2 | - | 26 |
| 1965 | 11 | - | 2 | 12 | - | 25 |
| 1975 | 15 | 5 | 11 | 22 | - | 53 |
| 1978 | 15 | 6 | 20 | 30 | 2 | 73 |
| 1984 | 16 | 5 | 22 | 39 | 4 | 86 |

*Table 2. Counts of breeding pairs of Great Crested Grebes.*

These data show a continuing expansion, especially between 1965 and 1984.

However, coverage during the 1965 survey was not complete, e.g. at Blashford Lakes, where seven pairs bred in 1961. The true county population at that time probably approached 40 pairs. The increase is largely attributable to the colonisation of newly-created gravel pits, principally in the Blackwater valley along the county boundary with Surrey and Berkshire, and in the Avon valley at Blashford. The species has also colonised slow-flowing stretches of the River Avon, where 12 territories were identified between Breamore and Sopley during the Atlas Survey. However, as the Atlas Map shows, breeding has ceased at several lakes. These may have become unsuitable due to increased human disturbance (e.g. at Hawley Lake and Heath Pond) or habitat change (e.g. at Alresford Pond, which has silted up and is now too shallow). The total summering population in 1991, including all the Blackwater valley gravel pits, was probably around 220 birds with 90-95 breeding pairs. The British population was estimated at 8000 individuals in 1988-91 (New Atlas).

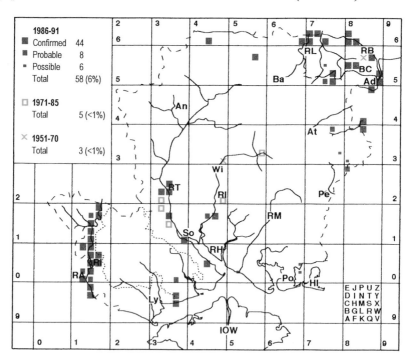

Groups of up to 20, consisting of failed and non- breeders and juveniles, form on favoured gravel pits from June onwards. A few individuals may return to the coast by this time, and several summer in Langstone Harbour each year. Numbers were particularly high there in 1988 and 1989, with peaks of 20 in June and 27 in July respectively.

Outside the breeding season, the highest numbers are most consistently recorded at Langstone Harbour, where there is a build up from late September onwards to a peak, usually in November but in some years as late as January. Numbers decline rapidly thereafter, especially in severe weather, when counts may drop into single figures. This may be due to a movement on to the open sea between Black Point and Southsea, or further west to the Hill Head/Brownwich area or Southampton Water. At the latter two localities, numbers usually peak later in the winter than at Langstone and are at their highest in severe weather. Winter counts at coastal localities increased considerably in the 1980s (Table 3); this presumably reflects not only the increased local breeding population but also above average numbers of continental birds forced westwards by freezing conditions in their usual wintering areas.

Most coastal wintering birds leave by mid-March but passage is indicated in April and May by secondary peaks, e.g. 39 at Langstone Harbour on Apr. 10th 1971, and occasional sightings of birds offshore or moving through The Solent. Between 1981 and 1989, 18 were noted flying east on dates between Mar. 25th and May 31st.

At the principal inland waters, passage peaks are occasionally evident in October and November, while in some years the maximum count is made in mid-winter. During severe weather, most depart, presumably for the coast, but sometimes large gatherings form on small ice-free pools, e.g. 35 at Fleet Pond on Jan. 19th 1989 and 44 at Spinnaker Lake (Blashford) on Feb. 9th 1991. Peak numbers usually occur in March, presumably due to a movement of birds which have wintered elsewhere returning to breed. Counts at various localities between 1955/56 and 1989/90 are summarised in table 3.

| | 55-60 | 60-65 | 65-70 | 70-75 | 75-80 | 80-85 | 85-90 | Peak counts | |
|---|---|---|---|---|---|---|---|---|---|
| Langstone Harbour | 53 | 62 | 54 | 66 | 40 | 50 | 98 | 147, | Jan. 1990 |
| Hill Head / Brownwich | 17 | 19 | 14 | 21 | 22 | 42 | 77 | 217, | Jan. 1987 |
| Southampton Water | 9^ | 50* | - | 26 | 36 | 34 | 74 | 126, | Mar. 1986 |
| Blashford Lakes | - | - | - | 23 | 36 | 37 | 33 | 57, | Feb. 1984 |
| Fleet Pond | 15^ | 21^ | 16^ | 15 | 23 | 31 | 31 | 39, | Nov. 1989 |
| Yateley / Eversley G Ps | - | - | - | 18 | 27 | 26 | 26 | 43, | Nov. 1989 |

*Table 3. Five year means of winter maxima and peak counts of Great Crested Grebes, 1955/56-89/90.*

Other localities where counts have exceeded 20 (maxima in brackets) are Southsea (55, January 1963), Lymington/Hurst (23, November 1969), Black Point (40, December 1983) and Hayling Bay (34, November 1986).

The only ringing recovery involved an adult ringed in Gloucestershire on July 4th 1964 and found dead at Ewhurst Lake on May 12th 1965.

# Red-necked Grebe                                    *Podiceps grisegena*

A very scarce but regular winter visitor and passage migrant.

K & M described the Red-necked Grebe as "an occasional visitor to the coast in winter". However, they only cite one occurrence from within the present day boundaries, that of a specimen obtained in Langstone Harbour on Dec. 19th 1894. There appears to be no further record until 1949, when one was at Frensham Great Pond on Jan. 23rd. In 1953, one was at Hurst on Feb. 1st and two were seen on the Lymington River on Dec. 20th. From then until 1978/79, the species was recorded in all but two winters (fig. 4). Most reports were of one or two individuals on one date only, usually in mid-winter. However, there was an exceptional gathering of ten off Hill Head from Jan. 12th-19th 1957.

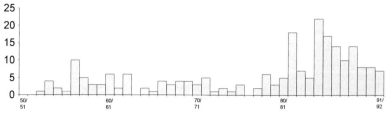

*Figure 4. Winter totals of Red-necked Grebes, 1950/51-91/92.*

Since an influx into Britain during severe weather in early 1979 (Chandler 1981), the species' status has changed significantly in Hampshire. The average number recorded per winter increased from three in the period 1950/51-77/78 to 11 in 1978/79-91/92. Although most occurred in hard weather, there has also been an increase in mild seasons and during September, October and April, suggesting passage. In contrast to the earlier period, individuals often remained in the same area for several weeks. It seems likely that the increase is connected with the slow expansion of its breeding range in north-western Europe. In the last 15 years, nesting has taken place in France, Belgium and the Netherlands and been attempted on several occasions in Britain (Spencer *et al* 1993).

Sightings have been made all along the coast, particularly favoured localities being the Black Point/Hayling Bay/Langstone Harbour area, Hill Head/Warsash, Lymington/Hurst and the upper reaches of Southampton Water. All reports involved one or two apart from four at Hill Head on Dec. 19th 1981, three off Mayflower Park (Southampton) on Jan. 20th 1982, five at Warsash two days later, three off Hurst Beach on Jan. 20th 1985, three in Hayling Bay on Jan. 1st 1989 and three there on Apr. 22nd 1989.

Inland sightings (including those on freshwater close to the coast) were made in six years from 1959-74 and in every year but two from 1979-92. Records, all of single birds, came from Frensham Great Pond (5), Hatchet Pond (4), Sinah Gravel Pit and Sowley Pond (3 each), Shepherds Spring (2), and the River Avon at Bickton and Ringwood, Broadlands Lake, Dogmersfield Lake, Ellingham Lake, New Milton and Wellington Country Park (1 each). Ten of these were seen on one date only, but others were present for two weeks or more, the longest stays being at Sinah from Mar. 2nd-Apr. 6th 1983, Frensham Great Pond from Jan. 4th-21st 1984 and Feb. 8th-Mar. 2nd 1990 and Shepherds Spring from Jan. 18th-Mar. 15th 1987.

The cumulative monthly totals of all records for 1950/51-91/92 are shown below.

|  | Sep | Oct | Nov | Dec | Jan | Feb | Mar | Apr | May |
|---|---|---|---|---|---|---|---|---|---|
| Coast | 5 | 9 | 27 | 43 | 92 | 54 | 21 | 13 | 0 |
| Inland | 1 | 1 | 3 | 4 | 6 | 9 | 4 | 1 | 1 |

The extreme dates for the county are Sep. 5th (1982, 1, Titchfield Haven) and May 9th (1968, 1, Frensham Great Pond).

## Slavonian Grebe                                    *Podiceps auritus*

A scarce winter visitor and passage migrant.

Slavonian Grebes are present along the coast from early November until late

March or early April. Sightings outside this period mostly refer to presumed migrants which stay for only a day or two, although two were at Sinah Gravel Pit from Sep. 29th-Oct. 18th 1984, one remaining until Nov. 1st. Other early birds were two at Warren Flats (Needs Ore) in the first half of August 1936 and singles at Frensham Great Pond on Aug. 1st 1965, off Pennington Marsh on Oct. 6th and 7th 1972 and in Langstone Harbour on Sep. 25th 1988. The latest in spring were single birds at Hill Head on May 21st and 22nd 1959 and off Hurst Beach on Apr. 30th 1971 and May 11th 1978.

The principal wintering area is between Black Point and Hayling Bay. In the period 1950-79, the highest counts there were of 13+ on Mar. 30th 1956 and nine on Feb. 5th 1972. Since then, numbers have increased, with 22 on Feb. 14th 1982, 26 on Jan. 4th 1986, 24 on Mar. 21st 1987 and lower double-figure counts in five other winters. In some years, such as 1987, the peak occurred in March, which suggests that some passage is involved. Other favoured areas (maximum counts in brackets) are Langstone Harbour (9, Dec. 8th 1979), Southsea (8, Jan. 13th 1982), Hill Head/Warsash (6, Feb. 8th 1970), Southampton Water, especially between Weston and Dibden Bay (5, Jan. 16th and Nov. 1st 1979), Lepe/Needs Ore (5, Feb. 11th 1988), Pitts Deep (7, Feb. 14th 1982) and Lymington/Hurst (7, Nov. 24th 1957). As at Hayling, most of these sites have shown an increase in the 1980s, probably due to a combination of improved observer coverage and more frequent hard winters.

Between 1951 and 1992, 47 were recorded on freshwater, at Frensham Great Pond (24), Broadlands Lake, Fawley Reservoir and Heath Pond (3 each), Lakeside (Eastleigh), Sinah Gravel Pit, Sowley Pond and Winnall Moors (2 each) and Fleet Pond, Hatchet Pond, Mockbeggar Lake, Timsbury Gravel Pit, Tundry Pond and Wellington Country Park (1 each). Most occurred at passage times or during severe weather. The cumulative monthly totals are shown below.

| Aug | Sep | Oct | Nov | Dec | Jan | Feb | Mar | Apr |
|-----|-----|-----|-----|-----|-----|-----|-----|-----|
| 1 | 1 | 7 | 10 | 5 | 12 | 7 | 4 | 5 |

At Frensham, Slavonian Grebes were reported in 15 years between 1951 and 1978, but only twice since. Although most records referred to single birds on one date only, two were seen together on five occasions, and stays of a week or more occurred five times, the longest being from Jan. 28th-Feb. 15th 1973 and Feb. 12th-Mar. 3rd 1974. Elsewhere, the longest stay was at Winnall Moors from Jan. 10th-Feb. 23rd 1979. There were six other instances of stays of a week or more, but 14 were seen on one date only.

During the 1980s, the wintering population has usually been in the range 20-40, which represents 5-10% of the estimated British total of 400 (Winter Atlas). Hampshire birds, and those elsewhere in south-eastern England, probably originate around the Baltic Sea (BWP).


## Black-necked Grebe                           *Podiceps nigricollis*

A scarce winter visitor and passage migrant; rare in summer but has bred.

The main locality for Black-necked Grebes is Langstone Harbour. This site regularly holds at least 30% of the British wintering population, which has been estimated at 120 (Prater 1981, Winter Atlas). The highest count was of 58 on

Nov. 17th 1957, but this presumably included some passage birds as subsequent counts in that winter did not exceed 31. Winter maxima fluctuated during the 1960s and 1970s but stabilised at 35-39 from 1979/80-1987/88. Since then, a slight decline has occurred (fig. 5).

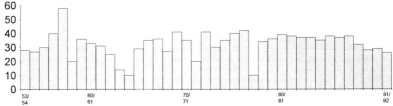

*Figure 5. Peak counts of Black-necked Grebes in Langstone Harbour, 1953/54-91/92.*

The first normally arrive between late September and late October, but in 13 years there were earlier sightings of up to three (once, five) in the period Aug. 3rd-Sep. 14th. These probably moved on to wintering sites elsewhere as there was often a considerable interval before the next were recorded. Most of the wintering population is present by mid-November; numbers then remain fairly constant until early March except during severe weather, when most leave the harbour. The evidence suggests that they may not move far. In 1963, none was seen in Langstone during the severe weather but 22 were in Hayling Bay on Jan. 5th. In 1985, there was a reduction from 35 on Jan. 11th to eight on Feb. 16th, but the onset of milder weather resulted in an increase to 35 by Mar. 9th. A flock of 30 small grebes in Hayling Bay on Feb. 10th may have been the missing birds. The departure is normally complete by late March or early April, there being sightings after Apr. 9th in only nine years with the latest on Apr. 25th 1958 and May 11th 1990. The flock is normally confined to Langstone Channel and is most readily observed from Hayling Oyster Beds.

The species formerly wintered regularly in the Lymington/Hurst area. The maximum count was of nine on Dec. 26th 1960, but in subsequent winters there was a gradual decline. Since 1974 it has been infrequently recorded there. In recent years, one or two have been seen in most winters in the Weston Shore/Dibden Bay area of Southampton Water, with a maximum of five on Feb. 3rd 1980. At other coastal sites it is decidedly rare; noteworthy records include those of five off East Hayling on Feb. 2nd 1975, ten in Portsmouth Harbour on Jan. 7th 1983, four off Hill Head on Mar. 27th 1983 and one at Paulsgrove Reclamation from June 15th-July 16th 1984.

Between 1956 and 1992, 47 have been sighted at inland localities, records coming from Frensham Great Pond (27 birds), Mockbeggar Lake (8), Fleet Pond and Winchester Sewage Farm (3 each) and Broadlands Lake, Bourley Reservoir, Ibsley, Spinnaker Lake, Timsbury Gravel Pit and Tundry Pond (1 each). As the cumulative monthly totals below show, most occurrences were in spring and autumn.

| Jul | Aug | Sep | Oct | Nov | Dec | Jan | Feb | Mar | Apr | May |
|-----|-----|-----|-----|-----|-----|-----|-----|-----|-----|-----|
| 1 | 8 | 14 | 2 | 4 | 1 | 0 | 1 | 8 | 3 | 5 |

At Frensham Great Pond, the species was reported in 11 years between 1956 and 1977, but only twice since. Most records were of one or two birds during August-November, but three were there on Aug. 19th and Sep. 9th 1956 and six on Mar. 24th 1984. Elsewhere, most were present for up to four days, but longer stays involved three at Winchester Sewage Farm from May 1st-7th 1983, one at Timsbury Gravel Pit from Mar 15th-Apr. 16th 1987 and one at Mockbeggar Lake from Aug. 21st-31st 1988. The extreme dates were July 30th (1978, 1, Fleet Pond) and May 10th (1986, 1, Spinnaker Lake).

In 1987, breeding was recorded for the first time when a pair raised two young at Winchester Sewage Farm. Between 1986 and 1990, the known British breeding population varied between 33 and 40 pairs (Spencer *et al* 1991, 1993).

The origin of Black-necked Grebes wintering in Hampshire is unknown. The nearest breeding colonies are in northern Britain and the Netherlands.

## Fulmar                                              *Fulmarus glacialis*

A scarce passage migrant, most frequent in spring, but recorded in all months except November.

The first for Hampshire was a corpse found at Southsea on Dec. 28th 1954. The next were single birds seen in Hurst Narrows on Jan. 15th and Aug. 27th 1956, to be followed by one picked up in weak condition in the grounds of Southampton University and released from the Royal Pier in January 1957.

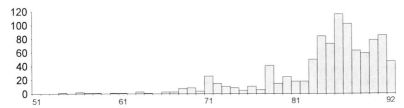

*Figure 6. Annual totals of Fulmars, 1951-92.*

Between 1958 and 1966, up to three were seen annually, all in spring, but higher numbers were recorded in the 1970s (fig. 6). This was largely accounted for by an increase in sightings off Hurst Beach. Between 1971 and 1992, 330 were seen off Hurst in spring, with 121 moving east, 29 west and 180 offshore. However, very few were actually seen to enter The Solent through Hurst Narrows. A further increase was evident from 1983, when regular sea-watching started at Hayling Bay. Between 1983 and 1992, 403 were seen there in spring, with 124 moving east, 264 west and 15 offshore. This is presumably part of the movement observed from Selsey Bill (West Sussex) and St. Catherine's Point (Isle of Wight), which has involved over 100 birds every year since 1965 and reached a maximum of 572 (73 east and 499 west) off Selsey in 1986. Few of these evidently penetrate far into the east Solent, for off Gilkicker Point and Hill Head, where spring sea-watching has been regular since 1966, only 137 were recorded up to 1992, with 54 flying east, 61 west and 22 offshore.

Spring records peak between mid-April and early May (fig. 7). At Hayling Bay, day totals have exceeded 15 on four occasions, with a maximum of ten east and 11 west on Apr. 28th 1990, while off Hurst Beach the peak was of 12 east on Apr. 7th 1985.

A small peak is evident in August and early September, but at other times of the year very few are recorded.

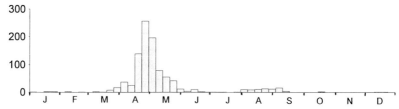

*Figure 7. Cumulative weekly totals of Fulmars, 1951-92.*

There have been four inland records. Single birds flew south over Ringwood on May 26th 1976, north-west over Fleet Pond on June 17th 1979 and south-west over Denny Inclosure on May 26th 1985, and one was at Mockbeggar Lake on Sep. 13th 1989. The only record for Southampton Water is of one flying south at Hythe on Aug. 16th 1988.

The increased numbers of Fulmars seen in Hampshire since the 1970s can be attributed to both increased observer effort and the establishment of breeding colonies in Dorset, the Isle of Wight and Sussex.

## Cory's Shearwater                                  *Calonectris diomedea*

One record. One was seen off Hurst Beach on May 12th 1982.

The Cory's Shearwater breeds on islands in the Mediterranean and off the North African coast.

## Sooty Shearwater                                  *Puffinus griseus*

One record. One was found long dead at Warsash on July 22nd 1974.

The Sooty Shearwater breeds on sub-Antarctic islands and winters in the North Atlantic and Pacific Oceans.

## Manx Shearwater                                  *Puffinus puffinus*

A very scarce passage migrant, not recorded every year.

K & M listed a few records but the next was not until 1949, when one was found dead at Needs Ore on June 21st. In the following year, a storm-driven bird was picked up alive at Avington Park on Sep. 5th. Since then, annual totals have been variable but shown an upward trend in line with the increase in birdwatching activity (fig. 8).

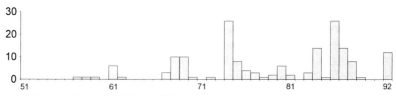

*Figure 8. Annual totals of Manx Shearwaters, 1951-92.*

Most have been recorded in spring, but a small peak is also evident in early autumn, largely involving storm-driven birds (fig. 9). 102 were recorded off Hurst Beach, including 22 on May 4th 1974 and ten on May 17th 1986. Other coastal sightings were made from Southsea/Eastney (18 birds, including ten flying west on Mar. 29th 1987), Hill Head (10), Hayling Bay (15), Pennington Marsh (12, including eight flying west on June 24th 1975), Gilkicker Point (2), Langstone Harbour (3, all dead or injured), Lepe (1) and Calshot (1). 11 were found dead or in poor condition at inland localities as far north as Andover and Alton following September gales. All records were in the period between Mar. 29th and Oct. 30th.

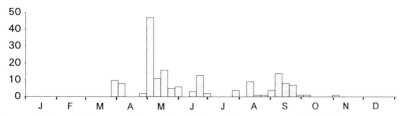

*Figure 9. Cumulative weekly totals of Manx Shearwaters, 1951-92.*

The nearest large colonies are on Skokholm and Skomer Islands, Dyfed. Smaller numbers breed in the Isles of Scilly, the Channel Islands and north-west France.

## Mediterranean Shearwater                    *Puffinus yelkouan*

Four records. Single birds were seen flying west off Oxey Creek (Lymington) on July 21st 1971 and off Hurst Beach on Aug. 2nd 1981, May 11th 1982 and July 4th 1993.

This species has recently been separated from the Manx Shearwater (BOURC 1992). It breeds in the Mediterranean and disperses into the North Atlantic.

## Storm Petrel                    *Hydrobates pelagicus*

A rare visitor, usually occurring after autumn gales.

K & M mention one found near Stockbridge about 1884, but the next was not until 1954. Since then there have been 16 records involving 18 birds. One flew west off Hurst Castle on Aug. 14th 1954 and another was seen off Hythe Pier on Oct. 9th 1955. A corpse was found on the shore at Lee-on-the-Solent on Jan. 1st 1957 after a storm two days earlier. One flew west at Gilkicker Point on Nov. 26th 1960 and two were off Hurst on Oct. 28th 1967. The next was not until 1980, when one fed over the river at Titchfield Haven during a force nine gale on Jan. 21st and eventually moved inland. One was seen in the Hamble Estuary on Sep. 3rd 1983 and one flew west off Pennington Marsh on Oct. 4th 1985. An exhausted bird was found on the container ship Kowloon Bay at Southampton Docks after a crossing from Le Havre on Nov. 27th 1986. It was fed and rested overnight, and released south of the Isle of Wight the next day. Two singles were seen in the aftermath of the great storm of Oct. 15th/16th 1987 – one off Stokes Bay on 17th and another off Hurst Castle the next day. One flew east at Lepe on May 1st 1988, the only spring record. Three appeared following gales in late 1989: one flying west off Hill Head on Oct. 21st, one picked up there on Dec. 21st and one off Farlington Marshes on Dec. 25th. Finally, two seen offshore at Gilkicker Point on Sep. 28th 1991 flew off east.

The cumulative monthly totals of all records for 1954-92 are shown below.

| Aug | Sep | Oct | Nov | Dec | Jan | Feb | Mar | Apr | May |
|-----|-----|-----|-----|-----|-----|-----|-----|-----|-----|
| 1 | 3 | 7 | 2 | 2 | 2 | 0 | 0 | 0 | 1 |

The nearest breeding colonies are in the Channel Islands, the Isles of Scilly and Brittany, France.

## Leach's Petrel                                    *Oceanodroma leucorhoa*

A rare autumn and winter visitor, usually appearing after gales.

K & M mentioned at least four Leach's Petrels which were picked up at inland localities in the second half of the 19th century. A further seven storm-driven birds were recorded between 1936 and 1949.

A massive "wreck" of this species was recorded throughout the country in late October and early November 1952 (Boyd 1954). In Hampshire, 18 dead or dying birds were discovered (14 at localities well inland) and five were seen offshore.

Between 1956 and 1988, there were 17 records involving 21 individuals. Most sightings were made off Hurst Beach or Pennington Marsh, where single birds were seen on Dec. 4th 1960, Oct. 28th and Nov. 3rd 1962, Oct. 28th 1967, Sep. 4th 1983, Sep. 28th 1986 and Oct. 9th 1988. Four were noted in the area on Oct. 17th 1987. Other coastal records involved single birds at Langstone Harbour on Oct. 29th 1972, Oct. 17th 1982 and Oct. 18th 1987, Hythe on Sep. 25th 1983 and two at Hill Head on Jan. 6th 1988, one of which flew off north up the River Meon. The remaining four birds were found inland, at Bisterne on Dec. 11th 1956, Fullerton on Sep. 27th 1963, Brambridge on Sep. 26th 1982 and Whitchurch on Sep. 9th 1986.

In 1989, two were seen off Hurst Castle during strong south-westerly winds on Oct. 21st and two flew east off Pennington Marsh the next day. An unprecedented influx occurred following severe gales from Dec. 16th onwards, with about 62 recorded. The largest numbers were ten at least flying east at Lee-on-the-Solent on 23rd, 12 in Hurst Narrows on 24th and at least 15, including eight together, between Hurst Beach and Milford-on-Sea on Christmas Day. Three were found dead inland at Stubbington, Queen Elizabeth Country Park and Hursley. A straggler from the wreck was picked up on Keyhaven Saltings on Jan. 3rd 1990; it was released later that day and flew off strongly.

In 1991 two flew west off Hill Head during a gale on Jan. 9th and one was found on a cargo ship in Southampton Docks on Nov. 29th which had arrived via the Bay of Biscay. It was released the next day at Hill Head.

The cumulative monthly totals of all records for 1952-92 are shown below.

| Sep | Oct | Nov | Dec | Jan |
|-----|-----|-----|-----|-----|
| 6 | 26 | 13 | 64 | 5 |

The nearest breeding colonies are in the Western Isles of Scotland and Mayo, Ireland.

## Madeiran Petrel                                                    *Oceanodroma castro*

One record. One was picked up dead at Milford-on-Sea on Nov. 19th 1911 (*Brit. Birds* 5: 252).

This is the only British record. The Madeiran Petrel breeds on islands in the East Atlantic and the Pacific Ocean.

## Gannet                                                                *Sula bassana*

A moderately common passage migrant and non-breeding summer visitor; rare in winter.

Gannets have been recorded in every month of the year, but by far the largest numbers occur in April and May and between July and September (fig. 10).

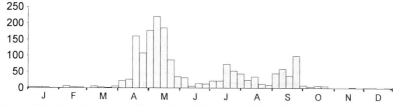

*Figure 10. Cumulative weekly totals of Gannets, 1971-92.*

In the period 1971-92, 1074 were seen between March and June, of which 393 flew east, 217 west and 464 were offshore, and 525 between July and October, of which 110 moved east, 217 west and 198 were offshore. 22 out of 43 which occurred between November and February were found dead or dying during severe cold weather or following gales.

The largest counts were made at the two ends of the Hampshire coastline. Between Hurst Beach and the Needles, there have been numerous reports from local commercial fishermen of large fishing flocks, mostly in May, July and August (E J Wiseman *in litt*); this is supported by records of 200 in that area in the last week of August 1953 and 150-200 there on July 10th 1969. The highest counts during 1971-92 were of 26 on July 19th 1987, 30 on Aug. 13th 1988 and 31 on May 9th 1992.

Increased sea-watching activity at Hayling Bay from 1983 onwards has revealed that regular movements occur offshore in both spring and autumn; this presumably forms part of the larger passage witnessed from Selsey Bill and St. Catherine's Point (*cf.* Fulmar). The highest day totals were of 79 moving west on May 10th 1986, 74 east on Apr. 20th 1990 and 59 south-west on Sep. 29th 1990.

Gannets are scarce in The Solent, e.g. off Hill Head, only 99 were seen between 1956 and 1992, including a flock of 22 which flew east on May 15th 1985 and a flock of 29 which flew east on Apr. 29th 1991.

Between 1933 and 1992, 14 individuals were recorded inland, seven between January and March and seven between July and November. Most appeared to be sick and/or storm-driven.

One of the inland birds, found dead on Broughton Down on Mar. 5th 1979, had been ringed as a chick on Little Skellig, Ireland in 1972. Two others, ringed as chicks on the Bass Rock, Scotland in 1949 and 1957, were found dead at

Milford-on-Sea in October 1949 and Calshot in October 1967. These recoveries indicate the origin of some of the birds seen in Hampshire, although others no doubt come from nearer colonies on Grassholm (Dyfed), Alderney and in Brittany.

## Cormorant                                   *Phalacrocorax carbo*

A moderately common non-breeding resident, passage migrant and winter visitor.

During the 1950s and 1960s, coverage of most sites was poor, but roost counts such as 257 on Fawley Pier on Sep. 19th 1955 and 250 at Dibden Bay on Jan. 12th 1963 indicate that Southampton Water was the principal area for the species. In Langstone Harbour, the maximum recorded was 80 on Nov. 28th 1953. Most birds from this site left at dusk to roost on the Spithead defence boom, where the highest count was of 120 on Mar. 15th 1958. A daily winter flight-line up the Avon valley was well established in the mid-1950s. Counts in excess of 20 were regularly recorded from 1952 onwards and 41 were night roosting in poplars at Avon on Feb. 8th 1959.

Since that period, numbers have increased in most areas of the county. Counts at various localities between 1970/71 and 1989/90 are summarised in table 4.

|  | 70-75 | 75-80 | 80-85 | 85-90 | Peak counts |
|---|---|---|---|---|---|
| Langstone Harbour | 57 | 49 | 65 | 142 | 201, Sep. 1988 |
| Portsmouth Harbour | - | 44^ | 41 | 51 | 64, Nov. 1986 |
| Southampton Water | 164^ | 159 | 205^ | 199^ | 221, Oct. 1988 |
| Avon valley | - | - | 53^ | 101 | 188, Feb. 1990 |
| Fleet Pond | 2 | 6 | 10 | 15 | 28, Jan. 1990 |

*Table 4. Five year means of winter maxima and peak counts of Cormorants, 1970/71-89/90.*

Other localities where counts have exceeded 30 are Warsash (maximum 33, February 1987), Titchfield Haven (37, October 1989), Broadlands Estate (45, February 1990) and Lymington/Hurst (58, October 1990).

At coastal localities, annual maxima are nearly always recorded between September and November, while the flight lines up the Avon and Test have their highest counts in mid-winter. Further inland, records during the 1970s and early 1980s showed peaks in spring and early autumn, but since 1982, birds from the Thames valley wintering population have flown in daily to sites such as Stratfield Saye, Fleet Pond and Eversley/Yateley Gravel Pits in increasing numbers. Numbers peaked at 53 at Fleet Pond on Nov. 8th 1990 and 34 at Stratfield Saye on Feb. 17th 1991. In the 1991/92 winter, a night roost was established at Fleet Pond with a maximum count of 43 on Nov. 9th.

Movement is regularly noted during spring sea watches, e.g. at Sandy Point, 48 flew east on Apr. 27th 1984, 40 east on May 5th 1984 and 114 east between 0510 and 1050 hrs. on May 3rd 1990. This is likely to refer, at least in part, to local birds leaving their roost site, for 59 flew west there between 1945 and 2020 hrs. on May 1st 1990.

The origin of our wintering population is indicated by the ringing data, which show 50 movements of over 100 km into Hampshire. 49 involved birds ringed between May and July, presumably as chicks, in Wales (38), Scotland (4), northern England (4), Ireland (2) and southern England (1). In addition, four, colour-ringed as chicks on St. Margaret's Island, Dyfed, have been seen at coastal sites since 1988, and another, colour-ringed as a chick at Vorso, Denmark in 1988, was at Fleet Pond in December 1989. The nearest breeding colonies are at Main Bench and Culver Cliff in the Isle of Wight and in Dorset, but ringing has not been attempted at these sites.

# Shag                                    *Phalacrocorax aristotelis*

A scarce winter visitor and passage migrant.

Before 1954, Shags were rarely recorded, but since then they have been seen annually. In autumn, most appear during and following gales, e.g. five flying east off Hill Head on Sep. 2nd 1989 and nine, the largest group recorded, moving east in Hayling Bay the next day.

Between November and March, the species is most frequent in the Black Point/Southsea area, where up to three are present in most winters and a maximum of six was recorded at Southsea on Jan. 2nd 1991. There are also occasional winter records from Southampton Water (often of birds roosting with Cormorants) and Hurst Beach.

In spring, most are seen off Hurst Beach, where the highest count was of four on May 18th 1974. A few are seen elsewhere along the coast, e.g. four flew east in Hayling Bay on Apr. 29th 1990.

There have been 16 inland records since 1961, with annual sightings from 1983-91. All were of single birds apart from those of three at Wellington Country Park on Nov. 29th 1987 and two at Fleet Pond on Sep. 3rd 1988. Several were storm-driven, and remained for a week or more before departing or dying. Long-staying individuals included a first-winter at Black Dam (Basingstoke) from Sep. 12th 1983-Apr. 1st 1984, which was then captured and released at Hurst Beach, and a second-winter at Blackwater from Feb. 16th-Mar. 2nd 1986. Other records came from Eversley Gravel Pit and Frensham Great Pond (2 each), and Alresford Pond, Basingstoke town centre, Black Dam, Fleet Pond, Heath Pond, Ovington/Winnall Moors, Pyestock and Shepherds Spring. The Basingstoke bird landed on the window sill of a sixth floor office on Jan. 18th 1985.

The cumulative monthly totals of all records for 1954/55-91/92 are shown below.

| Jul | Aug | Sep | Oct | Nov | Dec | Jan | Feb | Mar | Apr | May | Jun |
|-----|-----|-----|-----|-----|-----|-----|-----|-----|-----|-----|-----|
| 2 | 11 | 38 | 24 | 39 | 34 | 69 | 39 | 46 | 46 | 31 | 3 |

The origin of wintering birds is suggested by the recovery between October and April of nine ringed as chicks at the Isle of May (5), the Farne Islands (2), North Berwick (1) and the Scilly Isles (1). Eight were in their first winter and the other was in its second winter, thus demonstrating the dispersal of immatures from their natal colonies.

# Bittern                                    *Botaurus stellaris*

A very scarce but regular winter visitor.

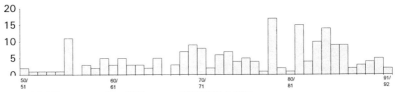

*Figure 11. Winter totals of Bitterns, 1950/51-91/92.*

From the mid-1950s until the late 1970s an average of about four Bitterns per winter was recorded, but during the 1980s this increased to eight (fig. 11). This upturn was in contrast to the fortunes of the British breeding population, which declined from over 100 pairs in the 1950s (Parslow 1973) to 20 pairs or booming males in 1990 (Spencer *et al* 1993). The increase coincided with the series of five severe winters between 1978/79 and 1986/87, when the highest numbers were recorded. Bibby (1981) showed that many wintering Bitterns originate from north-west Europe and that most occur in hard winters.

The first may arrive at any time between late October and December. However, during the 1970s there were regular records from Fleet Pond in July-September (earliest date, July 5th 1976); subsequently the only such records were of single birds near Romsey on July 31st and Aug. 1st 1989 and near Ringwood on Aug. 3rd 1991. The high numbers in January and February are partially accounted for by influxes in hard weather. Most have left by mid-March but one flew high to the east over Needs Ore on Apr. 21st 1974 and another remained at Sinah Gravel Pit from Dec. 18th 1981-Apr. 23rd 1982.

Many have been seen in, or close to, reed beds. In recent years, most reports have come from Fleet Pond and Titchfield Haven. At Fleet Pond, regular observations from 1968/69 onwards showed that one or two wintered annually, with three present in January 1973 and January 1974. After the 1978/79 winter, there were no further records until 1982/83. Since then, one has been present, sometimes for a few days only, in every winter apart from 1986/87, when two were seen, and 1989/90 and 1991/92, when none were recorded. At Titchfield Haven, the species has been seen in every winter but three since 1978/79. Usually one or two were recorded, but up to five were there in December 1983. The only other sites with records in more than five winters have been Sowley Pond (one or two in most winters from 1958/59-78/79, but only one since), Marsh Court (one in six winters from 1957/58-78/79, but none since) and Farlington Marshes (one or two in seven winters from 1955/56-86/87, always in severe weather). Further sightings have been made at other coastal reed beds and in the main river valleys, but Bitterns have also occurred along small streams, around gravel pits and lakes, on watercress beds and even in gardens, especially in hard weather when they are forced out of reed beds. Several have been found dead in such conditions. One was watched following a manure-spreader with Black-headed Gulls at Northfields Farm (Twyford) on Feb. 25th and 26th 1986.

The cumulative monthly totals of all records for 1950/51-91/92 are shown below.

| Jul | Aug | Sep | Oct | Nov | Dec | Jan | Feb | Mar | Apr | May | Jun |
|---|---|---|---|---|---|---|---|---|---|---|---|
| 5 | 8 | 11 | 14 | 28 | 57 | 105 | 77 | 40 | 13 | 4 | 0 |

K & M stated that the Bittern "was formerly a resident in suitable localities", but did not furnish any convincing evidence of nesting. There have been a few records suggestive of breeding during this century. At Titchfield Haven, booming was heard on Apr. 4th 1929 and May 16th 1970 and an old nest was found between 1950 and 1952. In the Test valley, a pair was present at Longparish in 1942. In the Avon valley, booming was heard at Breamore in early summer 1951 and at Somerley between March and May 1954; a nest typical of a Bittern's was found in the former area in July 1952.

## American Bittern                    *Botaurus lentiginosus*

Two records. Single birds were shot at Woodside, Lymington in January 1876 and a month later at Cadnam (K & M).

The American Bittern breeds in southern Canada and the USA and winters south to Mexico.

## Little Bittern                    *Ixobrychus minutus*

A rare vagrant. K & M listed birds obtained at Hilsea in 1851 and Fordingbridge in April 1869. Since then, there have been ten records of 11 birds, as follows:

1953:   immature, Titchfield Haven, Aug. 9th;
1954:   adult male, Titchfield Haven, June 13th/14th;
        female or immature, found dead, Eastern Road, Portsmouth, Aug. 12th;
        adult male found at Andover and released at Leckford, date unknown;
1960:   2, Titchfield Haven, May 21st and 22nd, 1 until May 26th;
1964:   adult female, Winchester Water Meadows, May 7th;
1966:   female, Titchfield Haven, Sep. 3rd;
1968:   adult male, Titchfield Haven, June 9th;
1970:   adult male, Farlington Marshes, May 2nd-6th;
1981:   adult male, Titchfield Haven, May 18th/19th.

The Little Bittern is a summer visitor to Europe; most British records involve birds overshooting their continental breeding grounds in spring. The decrease in records in Hampshire in the last 20 years, despite the great expansion of birdwatching, parallels the national situation. This is presumably connected with the recent decline in some breeding populations, e.g. in the Netherlands.

## Night Heron                    *Nycticorax nycticorax*

A rare vagrant. K & M listed birds shot at Ringwood on July 22nd 1868 and at Avon Castle in 1901. Since then, there have been 11 records, as follows:

1911:   New Milton, May-July 14th;
1961:   Lyndhurst, June 14th;
1966:   first-winter, Beaulieu area, Dec. 8th-June 18th 1967;
1972:   adult, Sowley Pond, Dec. 11th-Feb. 14th 1973†;
1980:   adult, Farlington Marshes, June 9th;
1981:   adult, Titchfield Abbey ponds, May 4th;
1988:   first-winter, Danes Stream (Milford-on-Sea) Oct. 30th-Nov. 16th†;

1990:    adult, Hucklesbrook, Feb. 24th-Mar. 25th;
         sub-adult, Arlebury Lake, Mar. 25th†;
         adult, Titchfield Haven, May 14th†;
1992:    first-winter, Woodmill/Itchen Country Park, Nov. 15th-Feb. 9th 1993.

The Night Heron is a summer visitor to Europe, although it is increasingly being recorded in winter. It breeds as close as northern France, Belgium and the Netherlands. Those occurring in 1990 were part of an early spring influx into southern England involving at least 30 birds (Rogers *et al* 1991).

## Squacco Heron                                      *Ardeola ralloides*

One record. An adult was at Needs Ore on June 11th and 12th 1982† (E J Wiseman *in litt*).

The Squacco Heron is a summer visitor to southern Europe; the above record is typical of the British pattern of overshooting spring migrants.

## Cattle Egret                                       *Bubulcus ibis*

Two records. One was present in the Titchfield Haven area from Nov. 4th 1986-Jan. 11th 1987 and another was at Farlington Marshes on May 22nd 1992†.

In Europe, the Cattle Egret is a resident and partial migrant which is slowly extending its range north across France.

## Little Egret                                       *Egretta garzetta*

A scarce, but increasing, passage migrant and winter visitor.

After the first at Langstone Harbour on June 2nd 1957, a further 32 Little Egrets occurred up to 1988 (fig. 12). Sightings were made between Apr. 19th and Oct. 6th, with a peak in late May and early June. Summering was recorded in 1976 (June 4th-Oct. 3rd), 1984 (June 15th-Oct. 1st) and 1985 (June 11th-Oct. 6th). Most were seen at coastal localities, especially Langstone Harbour, Titchfield Haven and in the west Solent area between the Beaulieu Estuary and Hurst, but single birds occurred inland at Bickton from May 21st-25th 1962, Bishopstoke on May 18th 1976†, Fleet Pond on Apr. 22nd 1982 and Leckford on Oct. 17th 1987. All records were of single birds apart from a flock of five which spent the day at Beaulieu Mill Pond on May 26th 1988.

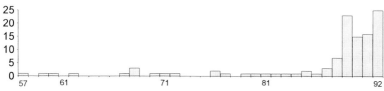

*Figure 12. Annual totals of Little Egrets, 1957-92.*

In 1989, one was at Langstone Harbour on May 24th, to be followed by an unprecedented influx from mid-July onwards which was recorded throughout southern England, and believed to have originated in north-west France (Combridge and Parr 1992). Most in Hampshire were in the west Solent area, where numbers peaked at 17 at Lymington on Aug. 28th. These dispersed during September and only one was recorded in October. A smaller arrival late in 1989 involved about seven birds which wintered: three at East Hayling, three in the west Solent area and one which moved up the Test valley from Eling to Longparish.

Since then, the pattern of a late summer influx with some birds staying through the winter has become established. Birds are now regular in the west Solent area and the Langstone Harbour/East Hayling area from July-March. Usually up to five have been recorded, but at Needs Ore there were seven on July 31st 1992, then 12 on Aug. 25th, decreasing to six on Sep. 5th. Reports from other coastal sites have mostly been of single birds, but three were at Lower Test Marshes on Aug. 30th 1992. Inland, one flew west over Acres Down on Aug. 11th 1992 and two were at Fleet Pond on Aug. 15th 1992.

Comparison of the cumulative monthly totals for 1957-88 and 1989-92 below shows how the pattern has changed. May and June, the months in which most of the early birds were recorded, is now the period when the species is least frequent.

|         | Jan | Feb | Mar | Apr | May | Jun | Jul | Aug | Sep | Oct | Nov | Dec |
|---------|-----|-----|-----|-----|-----|-----|-----|-----|-----|-----|-----|-----|
| 1957-88 | 0   | 0   | 0   | 2   | 18  | 8   | 4   | 7   | 5   | 4   | 1   | 0   |
| 1989-92 | 11  | 10  | 6   | 4   | 6   | 3   | 16  | 47  | 36  | 14  | 16  | 21  |

The Little Egret breeds in much of southern and central Europe, tropical Africa, southern Asia and Australasia. The French and Spanish populations are partially migratory, with most wintering in tropical West Africa.

## Great White Egret                                    *Egretta alba*

Two records. One flew from Thorney Island, West Sussex towards Hayling Island on June 15th 1985 and another was at Blackwater (Needs Ore) on July 17th 1992.

The Great White Egret is a resident and partial migrant which is increasing in western Europe and now breeds in the Netherlands.

## Grey Heron                                           *Ardea cinerea*

A moderately common resident, passage migrant and winter visitor. It is widely observed but a local, colonial breeder.

K & M gave details of heronries which held between 20 and 60 nests at Vinney Ridge in the New Forest, Mottisfont, Woolmer Forest, Hinton Admiral and Somerley. The first three were extinct by 1928, when 72 nests were found at nine sites during the course of the first national Heron Survey (Nicholson 1929). In 1954, when the next full census took place, 114 nests were counted in nine colonies with the largest at West Walk (30 nests), Tournerbury (20) and Alice Holt Forest (13) (Burton 1956).

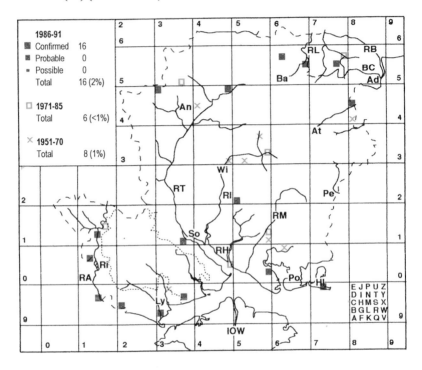

The census has been repeated annually ever since, although coverage has rarely been complete. Numbers declined after the severe winter of 1962/63. Subsequently, there was a steady increase which accelerated in the late 1970s and early 1980s. The population peaked at about 260 pairs in 1985, but by 1990, it had dropped back to about 155 pairs (fig. 13). Unfortunately, the county data for 1991 and 1992 are incomplete, but the national population in the former year was estimated to be 10,300 pairs (New Atlas).

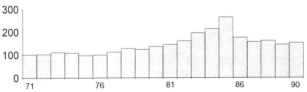

*Figure 13. Estimated totals of breeding pairs of Grey Herons, 1971-90.*

There is little doubt that the large increase in the early 1980s was the result of the expansion of fish farming, especially in the Test and Itchen valleys. Possibly the abundant supply of Rainbow Trout helped reduce winter mortality or improve nesting success, thus leading to an increase in the population. Antipredator netting is now used to protect the trout, which presumably accounts, at least in part, for the reduction since 1986. However, decreases at some sites can be specifically attributed to storm damage, disturbance by forestry thinning or other human activities.

The Atlas Map shows the 14 tetrads where nests were located during 1986-91 and those occupied at any time since 1951. Table 5 summarises counts of occupied nests at the main heronries during 1971-90.

| | | 71-75 | 76-80 | 81-85 | 86-90 | Peak count | |
|---|---|---|---|---|---|---|---|
| Elvetham Park | SU75S | 10^ | 8 | 8 | 9 | 11, | 1986 |
| Fort Elson | SU50W | - | 8^ | 51^ | 43^ | 75, | 1985 |
| Hinton Admiral | SZ29C | 24 | 19 | 12* | 5* | 25-28, | 1972 |
| Low Hill Farm / Marwell Park | SU52A | - | 8* | 37^ | 16* | 51/52, | 1985 |
| Ramridge Copse | SU34E | - | - | 29* | 20^ | 29/30, | 1985 |
| Round Copse | SU65X | - | - | - | 12^ | 14, | 1990 |
| Somerley Park | SU10I | 0 | 1* | 6 | 8 | 13, | 1990 |
| Sopley | SZ19N | 5 | 7* | - | 11 | 15, | 1990 |
| Sowley Pond | SZ39T | 13* | 27 | 41 | 27 | 51-54, | 1983 |
| Tournerbury | SZ79J | 15^ | 14 | 13 | 12 | 15-21, | 1973 |
| Trotts Wood | SU31Q | 7^ | 14 | 13^ | 8 | 25, | 1980 |

*Table 5. Counts of occupied nests of Herons: five year means and peak counts, 1971-90.*

Outside the breeding season, large feeding concentrations may gather at fish farms, lakes and gravel pits with low water levels, and favoured estuarine sites. Counts usually peak in late summer and autumn when the greatest numbers of juveniles are present. High counts have been most consistently recorded between the middle Test valley and Southampton Water, where flocks in excess of 50 were seen in eight years between 1976 and 1990. The highest counts at individual localities were of 53 at Dibden Bay on Oct. 10th 1976, 71 at Timsbury on July 29th 1979 and 80+ over Lower Test Marshes on Sep. 10th 1983. Between 1980 and 1985, large gatherings were regular in the vicinity of Avington fish farm, the peak counts being of 105 on Nov. 25th 1980, 153 on Jan. 22nd 1984 and 135 on Dec. 26th 1984. Since 1985, the only count in that area to have exceeded 50 was of 58 flying to roost from Alresford fish farm on June 13th 1990. At Langstone Harbour, the autumn maximum regularly exceeded 30 in the 1950s with a peak of 61 in October 1959. Between 1960 and 1977, a steady decline took place and in some years no more than 20 were recorded. Since then, there has been a recovery with a maximum of 48 on Oct. 18th 1986. The only other site to have held more than 50 is Mockbeggar Lake. In autumn 1989, exceptional numbers were attracted there by the easy feeding offered by the low water level, with a maximum count of 137 on Oct. 7th.

Not surprisingly, most of the large gatherings described above coincided with the period when breeding numbers were at their highest. At Langstone Harbour, the pattern of autumn numbers between 1953 and 1990 correlates closely with the fortunes of the local heronries at West Walk, Tournerbury and Fort Elson (Portsmouth Group 1991).

Coastal movement is observed almost annually in spring but much less frequently in autumn. Between 1971 and 1992, a total of 46 was recorded between mid-March and mid-May, with 31 moving in directions between north and east. In autumn during the same period, there were eight records between mid-August and early October involving ten moving east, eight west, one north and two flocks of 13 and 11 which flew high to the south-west over Titchfield Haven on Sep. 11th 1990.

British Grey Herons are mainly resident, although there is a post-fledging dispersal of young birds and some breeding in southern England winter in western France (Voisin 1991). There have been four recoveries of Hampshire-ringed pulli. One ringed at Alice Holt Forest in May 1962 was found dead at Creuse, France, 574 km SSE, on Feb. 16th 1963 and had presumably been forced south by the severe weather at the time, and another ringed at Low Hill Farm in May 1978 was found dead at Harpenden, Hertfordshire on Oct. 13th 1979. The other two had moved less than 10 km when recovered. Those ringed elsewhere in Britain and recovered in Hampshire total 15, of which eight travelled over 100 km, all in directions between west and SSW, from Bedfordshire, Essex (2), Kent, Norfolk, Suffolk and Sussex (2). The origin of some of our wintering birds is indicated by the recovery in Hampshire of 14 ringed as pulli in Belgium (2), Denmark (3), north-eastern France (2), western Germany (1), the Netherlands (2) and Sweden (4). Two more ringed as pulli in Denmark and Norway were found dead in Hampshire in summer.

## Purple Heron                                   *Ardea purpurea*

A rare vagrant. One was procured at Ashley Farm (Stockbridge) on June 30th 1875 (K & M). The next was not until 1964, since when a further 15 individuals have been recorded, as follows:

1964:   adult, Langstone Harbour, Aug. 3rd;
1967:   first-summer, Farlington Marshes, May 28th;
1968:   first-summer, Keyhaven, May 19th;
1969:   adult, Wildgrounds, Gosport, late Sep.-Oct. 15th;
1971:   adult, Farlington Marshes, Aug. 31st;
1976:   adult in flight over Hampton Ridge, May 1st;

| 1977: | first-summer, Marsh Court, May 7th; |
|---|---|
| | first-winter, Sowley Pond/Bishop's Dyke, Aug. 29th-Sep. 3rd; |
| | first-winter, Needs Ore, Oct. 14th-16th; |
| 1983: | sub-adult, Titchfield Haven, May 4th, left west; |
| 1984: | adult, Keyhaven, May 10th, flew off towards IOW; |
| | sub-adult soaring over Liss, May 30th; |
| 1986: | first-winter, Lower Pennington, Aug. 21st; |
| 1988: | adult, Needs Ore, Apr. 25th; |
| 1990: | first-summer in flight, Curbridge, Apr. 9th; |
| 1992: | adult flying south, Lower Test Marshes, May 5th. |

The Purple Heron is a summer visitor to Europe, with the nearest breeding colonies in north-eastern France and the Netherlands. Those occurring in spring are presumably migrants which overshoot those breeding grounds.

# Black Stork                                    *Ciconia nigra*

A rare vagrant. There have been six records, as follows:

| 1970: | Godshill, May 12th and Rhinefield, May 17th-19th; |
|---|---|
| 1975: | Farlington Marshes, Aug. 22nd; |
| 1985: | Plastow Green, Kingsclere, June 9th; |
| 1989: | New Forest, May 20th and 26th, Aug. 12th and 13th†; |
| 1990: | Avon valley/New Forest, Apr. 7th-July 11th; |
| 1993: | Frith End, July 1st and 2nd†. |

The Black Stork is a summer visitor to Europe, with the nearest breeding grounds in Spain and eastern Germany. It has been recorded in increasing numbers in Britain in recent years.

# White Stork                                    *Ciconia ciconia*

A rare vagrant. K & M list five records from within the present day county boundary. The first this century was shot near Southwick in summer 1931. The next was not until 1952, when one was following the plough near Damerham in early July. Since 1960, there have been 20 sightings, probably referring to 15 individuals, as follows:

| 1960: | flying north over Cosham, May 28th; |
|---|---|
| 1971: | Eling Great Marsh, Oct. 23rd†; |
| 1975: | Martyr Worthy, Apr. 11th-13th; |
| 1976: | flying north over Keyhaven, July 18th; |
| | flying south-west over Titchfield Haven, Sep. 18th; |
| 1978: | flying east over Regent's Park, Sep. 17th†; |
| | flying south over Horndean, Oct. 13th†; |
| 1979: | flying west over Farlington Marshes, Jan. 1st; |
| | in flight over Sway and Holmsley, Jan. 2nd†; |
| 1984: | adult, Titchfield Haven, May 5th, left east; |
| 1986: | flying south-west over Burley Lawn, May 30th; |
| | flying south over Winnall Moors, June 26th; |
| | soaring over Bishop's Dyke, July 1st; |
| | flying north-east over Buriton, July 1st; |
| | East Wellow, Aug. 15th; |
| 1988: | flying NNW over Portsmouth Harbour and Portsdown Hill, Mar. 30th; |
| | flying south-west over Tweseldown and Church Crookham, Sep. 6th; |
| 1989: | flying south over Hale, May 21st; |
| 1990: | East Hayling, Nov. 4th; |
| 1992: | flying west over Hayling Island, May 14th. |

The White Stork is a summer visitor to Europe which has declined in countries close to Britain. It winters in sub-Saharan Africa.

## Glossy Ibis                                    *Plegadis falcinellus*

Four records. K & M recorded a male shot at Tundry Pond in September 1881 and one killed near Romsey in October 1902. The only recent records were of one present in the Brockenhurst area from May 24th-Aug. 4th 1965† and one at Titchfield Haven on June 6th 1977.

The Glossy Ibis has a discontinuous worldwide distribution. Its nearest regularly-used nesting grounds are in south-eastern Europe although it has recently bred in the Camargue, France. Most European birds are probably trans-Saharan migrants but smaller numbers winter in the Mediterranean Basin west to Morocco.

## Spoonbill                                      *Platalea leucorodia*

A very scarce visitor, most frequent in summer but recorded in every month except February.

In the first half of this century, there were records in 16 years, including those of three at Needs Ore on Oct. 24th and 25th 1927 and up to three at Titchfield Haven from May 26th until early October 1939.

Between 1951 and 1992, a total of 65 was recorded (fig. 14). Sightings were made at Langstone Harbour/Farlington Marshes (30 birds), Titchfield Haven (24), the Lymington/Hurst area (15), Needs Ore (11), Warsash (4), Dibden Bay and East Hayling (3 each), Paulsgrove Reclamation and Pitts Deep (1 each) and at inland localities (4). Several individuals were seen at more than one place.

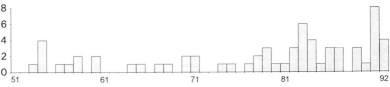

*Figure 14. Annual totals of Spoonbills, 1951-92.*

Most reports involved one or two birds and were in the period Apr. 23rd-Nov. 4th, with clear peaks in spring and autumn. Spoonbills were usually seen flying over or remained for a day or two, but some stayed for several weeks. One, colour-ringed as a nestling in the Netherlands in 1983, spent its first winter in Christchurch Harbour (Dorset), but was seen in Hampshire at Avon Causeway on Dec. 17th 1983 and near Avon Castle on Jan. 22nd 1984. It subsequently summered, being seen at Pennington Marsh, Needs Ore, Pitts Deep and Titchfield Haven between May 9th and Aug. 18th 1984. Long stays were also recorded in 1989, with an adult at Titchfield Haven from June 12th-Sep. 1st and a first-summer there from June 26th-Sep. 20th; and in 1992, with an adult and two first-summers at Titchfield Haven and Needs Ore between July 12th and Sep. 5th. The first-summer at Titchfield Haven in 1989 had been colour-ringed as a pullus at Terschelling, Netherlands in 1988. This individual was the adult recorded in 1992. In the interim period, it had been recorded in Dyfed in October 1988, Cornwall in November 1988, Algarve, Portugal in October 1989, the Coto Doñana, Spain in March 1990, the Netherlands in July 1990, Vendée, France in September 1990 and at Terschelling from May-July 1991, where it was breeding. Apart from the long-staying individual already mentioned, the only other winter records were of single birds at Titchfield Haven on Dec. 29th 1970 and Mar. 25th 1979, flying south over Ashley Walk, New Forest on Jan. 24th 1983, and at East Hayling and Langstone Harbour between Mar. 3rd and 12th 1989. One moving north then west over Bishopstoke on Apr. 26th 1981 is the only other inland record. The largest parties seen were flocks of four in Langstone Harbour on Aug. 15th 1954 and at Titchfield Haven and Langstone Harbour on Sep. 9th and 10th 1991. The cumulative monthly totals of all records for 1951-92 are shown below.

| Jan | Feb | Mar | Apr | May | Jun | Jul | Aug | Sep | Oct | Nov | Dec |
|-----|-----|-----|-----|-----|-----|-----|-----|-----|-----|-----|-----|
| 2   | 0   | 2   | 5   | 15  | 8   | 10  | 14  | 17  | 7   | 1   | 2   |

As the sightings of colour-ringed birds suggest, most birds occurring in Hampshire probably belong to the Netherlands breeding population, which winters mostly in north-west Africa (BWP).

# Mute Swan                                            *Cygnus olor*

A moderately common resident which has been increasing steadily since the 1970s and probably earlier.

The Mute Swan population has been the subject of four national surveys. In the first, in 1955, when coverage of the county was described as moderate, 63 breeding or territorial pairs and 171 non-breeders were located (Campbell 1960). In 1978, there were 121 pairs and 419 non-breeders (Clark 1979, Ogilvie 1981), and by 1983, this had increased to 166 pairs and 605 non-breeders (Smallbone 1984, Ogilvie 1986). In the most recent survey in 1990, 182 pairs and 801 non-breeders were counted (A C Smallbone *in litt*). The main increases have been in the Avon, Test and Itchen valleys (table 6). These rivers are highly fertile and used largely for fly fishing; there is no doubt that a steady and continuing increase has taken place on these and similar rivers in neighbouring counties since 1955 (Ogilvie 1986).

| | Breeding/Territorial Pairs | | | Non-breeders | | |
|---|---|---|---|---|---|---|
| | 1978 | 1983 | 1990 | 1978 | 1983 | 1990 |
| Avon valley | 31 | 48 | 56 | 174 | 260 | 346 |
| Test valley | 24 | 35 | 31 | 70 | 80 | 147 |
| Itchen valley | 14 | 27 | 25 | 18 | 33 | 106 |
| South-east Hants | 15 | 19 | 32 | 82 | 165 | 134 |

*Table 6. Results of Mute Swan surveys in four areas of Hampshire.*

In areas where course fishing is practised, notably the Blackwater valley gravel pits, the increase in the population, mostly of non-breeders, has only taken place since the ban on lead fishing weights was introduced in 1987.

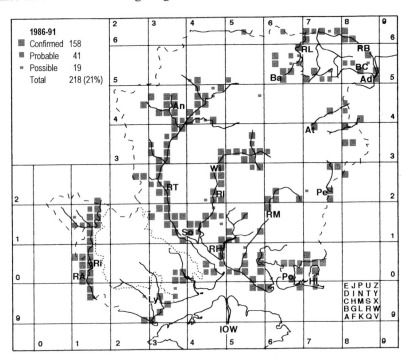

The Atlas Survey confirmed breeding during 1986-91 in 158 tetrads. Some of these regularly hold two or three pairs, but in others none were found during the 1990 survey. A few birds will have been missed in that year, so the population in 1990 was probably around 190 pairs and 800 non-breeders. This compares with a total estimate for Britain in 1990 of 5138 pairs and 15,422 non-breeders (WWT, preliminary report).

As breeding pairs establish their territories in spring, first-summer and other non-breeders are forced out of areas where they have wintered. Most of those in the three main river valleys move downstream to join moult gatherings at the coast. Evidence for this is provided by counts at Timsbury in the Test valley, where there were peaks of 55 on Apr. 8th 1979 and 82 on Apr. 5th 1987. Small herds of up to 20 occasionally moult at inland waters and in most years since the mid-1970s numbers have regularly exceeded 30 at Alresford Pond. Summer counts at various localities are summarised in table 7.

| | 71-75 | 76-80 | 81-85 | 86-90 | Peak counts | |
|---|---|---|---|---|---|---|
| Langstone Harbour | 45 | 40 | 60 | 64 | 82, | July 1990 |
| Itchen Estuary | - | - | 60 | 68 | 81, | Aug. 1986 |
| Eling Great Marsh | 59^ | 92 | 83 | 93 | 113, | Jun. 1976 |
| Alresford Pond | 19* | 24 | 52 | 29 | 69, | Jun. 1981 |

*Table 7. Five year means of summer maxima and peak counts of Mute Swans, 1971-90.*

Data for earlier years are far from complete but include maxima of 101 at the Itchen estuary on July 8th 1962 and the same number at Eling on Aug. 15th 1962. Peak counts at other localities used less frequently or with incomplete data include 57 at Baffins Pond (Portsmouth) in May 1983, 57 at Titchfield Haven in May 1984 and 73 at Emsworth in August 1986.

From August onwards, the summering flocks disperse, many birds returning inland. Counts such as 65 at Mottisfont on Oct. 17th 1976, 54 at Houghton on Oct. 24th 1982, 60 at Timsbury on Oct. 20th 1985 and 75 at Broadlands Estate on Oct. 15th 1988 show the movement up the Test valley, where the largest mid-winter gatherings are usually in the Longstock/Leckford area. In the Avon valley, the pattern which has developed since the mid-1980s involves a build-up on Blashford Lakes from late summer onwards, where they feed on the profuse growth of Canadian pondweed. By the new year, most have moved on to the water meadows at nearby Blashford and Ibsley and other sites in the valley. Winter counts at various localities are summarised in table 8.

| | 70-75 | 75-80 | 80-85 | 85-90 | Peak counts | |
|---|---|---|---|---|---|---|
| Baffins Pond (Portsmouth) | 2 | 2 | 34 | 60 | 79, | Feb. 1989 |
| Canoe Lake (Southsea) | 47 | 55 | 58 | 50 | 81, | Jan. 1980 |
| Lymington/Milford | 29^ | 69 | 60 | 30 | 120, | Jan. 1979 |
| Avon valley: Sopley/Bisterne | - | 52* | 51 | 78 | 106, | Nov. 1987 |
| Avon valley: Blashford/Bickton + Blashford Lakes | 73 | 126 | 98 | 168 | 194, | Nov. 1989 |
| Avon valley above Fordingbridge | - | 131^ | 144 | 185 | 215, | Jan. 1989 |
| Test valley: Longstock/Leckford | - | 41^ | 44 | 73 | 97, | Dec. 1986 |
| Eversley/Yateley Gravel Pits | 14^ | 26 | 44 | 50 | 80, | Nov. 1989 |

*Table 8. Five year means of winter maxima and peak counts of Mute Swans, 1970/71-89/90.*

Data for earlier years are very patchy, but noteworthy counts include 100 at Langstone Harbour in December 1952, 90 at Sturt Pond in severe weather in early January 1954, 180 at Fordingbridge in November 1955, 100 at Canoe Lake in January and February 1958, 72 at Gilkicker Pond in January 1966 and 80 at Emsworth Mill in January 1969.

Peak winter counts at other localities used less frequently or with incomplete data include 60 at Portsmouth Harbour in December 1971, 81 at Broadlands Estate in March 1988, 98 between Longstock and East Aston in February 1990 and 70 at Lakeside (Eastleigh) in March 1989.

Of 864 ringed in Hampshire and subsequently recovered, 314 had moved less than 10 km, 541 between 10 and 99 km and only nine further than this. These included an adult caught at Emsworth in August 1963 and found dead in

Schleswig Holstein, western Germany, 786 km ENE, in May 1964 and another ringed at Winchester in March 1967 and found dead in Loiret, France, 424 km ESE, in October 1969. The others had moved to Berkshire (2), Gloucestershire, Gwent, Kent, Somerset and Norfolk. A further 252 have been ringed outside Hampshire and recovered within the county, of which nine had moved more than 100 km, from Bedfordshire, Berkshire, Kent and Warwickshire (2 each), and Hertfordshire. Most of the short distance movements were up and down the main river valleys or along the coast between Poole, Dorset and Pagham, West Sussex, but there were also several to or from the Thames valley in Berkshire and West London.

## Bewick's Swan                                    *Cygnus columbianus*

A moderately common winter visitor and passage migrant.

Numbers of Bewick's Swans have increased since the 1960s, owing to the establishment of a wintering herd in the Avon valley. This has paralleled a major expansion in the Ouse Washes and at other sites in southern England, which has seen the total British wintering population increase from under 1000 in 1965/66 to over 9000 in 1991/92 (Owen *et al* 1986, Cranswick *et al* 1992).

Bewick's Swans were first recorded in the Avon valley in the 1961/62 winter. Until 1965/66, records were irregular and no more than ten were seen. From then until 1974/75, peak counts varied between 17 and 52. The following season produced the first three-figure count; in subsequent winters the flock failed to reach that level only once. Numbers reached their highest level during the severe cold spells in early 1985, 1986 and 1987 but since then have declined (fig. 15).

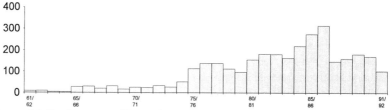

*Figure 15. Peak counts of Bewick's Swans in the Avon valley, 1961/62-91/92.*

The first normally arrive in the last few days of October, the earliest being 11 at Wattons Ford on Oct. 19th 1989. As many as 72 were back by Oct. 26th 1990. Numbers build up steadily, although counts have reached 100 before December in only three years. The peak count usually occurs in January or February, often coinciding with a cold spell of weather. In most years, all have left by mid-March but later records included 49 on Mar. 24th 1976 and 43 on Mar. 22nd 1986. Lingering individuals remained at Ibsley until May 28th 1965, Apr. 24th 1982 and May 10th 1986 (all first-winters) and at Avon Causeway until Apr. 24th 1991. There was also an adult at Hale on Sep. 8th and 15th 1985.

In the early years, all records were from the Ibsley/Hucklesbrook area, but since the late 1970s, swans have occurred regularly between Sopley and Watton's Ford. As numbers increased during the 1980s, herds appeared in other areas from time to time, especially at Blashford and Woodgreen.

Those feeding at Blashford, Ibsley and Woodgreen normally fly into Blashford Lakes to roost after dark, although following heavy rain they may remain overnight on floodwater in the meadows. In the Sopley/Wattons Ford area, they roost on slow moving stretches of the river or flashes adjoining it. The herd is most concentrated during hard weather, but at times of widespread flooding small groups may be found all the way up the valley.

The proportion of first-winters is usually low. Between 1976/77 and 1991/92, the percentage each winter varied between 5.3 and 25.3, with the average 14.2.

Prior to the establishment of the Avon herd, the species was a rare visitor, most often occurring in hard weather. Of several records listed by K & M, only one, of an adult and immature at Laverstoke in late 1880, is from within the present day county boundary. The next were not until 1954, when a flock of 22 moved north-east over Langstone Harbour on Mar. 20th. In early 1956, 76 moved west through Langstone Harbour in February, up to 34 were at Titchfield Haven in March and 32 were seen at three other sites. The next large herd seen was of 24 at Yateley Gravel Pit on Nov. 5th 1961. In the severe winter of 1962/63, 31 were recorded, including one which stayed at Winnall Moors until Apr. 28th, then moving to Avington Park where it was still present on May 6th. In the following year, 102 were seen, including 46 which left west from Langstone Harbour on Dec. 21st and 34 flying west at Black Point the next day.

As numbers increased on the Avon, observations elsewhere, especially of herds moving, became more frequent. Autumn records include those of 14 moving west over Gilkicker Point on Oct. 29th 1983 and 17 flying west over Havant on Oct. 26th 1990. Severe cold spells often induce further arrivals, as shown by 20 at Langstone Harbour on Jan. 29th 1972, 22 moving south-west over Stratfield Saye on Dec. 29th 1985 and 32 flying north-west over Farnborough Airfield on Jan. 9th 1986. Flocks may become established for several weeks, e.g. up to 11 at Timsbury from Dec. 16th 1978-Feb. 18th 1979, up to 12 in the Needs Ore/Sowley area from Dec. 19th 1981-Jan. 3rd 1982 and 12 at Titchfield Haven from Jan. 16th-Feb. 28th 1987. Most other records are in late February or early March and indicate the departure of the Avon herd or others from further west. Groups in excess of 20 have been recorded moving east or north-east on seven occasions since 1976, including 83 north-east over Martyr Worthy on Mar. 12th 1981, 57 east over Langstone Harbour on Mar. 9th 1985 and 66 south-east down Southampton Water on Feb. 23rd 1988. 20 were at Fleet Pond on Feb. 24th 1988.

In addition to the unseasonal records already mentioned, a presumed escape was regularly seen in the Winnall Moors/Itchen Stoke area between Sep. 25th 1983 and June 20th 1987, and a first-winter was at Lakeside (Eastleigh) from Feb. 10th-May 26th 1987.

Hampshire birds form part of the north-western European wintering population, which breeds in coastal western Siberia. Two birds colour-ringed as first-winters at Slimbridge, Gloucestershire have been sighted in the county. One, ringed in January 1982, was at Titchfield Haven from Jan. 14th-Feb. 18th 1987, and has also been seen in the Netherlands, Ireland, Norfolk and Northamptonshire. The other, ringed in November 1989, was seen on the Ouse Washes in February 1990 and wintered in the Avon valley in 1991/92.

One showing the characteristics of the Nearctic race *C. c. columbianus*, the Whistling Swan, was at Ibsley from Dec. 31st 1986 to Jan. 25th 1987.

## Whooper Swan                                                    *Cygnus cygnus*

A very scarce winter visitor.

K & M described the Whooper Swan as "a winter visitor to the coast .... sometimes numerous in severe weather". Hawker shot 38 in the Keyhaven area between 1822 and 1845, including nine in 1829/30 and 19 in 1837/38, both of which were severe winters.

There are few records for the first half of this century. In 1935, one summered at Needs Ore, in each winter from 1936/37-1939/40 from two to six were at Beaulieu, and in February 1940 six were in Cranbury Park.

Between 1950 and 1992, Whooper Swans were recorded in most winters but became increasingly scarce in the 1980s (fig. 16). Since 1981, the *HOSRP* has insisted on full descriptions of this species, especially of those seen only in flight. Prior to this, it is possible that some records may have referred to Bewick's Swans.

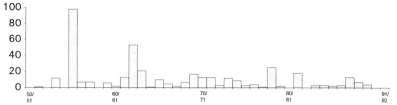

*Figure 16. Winter totals of Whooper Swans, 1950/51-91/92.*

The largest influx was in February 1956, when 98 were recorded, including 32 flying east at Hill Head on 4th, 18 flying west at Langstone Harbour on 18th, 20 flying south down the Itchen valley at Swaythling on 19th and up to 17 at Fullerton in the Test valley. The severe weather in early 1963 produced another notable influx, with 53 recorded including a flock of 27 on the sea off Hurst Beach on Jan. 19th. In the 1963/64 winter, up to eight were in the Blashford/Fordingbridge area and 13 flew south over Titchfield Haven and landed on the sea on Jan. 11th. From 1968/69-1973/74, up to six wintered at Titchfield Haven.

Since then, numbers have reached double figures in only three winters; all records were of less than four apart from 14 adults flying north-west over Fleet Pond during severe weather on Dec. 31st 1978, eight adults flying west past Southsea and into Portsmouth Harbour on Apr. 10th 1988 (following easterly winds and snow) and two adults and four first-winters at Langstone Harbour on Nov. 21st 1988. The only long staying birds were an adult in the Bishopstoke/Mansbridge area from Dec. 23rd 1981-Feb. 14th 1982, a first-winter in the Ibsley/Fordingbridge area from Nov. 26th 1984-Jan. 27th 1985, two adults between Avon and Woodgreen from Jan. 11th-27th 1985 and an adult between Sopley and Ibsley from Dec. 30th 1988-Jan. 15th 1989.

The earliest autumn records were of an adult flying north-east down the Wey valley at Bentley on Sep. 7th 1978 and a first-winter flying east over Farlington

Marshes on Oct. 21st 1961. In recent years, most records have been for November and early December. Of 53 recorded during 1980/81-91/92, 26 were in November. Sightings later in the winter usually coincide with severe weather. Apart from the Southsea record above, there were only two records after Mar. 12th, of adults which stayed at Winnall Moors from Mar. 12th-Apr. 9th 1963 and in the Sowley/Lymington area from Dec. 6th 1970 until early May 1971.

The cumulative monthly totals of all records for 1950/51-91/92 are shown below.

|         | Sep | Oct | Nov | Dec | Jan | Feb | Mar | Apr | May |
|---------|-----|-----|-----|-----|-----|-----|-----|-----|-----|
| Records | 1   | 2   | 22  | 26  | 38  | 31  | 7   | 3   | 1   |
| Birds   | 1   | 4   | 54  | 74  | 145 | 174 | 26  | 10  | 1   |

The Whooper Swan breeds in Iceland and from Fenno-Scandia to eastern Siberia. National ringing data suggest that most occurring in southern England are of Icelandic origin (Owen *et al* 1986), although birds from further east undoubtedly occur, especially when severe cold weather forces them west from their usual wintering grounds in the Low Countries.

# Bean Goose                                            *Anser fabalis*

A rare winter visitor, most frequently occurring in severe weather.

K & M considered the Bean Goose to be "an occasional winter visitor", but cited only one undated record from within the present day county boundary.

The first modern record was in 1960, since when there have been sightings in 15 winters involving 110 birds. In the 1960s, all sightings were made in the Portsmouth area. Five were at Farlington Marshes on Mar. 8th and 9th 1960 and up to 12 were in Langstone Harbour during severe weather between Jan. 20th and Mar. 17th 1963. Eight flew north over Black Point into Chichester Harbour on Feb. 1st 1964 and 17 flew south-east there on Mar. 2nd 1969.

One was at Ibsley on Jan. 10th 1971, but the next were not until 1976, when 15 were at Titchfield Haven in hard weather from Feb. 1st-8th, with six remaining until Feb. 22nd. The cold spell in early 1979 resulted in a notable influx, with two at Titchfield Haven from Jan. 6th-8th, 20-21 in the Lymore/Lower Pennington area between Jan. 27th and Feb. 3rd, two at Wellington Country Park from Feb. 3rd-25th and one at Moorcourt Farm (Nursling) from Feb. 17th-23rd.

In 1981, four were at Titchfield Haven on Feb. 28th and Mar. 1st, and in 1982, single birds were with Canada Geese at Heath Pond (Petersfield) on Mar. 8th, Elvetham Park on Apr. 11th and near Yateley Gravel Pit on May 5th. One was with Greylag Geese at Stratfield Saye from Jan. 2nd-Mar. 13th 1983, and in the same year two were in the Oxey/Salterns area near Lymington on Feb. 17th. The cold weather in early 1985 produced a further small influx, with two at Pennington Marsh from Jan. 11th-20th, up to eight at Titchfield Haven from Jan. 17th-22nd and one with White-fronted Geese in the Avon valley from Jan. 26th-Feb. 2nd. One was with Greylags at Stratfield Saye from Feb. 8th-Mar. 2nd 1986, and another was with Canadas at Wellington Country Park on Nov. 30th and Dec. 1st 1986 and at Tundry Pond on Dec. 24th 1986 and Jan. 5th 1987.

In the Avon valley, single birds were with White-fronts at Blashford on Jan. 17th 1987, Bewick's Swans at Ibsley from Feb. 23rd-Mar. 7th 1988 and White-fronts at Bisterne and Blashford from Jan. 18th-Feb 21st 1992. The only other recent record was of one with a Pink-footed Goose and Canadas at Sleaford Reservoir (Bordon) from Feb. 7th-Apr. 2nd 1988.

The cumulative monthly totals of all records for 1960-92 are shown below.

|         | Nov | Dec | Jan | Feb | Mar | Apr | May |
|---------|-----|-----|-----|-----|-----|-----|-----|
| Records | 1   | 1   | 11  | 14  | 9   | 2   | 1   |
| Birds   | 1   | 1   | 48  | 68  | 38  | 2   | 1   |

Of 52 which were racially assigned, 49 showed the characteristics of the tundra race *A.f. rossicus* and three those of the western race *A.f. fabalis*.

Some of the records of single birds almost certainly refer to feral or escaped individuals, especially those consorting with Canada or Greylag Geese.

The Bean Goose breeds from Fenno-Scandia to eastern Siberia. The large wintering flocks in the Netherlands and Germany are presumably the source of those seen in Hampshire.

## Pink-footed Goose                                   *Anser brachyrhynchus*

A rare winter visitor, although presumed feral birds have been recorded in every month except July and August.

The first Pink-footed Geese for the county were 24 which flew north over Titchfield Haven on Jan. 19th 1946. The next were seven with White-fronted Geese at Ibsley on Mar. 15th 1953. In severe weather in December 1961, one flew east at Gilkicker Point on 17th and eight flew south over Hurst Beach on 30th. Similar weather conditions no doubt accounted for the appearance of three at Sherfield-on-Loddon during February 1963. One was at Titchfield Haven on Feb. 13th 1966 and two flew north-east over Gilkicker Point on Jan. 10th 1968. In the same year, four were at Tournerbury on Dec. 22nd.

Between 1975 and 1990, there were reports in every year except three. Seven were at Dibden Bay on Feb. 1st 1976 and two were at Titchfield Haven from Nov. 8th-18th 1978. In the Blashford area, up to eight were with White-fronted Geese between Feb. 3rd and 23rd 1979 and single birds were with the White-front flock on Feb. 23rd 1982 and between Jan. 26th and Feb. 2nd 1985. Three were at Sleaford Reservoir on May 12th and 13th 1986 and eight were at Titchfield Haven from Dec. 19th 1987-Mar. 10th 1988. Most of these occurred during severe weather, and, with the possible exception of the Sleaford birds, were undoubtedly wild. The remaining records during this period, presumed to refer to feral or escaped individuals, have come mainly from the Test valley and north-east of the county. Single birds have been recorded intermittently in both areas since 1977.

The cumulative monthly totals of all records (excluding those of birds of suspect origin) for 1946-92 are shown below.

|         | Nov | Dec | Jan | Feb | Mar | Apr | May |
|---------|-----|-----|-----|-----|-----|-----|-----|
| Records | 1   | 4   | 4   | 6   | 2   | 0   | 1   |
| Birds   | 2   | 21  | 35  | 26  | 15  | 0   | 3   |

The Pink-footed Goose has two distinct populations: one, breeding in eastern Greenland and Iceland and wintering in Scotland and England south to Norfolk, and the other breeding in Spitsbergen and wintering in Denmark, western Germany and the Netherlands.

# White-fronted Goose                    *Anser albifrons*

A scarce winter visitor and passage migrant which has declined in recent years.

K & M described the White-fronted Goose as "the commonest of the grey geese to visit the coast". Today, most records are from the Avon valley, where a wintering flock of the Eurasian race *A.a. albifrons* became established around 1940 (Cohen). In the hard weather of February 1947 over 2000 were estimated to be present. Regular counting of the flock began in the early 1950s, with numbers peaking in the late 1960s (fig. 17). This may have been the result of wardening organised by the Hampshire Naturalists' Trust (N W Orr *in litt*), but the total number wintering in Britain also peaked at that time, reaching a maximum of 13,000 in January 1970 (Ogilvie 1978, Owen *et al* 1986). Since then, there has been a considerable decline, relieved only by influxes in severe weather in early 1979, 1982 and 1986. This follows the pattern shown at most British haunts, which is in contrast to the overall trend of the north-west European wintering population. This has increased from 81,500 in 1969/70 (when Britain held 16%) to an estimated 500,000 in 1990/91 (when Britain held less than 1%). The reduction in Britain is attributed to improvements in feeding conditions and increased protection in the Netherlands and Nord-Rhein Westfalia region of Germany (Kirby *et al* 1991).

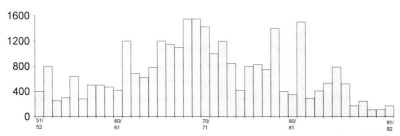

*Figure 17. Peak counts of White-fronted Geese in the Avon valley, 1951/52-91/92.*

In the Avon valley, the first normally arrive in the second half of November; earlier records include 25 on Nov. 1st 1959 and five on Oct. 26th 1990. In 1986, 170 were back by Nov. 22nd, but counts do not usually reach this level until mid-December or later. In most years peak numbers occur between mid-January and mid-February and often coincide with severe weather. Until the mid-1970s, several hundreds normally stayed until mid-March, 290 on Mar. 18th 1958 being the latest record. Since then, the departure has been earlier, and, especially in mild winters, the last birds have sometimes left before the end of February. One, presumably injured, was at Blashford Lakes from Apr. 20th-Sep. 6th 1978.

The geese feed in riverside meadows, and, at the present time, utilise two main areas: around Blashford and between Avon and Watton's Ford. Until the early 1980s, they also occurred regularly between Ibsley and Hucklesbrook, but increased fishing pressure is probably responsible for their non-appearance in this area at present. They normally remain in the fields overnight, but occasionally fly into Blashford Lakes to roost, arriving well after dark and departing at the first hint of sunrise.

Elsewhere in the county, most reports are of birds in flight, probably to or from the Avon. In autumn and early winter, such records normally involve small skeins of up to 50 moving in a westerly direction, but in 1952, 16 arrived at Farlington Marshes on Oct. 5th and were seen again on Oct. 11th. During severe weather, larger movements may take place (e.g. a total of 824 was noted over five sites flying in directions between north and west from Dec. 30th 1978-Jan. 1st 1979) and sizeable flocks may take up residence on coastal marshes. The largest such counts were of 150+ at Keyhaven on Feb. 22nd 1956 and 150 at Needs Ore on Jan. 3rd 1963, but in recent years smaller numbers have been recorded, e.g. 56 at Titchfield Haven on Jan. 28th 1979 and 40 at Farlington Marshes from Dec. 19th-21st 1981. From mid-February, flocks may be seen moving eastwards en route to their Siberian breeding grounds, e.g. 400 over Farlington Marshes on Feb. 29th 1964 and 130 over Frensham Great Pond on Feb. 18th 1968. Occasional migrants are seen after the departure of the Avon flock, e.g. 12 at Titchfield Haven on Apr. 1st 1985 and three which flew north over Calshot on May 20th 1984.

There is one Hampshire ringing recovery, which involved an adult trapped at Arkemheen, Netherlands on Feb. 13th 1963 and shot at Ringwood on Jan. 18th 1969. The main breeding ground of the north-west European wintering population is the tundra of western Siberia.

## Greylag Goose                                   *Anser anser*

A moderately common and increasing resident, passage migrant and winter visitor.

Until the mid-1960s, the Greylag Goose only occurred as a rare winter visitor. Subsequently, a feral population became established and expanded rapidly during the 1980s.

Breeding was first recorded at Stratfield Saye, where an introduced pair raised several young in 1964. Nesting continued annually thereafter; by 1971, the post-breeding flock had grown to 29. The increase continued and during the winter of 1979/80 up to 80 were present. In 1980, five pairs bred, raising 17 young, but numbers rose steadily in autumn to a peak of 127 on Oct. 31st, clearly showing immigration from other areas. The most productive years for breeding were 1982-84, when respectively ten, ten and 15 pairs bred, raising a total of 181 young. The peak count in 1984 was of 313 on Oct. 14th. Since that year, eggs have been removed from most nests, so that few young have been raised. However, autumn numbers have exceeded 200 in every year with a peak of 322 on Oct. 3rd 1987.

The pattern which has emerged is of a gradual decline through the winter months, then a rapid departure of most of the flock in March and April. The spring exodus has been especially marked since control measures were introduced. In 1991, the WWT Introduced Goose Survey revealed a summering population of only 12 adults, which were accompanied by four broods totalling eight young, but by Sep. 29th numbers had risen to 318. It has now been shown that the Stratfield Saye wintering flock includes birds from Sevenoaks, Kent. In the winter of 1989/90, four colour-ringed birds were present which proved to have been trapped as moulting adults at Sevenoaks in previous summers. These,

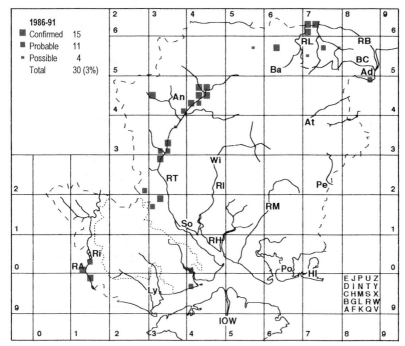

1986-91
- ■ Confirmed  15
- ■ Probable   11
- ▪ Possible    4
- Total       30 (3%)

and three additional birds, were recorded at Stratfield Saye in subsequent winters, but none of them have been sighted again in the Sevenoaks area.

The second flock to become established was in the upper Test valley at Bransbury Common. Up to 78 were there in October and November 1974 but the earlier history of this flock is not known. Numbers increased in subsequent winters to reach a maximum of 213 on Nov. 15th 1981. Breeding was first recorded in 1979, when three pairs raised 14 young. In the 1980s, a gradual increase and spread to other sites in the Test valley took place. During the 1991 survey, 34 adults and six young were found at Kentford Lake and two adults at Timsbury. Unfortunately, coverage in the main area was poor and none were found. The winter flock is now more dispersed. In the late 1980s, the highest count at Bransbury was of 125 on Nov. 18th 1989 but sizeable groups appeared elsewhere, e.g. 40 between Mottisfont and Bossington from Mar. 1st-4th 1985 and 54 at Longparish on Mar. 31st 1985. Although coverage of the Test flock is not as good as at Stratfield Saye, it is clear that a similar pattern occurs: small numbers remaining to breed, with others leaving in spring to breed and/or moult elsewhere and then returning in autumn.

During the 1970s and 1980s, up to four were present in the Avon valley around Blashford. In the 1984/85 winter up to seven were in the Bisterne/Avon area to the south, then up to ten in 1986/87 and 18 in the following winter. Two pairs with 12 young were seen in 1989 and 38 were present in December 1989 and January 1990. The 1991 survey located 19 adults and ten juveniles but by December there were 85 in the area.

At the Beaulieu Estuary, six were released in 1987 (J Venner pers. comm.) and 32 were there by November 1988. In summer 1991, there were 85 adults and 28 young although the maximum seen during the following winter was 84 on Feb. 20th 1992.

As the Atlas Map shows, most breeding records during 1986-91 were confined to the four areas described above. Probably no more than 30 pairs attempted breeding in 1991, but during the subsequent winter 600-700 were present. The whereabouts of most of these birds during the summer remains a mystery. Following the Introduced Goose Survey in 1991, the British population was estimated at 22,000 individuals (New Atlas).

Prior to the establishment of the feral population, few were seen. Between 1951 and 1970, there were records in eight winters, often during cold spells, including nine flying north-west off Hythe on Dec. 31st 1952 and up to eight at Langstone Harbour from Feb. 12th-18th 1961.

Since 1971, there has been a considerable increase in records away from the regularly used sites. Cumulative monthly totals for 1971-92 are shown below.

|         | Jan | Feb | Mar | Apr | May | Jun | Jul | Aug | Sep | Oct | Nov | Dec |
|---------|-----|-----|-----|-----|-----|-----|-----|-----|-----|-----|-----|-----|
| Records | 15  | 26  | 43  | 44  | 29  | 12  | 5   | 1   | 9   | 16  | 19  | 20  |
| Birds   | 73  | 83  | 127 | 93  | 68  | 27  | 14  | 2   | 20  | 28  | 81  | 102 |

There is a clear peak in spring, which may reflect passage of birds which have wintered elsewhere (e.g. five flying east off Hurst on May 2nd 1981), but probably refers mostly to the dispersal of the local population prior to moulting. The low totals for August-October are surprising, since this is when the main influx occurs at Stratfield Saye and the upper Test. Those for November-February are distorted by a few large flocks, but suggest passage in the last two months of the year. The largest flocks recorded were of 20 flying north-west over Farlington Marshes on Dec. 22nd 1979, 35 at Keyhaven on Dec. 4th 1982, 23 at Winnall Moors on Mar. 16th 1986 and 34 flying south over Keyhaven towards the Isle of Wight on Jan. 19th 1991. Some of the records may involve birds displaced from feral populations elsewhere in south-eastern England, but a flock of ten at Keyhaven from Oct. 24th-Nov. 3rd 1990 included one with a neck-band which was first caught in Skana, southern Sweden on June 18th 1986. It was observed in Skana on Oct. 19th 1990, and so had flown to Keyhaven in five days or less. Subsequently it was found wintering in the Coto Doñana, Spain.

## Snow Goose                                    *Anser caerulescens*

A scarce resident

A small feral population of Snow Geese is now established in the north-east of the county. The first to be recorded was one which flew south over Fleet Pond on Apr. 12th 1973. By 1977, up to seven (of unknown origin) were seen regularly at Stratfield Saye and elsewhere, and in 1978 they were joined by a blue-phase bird. In 1979, a pair of pinioned birds raised free-flying young at Stratfield Saye. During the Atlas Survey, single pairs bred successfully there in 1986, 1987 and 1991, by which time numbers had increased to 34. The flock is most frequently seen at Stratfield Saye and Eversley Gravel Pit but one or two are occasionally seen elsewhere in the area.

Sightings elsewhere in the county have also increased in frequency since the first was recorded in 1972. Most records have been of one to three individuals (of white and blue phases), but larger flocks reported include ten at Oxey Marsh (Lymington) on Mar. 31st 1980, 14 in flight over Titchfield Haven on Jan. 21st 1983 and at Fareham Creek two days later and seven at Leckford on Jan. 17th 1984.

## Canada Goose                                        *Branta canadensis*

A common resident and partial migrant whose population has been increasing since the 1950s. The most rapid expansion was in the 1970s and early 1980s, but since then control measures taken in several areas have stemmed the increase.

Early records of the Canada Goose in Hampshire include a pair which nested at Hurstbourne Priors regularly until 1890, one at Fleet Pond on May 4th 1905 and one at Keyhaven in April 1926. In 1936, single pairs nested at Heath Pond (Petersfield) and Fleet Pond, with counts at these sites reaching 32 in March 1947 and 44 in November 1950 respectively. In 1947, the first pair was seen at Stratfield Saye Park (Duke of Wellington pers. comm.), since when they have bred there every year. During the late 1950s, breeding was recorded at Bramshill Police College Lake, Elvetham Lake, Fleet Pond, Heath Pond, Stratfield Saye and Yateley Gravel Pit with probably no more than 15 pairs in total in any one year. The winter of 1957/58 produced the first records of any number away from the north-east, with up to 20 at Sowley Pond.

In 1961, two flying west over Farlington Marshes on May 30th were the first to be recorded in the Portsmouth area, while a flock of 112 at Tundry Pond on Dec. 9th was the first to reach three figures. During the cold spell of early 1962, 31 were grazing on Portsmouth Airfield on Jan. 6th, but numbers in that area did not reach that level again until 1976. The severe weather in early 1963 produced the first numbers of note in the west of the county. At Hurst, flocks of 24 and 34 flew east on Jan. 5th and 12th respectively, 28 moved north up the Avon valley at Blashford on Feb. 17th and up to 51 were present at Fullerton in the upper Test valley in mid-February.

In 1964, 47 were released at the Beaulieu Estuary and two pairs subsequently bred. By November 1968, the flock had grown to 104, and in 1971, 20 pairs attempted breeding in the area, although most of the nests were destroyed by the farmer.

In the north-east, Stratfield Saye was emerging as the main locality, with counts of 406 on Sep. 11th 1965 and 510 on Jan. 15th 1968. Flocks of 100-300 were also recorded at Elvetham Lake, Fleet Pond, Tundry Pond and Yateley Gravel Pit between 1965 and 1970. What few breeding records there are suggest that about 50 pairs were nesting in the area at the end of that period, the remainder of the population being non-breeders.

During the Breeding Grebes and Wildfowl Survey in 1978, 247 pairs were located in the county, of which 168 raised a total of 638+ young (Clark 1979). Of these, 180 pairs were in the north-east, with 116 raising 479 young. The main breeding concentrations were at Elvetham Lake (65 pairs, 30 raised 122 young) and Yateley/Eversley Gravel Pits (42 pairs, 34 raised 148 young). Elsewhere, the largest colony was at Blashford Lakes, where 17 pairs were found, 16 raising 72 young. In 1982 and 1983, about 500 young were raised in the north-east, but the main site was Stratfield Saye, with 108 and 143 young respectively, where the eggs had been removed from nests in 1978. By 1982, a considerable increase had occurred in the Avon valley, where 29 pairs raised 120 young. In the following year, 20 pairs were found at six sites in the Itchen valley, raising 75 young, and in 1986, 38 pairs were located there, but neither of these surveys were complete.

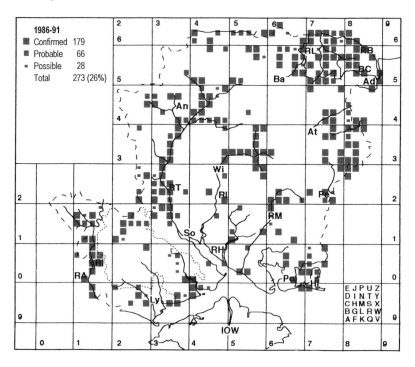

As the Atlas Map shows, Canada Geese are now widespread in Hampshire. The largest breeding colonies occur at gravel pits and lakes with plenty of islands. In recent years, they have taken to smaller waters in parks, on farmland and in the New Forest, and also increasingly nested alongside rivers and streams. The WWT Introduced Goose Survey in 1991, which involved counts of adults with young and moulting non-breeders, produced a total of 2350 adults and 761 young in the county (A C Smallbone *in litt*), with the main concentrations 572 adults and 279 young at Yateley/Eversley Gravel Pits and 371 adults and 210 young in the Avon valley. Unfortunately, coverage was not complete, especially in the Test and Itchen valleys and around Bordon and Liphook. Probably in the region of 500 adults and young were missed, giving a total post-breeding population of around 3600. Following the survey, the total British population was estimated at 60,000 (New Atlas).

Counts in recent years have shown that the largest numbers are present in the autumn, when the local population is augmented by birds from elsewhere. Many of these are immature and other non-breeders which were raised in Hampshire but leave the county in spring to moult. Table 9, which summarises the peak autumn counts in various parts of the county, shows the vast increase which took place in the 1970s and early 1980s. Since then, this has slowed, presumably due to the control measures taken at several sites because of damage to grazing and cereals caused by the species.

| | 71-75 | 76-80 | 81-85 | 86-90 | Peak counts | |
|---|---|---|---|---|---|---|
| North-east Hants | 957 | 1536 | 2713 | 2991 | 3300, | aut. 1988 |
| Stratfield Saye | 469 | 1043 | 1978 | 1440 | 2450, | Sep. 1983 |
| Petersfield area | 56 | 117 | 147 | 189 | 288, | Sep. 1989 |
| Portsmouth area | 25 | 49 | 73 | 149 | 246, | Sep. 1990 |
| Titchfield Haven | 5 | 18 | 58 | 312 | 440, | Oct. 1989 |
| Itchen valley | 18 | 83 | 217 | 247 | 420, | Nov. 1985 |
| Test valley | 75 | 202 | 262 | 260 | 363, | Sep. 1983 |
| Beaulieu Estuary/Hurst | 87 | 101 | 70 | 187 | 242, | Dec. 1988 |
| Avon valley | 124 | 207 | 322 | 348 | 370, | Nov. 1984 |
| Total | 1224 | 2109 | 3916 | 4630 | 5100, | aut. 1988 |

*Table 9. Five years means of autumn maxima and peak counts of Canada Geese, 1971-90.*

Counts at Stratfield Saye, the major site in the county, are included in the north-east Hants totals but also shown separately. Counts have reached 1000 at four other north-east sites: Eversley/Yateley Gravel Pits (1225, September 1987), Fleet Pond (1000, October 1988), Wellington Country Park (1200, December 1989) and Tundry Pond (1100, October 1990). All except the last named are used as nocturnal roost sites in autumn and winter.

Over 1300 Canada Geese have been ringed in Hampshire, the vast majority during the annual round-ups of moulting birds at Elvetham Park and Stratfield Saye between 1977 and 1981. This has produced controls in subsequent years in Staffordshire (2), Northumberland and the Beauly Firth, Highland (all in July, which shows the northward moult migration undertaken by some of the population), and a recovery in Devon in November. Other movements of note involved three adults ringed at Needs Ore in June 1964 which were recovered in Somme, France in September 1964, Pas-de-Calais, France in March 1965 and Valley, Anglesey in November 1965. The longest movements to Hampshire were of an adult trapped at Kendal, Cumbria in June 1957 and found dead at Farlington Marshes in January 1962, a juvenile ringed at Hoveringham, Nottinghamshire in June 1980 and controlled at Elvetham in July 1982 and an adult trapped on the Beauly Firth in July 1984 and shot near Liphook in January 1986.

## Barnacle Goose *Branta leucopsis*

A scarce resident (feral population) and rare winter visitor (wild populations).

An expanding feral population of Barnacle Geese in Hampshire and elsewhere in southern England now makes the separation of genuine wild birds highly problematical.

The largest feral flock in the county has become established in the north-east. As long ago as October 1950, one was seen at Fleet Pond, and between 1964 and 1974 at least two were present in the area. Numbers increased to ten in 1977, 16 in 1982, 35 in 1985, 54 in 1987 and 87 in 1991. Breeding was first recorded at Potbridge Fishery in 1979, Stratfield Saye in 1981 and Eversley Gravel Pit in 1990; at least eight pairs bred at these sites in 1991. During the winter months, the flock usually moves between Stratfield Saye and Eversley, but small parties are occasionally seen elsewhere.

Since the mid-1970s, a few feral or escaped birds have been present in the Avon, Test and Itchen valleys, between Hurst and the Beaulieu River and in the south-east of the county. In the latter area, most records probably refer to a free-flying flock based at Baffins Pond (Portsmouth) which numbered 16 in 1986 and 27 in 1990. The only reports of breeding involved a pair which bred at Sowley Pond in 1988 and 1991. One, ringed at Poole Park, Dorset on Jan. 12th 1985 was seen at Baffins Pond on Mar. 29th 1987 and Dec. 30th 1989.

Wild Barnacle Geese are most likely to occur when hard weather forces a westward movement from their usual wintering grounds in the Netherlands. Between 1946 and 1992, there were eight records of two or more birds which were probably wild, including six at Eling Great Marsh on Nov. 16th and 17th 1961, 21 at Tournerbury from late February to Mar. 9th 1975 and 20 with White-fronted Geese at Bisterne from Dec. 15th 1991-Jan. 26th 1992.

Occasional birds in flocks of White-fronts or Brents may be wild. Since the 1963/64 winter, one or two have wintered with the White-fronts in the Avon valley on nine occasions, but only three times since 1978, when feral birds were first recorded with Canadas there. Single birds have also been seen with Brents at Keyhaven (twice) and Portsmouth Harbour (once), and one flew over Park Corner Farm (Odiham) with a flock of 34 Bewick's Swans on Mar. 2nd 1984.

A flock of ten ringed birds at Pennington Marsh from Dec. 14th 1981-Feb. 14th 1982 arrived in cold weather; they proved to be part of the feral flock at Slimbridge, Gloucestershire.

## Brent Goose                                           *Branta bernicla*

A numerous winter visitor.

The numbers of Brent Geese wintering in the county have increased twenty-fold since regular watching began in the early 1950s. This reflects a similar expansion of the whole population of the race involved, the Dark-bellied Brent Goose *B.b. bernicla*, which breeds on the coast of western Siberia and winters on the North Sea and English Channel coasts. Although they occur all along The Solent coast, the principal sites are Langstone and Chichester Harbours, which hold internationally important numbers.

K & M described the Brent Goose as "a common winter visitor to the coast .... sometime occurring in great numbers". This statement was based largely on Hawker's diaries (1893), which contain references to flocks of 2000 at Keyhaven in February 1829 and January 1838, when he shot 180 and 310 geese respectively. His total bag between 1813 and 1850 was 1327 birds. Between 1880 and 1950, winter peaks for the whole county probably did not exceed a few hundred, with flocks of 100 or more generally occurring only in Langstone and Chichester Harbours (Tubbs & Tubbs 1982). Mudge's diaries, which catalogue his wildfowling exploits in Southampton Water and the Beaulieu Estuary in the first half of this century, suggest peaks in the 1920s and early 1930s and again in the 1940s. However, his highest bag in a season was 52 and the largest flock he saw was of 80 on the Beaulieu Estuary in 1933-34 (Tubbs 1992).

The first reliable counts for Langstone Harbour were made in early 1953, when a maximum of 70 was recorded in February (Portsmouth Group 1991). The low numbers at that time were almost certainly due to the widespread die-off of eelgrass *Zostera*, the preferred food, in the 1930s (Tubbs & Tubbs 1982). There was a gradual increase through the 1950s and early 1960s, with counts reaching 2400 in February 1967. The early 1970s saw the most rapid rise, with 6075 the maximum during the 1973/74 winter. Since then, the increase has continued, albeit rather more slowly, with counts exceeding 8000 for the first time in 1985/86 (table 10).

Several factors have probably combined to produce this phenomenal increase. The 1954 Protection of Birds Act reduced hunting pressure in Britain, and this was followed by an increase in the frequency of successful breeding seasons. Between 1954/55 and 1968/69, the percentage of first-winters present in wintering flocks exceeded 30% in six winters out of 15, but between 1969/70 and 1979/80, the period of the greatest expansion, this level was exceeded in eight out of 11 seasons. However, in the following ten seasons there were only two good years and yet the slow increase in numbers continued.

In the early 1950s, Langstone was the only south coast site to attract Brents as *Zostera* just about survived there. The subsequent recovery of *Zostera* also coincided with a change to grazing on the marine algae *Enteromorpha* and *Ulva*, which supported the geese after *Zostera* was exhausted in late autumn. During the 1969/70 winter, up to 100 birds grazed on pasture on Farlington Marshes. This habit was not noted again until early 1974, when up to 200 were present there. Two years later, the number grazing had increased dramatically to 2500. The birds arrived on the fields shortly after dawn and remained until dusk, regardless of the state of the tide. Geese were soon grazing on virtually every area of grass around the harbour, including a golf course, playing fields and roadside verges. They also moved on to winter wheat on Hayling Island, where considerable damage was caused, especially in wet conditions when the heavy soils puddled on the surface. In 1985/86, over 500 were grazing on winter barley just north of Portsdown Hill; since then up to 1500 have used that area.

Between 1951 and 1968, Brents were very scarce west of Langstone Harbour. No recorded flock exceeded 100 and the only regular sightings were in the Lymington/Hurst area. In December 1968, 200 were in Portsmouth Harbour, a site that was very poorly covered until that time, and in January 1970, numbers at Lymington/Hurst peaked at 284. In the following seasons, there was a rapid increase at these sites, and subsequently in Southampton Water, the Beaulieu Estuary and between Sowley and Lymington (table 10). 1980/81 saw the first geese grazing on pasture at the Beaulieu Estuary, and in 1982/83 large numbers started feeding on winter cereals and grass leys in the Keyhaven/Hurst area and at Brownwich, with over 1000 present in both areas. The numbers feeding inland at these two sites have continued to increase. The Brownwich flock flights across Southampton Water at dusk to roost at Calshot (Duffin 1991).

Clearly, the change from marine feeding to inland grazing is a major contributory factor to the expansion of this population. In the five winters from 1985/86-89/90, the proportion of the British wintering population in Hampshire, based on January counts, averaged 24.7%.

| | 55-60 | 60-65 | 65-70 | 70-75 | 75-80 | 80-85 | 85-90 | Peak counts |
|---|---|---|---|---|---|---|---|---|
| Chichester Harbour | 197 | 1030 | 2180 | **4656** | **7076** | **9396** | **10361** | 11849, Jan. 1984 |
| East Hayling | - | 566 | 1286 | - | **3376** | **3698** | **3559** | 4716, Dec. 1981 |
| Langstone Harbour | 590 | 928 | 2240 | **5014** | **5895** | **7100** | **7977** | 8646, Jan. 1986 |
| Portsmouth Harbour | - | - | - | 174 | **1811** | **2017** | **2146** | 3316, Dec. 1981 |
| Southampton Water | - | - | - | 15 | 304 | 953 | **2000** | 2000, Nov. 1988 |
| Hill Head/Brownwich | - | - | - | 15 | 113 | *851* | *1473* | 2000, Nov. 1988 |
| Hamble Estuary | - | - | - | - | 195 | 393 | 596 | 1200, Jan. 1990 |
| Fawley/Calshot | - | - | - | 12 | 293 | 595 | 710 | 900, Feb. 1984 |
| Beaulieu Estuary | - | - | 3 | 22 | 226 | 378 | 778 | 1140, Jan. 1989 |
| Sowley/Lymington | - | - | - | 60* | 285 | 416 | 401 | 600, Feb. 1989 |
| Lymington/Hurst | 37 | (38) | 120 | *356* | *798* | *1280* | **2020** | 2500, Jan. 1987 |

*Table 10. Five year means of winter maxima and peak counts of Brent Geese, 1955/56-89/90.*

As the population has increased, so the arrival date has become earlier. The first are now recorded in Langstone Harbour in the second half of September, and a rapid increase takes place through October. In 1986, 8567 were counted on Oct. 18th, and this proved to be the winter maximum. Flocks of up to 100 are regularly seen moving west along the coast between October and December. Larger movements include 130+ west off Hill Head on Nov. 27th 1978 and 344 west there on Dec. 31st 1978, the latter induced by cold weather. The peak count at Langstone Harbour occurred before the end of the year in seven of the 12 seasons from 1980/81-91/92, but in Chichester Harbour and at most sites to the west the peak is normally reached in January or later. This suggests some dispersal away from Langstone as *Zostera* is exhausted.

Most usually leave by late March. Their departure coincides with the heaviest easterly movements observed during spring sea-watches: 268 at Hurst Beach on Mar. 24th 1984, 394 at Sandy Point on Mar. 24th 1985 and 496 off Hurst Beach on Apr. 4th 1987. At the Beaulieu Estuary, a build-up occurs in late April and early May. In 1986, 478 were there on May 6th; counts there exceeded 50 at this time in every subsequent year up to 1992, when 520 were present on May 3rd. On the same day, 128 flew east at Sandy Point.

Since 1973, small but increasing numbers have summered in Langstone Harbour, with up to nine until 1985 and up to 14 subsequently. Occasionally, birds are seen at other localities.

Prior to 1972, the only records from well inland were of 14 at Itchen Stoke and six at Frensham Great Pond in February 1940, and ten near Ibsley on Jan. 20th 1941. Between 1972 and 1992, there were 37 records involving a total of 462 birds. The cumulative monthly totals of these records are shown below.

| | Sep | Oct | Nov | Dec | Jan | Feb | Mar | Apr |
|---|---|---|---|---|---|---|---|---|
| Records | 1 | 3 | 5 | 7 | 9 | 5 | 5 | 2 |
| Birds | 1 | 184 | 49 | 115 | 38 | 7 | 66 | 2 |

The largest flocks were all moving over at the time of the main autumn arrival on the coast: 100 west over Ashley Walk on Dec. 1st 1980, 150 south there on Oct. 17th 1988, 45 SSE over Woolmer on Nov. 11th 1983 and 30 west over Tunworth on Oct. 29th 1986. Most of the other records have come from two areas. In the Avon valley, there have been seven records of one to three (usually with White-fronts) and ten were at Mockbeggar Lake on Dec. 26th 1987. At Frensham Great Pond, one to six have been seen on six occasions and there were

16 on Mar. 7th 1981, 35 on Mar. 9th 1983 and 12 on Mar. 20th 1992. The latter three records indicate spring passage, as does the observation of 100 leaving inland high to the north-east from Langstone Harbour on Mar. 17th 1983 (not included in the above analysis). The other inland records were of one or two birds apart from those of ten flying NNW over Regents Park (Southampton) on Jan. 3rd 1987 and 16 grazing at Eastleigh Sewage Farm in severe cold weather on Jan. 26th 1987.

Individuals showing the characteristics of other races are occasionally recorded. 20 of the pale-bellied race *B.b. hrota* were at Keyhaven on Mar. 3rd 1929. In the mid-1950s, there were several records, probably referring to the same group, including 11 at Langstone Harbour on Mar. 9th 1955 and ten in Chichester Harbour off Emsworth on Feb. 10th 1957. Between 1969/70 and 1991/92, there have been records in 16 winters, mostly of one to three birds but of five at Pylewell on Mar. 28th 1980 and eight at Weston Shore on Nov. 15th 1983. One of the Nearctic race *B.b. nigricans*, the Black Brant, was in Chichester Harbour from Nov. 2nd 1986-Mar. 8th 1987 and during the following six winters. It was regularly seen on the Hampshire side of the county boundary at East Hayling and was also seen in Langstone Harbour from Feb. 7th-12th 1987 and on Jan. 8th 1990.

Records of colour-ringed birds have come from intensive studies into the species' ecology by the Brent Goose Research Group of the IWRB (B Ebbinge *in litt*). Birds were first ringed at Foulness, Essex, in the early 1970s as part of a project looking into the possible siting there of London's third airport. In later years, large numbers were ringed in the Netherlands and Schleswig Holstein, Germany and more recently on the breeding grounds in northern Taymyr, Siberia. Up to the end of the 1991/92 winter, some 169 individuals had been identified in Hampshire, from Germany (57), Netherlands (54), Essex (39), Siberia (12), Lincolnshire (6) and Norfolk (1). One of very few colour-ringed in Hampshire was later seen in Germany. Of particular note was a bird ringed on Texel, Netherlands, in May 1986, which was seen in the Netherlands on Nov. 29th 1987 and later that day arriving at The Kench (Langstone Harbour).

## Red-breasted Goose                    *Branta ruficollis*

Four records. The first was seen with White-fronted Geese at Blashford and Ibsley from Jan. 18th-Feb. 9th 1967. Another was at Blashford from Jan. 11th-19th 1969. One wintered with Brent Geese in Langstone Harbour and at North Hayling from Nov. 8th 1975-Feb. 29th 1976; this was probably the bird present in Essex from Oct. 12th-Nov. 7th 1975. Finally, one was with White-fronts at Bisterne and Blashford from Dec. 27th 1983-Jan. 15th 1984. Like the two previous birds recorded in the Avon valley, this individual was also seen at Slimbridge, Gloucestershire in the same winter.

The Red-breasted Goose breeds in arctic central Siberia and winters principally on the Black and Caspian Seas.

## Egyptian Goose                    *Alopochen aegyptiacus*

A very scarce visitor.

There is a long established feral population of Egyptian Geese in Norfolk but the increasing number of Hampshire records probably refers to birds which have escaped from wildfowl collections in southern England. The first was at Pennington Marsh on Aug. 13th 1971. There were no further reports until 1977, since when there have been sightings in every year but three. Reports have come from all parts of the county and are usually of one or two birds, but there were three at various localities in the Avon valley between Feb. 17th and May 21st 1985, five in the Nursling/Lower Test Marshes area from Dec. 20th 1985-Feb. 17th 1986 and up to five at Stratfield Saye in 1990 and 1991. The latter were believed to have originated from a small breeding population established at nearby Dinton Pastures in Berkshire.

## Ruddy Shelduck                    *Tadorna ferruginea*

A rare visitor.

Prior to 1970, there were only two records of the Ruddy Shelduck this century, but between 1971 and 1992 there were sightings in 14 years. Most reports involved one or two birds but four were at Langstone Mill Pond from Sep. 15th-21st 1975, four were at Langstone Harbour from Oct. 16th-Nov. 25th 1979 and five flew west over Pennington Marsh on Aug. 29th 1988. Most had probably escaped from wildfowl collections but it is possible that some originated from the feral population in the Netherlands.

## Shelduck                    *Tadorna tadorna*

A moderately common breeder whose numbers are greatly augmented in winter.

During the Atlas Survey, Shelducks were located in 115 tetrads but breeding was confirmed in only 46. Most of these records were of pairs with broods. The remaining registrations mainly referred to territorial pairs, many of which will not have attempted breeding.

At the coast, breeding was confirmed in 25 tetrads. The largest concentrations of successful pairs reported in any one year during 1986-92 were 18 in the Beaulieu Estuary, six between Sowley and Lymington and five on the Langstone Harbour islands. Probably around 50 pairs breed annually.

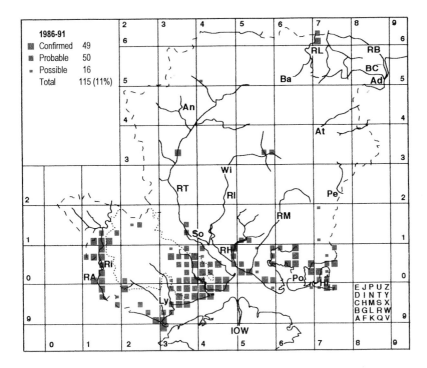

| 1986-91 | |
|---|---|
| ■ Confirmed | 49 |
| ■ Probable | 50 |
| ▪ Possible | 16 |
| Total | 115 (11%) |

In the New Forest, 12 pairs were located in 1959. During the Atlas Survey, pairs were found in 25 tetrads but breeding was confirmed in only seven. Probably about 15-20 pairs are present each spring, mainly associated with the valley mires in the southern half of the Forest, but not all attempt breeding and only one or two broods are reported annually.

In the Avon valley, breeding was first recorded at Blashford Lakes in 1976. Since then, it has occurred regularly there and in the valley between Kingston and Sopley, with occasional pairs at Somerley and Hamer Warren Sand Pits in Ringwood Forest. Records during the Atlas Survey indicate a summering population of five to ten pairs in the Blashford area, where a maximum of five broods was seen in 1986, and a similar number in the valley between Sopley and Kingston, where no more than two broods were recorded in any one year.

Elsewhere, occasional pairs hold territory in the south-east of the county around Portsdown Hill, in the Wallington valley and at Havant Thicket and Rowland's Castle. Broods were seen near Pigeon House Farm (Widley) in 1987 and nearby at Sheepwash Farm in 1988. Further inland, breeding is sporadic. Broods were reported at Farley Mount in 1960, Winchester Sewage Farm in 1970 and 1971, Marsh Court in 1990 and Stratfield Saye in 1991.

The total breeding population in Hampshire is thus probably in the range 80-100 pairs. In 1988-91, the British population was estimated at 10,600 pairs (New Atlas).

Coastal localities also hold a considerable non-breeding population. The largest numbers are recorded at Langstone Harbour, where 100-200 are present in May each year, and in the Fawley/Calshot area, where counts exceeded 150 in six years between 1974 and 1986 (peak 241 in 1976), but have not exceeded 69 since. Numbers decrease in June and July as birds depart for the moulting grounds at Heligoland Bight in the German Waddensee. However, in the 1970s, large pre-moult gatherings built up at Dibden Bay, with peaks of 306 on July 1st 1974 and 370 on June 15th 1977. In the latter year, at least 50 adults were present throughout the summer and presumably moulted there. Normally in August and September the only birds present are locally-bred juveniles.

The wintering population builds up slowly from October onwards with the main arrival in December. Peak counts are usually made in January or February and are greatest in severe weather, presumably due to the arrival of further birds from the continent or elsewhere in Britain. This was indicated by a cold weather movement between Jan. 10th and 12th 1987, when 117 moved west off Lepe and Pennington Marsh. In the five winters from 1985/86-89/90, the proportion of the British wintering population in Hampshire (based on January counts) averaged 7.1%. Table 11 summarises counts at the main localities.

| | 55-60 | 60-65 | 65-70 | 70-75 | 75-80 | 80-85 | 85-90 | Peak counts | |
|---|---|---|---|---|---|---|---|---|---|
| Chichester Harbour | - | - | 3540 | 3103 | 2122 | 3052 | 2813 | 4900, | Mar. 1968 |
| East Hayling | 2000* | 1500^ | 1500* | - | 1087 | 1750 | 1545 | 2713, | Feb. 1982 |
| Langstone Harbour | 2700 | 2385 | 3280 | 1567 | 1190 | 1662 | 1468 | 4000, | Feb. 1968 |
| Portsmouth Harbour | - | - | 1050^ | 260^ | 295 | 322 | 179 | 1200, | Dec. 1968 |
| Dibden Bay | 190^ | - | 185^ | 305 | 278 | 125 | 0 | 562, | Dec. 1977 |
| Fawley/Calshot | - | 183^ | 309^ | 420 | 459 | 363 | 212 | 710, | Jan. 1979 |
| Beaulieu Estuary | - | 78 | 108 | 81 | 104 | 126 | 207 | 300, | Dec. 1989 |
| Lymington/Hurst | - | 250* | 377^ | 480 | 650 | 324 | 367 | 1100, | Jan. 1979 |

*Table 11. Five year means of winter maxima and peak counts of Shelducks, 1955/56-89/90.*

In spring, there is a regular movement east through The Solent which peaks in late April and early May. During 1971-92, the recorded annual totals varied between 13 and 258 with an average of 88. The largest day totals logged were of 80 at Hurst Beach on Apr. 25th 1973, 67 there on Apr. 28th 1974 and 66 at Hill Head on May 4th 1980.

In the Avon valley, Shelducks are usually absent from August until late November, when numbers at Blashford Lakes start to build up. Mid-winter counts there and in the nearby water meadows are normally in single figures but

reached 21 in February 1988 and 25 in February 1990. In the Sopley/Bisterne area, counts may be even higher, maxima there including 34 in February 1988 and 50 in March 1990. At other inland breeding localities, the first returns are not usually recorded before April.

Elsewhere inland, Shelducks may turn up at any time although they are most frequent in spring and during severe weather. The cumulative monthly totals for 1971-92 of all inland records away from breeding areas are shown below.

| Jan | Feb | Mar | Apr | May | Jun | Jul | Aug | Sep | Oct | Nov | Dec |
|-----|-----|-----|-----|-----|-----|-----|-----|-----|-----|-----|-----|
| 65  | 118 | 72  | 130 | 110 | 24  | 6   | 53  | 52  | 23  | 30  | 42  |

Most records involve single birds or small parties in flight or pausing for a few hours. However, longer stays, sometimes of several weeks or even months, are often recorded, Alresford Pond being a particularly favoured locality. The largest flocks recorded were of 17 at Heath Pond (Petersfield) on Feb. 4th 1978, 21 flying north up the Test valley from Eling on Sep. 1st 1980 and 11 arriving at Frensham Great Pond from the south-west on Aug. 28th 1989.

Five Shelducks ringed abroad have been recovered in Hampshire. Adults trapped on the Weser Estuary, western Germany in August 1958 and September 1964 were found dead at Emsworth in February 1962 and Farlington Marshes in August 1965. A juvenile ringed in Denmark in July 1962 was found dead near Southampton in January 1963. An adult ringed at Somme, France in November 1981 was recovered at Langstone Harbour in December 1986 and another ringed at Rostock, eastern Germany in July 1985 had moved to the same place by February 1986. Two Hampshire-bred birds have been recovered. One, ringed at Farlington Marshes in July 1973, was found dead at Neuwerk, western Germany in October 1979 and another, ringed at Southampton Docks in June 1978, was found dead at Hurst Castle in January 1987.


# Mandarin                                    *Aix galericulata*

A moderately common and increasing resident.

This introduced species is now well established and increasing in the county. It nests in holes in mature, open, broadleaved woodland and parkland and has several times been recorded using nest boxes. It is easily overlooked when breeding, so will have gone unrecorded in a number of tetrads during the Atlas Survey. Assuming an average of two pairs per tetrad where breeding was confirmed or probable, and making an allowance for those which were missed, a county population of around 200 pairs is indicated. The most recent estimate of the British population was 7000 individuals (Davies 1988).

The species apparently first bred in a wild state in the county around Leckford, following the escape of birds from the wildfowl collection there in the 1950s (Taverner 1962). 25 were there on Dec. 25th 1972, and during the Breeding Grebe and Wildfowl Survey in 1978, seven pairs were located, of which five bred successfully (Clark 1979). During the Atlas Survey, breeding was not confirmed, but a count of 17 there on Oct. 14th 1990 shows that the species still survives in the area.

In the north-east, breeding was first recorded in 1964, when a pair raised four young at Stratfield Saye. A regular post-breeding gathering there peaked at

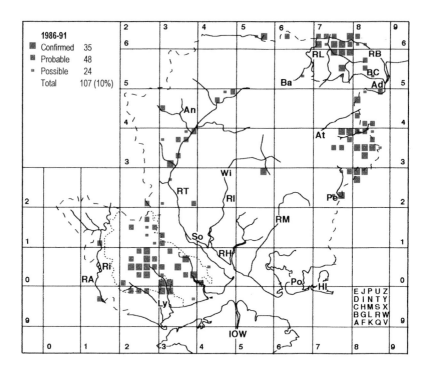

22 in October 1976, 39 in September 1980 and 72 in September 1987. Since then, very few have been seen, possibly due to a drop in water level on the preferred lake following damage to a weir during the great storm of October 1987. During the 1980s, there has been a gradual spread up the Blackwater and Hart valleys. In 1989, four nests were found in the Eversley/Bramshill area, three in nest boxes and one in a natural hole. Mandarins are now regular at Fleet Pond, where the highest count to date was of 34 in January 1992.

The population in east Hampshire was originally discrete from that based at Stratfield Saye, and is believed to have spread there from Cutt Mill and Witley Park in south-west Surrey. Breeding was first recorded at Waggoners Wells in 1981, and the species is now widespread in the Wey valley. The largest gatherings form at Passfield Pond, where there were 61 on Oct. 18th 1984, 37 on Oct. 2nd 1987 and 42 on Oct. 13th 1991.

In the New Forest area, single birds have occasionally been seen (mostly at Sowley Pond) since 1961, but breeding was not recorded until the early 1980s. By 1991, the species was widespread along the woodland streams in the centre and east of the Forest, extending into the Beaulieu, Exbury and Cadland Estates (C R Tubbs *in litt*). An indication of the possible density is given by a count of six pairs, of which two bred successfully, at Roydon Woods (Brockenhurst) in 1990. The largest wintering gathering reported so far was of 40-60 feeding in an area of wet woodland near Lyndhurst in January and February 1988.

Small numbers are regularly reported in other areas of the county. Many of these are tame and probably escaped from wildfowl collections.

# Wigeon                                   *Anas penelope*

A common winter visitor and passage migrant; a few summer each year.

The largest flocks of Wigeon occur at coastal sites and in the Avon valley; in most of these areas numbers have increased since the mid-1950s (table 12). This is probably due to a combination of factors, including the increased frequency of harsh winters, much reduced wildfowling, recovery of eelgrass *Zostera* (a favoured food) in Langstone Harbour, and management and lack of disturbance at sites such as Titchfield Haven which have been declared as nature reserves.

| | 55-60 | 60-65 | 65-70 | 70-75 | 75-80 | 80-85 | 85-90 | Peak counts | |
|---|---|---|---|---|---|---|---|---|---|
| Chichester Harbour | - | - | 736 | 771 | 737 | 1082 | 1264 | 2485, | Jan. 1987 |
| East Hayling | - | - | - | - | 85 | 121 | 247 | 541, | Oct. 1989 |
| Langstone Harbour | 788 | 890 | 848 | 1290 | 1228 | 1530 | 1554 | 2340, | Oct. 1988 |
| Titchfield Haven | 962 | 1046 | 477 | 196 | 954 | 1569 | 1711 | 3300, | Jan. 1987 |
| Eling/Lower Test | 300^ | 770^ | - | 238 | 190 | 432 | 598 | 1011, | Jan. 1963 |
| Beaulieu Estuary | 500^ | 920 | 907 | 840 | 652 | 504 | 523 | 2000, | Jan. 1963 |
| Sowley/Lymington | - | 500^ | - | 375^ | 287 | 271 | 409 | 700, | Nov. 1988 |
| Lymington/Hurst | 320^ | - | 180^ | 118 | 430 | 380 | 435 | 1000, | Jan. 1987 |
| Avon valley: Bisterne area | - | - | - | - | 55^ | 1661 | 2006 | 4130, | Jan. 1987 |
| Avon valley: Blashford/ Bickton + Blashford Lakes | 600^ | 800^ | 1037^ | 1910 | 2120 | 3200 | 1473 | 4800, | Jan. 1985 |

*Table 12. Five year means of winter maxima and peak counts of Wigeon, 1955/56-89/90.*

Elsewhere on the coast, counts have exceeded 200 at Portsmouth Harbour (max. 593, December 1978), Hythe (max. 475, November 1986) and Fawley/Calshot (max. 450, December 1979), but usually fewer are present. In the Avon valley above Fordingbridge, 100 or more are occasionally recorded, the largest flock being of 250 in February 1980. In the Test valley, three-figure counts are most frequent at Broadlands (max. 479, January 1977), but have also been recorded further upstream at Timsbury (max. 150, February 1974) and between Mottisfont and Marsh Court (max. 176, December 1990). In the upper Itchen valley, 50-80 (once, 100) regularly wintered at Avington Park until the mid-1970s, but subsequently very few have occurred. At Stratfield Saye, counts twice exceeded 100 in the 1960s (max. 160, January 1964), but since then the winter peak has typically been 30-60. At other north-east sites, records increased in frequency during the 1980s but most referred to small flocks passing through, apart from a gathering of 169 at Greywell in severe weather in January 1985. However, since 1987, a wintering flock has become established at Eversley/Yateley Gravel Pits, with a maximum count of 52 on Nov. 7th 1992.

Wigeon begin to return from their breeding grounds in late August. In autumn, Langstone Harbour holds the highest numbers, but in most years these then decline as *Zostera* is exhausted. Movement is occasionally recorded at this time, e.g. 162 flew west off Pennington Marsh on Sep. 21st 1980 and 173 arrived from the east at Black Point on Nov. 20th 1985. At other localities, the winter peak is usually recorded in December or January. The onset of severe weather may result in a large arrival and heavy cold weather passage, e.g. between Jan. 10th and 13th 1987, when a minimum of 923 moved west through The Solent. Extensive flooding in the Avon valley, especially as a result of snow melting, may attract several thousand, e.g. 6200 in January 1982, 7100 in

January 1985 and 6880 in January 1987. Wintering flocks disperse from mid-February onwards unless severe weather delays their departure. Evidence of passage is occasionally noted, e.g. 157 flew east off Hayling Bay on Mar. 12th 1984. Most have left by early April; 124 at Ivy Lake (Blashford) on Apr. 1st 1979 is the only three-figure count for that month apart from a passage peak of 800+ at Langstone Harbour on Apr. 4th 1958.

A few birds, some presumably sick or injured, summer every year, most frequently at Langstone Harbour, Titchfield Haven, the Beaulieu Estuary and Mockbeggar Lake (Blashford). A pair summered at Winnall Moors from 1979-85 but there was no indication that breeding was attempted.

National ringing data indicate that most of the Wigeon wintering in south-east England originate from Finland, the Baltic States, the Ukraine and north-west Russia (Owen *et al* 1986). However, the nine birds recovered in Hampshire had been ringed in the Netherlands (5), Essex (3) and Suffolk (1), thus only giving an indication of the route taken on migration. In recent mild winters, the Hampshire population has been around 5000, representing about 2% of the British total. However, during the cold spells of early 1982, 1985 and 1987, the county total peaked at 12,000-15,000, which formed between 4.5% and 5.7% of those counted in the whole country at those times.

## American Wigeon                               *Anas americana*

A rare vagrant. There have been six records, all of single drakes, as follows:

| | |
|---|---|
| 1963: | Titchfield Haven, Dec. 22nd; |
| 1977: | Dibden Bay, Apr. 14th-18th; |
| 1978: | Titchfield Haven, Oct. 27th; |
| 1984: | Bisterne, Jan. 5th-14th and Ivy Lake (Blashford), Feb. 12th-19th; |
| 1987: | Titchfield Haven, May 7th-July 19th; |
| 1991: | Eling/Lower Test Marshes, Feb. 9th-Apr. 11th. |

The first was considered by the *BBRC* to be one of three birds that had escaped from a collection in Portsmouth in August 1962.

The American Wigeon breeds in North America and winters south to Panama.

## Gadwall                                      *Anas strepera*

A scarce resident and moderately common winter visitor which has increased considerably in recent years.

K & M considered the Gadwall to be "a rather scarce winter visitor"; this remained true until the 1970s. Between 1951 and 1968, most sightings were of single birds or small groups of up to six which rarely stayed for more than a few days. Most occurred in mid-winter, but there was evidence of passage in April and May and a few summer records, including one of 12 at Titchfield Haven on Aug. 4th 1966.

In 1968/69, a flock of up to 16 wintered at Marsh Court; in subsequent years this continued to increased. Elsewhere, the species remained irregular until the 1976/77 winter, when up to 27 were at Blashford Lakes. Since then, the Blashford flock has expanded rapidly and numbers in excess of 50 have been recorded at six other sites. Fig. 18 illustrates the increase over the period 1950/51-91/92.

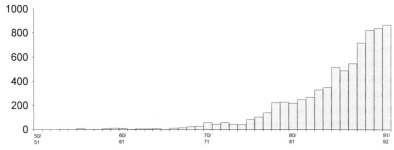

*Figure 18. Winter totals of Gadwall, 1950/51-91/92.*

Counts at various localities during 1970/71-89/90 are summarised in table 13.

| | 70-75 | 75-80 | 80-85 | 85-90 | Peak counts | |
|---|---|---|---|---|---|---|
| Titchfield Haven | 2 | 10 | 13 | 51 | 82, | Dec. 1989 |
| Blashford Lakes | 0 | 46 | 91 | **236** | 366, | Dec. 1989 |
| Marsh Court | 25 | 48 | 36 | 36^ | 71, | Feb. 1979 |
| Laverstoke/Overton | 0 | 0 | 42^ | 74 | 115, | Dec. 1987 |
| Allington Gravel Pit | 0 | 0 | 15 | 25 | 33, | Nov. 1989 |
| Winchester Sewage Farm | 0 | 0 | 9 | 44 | 69, | Feb. 1990 |
| Alresford Pond | 2 | 6 | 19 | 44 | 66, | Nov. 1988 |
| Eversley/Yateley Gravel Pits | 3 | 2 | 22 | 79 | 169, | Jan. 1990 |

*Table 13. Five year means of winter maxima and peak counts of Gadwall, 1970/71-89/90.*

After the period covered by table 13, numbers continued to rise at several localities, reaching 557 at Blashford Lakes and 88 at Allington Gravel Pit in December 1992, 73 at Winchester Sewage Farm in February 1991 and 243 at Eversley/Yateley Gravel Pits in January 1991.

Flocks of 20-50 have also been recorded on or near the coast at Farlington Marshes, Fawley Reservoir, the Beaulieu Estuary, Sowley Pond and Lower Pennington, in the Test valley at Leckford and Bransbury Common, in the Itchen valley at Winnall Moors, Ladywell Lake, Northington Lake and Brown Candover, and in the north-east at Stratfield Saye, Wellington Country Park, Fleet Pond, Tundry Pond and Dogmersfield Lake.

It has recently emerged that the Marsh Court flock originated, at least in part, from a wildfowl collection at nearby Ashley Manor (T J Norriss pers. comm.). However, since few were observed there outside the winter months, immigrants from elsewhere must also have been involved. Despite the presence of a pair at Marsh Court in May and June in most years from 1971-82, successful breeding has never been recorded there. Summering became more widespread from 1977 onwards, and breeding was finally proved in 1983, when two broods were raised at Winchester Sewage Farm and one at Northington Lake. In the following two years, breeding was again confined to the upper Itchen valley, with single broods at Winchester Sewage Farm, Alresford Pond and Northington Lake in 1984 and two broods at Winchester Sewage Farm and one at Winchester College Water Meadows in 1985.

During the Atlas Survey, the breeding population continued to expand, with successful nesting reported from 15 localities with a maximum of 13 broods

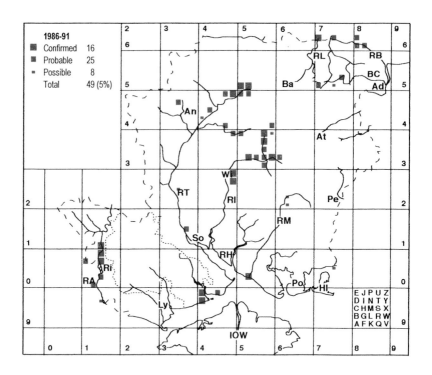

1986-91
■ Confirmed 16
■ Probable 25
▪ Possible 8
Total 49 (5%)

reported in both 1987 and 1988. The total summering population in 1990 and 1991 was in the range 100-150 birds with concentrations of 20 or more at Blashford Lakes, around Overton in the upper Test valley and in the Alresford/Northington area. In the former year, the British breeding population was estimated at 770 pairs (New Atlas).

Post-breeding flocks build up in the main breeding areas in late summer, e.g. as many as 98 were at Alresford Pond in August 1988. Winter visitors arrive from mid-September and reach a peak at most localities in December. In severe weather, as in early 1986 and 1987, many vacate inland sites, some appearing at coastal localities but most apparently leaving the county. Even in mild winters, numbers decline from mid-January onwards and all but the summering population has gone by early April. Passage is suggested at this time by the small numbers which move east through The Solent, a total of 39 being recorded during 1971-90 on dates between Apr. 8th and May 11th.

The increase in the breeding and wintering populations of Gadwall in Hampshire is part of a wider expansion in Britain and north-west Europe. Over the period 1960-85, the post-breeding population in south-east England increased by 9% per annum (Fox 1987). However, during the last two decades, the increase in wintering numbers in Britain has been over three times greater than can be explained by the expansion of the nesting population alone. This appears to be related to the proliferation of lowland artificial waters such as gravel pits and reservoirs (Fox & Salmon 1989); certainly the most spectacular increases in Hampshire have been on the gravel pit complexes at Blashford and

Eversley/Yateley, where Gadwall are attracted to the profuse growth of Canadian pondweed. In the five winters from 1985/86-89/90, the proportion of the British wintering population in Hampshire (based on January counts) averaged 8.5%.

Ringing data suggest that the national wintering population consists of immigrants from the Netherlands, Scandinavia and central Europe and a proportion of British-bred birds, the remainder of which move south into France (Owen *et al* 1986). There have not been any Hampshire recoveries of foreign-ringed birds, but one ringed at Titchfield Haven in December 1986 was shot 234 km east in France in September 1987. Five birds, ringed in Norfolk in July, Essex in September and January and Gloucestershire in November (2), have been recovered in Hampshire in winter.

## Teal                                                      *Anas crecca*

A scarce resident and common winter visitor.

The favoured breeding sites are small, peaty heathland pools, and lakes and rivers fringed with reeds, rushes or other thick vegetation, but they may also nest some distance from water. Teal are secretive and only thinly scattered through the available habitat, so many pairs are likely to be overlooked. Confirmation of breeding is difficult to obtain, since most broods stay hidden in vegetation and do not venture out on to open water.

Eight pairs were found in part of the New Forest in 1960. During the Breeding Grebe and Wildfowl Survey in 1978, 17 pairs were located, including

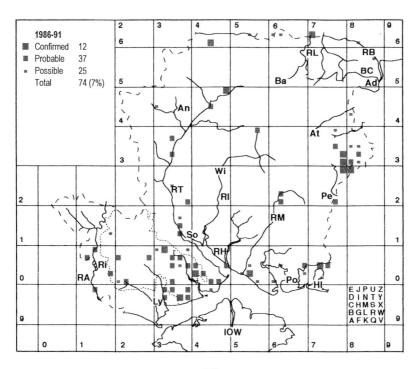

1986-91
Confirmed 12
Probable 37
Possible 25
Total 74 (7%)

only four in the New Forest, where coverage was poor. Three pairs were known to have bred successfully. The county population was estimated at 30 pairs (Clark 1979).

The results of the Atlas Survey show confirmed or probable breeding in 47 tetrads, although some of these were not occupied in every year. C R Tubbs (*in litt*) estimated that 10-15 pairs were present, and presumed to be attempting to breed, in the southern half of the New Forest in 1986. There are probably at least 20 pairs elsewhere, which indicates a minimum total of 30-35 pairs. The total British population in 1988-91 was estimated at 1500-2600 pairs (New Atlas).

Flocks build up from late July onwards and may reach three figures during August at favoured sites such as Langstone Harbour, Titchfield Haven and Alresford Pond. In Langstone Harbour, where numbers have increased considerably since the 1950s, numbers normally peak in autumn, but most other coastal localities have their highest counts in mid-winter. Counts at the principal wintering sites are summarised in table 14.

| | 55-60 | 60-65 | 65-70 | 70-75 | 75-80 | 80-85 | 85-90 | Peak counts | |
|---|---|---|---|---|---|---|---|---|---|
| Chichester Harbour | - | - | 199 | 494 | 1463 | **2382** | 1751 | 3253, | Dec. 1981 |
| East Hayling | - | - | - | - | 888 | 1175 | 892 | 1800, | Dec. 1981 |
| Langstone Harbour | 182 | 224 | 518 | 755 | 696 | 948 | 698 | 1300, | Sep. 1981 |
| Portsmouth Harbour | - | - | - | 14 | 73 | 180 | 382 | 700, | Nov. 1986 |
| Southampton Water | - | - | - | 1437 | 1903 | 1850 | 1704 | 3050, | Dec. 1982 |
| Titchfield Haven | 1086 | 1123 | 300 | 708 | 1171 | 562 | 465 | 2300, | Jan. 1962 |
| Eling/Lower Test | - | - | - | 28 | 132 | 82 | 343 | 660, | Dec. 1989 |
| Dibden Bay | 475^ | 600* | 338* | 87 | 309 | 138 | 0 | 800, | Jan. 1978 |
| Fawley/Calshot | 725^ | - | 250^ | 1118 | 1428 | 1382 | 1087 | 3000, | Dec. 1982 |
| Beaulieu Estuary | 200* | 275^ | 433 | 525 | 670 | 447 | 541 | 1200, | Dec. 1976 |
| Sowley/Lymington | 395^ | 650^ | 625^ | 568^ | 1426 | 746 | 519 | 4000, | Jan. 1979 |
| Lymington/Hurst | - | - | - | 194 | 812 | 836 | 670 | 1500, | Dec. 1978 |
| Avon valley: Bisterne | - | - | - | - | 408^ | 564 | 225 | 1300, | Jan. 1982 |
| Avon valley: Blashford/ Bickton + Blashford Lakes | 700* | 1500* | 625^ | 645 | 271 | 363 | 242 | 1500, | Jan. 1961 |
| Avington Park | 47 | 76 | 56 | 100 | 124 | 135 | 155 | 305, | Dec. 1989 |
| Alresford Pond | 125^ | 161 | 114 | 123 | 208 | 186 | 155 | 330, | Jan. 1979 |
| Stratfield Saye | 209* | 378^ | 293^ | 102 | 25 | 69 | 177 | 524, | Dec. 1966 |

*Table 14. Five year means of winter maxima and peak counts of Teal, 1955/56-89/90.*

In addition to the sites in the table, the Hamble Estuary held 400 in December 1981, but numbers there do not usually exceed 100. Inland, three-figure flocks are sometimes recorded in the Test valley, the maximum being 316 at Broadlands in January 1977. Teal have gradually become more numerous in the Dogmersfield Lake/Fleet Pond area, with maxima of 140 at Dogmersfield in December 1986 and 154 standing on ice at Fleet in January 1992. Away from the main haunts in the Itchen valley, counts peaked at 228 at Winchester Sewage farm in severe weather in February 1991 and 120 at Allington Gravel Pit in January 1992.

Several of the localities listed in table 14 have shown great fluctuations due to changing conditions, but overall the wintering population in the county peaked between 1976/77 and 1985/86, with a January total of 5000-7000 in every year except 1979. The severe weather in early January of that year resulted in a large influx, with an estimated 9000 in the county including 4000+

at Sowley Pond and 2000+ between Tanners Lane and Hurst, but most of these quickly moved on. In the five winters from 1985/86-89/90, the proportion of the British wintering population in Hampshire (based on January counts) averaged 6.4%.

Most Teal depart in late February and March, with very few remaining in April. The only localities to have held over 100 in that month are Titchfield Haven, where three-figure flocks have been recorded in six years since 1971 with a maximum of 300 on Apr. 12th 1977, and the Avon Valley, where a total of 430 was counted on floods at Sopley and Hucklesbrook on Apr. 1st 1979.

Hampshire ringing data give some indication of the origins and migration routes of wintering birds. 17 birds ringed in winter, including ten at Titchfield Haven, have been recovered abroad, in Denmark (5), Finland (3), northern France (2), and Estonia, southern France, western Germany, Latvia, the Netherlands, western Russia and Sweden (1 each). One of these, ringed at Sowley Marsh on Dec. 22nd 1986, was shot 813 km south in the Pyrenées Atlantique, France, on Jan. 12th 1987, and had presumably been forced south by the severe cold weather at the time. Of the others, single birds were shot in Germany and the Netherlands in December and the remainder were shot or found dead between August and October. Nine foreign-ringed birds have been recovered in Hampshire in winter, from the Netherlands (4), Denmark and Poland (2 each), and eastern Germany (1). The two from Poland were both ringed in July but the remainder were ringed between August and December.

There have been 13 records of drakes of the Nearctic race *A.c. carolinensis*, the Green-winged Teal, as follows:

1956: Titchfield Haven, Mar. 18th;
1962: Avington Park, Jan. 30th-Mar. 25th;
1978: Farlington Marshes, Dec. 30th-Jan. 14th 1979;
1980: Ivy Lake (Blashford), Jan. 12th;
1982: Dibden Bay, Feb. 6th and Mar. 13th;
        Stratfield Saye, Mar. 14th-17th;
1985: Dogmersfield Lake, Mar. 24th-30th;
1987: Emer Bog (Romsey), Feb. 28th;
1989: Titchfield Haven, May 5th, 7th and 28th;
        Titchfield Haven/Farlington Marshes/Needs Ore, Oct. 29th-Mar. 4th 1990;
1991: Titchfield Haven, Jan. 6th and Feb. 13th-16th;
1992: Titchfield Haven, Feb. 16th-Mar. 16th;
1993: Needs Ore, Mar. 27th-Apr. 15th.

The last five records presumably refer to the same returning individual.


# Mallard                                               *Anas platyrhynchos*

A common resident and winter visitor.

The Atlas Survey shows the Mallard to be widespread in Hampshire. The main gaps in its distribution are on the chalk, where it is found only in the river valleys and at isolated village or farm ponds. The largest concentrations occur at wetland sites, but nesting also occurs in dry areas such as heathland and woodland which may be some distance from water. Breeding season counts made in recent years include 133 pairs found on the Itchen above Mansbridge during a survey of the valley in 1976 (Cloyne 1977), 53 pairs in the Longstock/

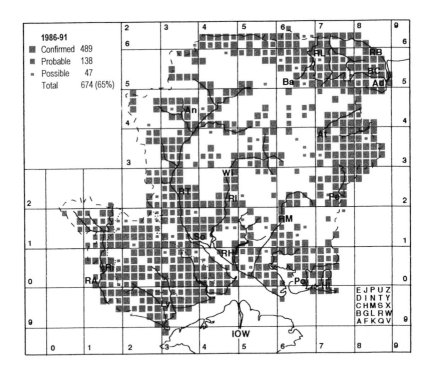

Leckford area of the Test valley in 1978, a total of 76 broods at 16 sites in the north-east in 1978, and 40 pairs in the Wallington valley in 1983. Estimates of 20-30 pairs have also been made for Bramshill, Eversley/Yateley Gravel Pits, Timsbury, Titchfield Haven, Winchester College Water Meadows and Winnall Moors, but no data are available for several other sites which probably hold similar numbers. Although some tetrads only hold one or two pairs, there may be 20 or more pairs in those with a large expanse of suitable habitat. An average of five to ten pairs per tetrad where breeding was confirmed or probable equates to a county population in the range 3000-6000 pairs. The British population was estimated at 100,000 pairs in 1986 (New Atlas).

After the breeding season, large gatherings of the local population form on undisturbed inland waters. At some localities these include hand-reared birds released by wildfowlers. Usually these flocks roost by day and fly out to feed on stubble fields at dusk. Counts vary markedly at individual sites from year to year, presumably depending on the availability of local food supplies. However, at Stratfield Saye, where counts exceeded 1000 in 16 autumns between 1959 and 1980, Sowley Pond and Marsh Court, numbers have declined in recent years. As the winter progresses, numbers dwindle at most inland sites, although many of the high counts at Fleet Pond have been of birds standing on ice during severe weather. At coastal sites, the highest numbers are usually present between November and January, then declining rapidly as the return to breeding sites gets underway. Table 15 summarises counts at the principal localities.

| | 55-60 | 60-65 | 65-70 | 70-75 | 75-80 | 80-85 | 85-90 | Peak counts | |
|---|---|---|---|---|---|---|---|---|---|
| Titchfield Haven | 343 | 278 | 148 | 135 | 234 | 281 | 264 | 700, | Dec. 1959 |
| Lower Test Marshes | - | - | - | - | 375^ | 363^ | 591^ | 977, | Dec. 1989 |
| Beaulieu Estuary | - | 258^ | 371 | 405 | 390 | 499 | 482 | 620, | Nov. 1969 |
| Sowley Pond | 600* | 684 | 750^ | 247^ | 254 | 393^ | 298 | 1000, | Jan. 1970 |
| Blashford Lakes | - | 450* | - | 412 | 346^ | 409 | 560 | 827, | Sep. 1987 |
| Broadlands | - | - | - | 927^ | 898^ | 678^ | 833 | 977, | Oct. 1975 |
| Marsh Court | - | - | - | - | 724 | 430^ | - | 1050, | Sep. 1978 |
| Longstock/Leckford | - | - | 1000* | - | 483^ | 407 | 365 | 1000, | Oct. 1968 |
| Avington Park | 460^ | 564 | 405 | 318 | 240 | 139 | 199 | 795, | Nov. 1963 |
| Alresford Pond | 305^ | 322 | 465 | 296 | 371 | 418 | 293 | 850, | Aug. 1982 |
| Northington | 565^ | 361 | 768 | 684 | 652 | 425 | 552 | 1250, | Aug. 1966 |
| Stratfield Saye | 655^ | 1192 | 1372^ | 1054 | 1214 | 886 | 586 | 1800, | Sep. 1979 |
| Fleet Pond | - | - | - | 252 | 462 | 407 | 482 | 685, | Dec. 1987 |

*Table 15. Five year means of autumn/winter maxima and peak counts of Mallard, 1955/56-89/90*

There have been 222 ringing recoveries/controls involving Hampshire birds. 130 moved within the county, 74 to or from other parts of southern England and 18 to or from continental Europe. Long distance movements include one ringed at the Volga Delta, Ukraine on Aug. 24th 1941 and shot at Otterbourne, 3728 km west, on Feb. 12th 1944, a hand-reared bird released at Damerham on July 5th 1955 and shot in Estonia, 1972 km ENE, on Sep. 15th 1958, and one, ringed as a chick at Murmansk, Russia on July 8th 1972 and found dead at Totton, 2617 km south-west, on Jan. 30th 1977. These recoveries show the great distances covered by some individuals of this species.

# Pintail                                          *Anas acuta*

A moderately common winter visitor and passage migrant which occasionally summers.

Both K & M and Cohen considered the Pintail to be scarce, but by the time the latter wrote there was some evidence of an increase, with flocks of 57 in Langstone Harbour in January 1955 and 110 in the Avon valley in January 1961. Numbers have continued to increase except in the Avon valley, where there has been a decline through the 1980s due to the lack of consistent winter flooding (Table 16). During the five winters from 1985/86-89/90, the proportion of the British wintering population in Hampshire (based on January counts) averaged 2.2%.

| | 55-60 | 60-65 | 65-70 | 70-75 | 75-80 | 80-85 | 85-90 | Peak counts | |
|---|---|---|---|---|---|---|---|---|---|
| Chichester Harbour | - | - | 66 | 115 | 161 | 152 | 138 | 251, | Jan. 1987 |
| East Hayling | - | - | - | - | 13 | 20 | 14 | 62, | Dec. 1982 |
| Langstone Harbour | 16 | 19 | 44 | 123 | 87 | 165 | 250 | 304, | Jan. 1989 |
| Beaulieu Estuary | | 15 | 27 | 43 | 68 | 92 | 91 | 140, | Dec. 1989 |
| Lymington/Hurst | - | - | - | 7 | 27 | 45 | 48 | 100, | Jan. 1982 |
| Avon valley: Blashford / Bickton + Blashford Lakes | - | 110* | 37^ | 52 | 131 | 56 | 13 | 190, | Feb. 1978 |

*Table 16. Five year means of winter maxima and peak counts of Pintail, 1955/56-89/90.*

Gatherings of more than 20 (maximum count in brackets) have also been recorded at Paulsgrove Reclamation (35, January 1987), Titchfield Haven (27,

January 1985), Eling/Redbridge (46, December 1963), Dibden Bay (75, February 1977), Sowley Pond (75, January 1982), Tanners Lane (32, March 1978) and in the Avon valley at Bisterne (52, February 1978). Apart from Sowley Pond, which is regularly used by the Beaulieu Estuary flock, numbers at these localities are usually much lower or the species is absent completely. Several of the counts were made in unusual circumstances, e.g. during hard weather (at Titchfield Haven), when temporary conditions offered by reclamation pans proved particularly attractive (at Paulsgrove and Dibden Bay) or on extensive floods (at Bisterne).

Away from the coast and Avon valley, Pintails are scarce; the only double-figured counts have been of 15 at Alresford Pond and Northington Lake on Jan. 12th 1969, 16 at Fleet Pond on May 1st 1984 and 11 at Alresford Pond from Mar. 1st-5th 1992.

Returning birds are present in most years from late August. Small movements are sometimes detected in autumn, e.g. ten flew east at Pennington Marsh on Aug. 18th 1971 and flocks of 10-16 have been seen moving west in the west Solent area on five occasions between Sep. 21st and Oct. 25th. The winter maximum is normally reached between mid-December and early March. Small cold weather movements are occasionally witnessed but exceptionally 160 flew east at Pennington Marsh on Dec. 28th 1989 in mild conditions. Most have departed by early April and there is little evidence of through passage, the only noteworthy records being of 56 flying east off Sandy Point on Mar. 31st 1990 and the Fleet Pond record above.

Summer records are unusual, mostly coming from coastal localities, especially Langstone Harbour. The cumulative monthly totals for May to August over the period 1971-92 were 15, 11, 25, 99, the high August total reflecting the early arrival of wintering birds. A pair present at Farlington Marshes throughout May and June 1983 is the only suggestion of breeding.

National ringing data indicate that most birds wintering in Britain originate from western Siberia (Owen *et al* 1986). In Hampshire, there have been six recoveries of foreign-ringed birds. One ringed at Oulu, Finland on July 5th 1970 was shot at Ringwood, 2213 km south-west, on Jan. 25th 1971, and another ringed at Murmansk, Russia on July 28th 1972 was shot in Langstone Harbour, 2604 km south-west, on Dec. 16th of that year. Four others trapped in autumn, three in the Netherlands and one in Sweden, had moved to Hampshire in the following or subsequent winters.

## Garganey                                                      *Anas querquedula*

A scarce passage migrant and rare summer visitor.

Analysis of the records for 1951-92 shows that numbers have declined since the early 1970s, especially in autumn (fig. 19).

The first normally arrive in mid or late March; earlier records include a drake at Needs Ore on Mar. 4th 1954, 11 at Blashford Lakes on Mar. 5th 1961 and a pair at Titchfield Haven on Mar. 5th 1977. Peak numbers usually occur between late March and mid-April (fig. 20). However, in some recent years the first were not seen until late April or May and in 1979 none was recorded before June 10th.

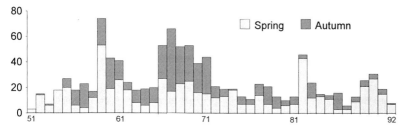

*Figure 19. Spring and autumn totals of Garganeys, 1951-92.*

Most occur at coastal sites, particularly the Pennington/Keyhaven area, Titchfield Haven and Farlington Marshes. Records are usually of up to four, but larger counts include 13 at Keyhaven on Mar. 22nd 1954, nine at Farlington Marshes on Apr. 17th 1959, 11 at Pennington Marsh on Mar. 22nd 1966, nine at Paulsgrove Reclamation on Mar. 27th 1982 and six at Titchfield Haven on Apr. 27th 1984. Birds are occasionally recorded moving east offshore; between 1968 and 1992, 34 were noted in the period Mar. 14th to May 31st, 18 of them between Apr. 11th and 23rd.

Inland, Garganeys are scarce. Since 1951, the species has been recorded in spring at 29 localities. In the Avon valley, there were sightings in 11 years including the flock of 11 at Blashford above, ten still there on Mar. 12th 1961 and eight at Ibsley on Mar. 21st 1971. Other localities with records in five to seven years were Nursling Gravel Pit, Fleet Pond, Alresford Pond, Timsbury Gravel Pit and Winnall Moors.

Although the underlying trend appears to be downwards, the total recorded in spring fluctuates markedly from year to year, with the highest numbers occurring in warm springs with anticylonic conditions, e.g. 1959 (53), 1982 (43) and 1990 (27).

Return passage peaks between late July and late August (fig. 20). Until 1971, autumn totals regularly exceeded 20, with a maximum of 49 in 1967 (fig. 19). In the Pennington/Keyhaven area, counts reached double figures in four years between 1966 and 1971 with a maximum of 15 on Aug. 7th 1967. Maxima at other coastal sites included 12 at Dibden Bay on July 23rd 1960, 12 at Titchfield

129

Haven on July 23rd 1967 and eight at Farlington Marshes on July 30th 1970. Inland, there were records from seven localities including eight at Fleet Pond on Aug. 8th 1967 and seven at Stratfield Saye on Aug. 21st 1970.

Since 1972, the highest autumn total has been 14, and in 15 years no more than six were recorded (fig. 19). At coastal sites, the only count to exceed four was of eight at Pennington Marsh on Aug. 10th 1986, while inland, there were records from six localities, all of one or two birds apart from five at Timsbury Gravel Pit from Aug. 20th-26th 1978.

The last are usually recorded in late September or early October, the only later birds in recent years being one at Mockbeggar Lake on Oct. 19th 1979 and another at Farlington Marshes from Sep. 13th-Oct. 20th 1985. However, in 1963, four were at Farlington Marshes on Nov. 9th and one was still present on Nov. 17th. In 1957, one remained at Titchfield Haven until at least Nov. 20th, but the latest ever was a drake at Needs Ore on Nov. 29th 1953.

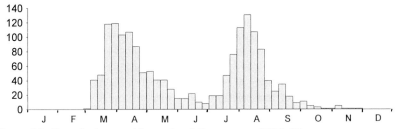

*Figure 20. Cumulative weekly totals of Garganeys, 1951-92.*

K & M and Cohen mentioned a total of six breeding records, the most recent in 1940. In 1976, a pair possibly attempted nesting near Broadlands Lake. Between 1982 and 1990, there were June records involving up to four birds in five years, but mostly on one date only. Records for 1991 indicate that breeding may have taken place in the county. At one site, a pair was present in late May, but there were no further reports until Aug. 4th, when a drake and a juvenile were seen. In recent years, the reported British breeding population has been in the range 40-111 pairs (Spencer *et al* 1993).

Garganeys breeding in Britain and the near continent winter mainly in tropical West Africa.

## Blue-winged Teal                                                  *Anas discors*

A rare vagrant. There have been five records, as follows:

1972:   drake, Pennington/Keyhaven area, May 30th-June 28th and at Needs Ore, June 4th;
1978:   drake, Farlington Marshes, May 28th;
1980:   pair, Fleet Pond, May 4th;
1989:   immature, Frensham Great Pond, Oct. 29th-Nov. 26th;
1992:   female, Dibden Bay, May 18th-21st†.

The Frensham bird was considered likely to have escaped from captivity by the *BBRC*.

The Blue-winged Teal breeds in North America and winters from the southern USA to Peru and Brazil.

# Shoveler                                    *Anas clypeata*

A moderately common winter visitor and passage migrant; a few pairs probably attempt breeding annually.

Since the 1950s, Titchfield Haven, the Beaulieu Estuary/Sowley Pond area and the Avon valley around Blashford have held wintering flocks in excess of 50 fairly regularly, as has Langstone Harbour since 1971. Other sites have held larger numbers for shorter periods while conditions were attractive, notably on the lagoons on reclaimed land at Dibden Bay (1975-82) and Paulsgrove (1981-88). Overall, numbers reached a peak of over 650 in early 1961 when there was heavy flooding in the county, then fell to a low level through the rest of that decade. A gradual increase took place in the early 1970s which accelerated to reach a peak of about 700 in 1981/82, since when numbers have fallen again. During the five winters from 1985/86-89/90, the proportion of the British wintering population in Hampshire (based on January counts) averaged 8.3%. Table 17 summarises counts at the main localities.

| | 55-60 | 60-65 | 65-70 | 70-75 | 75-80 | 80-85 | 85-90 | Peak counts | |
|---|---|---|---|---|---|---|---|---|---|
| Langstone Harbour | 14 | 10 | 22 | 54 | 105 | 128 | 129 | 213, | Dec. 1981 |
| Portsmouth Harbour | - | - | - | 0 | 6 | 62 | 41 | 136, | Feb. 1988 |
| Titchfield Haven | 51 | 58 | 15 | 9 | 47 | 58 | 75 | 224, | Feb. 1961 |
| Dibden Bay | 23* | - | 22* | 8 | 80 | 59 | 2 | 136, | Dec. 1977 |
| Beaulieu Estuary | 48 | 39 | 21 | 19 | 19 | 29 | 51 | 84, | Nov. 1985 |
| Sowley Pond | 49 | 140* | - | 1 | 15 | 25 | 42 | 140, | Jan. 1961 |
| Lymington/Hurst | - | - | - | 5 | 35 | 39 | 35 | 50, | Dec. 1981 |
| Avon valley: Blashford / Bickton + Blashford Lakes | 35* | 133^ | 22^ | 70 | 152 | 191 | 110 | 285, | Feb. 1978 |

*Table 17. Five year means of winter maxima and peak counts of Shoveler, 1955/56-89/90.*

Flocks of 20-60 have also been recorded near the coast at Baffins Pond and Fawley Reservoir, in the Avon valley at Bisterne, in the Test valley at Broadlands Lake, Timsbury Lake and Marsh Court, in the Itchen valley at Allington Gravel Pit, Winnall Moors, Avington Lake, Alresford Pond and Northington Lake, and in the north-east at Stratfield Saye, Fleet Pond, Tundry Pond and Dogmersfield Lake. In the north-east, Shovelers were very scarce until the mid-1970s, but since then, numbers have increased and they are now regular at Stratfield Saye (max. 55, December 1983) and Fleet Pond (max. 53, December 1992).

Although maximum numbers normally occur between December and February, passage peaks are sometimes noted in early autumn, especially at Blashford Lakes and Langstone Harbour. At the latter site, numbers rose to 90 on Sep. 1st 1987 but did not exceed 65 during the rest of that year. Evidence of spring passage is occasionally provided by easterly movement along the coast. During the period 1971-92, a total of 313 was recorded on dates between Mar. 19th and May 15th with most in the last few days of March and early April. Day totals did not exceed 17 except on Mar. 31st 1990, when at least 131 passed through the county.

During the Atlas Survey, breeding was confirmed in three tetrads, with single broods seen at Winchester Sewage Farm in 1986 and Farlington Marshes in 1987 and 1988, and two broods at Needs Ore in 1988. Pairs were also recorded at Mockbeggar Lake and Titchfield Haven but with no evidence of breeding. The only other post-war records of young being raised were at Breamore in 1952, Needs Ore from 1966-69, Winnall Moors in 1974, Farlington Marshes in 1975 and 1978 and Winchester Sewage Farm in 1979.

National ringing data suggest that most wintering birds originate from Russia (Owen *et al* 1986). The only confirmation of this from Hampshire is of one ringed at Titchfield Haven on Jan. 4th 1984 and found dead at Arkhangelsk, 3133 km north-east, on May 15th 1984. Other recoveries involved one ringed in the Netherlands in August 1967 and found dead at Keyhaven, 464 km WSW, in January 1969, a female ringed at Fawley in October 1974 and shot at Charente Maritime, France, 613 km south, in December 1974, and one ringed at Titchfield Haven in January 1984 and found dead at Somme, France, 207 km south, in December 1986.

## Red-crested Pochard                                  *Netta rufina*

The first for the county was a drake at Dogmersfield Lake from Apr. 5th-13th 1965. Three were seen in 1968 and since 1971 there have been records in every year except 1973. The cumulative monthly totals for 1965-92, excluding long-staying, tame individuals strongly suspected as being escapes, are shown below.

| Jan | Feb | Mar | Apr | May | Jun | Jul | Aug | Sep | Oct | Nov | Dec |
|-----|-----|-----|-----|-----|-----|-----|-----|-----|-----|-----|-----|
| 18  | 9   | 11  | 9   | 3   | 2   | 2   | 7   | 9   | 7   | 7   | 5   |

In all, some 58 were recorded, including 17 at sites in the north-east, nine at Titchfield Haven, eight at Sinah Gravel Pit, seven at Blashford Lakes and Timsbury Gravel Pit and the remainder at eight other sites. All records involved one or two apart from three at Sinah on Oct. 12th 1974 and eight, including six drakes, on the sea off Hill Head in severe weather on Jan. 13th 1982. The latter flock may have been displaced from the Netherlands, where there is a small breeding population. However, the majority seen in Hampshire probably originate from feral populations such as those at Cotswold Water Park, Gloucestershire and St. James' Park, London, or from local wildfowl collections such as that at Paultons Park (Ower) where 50 were counted on Jan. 9th 1989.

## Pochard                                              *Aythya ferina*

A scarce breeder and moderately common winter visitor.

Pochards nest in dense, tall, emergent vegetation in the fringes of rivers and lakes. Breeding was first confirmed in 1935, when a pair nested in the Test valley near Romsey. In 1966, the population in the Test valley was well established, with 17 broods reported, and the species had also spread to the upper Itchen, where two pairs bred at Alresford Pond for the first time.

The Breeding Grebes and Wildfowl Survey in 1978 produced 56 pairs, of which 39 bred successfully, 27 in the Test valley, six at Alresford Pond, three at Fleet Pond, two at Warnford Park Lake and one at Winnall Moors. The total population was estimated at 70-80 pairs (Clark 1979).

The results of the Atlas Survey show a broadly similar distribution, although one pair bred successfully at Ellingham Lake in 1986, the first in the Avon valley. The total population does not appear to have increased since 1978; fewer

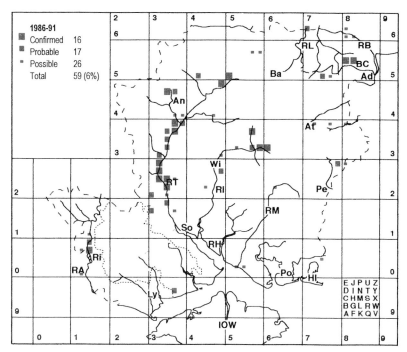

broads are now seen at Fleet Pond (max. 10 in 1980) and Alresford Pond (max. 9 in 1983), but quantitative data are lacking for the Test. The total population in 1991 was probably in the range 40-50 pairs, giving Hampshire over 10% of the British total, which was estimated at 400 pairs in 1988-91 (New Atlas).

| | 55-60 | 60-65 | 65-70 | 70-75 | 75-80 | 80-85 | 85-90 | Peak counts | |
|---|---|---|---|---|---|---|---|---|---|
| Sinah Gravel Pit | 50* | 79^ | 58^ | 64 | 55 | 156 | 150 | 205, | Jan. 1982 |
| IBM Lake/Paulsgrove Reclamation | - | - | - | - | 116 | 150 | 53 | 297, | Jan. 1985 |
| Fawley Reservoir | 36* | - | - | 102 | 175 | 127 | 113 | 260, | Jan. 1979 |
| Sowley Pond | 46* | 103^ | 188^ | 178^ | 81 | 54 | 78 | 350, | Dec. 1970 |
| Blashford Lakes | 155^ | 138^ | 91^ | 267 | 315 | 301 | 479 | 655, | Nov. 1988 |
| Broadlands Lake | - | - | - | - | 81 | 81 | 35 | 138, | Jan. 1979 |
| Timsbury Lake/Gravel Pit | - | 40^ | 74^ | 70 | 76 | 86 | 149 | 210, | Feb. 1987 |
| Allington Gravel Pit | - | - | - | 21^ | 43^ | 104 | 90 | 196, | Feb. 1985 |
| Alresford Pond | 21 | 26 | 38 | 41 | 75 | 64 | 56 | 129, | Feb. 1977 |
| Stratfield Saye | 12* | 29* | 36 | 21 | 55 | 81 | 61 | 126, | Jan. 1985 |
| Wellington Country Park | - | - | - | - | 104^ | 43 | 37 | 164, | Feb. 1979 |
| Dogmersfield Lake | - | - | - | 48^ | 45 | 67 | 56 | 173, | Dec. 1985 |
| Fleet Pond | 35^ | 58^ | 38^ | 71 | 94 | 96 | 95 | 198, | Dec. 1985 |
| Yateley/Eversley Gravel Pits | - | 45* | 74^ | 96 | 96 | 107 | 99 | 191, | Dec. 1985 |

*Table 18. Five year means of winter maxima and peak counts of Pochard, 1955/56-89/90.*

Winter visitors begin to arrive from mid-September onwards. In some years, passage is indicated by the appearance of sizeable flocks, often consisting largely of adult males, in early autumn, which then disperse, e.g. in 1992, a flock at Fleet Pond peaked at 210 on Oct. 11th but no more than 38 were seen in subsequent months. The main influx is usually in November; maximum counts at individual waters may occur at any time from then until February, but the departure is early and rapid, most having left by mid-March. As table 18 shows, numbers have increased considerably since the 1950s and 1960s. Although this is most likely to be connected with the large expansion in the area of gravel pits, the rise has also been recorded at other waters, such as Sinah Gravel Pit, Alresford and Fleet Ponds and Stratfield Saye. During the five winters from 1985/86-89/90, the proportion of the British wintering population in Hampshire (based on January counts) averaged 3.8%.

Most localities hold their highest numbers during severe weather. In such conditions, birds congregate in ice-free areas of still water, or move to rivers or the sea. Favoured haunts on rivers include the Avon between Sopley and Bisterne and Ibsley and Bickton, both of these stretches holding up to 200 in January 1979; the Test at Mottisfont, where the usual small flock swelled to 153 in January 1987; and on the Meon at Titchfield Haven, where up to 169 were present in January 1987. Records from saltwater include peaks of 257 at Eling on Feb. 18th 1963, 150 in Langstone Harbour entrance on Feb. 13th 1985, 100 in the Beaulieu Estuary on Feb. 27th 1985 and 150+ off Netley on Feb. 10th 1986. The only other sites to have held over 100 are Salterns Pond (Lymington), where birds regularly flighted in from the east at dusk during the early 1970s and reached a peak of 160 on Nov. 13th 1973; Rooksbury Mill (Andover), with 117 on Nov. 13th 1976; and Winchester Sewage Farm, where ice-free conditions attracted maxima of 142 in February 1985 and 118 in March 1986.

Small flocks are occasionally noted moving east through The Solent in spring, e.g. 11 at Hurst Beach on May 10th 1980, ten at Hill Head on May 10th 1981 and 12 there on Apr. 3rd 1985.

National ringing data indicate that most wintering Pochard originate from the Baltic countries and Russia (Owen *et al* 1986). Recoveries involving Hampshire birds include one ringed in Latvia in June 1976 and found dead at Leckford, 1734 km WSW, in January 1977, another ringed in Denmark in April 1984 and shot at Ringwood, 1091 km WSW, in January 1985 and a third trapped at Titchfield Haven in February 1986 and shot near Moscow, Russia, 2752 km east, in August 1988. Seven others were ringed at Abberton Reservoir, Essex, where there is a large post-breeding moult gathering, between May and September and shot in Hampshire in subsequent winters.

## Ring-necked Duck                                                   *Aythya collaris*

134

A rare visitor. Since the first was recorded in 1979, there have been records in 11 years, but probably only five individuals, all drakes, are involved.

1979:   adult, Blashford Lakes, Dec. 15th-Feb. 17th 1980, also seen at Sopley, Jan. 10th 1980;
1980:   adult, Blashford Lakes, Dec. 29th-Jan. 11th 1981;
1985:   adult, Spinnaker Lake (Blashford), Jan. 31st;
        first winter, Frimley, Ash Vale and Badshot Lea Gravel Pits, Fleet Pond and
        Dogmersfield Lake, Nov. 17th-Apr. 19th 1986;
1986:   adult, Frimley and Ash Vale Gravel Pits, Fleet Pond and Dogmersfield Lake, Sep. 9th-
        Apr. 25th 1987;
1987:   first winter, Mockbeggar Lake (Blashford), Nov. 16th and 17th, then moving to
        Timsbury Gravel Pit, where it remained until Mar. 20th 1988;
1988:   adult, Timsbury Gravel Pit, Nov. 25th-Apr. 26th 1989;
1989:   adult, Timsbury Gravel Pit, Dec. 16th-Jan. 28th 1990; also seen at Alresford Pond on
        Jan. 27th 1990;
1990:   adult, Timsbury Gravel Pit, Dec. 22nd-Mar. 7th 1991;
1991:   adult, Linbrook Lake (Blashford), Nov. 16th, then moving to Timsbury Gravel Pit,
        where it remained until Apr. 5th 1992;
1992:   adult, Timsbury Gravel Pit, Oct. 14th-Mar 14th 1993 and May 17th-June 17th 1993;
1993:   adult, Fleet Pond, May 18th and 19th.

The Ring-necked Duck breeds in North America and winters south to Costa Rica.

## Ferruginous Duck                                        *Aythya nyroca*

A rare winter visitor. The 11 records probably refer to only five individuals.

The first for the county was a drake at Frensham Great Pond from Dec. 29th 1960-Jan. 25th 1961. The next was a drake at Fawley Reservoir from Nov. 25th-Dec. 17th 1972. This may have been the bird seen in the following two winters at Allington Gravel Pits from Oct. 1st-Dec. 26th 1973 and again between Nov. 19th and Dec. 23rd 1974, and at Fawley Reservoir on Dec. 14th 1974. Another drake was seen on the River Test just above the M27 at Nursling on Mar. 5th 1979. An elusive female was present in the Eversley/Yateley Gravel Pit complex between Dec. 28th 1985 and Mar. 16th 1986, and what may have been the same bird was at Dogmersfield Lake on Sep. 16th 1986, Fleet Pond five days later and on Jan. 9th 1987. Finally, a drake was at Mockbeggar Lake from Dec. 13th-16th 1987 and on the River Avon at Sopley from Dec. 28th 1987-Feb. 6th 1988.

Several other claims of this species have not been included, either because they were believed to be escapes from captivity or the *HOSRP* felt that the possibility of *Aythya* hybrids had not been ruled out. Wild Ferruginous Ducks occurring in Britain probably originate from eastern Europe (Owen *et al* 1986).

## Tufted Duck                                             *Aythya fuligula*

A moderately common breeding species whose numbers increase considerably in winter.

The first breeding record of Tufted Ducks in Hampshire was at Northington Lake in 1890 (K & M). This was followed by a slow spread, with breeding recorded at several lakes and ponds in the north of the county up to 1960. Subsequently, the expansion of gravel extraction activities, particularly in the Avon and Blackwater valleys, provided much suitable habitat, and the breeding population increased substantially. In 1966, when no real search was made, 21 pairs were recorded. In 1976, a survey of the Itchen valley located 27 pairs, of which at least 15 bred successfully, and elsewhere a further 40 broods were recorded, including 23 at Eversley/Yateley Gravel Pits and 11 at Broadlands Lake, but coverage was far from complete.

During the Breeding Grebes and Wildfowl Survey in 1978, at least 243 pairs were found, of which 113 bred successfully. The main concentrations were in the Test valley (93), at Eversley/Yateley Gravel Pits (45), in the Itchen valley (23), in the Andover area (16) and at Blashford Lakes (10). Allowing for pairs missed, the total population was estimated at 300-350 pairs, plus 200 apparently non-breeding birds (Clark 1979).

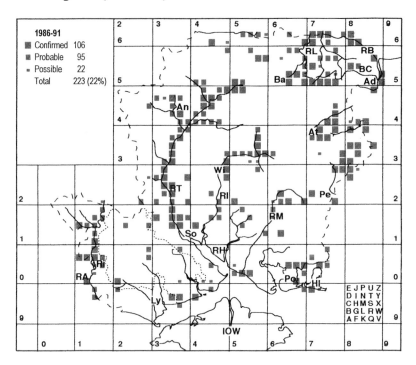

Since the 1978 survey, the Tufted Duck has continued to increase and spread to new sites. Records during the Atlas Survey indicate summering populations of at least 50 pairs at both Blashford Lakes and Eversley/Yateley Gravel Pits, and five to ten pairs at Needs Ore, Broadlands Estate, Timsbury, Longstock, the Overton area, Allington Gravel Pit, Winnall Moors and Stratfield Saye. Assuming an average of two pairs in each of the remaining tetrads where breeding was confirmed or probable, this gives a total population in the range 500-540 pairs. In 1988-91, the British breeding population was estimated at 7000 pairs (New Atlas).

Post-breeding gatherings may exceed 200 at Eversley/Yateley and Blashford, but counts at these sites often show a noticeable reduction before the main arrival of wintering birds from mid-October onwards. This suggests that some of our breeders winter elsewhere, although Owen et al (1986) stated that the

breeding population of southern England is largely resident. Unfortunately, very few, if any, Hampshire-bred Tufted Ducks have been ringed, so the location of their wintering grounds remains uncertain.

Winter flocks usually build up to a peak in January or February, although at some localities the maximum occurs in November, indicating passage. The highest ever count was of 705 at Blashford Lakes on Nov. 5th 1988, but a gradual reduction occurred thereafter. As table 19 shows, winter numbers have shown a steady rise since the 1950s. During the five winters from 1985/86-89/90, the proportion of the British wintering population in Hampshire (based on January counts) averaged 4.0%.

| | 55-60 | 60-65 | 65-70 | 70-75 | 75-80 | 80-85 | 85-90 | Peak counts | |
|---|---|---|---|---|---|---|---|---|---|
| Sinah Gravel Pit | - | 90* | 34* | 53 | 58 | 114 | 130 | 162, | Jan. 1986 |
| IBM Lake/Paulsgrove Reclamation | - | - | - | 0 | 26 | 95 | 82 | 221, | Jan. 1987 |
| Fawley Reservoir | 21* | - | - | 163 | 190 | 109 | 63 | 290, | Jan. 1979 |
| Blashford Lakes | 44^ | 41^ | - | 69 | 197 | 334 | 487 | 705, | Nov. 1988 |
| River Test: Broadlands | - | - | - | 10^ | 131 | 146 | 178 | 380, | Jan. 1987 |
| Timsbury Lake/Gravel Pit | - | 29^ | - | 40 | 74 | 124 | 230 | 275, | Dec. 1989 |
| River Test: Leckford/ Longstock | - | - | - | - | 75^ | 125 | 85 | 170, | Jan. 1982 |
| Allington Gravel Pit | - | - | - | 31^ | 37 | 70 | 91 | 100, | Jan. 1987 |
| Stratfield Saye | 21^ | 25* | 27^ | 18 | 58 | 88 | 96 | 125, | Feb. 1986 |
| Eversley/Yateley G Ps | 20* | 63* | 48^ | 161 | 232 | 241 | 281 | 352, | Feb. 1990 |

*Table 19. Five year means of winter maxima and peak counts of Tufted Ducks, 1955/56-89/90.*

The largest concentrations occur on still fresh water, although parties of up to 20 or more are scattered along the larger rivers, especially the Avon and Test. During severe weather, these are joined by others forced off frozen lakes and gravel pits. In addition to those in table 19, favoured stretches of river include the Avon between Ibsley and Bickton and the Test at Mottisfont, which held up to 150 in January 1985 and February 1986 respectively. Extreme cold spells may also induce movements to sheltered areas of the coast. In February 1963, numbers peaked at 428 at Eling, 300 off Hill Head and 127 in the Beaulieu Estuary. In January 1982, there were 180 in Langstone Harbour entrance and

102 off Netley, and in January 1985 counts peaked at 250 in Haslar Creek (Portsmouth Harbour), 110 in Langstone Harbour entrance and 79 off Hayling Oyster Beds. Most recently in January 1987, 155 were counted off Hill Head and 160 off Netley, but these records may have involved the same flock. The only other sites to have held more than 100 are Sowley Pond (106, February 1963), Highwood Reservoir (135, January 1987) and Winnall Moors (108, February 1990).

The departure of wintering birds is somewhat later than other wildfowl, with the majority leaving in March and early April. Spring passage is indicated by occasional April peaks at some waters and small movements east through The Solent, e.g. 14 off Hill Head on Apr. 23rd 1978.

National ringing data show that British wintering birds originate from a wide area between Iceland and central Russia. There have been two recoveries of foreign-ringed juveniles in Hampshire: one ringed at Lake Myvatn, Iceland in July 1949 was shot at Keyhaven, 1881 km SSE, on Oct. 29th 1949, and another, ringed in Estonia in June 1979, was shot at Nursling, 1829 km WSW, on Nov. 30th of that year. There have been 11 recoveries in Hampshire of birds ringed elsewhere in England; all involved movements of less than 250 km.

## Scaup                                                    *Aythya marila*

A scarce winter visitor and passage migrant.

Since 1950, the total recorded in mild winters has rarely exceeded 20, but considerable influxes have occurred in most prolonged spells of hard weather (fig. 21).

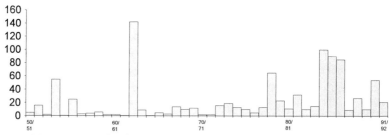

*Figure 21. Winter totals of Scaup, 1950/51-91/92.*

The first normally arrive in November or December, but there have been October records in six years. Earlier records include those of a female at Keyhaven from Aug. 17th-21st 1992, a drake at Mockbeggar Lake on Sep. 18th 1988 and a duck at Titchfield Haven from Sep. 30th-Oct. 19th 1990. The eastern harbours and Southampton Water have been the favoured localities. Flocks to exceed 20, all recorded in hard weather, include 38 in Dibden Bay on Feb. 6th 1954, 29 at Black Point on Jan. 26th 1963, up to 25 (including 10 adult drakes) in Portsmouth Harbour between January and March 1985, 38 (10 drakes) off Tanners Lane on Feb. 9th 1986, and up to 31 (10 drakes) in the Hythe/Dibden Bay/Marchwood area of Southampton Water in January and February 1987. 26 off Brownwich on Feb. 15th 1987 were probably part of this flock. Hard weather has also induced movements along the coast, e.g. 20 east off Gilkicker Point on Dec. 31st 1962, 46 west off Hurst Beach on Feb. 9th 1963 and 15 east there on Jan. 15th 1979.

The main departure is in March, but a few stragglers or passage migrants are seen in April and May. Noteworthy flocks seen at this time include 15 in Langstone Harbour on Apr. 15th 1952, 12 flying east off Hurst Beach on Apr. 20th 1963, 12 there on May 9th 1974 and 11 east off Sandy Point on Mar. 25th 1985. Late records include those of two in Langstone Harbour on May 19th 1977 and a drake at Ellingham Lake from Mar. 5th-May 18th 1978. There were two summer records, of a female at Fawley Reservoir on July 28th 1971 and a drake at Titchfield Haven on June 23rd 1979.

As well as the harbours and open sea, there have been regular records from freshwater pools close to the shore, especially at Sinah Gravel Pit, where there have been records in ten winters since 1972/73 with a maximum of nine on Mar. 3rd 1991. Further inland, 67 have been recorded, only six prior to 1971. Records came from Blashford Lakes and the River Avon (29 birds, including five at Harbridge on Feb. 16th 1974 and four at Sopley on Feb. 24th 1991), Timsbury Gravel Pit (10, including up to four in each of the winters 1987/88-90/91), Eversley/Yateley Gravel Pits and Highwood Reservoir (5 each), Dogmersfield Lake (4, including 3 from Nov. 6th-16th 1980) and nine other localities. Claims of Scaup inland, especially females, may refer to misidentified *Aythya* hybrids. However, the *HOSRP* has scrutinised such records carefully since the late 1970s and all those included for that period have been well described or seen by experienced observers.

The cumulative monthly totals of all records for 1950/51-91/92 are shown below.

|        | Sep | Oct | Nov | Dec | Jan | Feb | Mar | Apr | May | Jun | Jul |
|--------|-----|-----|-----|-----|-----|-----|-----|-----|-----|-----|-----|
| Coast  | 1   | 9   | 71  | 120 | 301 | 373 | 145 | 40  | 24  | 1   | 1   |
| Inland | 1   | 5   | 6   | 12  | 20  | 32  | 20  | 5   | 2   | 0   | 0   |

The Scaup has a circumpolar breeding distribution. Those wintering in Britain mostly originate from Iceland. However, the large influxes recorded in cold winters are probably of continental origin (Owen *et al* 1986).


# Eider                                    *Somateria mollissima*

A moderately common winter visitor and passage migrant along the coast; non-breeding birds summer in some years.

Until the mid-1950s, the Eider was very rarely recorded (K & M, Cohen). From that time, the species underwent a dramatic extension of its winter range, with greatly increased numbers occurring in eastern and southern England. This was attributed to the large increase in the breeding population on the Friesian Islands off the coast of the Netherlands (Taverner 1959, 1963). However, this has now declined and the main source of our wintering birds is thought to be the Baltic Sea (Owen *et al* 1986, Lack 1986).

The first double-figure counts were made in 1957/58, when 70 wintered, including a maximum of 35 in Chichester Harbour in January. Since then, the number recorded each winter has fluctuated greatly (fig. 22), often being swelled by flocks moving through the county in autumn or spring.

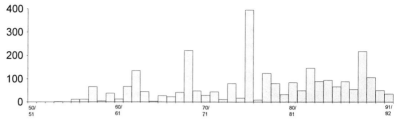

*Figure 22. Winter totals of Eiders, 1950/51-91/92.*

Wintering birds normally arrive from early October onwards, although in 1979 up to 14 were off Pennington Marsh from Aug. 18th-Sep. 15th. Passage through the county has been demonstrated by three large movements observed from Hurst Beach: 61 west in two flocks on Oct. 22nd 1975, a single flock of 130 west on Nov. 10th 1975 and 97, including six adult males, there on Dec. 4th 1982. Small westerly movements of up to ten have also been noted on four other occasions on dates between Oct. 10th and Nov. 3rd.

In the 1980s, the favoured wintering area was between Chichester Harbour and Hayling Bay, where the maximum exceeded 20 in six seasons, with peaks of 54 in March 1985, 55 in January 1987 and 146 in March 1989. Prior to this, similar numbers occurred at Hurst Beach (71 in February 1963), Hill Head (130 in February 1968; 79 in February 1976) and Pitts Deep (41 in March 1976), but in recent years, winter flocks at these sites have rarely reached double figures.

Return passage is indicated in late March, April and the first half of May by increases in wintering flocks and eastward movement along the coast. 37 off Hurst Beach on Apr. 26th 1975 were clearly migrants as no more than six had been seen there during the previous winter. Hayling Bay is another favoured area for spring flocks, and although most seen there may be lingering wintering birds, increases do occur, e.g. in 1989 a flock of 42 on Apr. 15th grew to 101, including 32 drakes, by Apr. 22nd. Easterly movements along the coast are small. Between 1971 and 1992, there were records in 18 years totalling 275 birds. The maximum day total was of 43 off Hurst Beach on Apr. 18th 1978, but no other counts exceeded 14.

The first summer record was of a female off Hill Head on July 6th and 7th 1958. Ten were seen between June and August 1962, and three in summer 1963. Since 1971, non-breeding birds have summered in 12 years. In most years, fewer than ten were recorded, but between May and September 1976, there were up to 23 off Pennington Marsh, 13 between Sowley and Pylewell and six at Needs Ore. The best year was 1989, when up to 32 were off Pennington Marsh and 70 in Chichester Harbour. These flocks may stay until the following winter or disperse in the autumn. 55 were still at Chichester Harbour in October 1989 but only three remained there in December.

The only inland record was of a drake in partial eclipse plumage at Frensham Great Pond on June 10th 1965.

The cumulative monthly totals of all records for 1950/51-91/92 are shown below.

| Sep | Oct | Nov | Dec | Jan | Feb | Mar | Apr | May | Jun | Jul | Aug |
|-----|-----|-----|-----|-----|-----|-----|-----|-----|-----|-----|-----|
| 189 | 352 | 647 | 891 | 984 | 825 | 638 | 766 | 234 | 120 | 187 | 177 |

# Long-tailed Duck                            *Clangula hyemalis*

A scarce winter visitor and passage migrant along the coast; rare inland.

K & M described the Long-tailed Duck as "a rare winter visitor" and Cohen listed only one record for the first half of this century. Systematic watching since the early 1950s has produced records in every winter but three. Numbers have been variable; the largest influxes so far were in 1988/89 and 1991/92, both mild seasons (fig. 23). Less than 20% have been adult drakes.

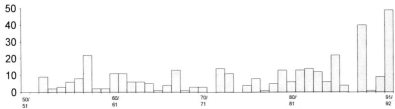

*Figure 23. Winter totals of Long-tailed Ducks, 1950/51-91/92.*

The first usually arrive in late October or November; earlier records include those of one flying east off Hurst Beach on Sep. 23rd 1961 and four off Brownwich on Oct. 14th 1973.

The favoured areas for wintering birds are Chichester and Langstone Harbours and between Lymington and Hurst, although there are several records of individuals staying for several weeks on lakes and small pools adjacent to the coast. Sightings usually involve up to four birds, but six were in Langstone Harbour in December 1972 and January 1973, five were there in February 1986 and five were off Hill Head on Dec. 23rd 1981. During the 1988/89 winter, a flock in Chichester Harbour peaked at 15 (including eight drakes) in early February, five were in the Lymington/Hurst area and up to four were between Eling and Bury Marshes and in Langstone Harbour. A larger influx in 1991/92 showed a similar pattern, with peaks of 20 (including seven drakes) in Chichester Harbour on Feb. 6th, 15 between Lymington and Hurst on Feb. 22nd, and five in Langstone Harbour and the Beaulieu Estuary. Most wintering birds leave by mid-April.

In April and early May, birds are occasionally recorded moving east along the coast. Most records have been of one or two, but five flew east off Sandy Point on Apr. 15th 1989. The latest record is of two flying east off Sandy Point on May 23rd 1987, although one summered in Langstone Harbour in 1988, being present from May 25th-Nov. 27th.

Long-tailed Ducks are rare inland. Since 1961, there have been records of 19 birds in ten different winters. Sightings were made at Blashford Lakes and the nearby River Avon (9), Frensham Great Pond (4), Broadlands Lake (2), Charlton Gravel Pit, Cranmer Lake, Dogmersfield Lake, Southampton Common and Timsbury (1 each). Usually single birds were involved, but there were two at Frensham Great Pond from Oct. 28th-Nov. 20th 1967, these being joined by a third from Nov. 2nd-5th, and two at Blashford Lakes from Nov. 29th-Dec. 5th 1981. Several remained for weeks or even months, e.g. at Broadlands Lake and Timsbury Gravel Pit from Dec. 11th 1976-May 22nd 1977 and at Blashford Lakes from Dec. 24th 1991-May 3rd 1992. Most of those present for one or two days only occurred in November, suggesting passage. Additionally, a female was at Eversley Gravel Pit from July 21st-28th 1992.

The cumulative monthly totals of all records for 1950/51-91/92 are shown below.

|        | Sep | Oct | Nov | Dec | Jan | Feb | Mar | Apr | May | Jun | Jul | Aug |
|--------|-----|-----|-----|-----|-----|-----|-----|-----|-----|-----|-----|-----|
| Coast  | 2   | 29  | 113 | 155 | 135 | 130 | 93  | 78  | 23  | 1   | 1   | 1   |
| Inland | 0   | 2   | 13  | 8   | 4   | 3   | 3   | 3   | 3   | 0   | 1   | 0   |

Long-tailed Ducks wintering in Britain are believed to originate from Fenno-Scandia and Russia (Owen *et al* 1986).

## Common Scoter                                    *Melanitta nigra*

A moderately common spring passage migrant; scarce at other times of the year.

By far the largest numbers of Common Scoters occur on spring passage between late March and mid-May, the heaviest movements occurring on days with strong south-easterly or southerly winds. Flocks are regularly present off Hurst Beach during this period, with counts exceeding 100 in 19 years between 1966 and 1992. The largest gatherings recorded were of 400 on Apr. 4th 1987 and 600 on Apr. 10th 1991, while over 300 were present in five other years on dates between Mar. 27th and Apr. 18th. Sea-watching has shown that some of these do not move east through Hurst Narrows into The Solent, but return out to sea and continue their migration past St. Catherine's Point, on the southern side of the Isle of Wight. Between 1966 and 1992, the total recorded moving into The Solent exceeded 200 in only six years. The heaviest passage was in 1966, when 2229 were observed moving through the west Solent, including 1380 east at Hurst Beach on Apr. 5th and 765 off Needs Ore on Apr. 9th. Since then, high totals have been recorded in 1971, with 667 east including 267 on Apr. 22nd, and 1979, with 653 east including 279 on Apr. 10th. Since regular sea-watching began at Hayling Bay in 1983, this area has produced the heaviest movements, which probably include some of those taking the route to the south of Wight. In 1984, 563 moved east there, with peaks of 84 on May 16th and 71 on the late date of June 3rd. In 1987, 649 were logged at Hayling Bay on Apr. 4th. On that day, 400 were off Hurst but none was seen in The Solent. However, 1746 moved east at St. Catherine's Point.

At other times of the year, Common Scoters are somewhat irregular in their appearance. Most records involve small groups, but flocks of 50 or more are occasionally noted, usually in the west Solent area. The only recent evidence of summering was in 1991, when up to 100 were off Hurst Castle in June and July, and in 1992, when an unprecedented gathering of 1000 was present in early June and 200 were still there on July 3rd. From July-October, westerly movements predominate, e.g. 72 at Pennington Marsh on July 11th 1981, 60 at Hurst on Sep. 16th 1984 and 70 at Pennington Marsh on Aug. 3rd 1989. Movements to the east are also occasionally recorded at this time, the largest being of 133 at Hurst and Keyhaven on Sep. 14th 1986.

In mid-winter, small parties of up to ten are occasionally noted, but only during the 1988/89 winter did a sizeable flock become established, with 65 off Hurst Beach on Nov. 27th, rising to 95 on Dec. 21st and 100 on Jan. 21st. The only other comparable gatherings were of 300 in Hayling Bay in severe weather on Jan. 27th 1963, 120 off Hill Head on Jan. 8th 1966 and 150 flying east off Southsea three days later.

Common Scoters are recorded inland almost annually, most occurring at localities in the north-east. Between 1955 and 1992, there have been 29 records from Frensham Great Pond involving 56 birds, including eight on Nov. 18th 1959, five on Aug. 4th 1963, four on Apr. 6th 1971 and six on Apr. 5th 1981. Others were seen at Fleet Pond and Eversley Gravel Pit (8 birds), Heath Pond (5), Ivy Lake, Rooksbury Mill and Wellington Country Park (2 each), and Bramshill Gravel Pit, Kingsley Sand Pit, Timsbury Gravel Pit, Tundry Pond and Winnall Moors (1 each). All were present on one day only apart from three single birds which stayed for up to nine days. The cumulative monthly totals of all inland records are shown below.

| Jan | Feb | Mar | Apr | May | Jun | Jul | Aug | Sep | Oct | Nov | Dec |
|-----|-----|-----|-----|-----|-----|-----|-----|-----|-----|-----|-----|
| 3 | 1 | 6 | 34 | 5 | 2 | 6 | 11 | 1 | 9 | 12 | 0 |

The above analysis does not include the record of 50 flying south-east over Lee in the lower Test valley on Apr. 14th 1959.

Most of the Common Scoters occurring in Hampshire probably originate from the Fenno-Scandian and Russian breeding populations. The winter range includes the Atlantic seaboard of France, Iberia and north-west Africa.

## Surf Scoter                                         *Melanitta perspicillata*

One record. A drake flew east past Hurst Beach with a small flock of Common Scoters on May 15th 1976.

The Surf Scoters breeds in arctic Alaska and Canada and winters along the Pacific and Atlantic coasts of North America.

## Velvet Scoter                                          *Melanitta fusca*

A scarce passage migrant and winter visitor along the coast; rare inland.

K & M and Cohen listed very few records for the 19th and first half of the 20th centuries. Improved coverage from the mid-1950s onwards has produced records for every winter but two (fig. 24). The apparent upsurge in the 1970s and 1980s was due to increased spring sea-watching activity.

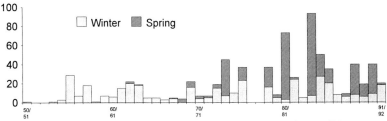

*Figure 24. Winter and spring totals of Velvet Scoters, 1950/51-91/92.*

The first Velvet Scoters are normally seen in late October or November, although the earliest ever were five flying east with Common Scoters off Hurst Beach on Sep. 29th 1991. Many late autumn records refer to passage flocks moving west or staying briefly before moving on, e.g. 18 at Pennington sewage outfall on Nov. 22nd 1975 and 14 which moved off west from Hill Head on Oct. 28th 1985.

Between mid-December and late March few are seen, although birds sometimes remain in favoured areas, e.g. between Hill Head and Woolston, for several weeks. Hard weather may produce greater numbers, but there is only one record of more than eight together: a flock of 21 flying east off Hill Head in freezing conditions on Jan. 29th 1956.

Prior to 1968, only three were recorded in April and May, but since then there have been records for this period in every year but five (fig. 24), with totals exceeding 30 in 1974 (38), 1981 (70), 1984 (86), 1989 (32) and 1991 (31). Most sightings involved small parties moving east along the coast, but some flocks stayed for a day or two, especially off Hurst Beach. The largest groups seen were of 30 flying east off Hurst on Apr. 12th 1974, 19 flying east at Hurst and Hill Head on Apr. 10th 1981, 20 off Hill Head on Apr. 25th 1981, 35 moving east off Sandy Point and 20 at Hurst on May 1st 1984, and 27 off Hurst on Apr. 10th 1991. Few are seen after the second week of May; the latest have been two flying east off Sandy Point on May 23rd 1984 and two flying east off Hill Head on June 6th 1985.

There have been five inland records: single birds at Frensham Great Pond from Nov. 4th-24th 1956 and on Mar. 26th 1961 and Mar. 8th 1989, two at Heath Pond on Jan. 18th 1961, one of which remained until Apr. 16th 1961, and one at Spinnaker Lake on Mar. 9th 1985.

The cumulative monthly totals for 1950/51-91/92, which clearly show the autumn and spring passage peaks, are shown below.

| Sep | Oct | Nov | Dec | Jan | Feb | Mar | Apr | May | Jun |
|-----|-----|-----|-----|-----|-----|-----|-----|-----|-----|
| 5 | 41 | 117 | 85 | 111 | 49 | 34 | 232 | 154 | 2 |

The Velvet Scoters occurring in Britain originate from Fenno-Scandia and western Siberia. Those migrating through Hampshire in spring and autumn may form part of the wintering population off north-western France and northern Iberia.

# Goldeneye                                      *Bucephala clangula*

A moderately common winter visitor; rare in summer.

The largest concentrations of Goldeneyes occur in the eastern harbours, Southampton Water, the Lymington/Hurst area and at Blashford Lakes in the Avon valley (table 20). The first are normally seen in the second half of October, but the main arrival is from mid-November onwards. Peak counts may be made at any time between mid-December and early March.

| | 55-60 | 60-65 | 65-70 | 70-75 | 75-80 | 80-85 | 85-90 | Peak counts | |
|---|---|---|---|---|---|---|---|---|---|
| Chichester Harbour | - | - | 83 | 122 | 77 | 75 | 54 | 225, | Jan. 1971 |
| East Hayling | - | - | - | - | 40 | 35 | 20 | 103, | Dec. 1975 |
| Langstone Harbour | 61 | 55 | 85 | 106 | 89 | 62 | 71 | 153, | Jan. 1970 |
| Portsmouth Harbour | - | - | 90^ | 59 | 47 | 62 | 45 | 130, | Dec. 1970 |
| Southampton Water | 30 | 24^ | 44 | 32^ | 27 | 50 | 55 | 120, | Feb. 1987 |
| Lymington/Hurst | - | - | - | 9 | 23 | 16 | 14 | 40, | Feb. 1980 |
| Blashford Lakes | - | - | - | 6^ | 22 | 39 | 33 | 64, | Mar. 1987 |

*Table 20. Five year means of winter maxima and peak counts of Goldeneyes, 1955/56-89/90.*

The data suggest that there has been a decline in the eastern harbours since the early 1970s; this is in contrast to Southampton Water and Blashford Lakes, where an increase occurred during the 1980s. This can be explained by a combination of influxes during the severe winters in that decade (which were not recorded in the eastern harbours), improved observer coverage and the continuing expansion of gravel extraction activities at Blashford. The Avon valley birds feed on the river during the day and usually return to the lakes to roost at dusk, which is when the highest counts have been made.

Small parties occur elsewhere along the coast. Most records have been of fewer than five, but in the Beaulieu Estuary there were 28 in severe weather on Feb. 20th 1963 and 21 on Mar. 17th 1969.

Away from the Avon valley, there have been records from 37 inland localities. In the north-east, small numbers have regularly wintered at Frensham Great Pond since the 1950s or earlier, and at Eversley/Yateley Gravel Pits since the early 1980s. At Fleet Pond, sightings are almost annual though principally in autumn. The cumulative monthly totals for 1970/71-91/92 at the three main sites and other inland waters are shown below.

| | Oct | Nov | Dec | Jan | Feb | Mar | Apr | May |
|---|---|---|---|---|---|---|---|---|
| Eversley/Yateley Gravel Pits | 0 | 18 | 14 | 17 | 13 | 14 | 7 | 0 |
| Frensham Great Pond | 11 | 35 | 39 | 50 | 51 | 49 | 18 | 1 |
| Fleet Pond | 10 | 15 | 10 | 9 | 2 | 2 | 3 | 0 |
| Other north-east sites | 4 | 7 | 8 | 8 | 21 | 3 | 1 | 0 |
| Elsewhere inland | 5 | 23 | 24 | 33 | 35 | 14 | 2 | 0 |

The highest counts during the period analysed were of seven at Frensham Great Pond on Jan. 6th 1974 and Jan. 9th 1983, five there on Oct. 14th 1973 and Oct. 29th 1980 and five at Eversley/Yateley Gravel Pits from Dec. 27th 1985-Jan. 7th 1986 and on Nov. 25th 1989. The only other sites where the total recorded exceeded ten were Broadlands Lake (25) and Timsbury (11). Few were recorded inland in earlier years except at Frensham, where the largest flock was of 16 on Nov. 14th 1952.

Most have left the county by mid-April, but between 1963 and 1992 there were summer records in 17 years involving 30 birds. The cumulative monthly totals are shown below.

| May | Jun | Jul | Aug | Sep |
|---|---|---|---|---|
| 13 | 12 | 7 | 11 | 4 |

Of these, 12 were at the coast, six in the Avon valley, five at Frensham Great Pond, four in the Test valley and one at Alresford Pond. Only two remained throughout the summer – in Langstone Harbour in 1970 and at Mockbeggar Lake in 1984. All records were of one or two birds, apart from an immature drake and two brownheads at Frensham Great Pond on Aug. 25th 1964 which were joined by another brownhead two days later.

Few adult drakes are recorded. Of 203 counts in Langstone Harbour totalling 6400 birds, 721 (11.3%) were adult drakes. At Blashford Lakes, of 460 recorded between 1975 and 1990, 81 (17.6%) were adult drakes.

National ringing data show that most Goldeneyes wintering in Britain originate from Scandinavia (Owen *et al* 1986).

# Smew                                    *Mergus albellus*

A very scarce winter visitor, not recorded annually.

The largest numbers of Smew occur during severe winters. At the onset of harsh conditions, a sudden influx may occur, with ones, twos and small parties occurring on unfrozen lakes and gravel pits, rivers and in sheltered estuaries and harbours. Especially at the start of an influx, many records refer to birds staying for only a few hours or flying over. However, once settled, they may remain in the same general area for several weeks until a thaw takes place. The return of mild weather usually results in their disappearance, equally as rapidly as their arrival. Fig. 25 shows the approximate totals recorded in each winter since 1950/51.

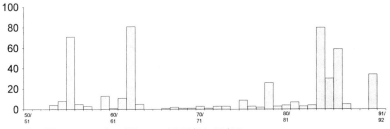

*Figure 25. Winter totals of Smew, 1950/51-91/92.*

The true numbers present during the severe spells in early 1956 and 1963 were almost certainly greater than shown, as coverage, especially of inland localities, was considerably less thorough than today. The former year produced the largest gathering yet seen in the county, at Titchfield Haven, which peaked at 34, including nine drakes, on Feb. 24th. In 1963, the highest counts were of eight flying east off Hurst Beach on Jan. 6th, up to ten at Titchfield Haven from Jan. 14th-Mar. 16th, up to ten at Eling from Jan. 19th-Mar. 2nd and up to seven at Needs Ore and Sowley Pond from Jan. 19th-Mar. 9th.

Since then, there have been notable influxes in five winters. Records from the most frequently used sites are summarised in table 21.

| | 78/79 | 84/85 | 85/86 | 86/87 | 90/91 | No. of winters with records, 1963/64-91/92 |
|---|---|---|---|---|---|---|
| Langstone Harbour/Sinah Gravel Pit | 0 | 1 | 2 | 1 | 1 | 6 |
| IBM Lake/Paulsgrove Reclamation | 0 | 5 | 2 | 5 | 6 | 10 |
| Titchfield Haven | 2 | 6 | 2 | 3 | 0 | 4 |
| Eling/Broadlands Lake | 5 | 6 | 6 | 4 | 8 | 8 |
| Sowley Pond/Needs Ore | 2 | 3 | 3 | 5 | 0 | 10 |
| Lymington/Hurst | 0 | 5 | 1 | 6 | 0 | 6 |
| Blashford Lakes | 3 | 10 | 8 | 6 | 5 | 12 |
| Allington Gravel Pit/Highwood Reservoir | 5 | 6 | 1 | 0 | 7 | 7 |
| Eversley/Yateley Gravel Pits | 1 | 1 | 1 | 2 | 7 | 7 |

*Table 21. Minimum totals of Smew recorded at various localities in five winters between 1978/79 and 1990/91.*

The only other places where counts exceeded four were Avon Castle (5, Jan. 26th 1985), Timsbury (6, Mar. 2nd 1986; probably from Eling) and Sopley (7, Jan. 15th 1987).

The earliest recorded were two at Paulsgrove Reclamation on Nov. 8th 1982. One or two Smews were present at this site or nearby IBM Lake in November in five consecutive years from 1981-85 and subsequently wintered; it seems likely that the same individuals were involved each year. Elsewhere, few have been seen before late December, and the largest numbers are present between mid-January and late February. Departure is usually complete by mid-March; there have been no records later than Mar. 21st apart from those of single redheads at Alresford Pond on Apr. 10th 1963 and flying east with Common Scoters off Hurst Beach on Apr. 8th 1979. The cumulative monthly totals of all records for 1950/51-91/92 are shown below.

| Nov | Dec | Jan | Feb | Mar | Apr |
|-----|-----|-----|-----|-----|-----|
| 11  | 33  | 224 | 271 | 72  | 2   |

Of some 491 Smew recorded in the period analysed above, 97 (19.7%) were adult drakes. The proportion of drakes was considerably higher in the seven winters with major influxes (23.1%) than in the other seasons (8.2%).

The Smew breeds from Fenno-Scandia to central Siberia. Birds from north-west Europe winter in the Baltic and North Sea, particularly in the Ijsselmeer in the Netherlands. This is the source of hard weather influxes into Britain.

# Red-breasted Merganser                    *Mergus serrator*

A moderately common winter visitor and passage migrant along the coast; rare inland.

The numbers of Red-breasted Mergansers wintering in the county increased considerably during the 1980s; this reflects the national trend and is probably connected with the expansion of the British breeding population. However, the limited national ringing data suggest that Scandinavian birds also occur (Owen *et al* 1986). The species is most numerous in Langstone Harbour but counts have also reached 50 in four other areas (table 22). During the five winters from 1985/86-89/90, the proportion of the British wintering population in Hampshire (based on January counts) averaged 9.9%.

Smaller parties also occur along other stretches of The Solent coast, but these only occasionally reach double figures. Larger gatherings include 55 at Needs Ore during severe weather on Mar. 2nd 1963, 24 off Sowley Shore on Feb. 28th 1981 and 35 off Lee-on-the-Solent on Feb. 3rd 1985.

| | 55-60 | 60-65 | 65-70 | 70-75 | 75-80 | 80-85 | 85-90 | Peak counts |
|---|---|---|---|---|---|---|---|---|
| Chichester Harbour | - | - | 30 | 49 | 47 | 73 | 95 | 126, Dec. 1986 |
| East Hayling | - | - | - | 54^ | 35 | 41 | 44 | 81, Nov. 1988 |
| Langstone Harbour | 27 | 42 | 49 | 53 | 88 | 164 | 203 | 334, Mar. 1989 |
| Portsmouth Harbour | - | - | - | 22^ | 46 | 60 | 94 | 142, Jan. 1990 |
| Hill Head area | 18^ | 24^ | - | 4^ | 10 | 15 | 24 | 37, Jan. 1987 |
| Southampton Water | - | - | - | 1^ | 7 | 25 | 49 | 68, Jan. 1988 |
| Lymington/Hurst | 30^ | 16^ | 20^ | 32 | 31 | 29 | 36 | 50, Nov. 1975 |

*Table 22. Five year means of winter maxima and peak counts of Red-breasted Mergansers, 1955/56-89/90.*

The main arrival of wintering birds normally starts in late October. However, in some years a few are seen in late September, while in 1986, 74 were in Langstone Harbour by Oct. 19th. Westerly movements may be recorded at this time, e.g. 37 off Keyhaven on Oct. 26th 1980. The pattern at the main wintering sites varies; in some seasons, peaks occur in November or March/April (suggesting passage), while in others the maximum count is made in mid-winter. At Langstone Harbour, the highest autumn and spring counts have been of 231 on Nov. 19th 1981 and 334 on Mar. 11th 1989, while the peak mid-winter count was of 214 on Dec. 19th 1987. Most of the high counts there were made on ebbing tides at dusk, when the birds left the harbour to roost on the sea, or at dawn, when they returned.

Visible migration eastwards along The Solent is recorded between mid-March and mid-May, with most sightings in late April. The numbers recorded are usually small; from 1971-92 they averaged 44 per year; the only totals to reach three figures were of 109 in 1971 and 140 in 1974. Day totals rarely exceed 20; higher counts (all recorded at Hurst Beach) include 71 on Apr. 13th 1971, 42 on Apr. 12th 1974 and 45+ on Apr. 4th 1987.

Most have left by mid-May but one or two are seen from June-August in most years. Between 1971 and 1992, there were records for 16 years, most frequently from Langstone Harbour (nine years) and the Lymington/Hurst area (nine years), and once only at Eling Great Marsh, Needs Ore, Portsmouth Harbour and Titchfield Haven.

The species is rare inland. Between 1954 and 1992, there were records in 16 years involving 48 birds, 12 of them adult drakes. Most were during cold spells but some coincided with passage movements at the coast. Records came from Frensham Great Pond (17 birds), Eversley/Yateley Gravel Pits (10), Blashford Lakes (9), Alresford Pond (5), Wellington Country Park and Winnall Moors (3 each) and Bishopstoke (1). Those to involve more than two birds were of four at Frensham Great Pond on Apr. 27th 1954, three at Blashford Lakes on Mar. 26th 1971, seven at Frensham Great Pond on Feb. 15th and 16th 1979 and seven at Eversley Gravel Pit on Dec. 1st 1991. Most were seen on one date only; the longest stay was of eight days. The cumulative monthly totals of all inland records are shown below.

| Oct | Nov | Dec | Jan | Feb | Mar | Apr |
|---|---|---|---|---|---|---|
| 2 | 3 | 17 | 2 | 15 | 4 | 5 |

# Goosander                                    *Mergus merganser*

A scarce and erratic winter visitor, most numerous in hard weather. Since the late 1970s, a wintering flock has become established in the north-east.

In the first half of the century, when observer coverage was poor, Goosanders were infrequently seen. However, there are two records of note for the period: 13 at Frensham Great Pond on Mar. 13th 1920 and the same number at Fleet Pond on Mar. 1st 1936.

In the 1950s and 1960s, they remained very scarce except during the severe weather of early 1963, when possibly as many as 190 were present (fig. 26). A flock on the River Avon at Woodgreen between Jan. 7th and Mar. 10th peaked at 100 on Feb. 26th. Sightings elsewhere in that year included 11 flying east at Gilkicker Point on Jan. 2nd, 20 in Langstone Harbour on Jan. 22nd and 16 at Eling on Feb. 24th. The only other double-figure count during this period was of 13 at Frensham Great Pond on Dec. 29th 1968.

Improved coverage in the north-east during the early 1970s produced occasional sightings of Goosanders, but usually they only stayed for a few hours. The winter of 1977/78 produced the first long-staying birds, with up to five at Tundry Pond and three at Wellington Country Park and nearby Stratfield Saye. At least 26 were present during the severe weather of early 1979, with maxima in the range 15-18 recorded at Stratfield Saye, Wellington Country Park, Eversley Gravel Pit and Fleet Pond. In subsequent winters, it emerged that a flock was based at Wellington, returning there to roost at night but radiating out to nearby rivers, lakes and gravel pits during the day. When still water was frozen, the roost transferred to the River Loddon at Stratfield Saye. The highest numbers occurred in cold winters, usually reaching a peak immediately after the thaw; the maximum so far recorded was on Feb. 1st 1985, when 42, including 16 adult drakes, roosted at Wellington and a pair at Eversley. Since the 1988/89 winter, Eversley Gravel Pit has been increasingly used as the main roost site and now very few are recorded at Wellington.

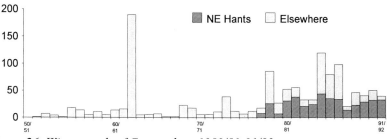

*Figure 26. Winter totals of Goosanders, 1950/51-91/92.*

Elsewhere in the county, numbers have continued at a low level except during occasional influxes, which have usually been associated with severe weather. At these times, many of the high numbers recorded have involved birds in flight, e.g. 25 over Calshot Spit and 16 over Goodworth Clatford on Jan. 4th 1979, 16 moving east over Bishopstoke on Jan. 20th 1979 and 15 moving west along Portsdown Hill on Jan. 16th 1985. Flocks have appeared reluctant to settle for long in one area, although single birds especially have sometimes stayed for several weeks or months and evidently returned in subsequent years. Since 1988/89, one or two have wintered at Langstone Harbour and up to five in the Allington Gravel Pit/Highbridge area. Records from the most frequently used sites are summarised in table 23.

| | No. of years with records | No. of years with birds present for more than 1 week | Maximum counts |
|---|---|---|---|
| Allington Gravel Pit/Highwood Reservoir | 10 | 4 | 11, Dec. 18th 1983 |
| Alresford Pond/Ladywell Lake | 6 | 1 | 17, Jan. 20th 1985 |
| Blashford Lakes | 10 | 4 | 15, Feb. 24th 1985 |
| Broadlands Lake/Eling | 10 | 2 | 23, Jan. 10th 1979 |
| Langstone Harbour/Sinah Gravel Pit | 10 | 3 | 6, Jan. 26th 1990 |
| Lymington/Hurst | 12 | 3 | 7, Jan. 17th 1987 |
| Sowley Pond | 8 | 5 | 14, Dec. 27th 1973 |
| Titchfield Haven | 12 | 3 | 8, Jan. 17th 1985 |

*Table 23. Summary of Goosander records at selected sites, 1969/70-91/92.*

The first Goosanders usually arrive in early or mid-November. However, there have been seven October records and two for September, while the earliest ever was a redhead in Langstone Harbour on Aug. 11th 1963. The highest numbers are present in January and February, although in December 1988, 44 were recorded. Most leave by mid-March although stragglers remain into April in most years, e.g. one at Keyhaven until Apr. 30th 1978. The latest ever were two flying east off Gilkicker Point on May 1st 1965.

Females and immatures predominate in most flocks. During the 1985 influx, of 108 which were sexed, 26 (24.1%) were adult drakes. In the north-east, these form a larger proportion of flocks and in two years predominated. Between 1980 and 1991, a total of 324 was recorded in the Wellington/Eversley area of which 117 (36.1%) were adult drakes.

Although the breeding population of the Goosander in Britain is increasing. those wintering in southern England probably originate from northern Scandinavia, the Baltic States and Russia (BWP).

# Ruddy Duck                              *Oxyura jamaicensis*

A scarce resident and winter visitor.

Following the escape of about 70 juvenile Ruddy Ducks from the Wildfowl and Wetlands Trust at Slimbridge between 1956 and 1963, a feral population became established, centred in Avon and the West Midlands (Kear 1990). The first to be seen in Hampshire was a female at Fleet Pond from Dec. 20th-27th 1971. There were no further sightings until 1977, since when there have been annual records.

A pair almost certainly bred at Fleet Pond in 1977, and in the following year a pair hatched six young there, of which one was raised successfully. Breeding was next recorded in 1983, when a pair raised two young at Timsbury Lake and another probably attempted breeding at Fleet Pond. In 1984, a pair was again successful at Timsbury Lake, raising one young.

Since 1985, breeding has occurred annually at Blashford Lakes, where a maximum of four pairs bred in 1989, raising 14 young. Ruddy Ducks are normally present throughout the year in this area, with the highest numbers in autumn, followed by a mid-winter decline, especially when the lakes freeze over, and a return from April onwards. The highest count so far recorded was of 28, including nine drakes, on Nov. 16th 1991.

During the Atlas Survey, breeding was also confirmed at Frensham Great Pond in 1987 (and suspected in other years), while at Timsbury Lake, displaying males were seen on several occasions but the only record of a pair was on May 7th 1989. In 1992, a pair bred at Casbrook Common.

Away from breeding sites, the species is most frequent in winter, particularly in severe weather, when it is known to disperse from the main population centres in Avon and the West Midlands (Owen *et al* 1986). The highest counts have been of 12 at Titchfield Haven from Jan. 17th-19th 1982, nine on the sea at Weston Shore on Jan. 15th 1982, seven at Yateley Gravel Pit on Dec. 17th and 18th 1982 and seven on the sea off Hill Head on Feb. 7th 1986. At other times of the year, records are widely scattered and normally involve fairly short stays. The cumulative monthly totals of all records (away from breeding sites) for 1977-92 are shown below.

| Jul | Aug | Sep | Oct | Nov | Dec | Jan | Feb | Mar | Apr | May | Jun |
|-----|-----|-----|-----|-----|-----|-----|-----|-----|-----|-----|-----|
| 6   | 6   | 3   | 15  | 25  | 37  | 60  | 26  | 11  | 12  | 3   | 5   |

# Honey Buzzard *Pernis apivorus*

A very scarce summer visitor and passage migrant.

The first reference to Honey Buzzards in Hampshire is Gilbert White's account of birds at Selborne in the 1780s. In 1780, the only egg was taken from the nest and the female shot, but in 1787 they apparently bred successfully.

Wise (1862) and K & M described the history of the species in the New Forest; unfortunately it is largely an unsavoury narrative of habitual persecution by egg and skin collectors. Between 1856 and 1872, 24 nests were recorded, of which at least 20 were plundered of eggs or young and the adults killed. By the time that Gerald Lascelles was appointed Deputy Surveyor of the New Forest in 1880, the Honey Buzzard had apparently become an infrequent breeder. Apart from references to breeding in 1887 and 1894 and the procurement of a freshly-killed specimen in the summer of 1903, there appears to be no other published occurrence during Lascelles' term of office up to his retirement in 1915.

Subsequently, single birds or pairs were recorded in most years between 1928 and 1939 and from 1946-48. Young were certainly reared in 1934 and at least one pair bred in 1948.

No data have previously been released by the group of observers who have constantly monitored the small Hampshire population since 1954. In recent years, there has been much unnecessary disturbance of the birds. In view of potential threats to the birds' welfare which may be generated by lack of information, it is now prudent to report the following facts. Between 1954 and 1960, up to four pairs were present during the breeding season, and from 1961-80, numbers varied between six and nine pairs. From 1981-92, no more than two pairs were recorded annually with the exception of two years when three pairs were present. Not all attempted to breed and additionally one or more unmated individuals were present in most seasons. Of 93 known breeding attempts between 1954 and 1992, most have been successful and at least 133 young have been reared to the flying stage. Failures have been attributed to abandoned or infertile eggs (at least 6 occasions), eggs broken in nest (1), eggs apparently taken by a predator, possibly a Carrion Crow (1), nest robbed by collectors (1), nest blown out (1) and uncertain (at least 2). In addition, there have been at least five other occasions when breeding has probably occurred during the period. Work continues to determine the cause of the apparent decline or fluctuation. The British population was estimated at 30 pairs in 1988-91 (New Atlas).

Breeding birds normally arrive in the Forest in mid-May although the earliest ever was one seen on Apr. 23rd 1960; what was presumably the same individual was seen by independent observers on Apr. 30th of that year. Aerial activity, including display, is most prominent in the second half of May and early June during the periods of pair-formation, nest building and egg-laying, and again in August, when the young are more than half grown (BWP). Most have left by mid-September; the latest date recorded is Sep. 18th.

Away from the New Forest, there have been few records although they have increased in frequency since the mid-1970s. One was seen on the downs to the east of Winchester on July 11th 1921. Cohen stated that a pair was present and may have nested near Ashmansworth in 1949. This probably stretches the available evidence a little too far – two were found digging out a wasps' nest on Aug. 9th but that was the only sighting (*Brit. Birds* 43: 189). In 1951, one flew north over Tidpit Down on May 10th and another was seen displaying over Woolmer Forest on Aug. 4th. The next was one at Needs Ore on Oct. 3rd 1959, but there were no further records until 1972, when one was in one area on three dates between June and August.

Between 1973 and 1992, there were records in every year except 1974, 1983, 1985 and 1987. No more than four were recorded per year apart from 1976 (6), 1988 (7) and 1989 and 1991 (5 each). The cumulative monthly totals for 1973-92 are shown below.

|  | May | Jun | Jul | Aug | Sep | Oct |
|---|---|---|---|---|---|---|
| Inland sites | 6 | 4 | 4 | 6 | 11 | 2 |
| Coastal sites | 2 | 1 | 0 | 0 | 8 | 4 |

Most of the May records involved migrants moving in a northerly direction, the earliest being one flying in off the sea at Milford on May 12th 1980. The records for June-August were all from inland localities apart from one over Weston

(Southampton) on June 24th 1982. Although some were seen over suitable habitat, there has been no suggestion of breeding and it is probable that most were wandering failed or non-breeders. The total of 25 seen in September and October includes seven moving over inland localities in a southerly direction and six leaving out to sea from the Hampshire coast. However, one moved north off the sea over Pennington Marsh on Oct. 21st 1973 and another, the latest recorded, flew west there on Oct. 30th 1976. All records referred to single birds apart from two flying south-west over South Warnborough on Sep. 12th 1976, two flying south over Timsbury on Sep. 14th 1986, two moving south-west over Baddesley Common on Sep. 3rd 1988 and two drifting north over Keyhaven two days later.

The Honey Buzzard breeds from western Europe to Kazakhstan and winters mainly in west and central Africa.

# Black Kite                                             *Milvus migrans*

A rare vagrant, recorded on 11 occasions, as follows:

1980:   flying north-west over Acres Down, New Forest, July 13th;
1986:   flying south over Ashley Walk, New Forest, June 12th;
1987:   flying west off Hurst Beach, May 4th;
1988:   Fleet Pond, Apr. 23rd;
1990:   Hawkhill Inclosure, New Forest, May 9th;
1991:   flying north-west over Langstone Harbour, Apr. 27th†;
1993:   flying north over Wendleholme (Warsash), Apr. 28th†;
        flying north-east over Harefield (Southampton), Apr. 30th†;
        flying north over Bishop's Dyke, May 7th;
        flying east over Fleet, July 3rd†;
        flying south-west over Pennington Marsh, Sep. 26th†.

The four sightings in spring 1993 probably refer to the same individual.

The increase in records of the Black Kite in the last decade parallels the national picture and is presumably connected with the gradual extension of its European breeding range towards Britain. Most European birds winter in Africa south of the Sahara.

# Red Kite                                                 *Milvus milvus*

A very scarce visitor.

The Red Kite was formerly resident in the county; K & M record that the last nest, from which the clutch of three eggs was taken, was found near Broughton in 1864.

The first this century was at Old Winchester Hill from Aug. 15th-17th 1956, but there were no further sightings until 1970, when one was seen between Preshaw and Dur Wood on Aug. 23rd. Since then, there have been occurrences in every year except five, with a total of 31 recorded. Sightings have increased in frequency since the late 1980s. In 1988, four were seen, including three in late March which were part of an influx to south-eastern England almost certainly of continental origin. In 1990, six were recorded, including one which stayed around Lower Whitehill Farm (Overton) from Jan. 12th-24th. The cumulative monthly totals for 1956-92 are shown below.

| Jan | Feb | Mar | Apr | May | Jun | Jul | Aug | Sep | Oct | Nov | Dec |
|-----|-----|-----|-----|-----|-----|-----|-----|-----|-----|-----|-----|
| 6   | 3   | 5   | 3   | 1   | 1   | 2   | 3   | 1   | 3   | 4   | 1   |

The recent increase may be connected with the dispersal of birds from the expanding Welsh population. However, the discovery of the corpse of one in Freefolk Wood (Whitchurch) in January 1978, which had been ringed as a pullus in Schwerin, eastern Germany in June 1976, confirms that continental birds do reach the county.

Since November 1991, at least three wing-tagged birds, released as part of the RSPB reintroduction scheme, have been seen in the north-west of the county. These are not included in the table above.

## White-tailed Eagle                              *Haliaeetus albicilla*

A rare visitor in the 19th century; only two records since.

K & M cited several records for the last century. Hawker encountered White-tailed Eagles in the west Solent on at least four occasions between 1827 and 1841, but failed to kill one. Meade-Waldo saw an adult over Wilverley Plain (New Forest) in July 1885 (which roosted throughout the summer of that year at Hengistbury Head, now in Dorset) and an immature near Micheldever Station in December 1895. One was shot at Cadland about 1886 and another was there for two or three months in the winter of 1888-89. An adult shot in Somerley Park (Ringwood) on Dec. 28th 1861 was included by K & M as a Spotted Eagle, but the specimen was later examined by C W Mackworth-Praed and proved to be of this species (Cohen).

The only records this century are of one at Highclere on Dec. 18th 1927 (*Oxford Ornithological Society Report*) and an immature at Somerley Park on Jan. 6th 1947 (Cohen).

Those seen in Hampshire were probably central European breeders, although in the 18th century it possibly nested on Culver Cliff in the Isle of Wight (Cohen). In recent years, the population in northern Germany has expanded and birds have regularly wintered in east central France.

## Marsh Harrier                              *Circus aeruginosus*

A scarce visitor, most frequently recorded in spring and autumn but also occasionally in mid-winter; has bred.

K & M described the Marsh Harrier as "a rare winter visitor" and listed four records for the 19th century. There do not appear to be any for the first half of this century.

Between 1952 and 1960, Marsh Harriers occurred regularly along the coast with records in every month of the year. In winter, individuals sometimes remained for several weeks at favoured sites such as Needs Ore and Titchfield Haven. At other times of the year, visits were usually of shorter duration, but at Needs Ore, a pair nested unsuccessfully in 1957 and there were also summer sightings there in 1955 and 1959. Although there was a great upsurge in observer activity in the county during this period, the increase was almost certainly connected with the expansion of the breeding colony which was established around Poole Harbour, Dorset in the 1940s. This built up to at least five pairs in 1954 but declined to one pair in 1962, the last year the species bred in the area (Prendergast & Boys 1983).

In the 1960s and early 1970s, no more than five were seen per year. This coincided with a slump in the British breeding population, which was virtually confined to East Anglia. Since then, there has been a steady increase in Hampshire (fig. 27); 1988, the best year so far, produced possibly 29 individuals. This parallels the expansion of the British population; in 1990, 73 breeding males and 110 breeding females were known (Spencer *et al* 1993).

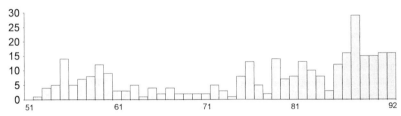

*Figure 27. Annual totals of Marsh Harriers, 1951-92.*

Records of Marsh Harrier peak between early April and early June and again between late August and mid-October (fig. 28). In spring, most pass through quickly; only rarely have individuals remained at a site for more than two days. Longer stays may be recorded in autumn but it is not always clear if the same birds are involved. In 1988, at least three female/immatures were seen at Titchfield Haven between Sep. 22nd and Nov. 4th; during this period there were several sightings at Langstone Harbour, Needs Ore and Pennington Marsh which may have involved the same birds. Most of the winter records shown in fig. 28 refer to the 1950s, but since 1987/88 such sightings have become more frequent, especially at Titchfield Haven and Lower Test Marshes.

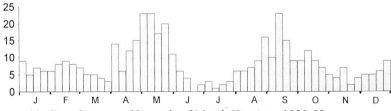

*Figure 28. Cumulative weekly totals of Marsh Harriers, 1951-92.*

Between 1961 and 1992, approximately 250 Marsh Harriers were recorded, although in some cases the same individual is known to have occurred at more than one locality. Of these, 188 were at coastal localities, including 64 at Langstone Harbour, 50 at Titchfield Haven, 38 in the Lymington/Hurst area and 13 at Needs Ore. Inland, there were 62, including 17 in the New Forest, ten in the Itchen valley and nine at Fleet Pond. 46 (21.4%) were recorded as adult or second-year males.

The Marsh Harrier breeds in much of Eurasia; ringing studies show that most north-west European birds winter in the Mediterranean Basin and tropical West Africa (BWP).

## Hen Harrier                                    *Circus cyaneus*

A scarce, but regular, winter visitor and passage migrant.

In the 1950s and 1960s, the number of Hen Harriers recorded per winter in Hampshire only once exceeded ten; this was in 1962/63 when some 15 were present including five in the New Forest. From 1973/74-77/78, the total was between ten and 15, but a large influx into England during the severe winter of 1978/79 produced around 40 in Hampshire (Davenport 1982). Subsequently, the wintering population (excluding passage birds) has usually been between 15 and 20 with more in severe winters, e.g. 30 in 1981/82 and 27 in 1984/85.

Hen Harriers are most frequently recorded on the heaths of the New Forest. From the late 1970s until the mid-1980s, the wintering population there was in the range 12-20 birds, but since then it has fallen to 8-12. Several roosts have been discovered which usually hold up to four birds, although a maximum of eight has been recorded. Counts for the Hen Harrier Winter Roost Survey from 1983/84-90/91 found that 52% at roost were adult males, compared to 37% for England as a whole. As an unknown number of harriers in brown plumage are first-winter males, the percentage of males will be greater in each case. Poor mammal populations in the New Forest may be limiting the numbers of female harriers which, being heavier and less agile than males, are less well adapted to take small passerines, the prey most readily available. It is likely that some harriers using these roosts range outside the New Forest to hunt. Large samples of pellets collected have revealed lizards, seven species of mammals and 32 species of birds. The number of bird species recorded in pellets is higher than for any other site yet studied in England (Clarke & Combridge, unpublished).

Elsewhere inland, the only known regularly-used roost site is in the east of the county. There, as in the New Forest, some birds leave the area during the day to hunt but return at dusk. In most winters, one or two individuals are recorded, but three were identified in 1982/83, 1984/85 and 1987/88 and four in 1991/92. Of 31 recorded since the 1973/74 winter, 14 were adult males and 17 were ringtails. In some years, birds have remained for several weeks at downland sites such as Cheesefoot Head, Old Winchester Hill and the Damerham/Martin area, but coverage of such areas is not sufficiently comprehensive to determine whether birds regularly winter in them. In severe weather, birds have often stayed at localities where they are not normally recorded, most notably in 1979 when up to three males and two ringtails were at Baddesley Common between Jan. 7th and Mar. 30th.

At coastal sites, Hen Harriers are normally irregular in appearance. However, in hard weather, individuals have remained for several weeks at Langstone

Harbour, in the Titchfield Haven/Calshot/Dibden Bay area and between Lepe and Hurst. Most records were of one or two birds but on Jan. 17th 1982 a male and four ringtails were seen together at Needs Ore and at least one other male was present in the area. Some of those seen along the shores of the north-west Solent and Southampton Water may be from New Forest roosts.

Other inland and coastal records (i.e. of birds moving over or staying for a few days only) show evidence of autumn passage (peaking between mid-October and early December), further arrivals during severe cold spells in mid-winter, and spring passage (peaking between mid-March and late April).

Until the mid-1970s, virtually all sightings of Hen Harriers were made between October and April. However, in the period 1974-92, there were ten records for September and 16 for May, while the extreme dates were Aug. 29th 1979, when a ringtail flew south-west over Martyr Worthy, and June 10th 1986, when a male was at Pennington Marsh.

The increased numbers wintering in south-eastern England in the last 20 years are presumed to be linked with the expansion of the Dutch and Fenno-Scandian breeding populations (Clarke & Watson 1990). However, a ringtail carrying a wing-tag at Farlington Marshes on Oct. 7th 1990 had been marked at Pitlochry, Perthshire on June 25th 1990. Two further sightings of wing-tagged birds in 1991 and 1992 involved one from Scotland and one from Wales.

Whether or not Hen Harriers have ever bred in Hampshire is open to debate. K & M give details of several 19th century nests in the New Forest, with the last in 1893. The Hart Collection included pairs with nests and eggs or young of both this species and the Montagu's Harrier which had been obtained in the Forest. However, Cohen stated that "there is practically no evidence to substantiate (breeding)" and leaves little doubt that he believed the records referred to Montagu's Harriers. Watson (1977) indicated that there is good evidence to show that breeding occurred in all the counties of southern England in the early 19th century, but that it had become sporadic by the 1860s. Witherby *et al* (1939) admitted one record for Hampshire for early in this century, but it has not been possible to trace the details.

## Montagu's Harrier          *Circus pygargus*

A very scarce passage migrant and summer visitor, formerly breeding in small numbers.

K & M described the Montagu's Harrier as "a regular summer visitor to certain districts of the mainland". They cite a pair, thought to have been breeding, which was shot at Newton Valence in May 1850, as being the first to be recognised on the Hampshire mainland. It should be remembered that it was not until 1802 that the Montagu's Harrier was separated as a distinct species.

K & M suggested that there was a rapid increase between 1860 and 1880 coinciding with a reduction of the "larger and more powerful Hen Harrier as a breeding species". They described several instances of successful breeding in the New Forest and Avon valley in the last three decades of the 19th century, but also unfortunately the shooting of a large number by collectors and gamekeepers. They also referred to a district in the north-east of the county where it was said to occur every year and a nest was found in 1875. Nests were found in the south-east of the county in June 1883, which was robbed, and in July 1898, which contained three young. This was possibly on Hayling Island where Kelso (1912), probably referring to the turn of the century, recorded the species as having nested for several years and been afforded protection. Kelso settled on Hayling in 1909 but by then Montagu's Harriers had ceased to breed there.

It is probable that Montagu's Harriers continued to breed in the New Forest throughout the early 20th century. In the 1930s and 1940s, pairs were found breeding or on territory there in at least ten years, while in the east of the county, a pair bred successfully at Liss Forest in 1945.

The late 1940s and early 1950s saw a remarkable upturn in numbers breeding in Britain, as well as a distinct redistribution of the population. The stronghold, previously in East Anglia, moved to the south-west between Hampshire and Cornwall. Between 1950 and 1961, there were reports from six areas in the New Forest, involving at least 22 pairs which were breeding or holding territory (table 24). 11 of these reared 35 young. Subsequently, pairs were present in five years up to 1967, but the only one known to have nested (in 1965) was robbed.

| | Pairs Present | Pairs Breeding | Pairs Successful | Young Reared |
|---|---|---|---|---|
| 1950 | 1 | 1 | - | - |
| 1951 | 1 | 1 | 1 | 3 |
| 1952 | 2 | 2 | 2 | 6 |
| 1953 | 1 | 0 | 0 | 0 |
| 1954 | 2 | 2 | 2 | 5 |
| 1955 | 3 | 2 | 1 | 3 |
| 1956 | 4 | 2 | 2 | 6 |
| 1957 | 2 | 0 | 0 | 0 |
| 1958 | 1 | 1 | 1 | 3 |
| 1959 | 2 | 2 | 0 | 0 |
| 1960 | 1 | 0 | 0 | 0 |
| 1961 | 2 | 2 | 2 | 9 |
| 1963 | 2 | 0 | 0 | 0 |
| 1964 | 1 | 0 | 0 | 0 |
| 1965 | 2 | 1 | 0 | 0 |
| 1966 | 1 | 0 | 0 | 0 |
| 1967 | 1 | 0 | 0 | 0 |

*Table 24. Breeding Montagu's Harriers in the New Forest, 1950-67.*

Between 1968 and 1992, sightings were made in the New Forest in 19 years involving approximately 29 birds (table 25). Most were reported on one date only, but in 1979 four individuals (two males and two females) were recorded on dates between Apr. 8th and Aug. 27th. In 1981, a male was seen between May 23rd and June 4th and a pair was in the same area on July 8th, and in 1985, three individuals, an adult male, an immature male and a female, were present in one area between Apr. 27th and June. 29th.

Most other recent breeding records refer to the chalk downlands. In one area, a pair bred successfully in 1952. A female was shot there in 1954, a male was present in 1955 and 1956, and a pair in 1957. Three pairs took up territory in 1958, but unfortunately one pair and a second female were shot. Single pairs were present in the next three years but with no indication of successful breeding. Thereafter, pairs were recorded in 1965, 1966, 1968, 1970, 1977 and 1978. Only those in 1966 and 1978 were known to be successful, the latter being the last known record of breeding for the county. Since 1978, birds have been seen in every year except 1984, 1988 and 1989. Most sightings involved males which were probably on hunting expeditions from a breeding site in an adjacent county, but pairs possibly summered in 1981 and 1982.

Elsewhere on the chalk, a pair bred in the Test valley in 1956 and 1971; the latter had three young in a nest in a grass crop but they died after the female disappeared. In the north of the county, a pair probably bred in a barley field at Sherborne St. John in 1965, and in the south-east a male was present in one area in June and July 1980.

The only other breeding record involves a pair which bred successfully in a young conifer plantation in 1963. A pair was present in the following year but it is not known whether breeding was successful. Also in 1963, a pair frequently hunted over a coastal site and was seen to carry away prey on several occasions.

Records away from breeding areas since 1951 (including those for the New Forest from 1968-92) are summarised in table 25. Such sightings have become more frequent in the last two decades, which may be connected with the increase in the breeding population in north-west France. Since 1970, there have been records for every year except 1976, with up to five seen annually. Excluding the New Forest, 36 have been recorded, with eight in the Pennington/Keyhaven area, three at Needs Ore, two at Farlington Marshes, Portsdown Hill, Tichborne and Ewshot, and the rest, apart from one at Lower Test Marshes, at widely scattered inland localities.

|  | Apr | May | Jun | Jul | Aug | Sep | Oct | Nov |
|---|---|---|---|---|---|---|---|---|
| Inland | 5 | 12 | 5 | 2 | 4 | 2 | 1 | 1 |
| Coast | 2 | 11 | 2 | 3 | 12 | 6 | 2 | 0 |
| New Forest (1968-92) | 3 | 15 | 8 | 3 | 4 | 1 | 0 | 0 |

*Table 25. Cumulative monthly totals of Montagu's Harriers at non-breeding localities, 1951-92.*

These birds presumably comprise passage migrants, non-breeders and birds which have lost eggs or young elsewhere.

Montagu's Harriers usually arrive in late April or May and depart in August or September. Early records include those of females at Needs Ore on Apr. 17th 1952 and Gilkicker Point on the same date in 1963, and a male in the New Forest on Apr. 8th 1979. There have been four records after the end of

September. In 1960, a female was at Micheldever from Oct. 1st-19th and a juvenile was there on Nov. 2nd. More recently, juveniles were at Langstone Harbour on Oct. 2nd 1974 and Needs Ore on Oct. 18th 1981.

There have been three ringing recoveries involving Hampshire birds. One, ringed as a pullus in the New Forest on Aug. 7th 1949, was shot at Champagne-le-Marais, France, 491 km south, on Sep. 22nd 1949. The remains of a young bird ringed in the New Forest on July 13th 1952 were found on Tresco, Isles of Scilly, 354 km WSW, on May 31st 1954. Another, ringed as a pullus in East Dorset on July 8th 1956, was shot at a breeding site in the county on June 7th 1958. British and west European breeding birds almost certainly winter in the savannas of tropical West and Central Africa, although there are few ringing recoveries to confirm this (BWP).

# Goshawk                                                    *Accipiter gentilis*

A very scarce visitor, possibly resident.

K & M did not include this species; a record of one said to have been shot by Marshall at Highclere in 1886 (Munn's diaries) was presumably discounted by them, while they would not have known about an adult female trapped at Lockerley in October 1896 (Meinertzhagen's diaries).

The first this century was one seen soaring over Sloden Inclosure in June 1938 (C & T). The next were in 1953, when a male was at Farlington Marshes on July 7th, a female was there on Oct. 24th and one was near Fordingbridge on Sep. 8th. In the following year, a juvenile was seen at Farlington Marshes on Aug. 3rd, 9th and 15th. In 1957, one flew south down the Avon valley at Fordingbridge on Feb. 8th, while in 1958, one was seen at Pilot Hill on Sep. 3rd.

Since the late 1950s, there have been many reports from the New Forest. It is difficult to assess the validity of the majority of them since they lack the necessary supporting detail. Nevertheless, it has been possible to identify the discontinuous presence of Goshawks in three broadly defined regions of the Forest during this period. There has probably been interchange of individuals between sites, thus further complicating the picture. In most years, one or two birds have been seen, but in 1983, possibly up to four were involved.

There are few authenticated records for areas outside the New Forest. Between 1972 and 1976, five birds were seen in widely separated areas, and additionally a pair was present near Basingstoke in the spring of 1975, but with no proof of breeding. One bird was seen in 1983, then two in 1984 and 1990, three in 1991 and one in 1992; most of these were seen on one date only but in 1991, a male and female were regularly recorded in a suburban area between Sep. 30th and Nov. 16th. On one occasion during this period, the female was watched eating a Woodpigeon. It later returned with a male; neither bird was wearing jesses or showed signs of having been kept in captivity.

The origin of Goshawks in Hampshire remains uncertain. The present British stock is believed to be descended from falconers' escapes and releases (Marchant *et al* 1990). It is known that at least one female was released in the New Forest prior to 1983 and a male, wearing jesses, was reported in that year. Elsewhere, females, both wearing jesses and bells, were seen at two sites in 1976. Hopefully, the Goshawk will soon establish a self-supporting breeding population in the county. Nationally, the population is expanding, despite persecution, and was estimated at 200 pairs in 1988 (New Atlas).

## Sparrowhawk                                        *Accipiter nisus*

A common resident, passage migrant and probable winter visitor.

K & M described the Sparrowhawk as "still a fairly common resident throughout the county". They commented on the species' ability to survive the constant war waged against it in the interests of game preservation. This has been the position throughout much of the present century; it did not receive legal protection in Britain until 1963. By this time there had been a marked decline in much of Britain, especially in eastern and southern England, where the proportion of tilled land was greatest. This was subsequently attributed to the widespread use of organochlorine pesticides (Presst 1965, Newton 1986). Cohen noted this decrease in Hampshire, particularly in the north of the county, although in the New Forest and adjacent woodlands numbers remained at a high level.

Following increased restrictions on the use of aldrin and dieldrin in 1962, 1965 and 1975, the national population recovered. This occurred in a wave-like pattern, west to east, first in areas with least tilled land (and the least marked decline) (Newton 1986). There are few quantitative data to identify the timing of the recovery in Hampshire. Regular records kept for Langstone Harbour from 1952-86 indicate a rapid increase from the mid-1970s onwards. In the period 1952-57 there was an average of 24 sightings per year, but in the 1958-75 this fell to only 2.5 per year. From 1976-86, there were 52 sightings per year: the species had fully recovered its former status and was apparently even more numerous than before (Portsmouth Group 1991), perhaps reflecting a reduction in illegal persecution in the vicinity. In 1971, only two nests were known in north-east Hampshire, but in 1982, 35 pairs were located in 300 km$^2$ in that part of the county.

The picture is rather different in the New Forest. During 1961-66, numbers remained at a high level, with around 40 known territories. Of these, about half were searched annually for nests. In that time, breeding attempts made in searched areas increased from 70 to 100% and successful attempts from 40 to 90%, perhaps reflecting an early and rapid recovery from the pesticides era. However, large declines in nesting pairs were detected in 1968-70 and again in 1975-80, though a high percentage of those found were successful (Tubbs 1986a). This may have been due to the maturing of preferred conifer stands. The loss of the shrub layer in the inclosures (due to increased grazing by large herbivores) and the resultant reduction of breeding habitat for prey species such as the Song Thrush and Blackbird may also have been a contributory factor (Tubbs 1986a). Since the late 1980s, or possibly earlier, there has been a strong recovery. Fieldwork carried out by the Forestry Commission in 1988-92 produced a total of 56 territories, with a maximum of 34 nests located in 1991. Allowing for areas as yet uncovered, the total population on Forestry Commission land in the New Forest is estimated at 45 pairs (A Page *in litt*).

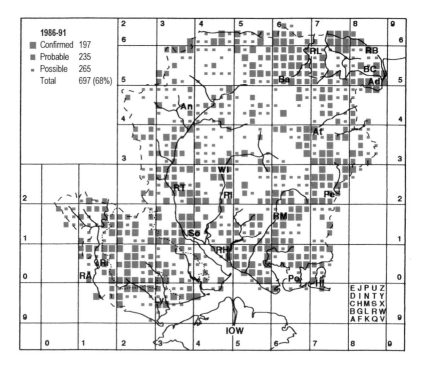

The Atlas Survey revealed that Sparrowhawks are now widespread throughout the county, although rather thinly scattered in the centre and north-west. The apparent scarcity in these areas is probably because of under-recording, but on the other hand it could be connected with continuing persecution on some estates where Pheasants and other game are reared (*cf.* Carrion Crow).

The optimum breeding habitat consists of large, fairly thick woods, but they will nest in small woods or clumps of trees, scrub patches and scattered trees, even in suburban parks, gardens and churchyards. Conifers are preferred for nesting, but, where these are scarce, they will utilise broadleaved trees (Newton

162

1986). It is difficult to estimate a population for Hampshire. Tetrads containing optimum wooded habitat may hold several pairs, whereas in less suitable areas, registrations in adjoining squares could relate to the same pair. Taking an arbitrary two pairs per occupied tetrad where breeding was confirmed or probable and one where it was possible suggests a total population of around 1100 pairs. Newton (1986) estimated the British population at 25,000 pairs and calculated a maximum possible total of 32,000 pairs when recovery is complete.

Ringing studies suggest that the Hampshire population is largely resident. Of 38 ringed in the county and subsequently recovered, 26 had moved less than 10 km and the remainder 10-99 km. 25 ringed elsewhere in southern England have been found in Hampshire and only one of these had moved more than 100 km: a bird ringed as a chick in Northamptonshire in July 1983 and found dead at Nether Wallop in February 1984. Most of these movements involved birds ringed as chicks and thus illustrate the expected pattern of dispersal for young birds.

Observations at coastal watch points give some indication of possible passage movements, especially in spring. Analysis of the records for 1976-92 shows that five seen between Apr. 3rd and 14th were all moving out to sea whereas 12 noted between Apr. 17th and May 20th (mostly late April) were all moving north. Of eight recorded between Sep. 29th and Nov. 6th five were moving south and three north. There were also records of two arriving from the south at Titchfield Haven in cold weather on Feb. 18th 1985 and one arriving off the sea at Hurst Beach on Dec. 22nd 1990. Many of these sightings probably refer to local movements between the mainland and Isle of Wight, but firm evidence that continental birds do reach the county is provided by the recovery of one foreign-ringed bird, which was ringed as a chick in Aust-Agder, Norway in June 1952 and shot at Ringwood, 1061 km south-west, on Sep. 17th of that year.

# Buzzard                                   *Buteo buteo*

A moderately common resident, passage migrant and possible winter visitor.

The Buzzard had virtually disappeared from lowland Britain by the mid-19th century apart from a small but viable population in south-west Hampshire, which persisted despite persecution by egg and skin collectors and even the Crown keepers. Wise (1862) recorded that it bred "in nearly all the old woods, but is becoming scarce". Persecution continued until 1880, when Gerald Lascelles was appointed Deputy Surveyor (the senior administrator) to the New Forest. Under Lascelles, new wildlife policies were instigated and full instructions for all keepers carefully drawn up. As a result, the Buzzard recovered in the Forest, although it was still being persecuted in adjacent areas when Lascelles retired in 1915.

Records of breeding Buzzards between the wars were few and often vague, e.g. the HFC Report for 1935 states: "New Forest numbers well maintained". B J Ringrose's diaries for the period, now in the possession of C R Tubbs, contain references to pairs or nests at 13 localities in the north and west of the Forest. Between 1962 and 1971, Tubbs found that 12 of these were still occupied and located only two additional pairs. This suggests that the total New Forest population in the late 1920s and early 1930s was little different from that of the mid-1960s (see below). Notes left by the late P Day tend to endorse the view that Buzzards were numerous during the 1940s, when he found pairs in seven localities around Burley. All these held birds between 1962 and 1971 (C R Tubbs pers. comm.).

The spread of myxomatosis in the mid-1950s apparently had little effect on the New Forest population. At least 25 pairs were located in 1958, 34 in 1959 and 28 in 1960. Since 1961, the population in a 288 km$^2$ study area has been continuously monitored by C R and J M Tubbs and others (Tubbs 1967a, 1972, 1974a, 1986a; Tubbs & Tubbs 1985). Some of the resultant data are portrayed in fig. 29.

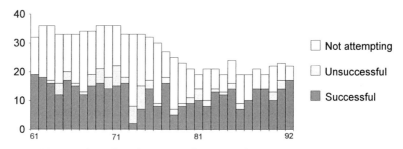

*Figure 29. Breeding data for Buzzard pairs in the New Forest, 1961-92.*

Until 1974, the population was relatively constant (32-36 pairs occupying territories). However, its density and the size of fledged broods were low compared with elsewhere. In 1973, there was a dramatic fall in breeding success: only eight breeding attempts were recorded and only two pairs fledged young. From then until the 1980s, breeding performance was erratic and significantly lower than between 1961 and 1972. The number of occupied territories fell from 33 in 1974 to 21 in 1982 (36% decline) and has since remained in the range 19-21. Between 1988 and 1992, breeding performance became more consistent from year to year, and brood sizes recovered.

From 1968, the number of successful breeding pairs fluctuated in relation to the amount of tree and shrub seed produced in the previous autumn. This in turn was reflected in the numbers of small rodents (wood mice and bank voles) surviving into the spring. Tubbs and Tubbs (1985) suggested that from the early 1970s Buzzards responded positively to these spring numbers of small rodents. At that time, they are re-establishing territories and constructing nests, but alternative prey sources are at their lowest densities, with few young rabbits, woodland passerines and reptiles available.

Until the late 1960s, the woodland inclosures of the Forest were secured against stock. After 1965, stock density increased sharply with the fencing of the Forest's perambulation; this was followed by a policy change which permitted animals into the woodlands. Gross habitat impoverishment followed and small rodent numbers declined. Tubbs and Tubbs (1985) suggested that it was these events which led directly to the decline in both breeding success and numbers of Buzzards, though the rodent population was buffered against decline between 1968 and 1971 by a sequence of remarkably good seed years. 1973, the year in which Buzzard productivity crashed, was preceded by the poorest seed autumn recorded during the entire study.

The interactions involved in the ecology of the New Forest Buzzard population are complex, and much remains to be explained, but numbers and productivity are clearly related to the peculiar conditions prevailing in the Forest.

Elsewhere in the county, there are few records of breeding for the period up to 1940. The cessation of gamekeeping activities in the Second World War may well have permitted an expansion. A pair probably bred near Droxford in 1948, and in the 1950s there were reports from Porton Down, Rushmore Down and Pilot Hill in the north-west, several sites around Winchester, Paultons Park, East Meon and the Martin/Damerham area. In 1961, five pairs were located to the west of the New Forest and one pair possibly bred at Stratfield Saye in the north. However, persecution was clearly limiting their spread; in 1963, five pairs in one central locality had their young destroyed.

Records for 1970-85 suggest a gradual increase, although this largely involved infilling into suitable habitat in the range already occupied rather than an eastward expansion. At least 50 different territories outside the New Forest were occupied at some time during this period.

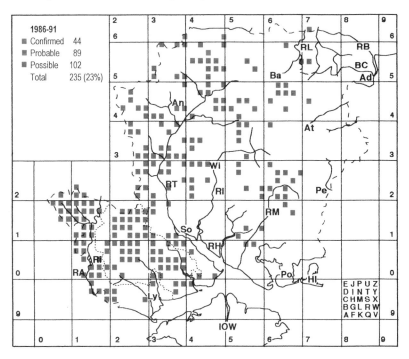

The Atlas Map shows the distribution recorded during 1986-91, with all registrations shown at the same level for security reasons. Despite the existence of much suitable habitat, Buzzards have still not spread into the north-east and east of the county. While persecution and the use of poison baits may be limiting expansion, it has been suggested that additional factors which we do not yet appreciate may be responsible (Taylor 1988). In 1992, 42 nests were known in the area bounded by the Avon valley, the boundary with Wiltshire, Southampton Water and the north-west Solent coast (C R Tubbs *in litt*). In the remainder of the county, there were registrations in 161 tetrads during the Atlas Survey. Many of those of possible breeding will have related to wandering individuals and some of those of probable or confirmed breeding will have referred to pairs breeding in adjacent tetrads. Taking this into account, the population in these areas is estimated at 60-90 pairs, indicating a total for the county in the range 100-130 pairs. As a result of a national survey organised by the BTO in 1983, Taylor (1988) estimated the British population at 12,000-15,000 territorial pairs.

Outside the breeding season, Buzzards are most conspicuous on the downs. Loose gatherings of up to eight are not unusual in favoured areas. In recent years, the largest numbers have been recorded in the Linkenholt/Ashmansworth area, with 12 on Nov. 12th 1978 and ten on Dec. 24th 1990. As well as local breeding birds, these gatherings may also include individuals from the New Forest, where the numbers wintering have declined since 1973 (Tubbs 1986a), and from further afield.

Ringing studies confirm that juveniles tend to wander, normally for short distances only, after the breeding season. Of 84 ringed as chicks in the New Forest between 1957 and 1969, seven were subsequently recovered, five within 60 km of their nests. Two ringed in 1962 moved much further afield, one to Hornsea, Yorkshire, where it was found dying on Sep. 17th 1962, and the other to Aisne, France, 436 km ESE, where it was found dead in a pole trap on Sep. 28th 1962. Evidence that birds may move long distances into Hampshire for the winter is provided by two recoveries. Birds ringed as chicks in Yorkshire in 1975 and Cardiganshire in 1976 were found in the county on Oct. 17th 1975 and Dec. 15th 1976 respectively. In some winters continental birds may reach the county but there have been no ringing recoveries to confirm this.

In most years, passage is indicated by the appearance of birds at coastal sites and in the north-east where breeding does not occur. Analysis of such records for 1971-92 (Table 26) shows a large autumn peak between late August and early October and a lesser spring peak between March and May.

| | Jan | Feb | Mar | Apr | May | Jun | Jul | Aug | Sep | Oct | Nov | Dec |
|---|---|---|---|---|---|---|---|---|---|---|---|---|
| Portsmouth area | 3 | 1 | 1 | 0 | 2 | 2 | 0 | 11 | 14 | 5 | 0 | 1 |
| Titchfield Haven/ Southampton Water | 2 | 5 | 7 | 9 | 2 | 0 | 0 | 5 | 12 | 9 | 2 | 1 |
| Regents Park (Southampton) | 2 | 0 | 0 | 5 | 2 | 2 | 0 | 1 | 4 | 2 | 0 | 0 |
| Lymington/Milford | 1 | 1 | 3 | 4 | 8 | 1 | 0 | 14 | 41 | 10 | 1 | 2 |
| North-east Hants | 4 | 1 | 6 | 2 | 3 | 1 | 2 | 5 | 14 | 10 | 5 | 5 |
| Totals | 12 | 8 | 17 | 20 | 17 | 6 | 2 | 36 | 85 | 36 | 8 | 9 |

*Table 26. Cumulative monthly totals of Buzzards recorded in various areas, 1971-92.*

The origin or destination of these birds is open to speculation although the likelihood is that most refer to local movements. In autumn, birds were recorded moving to all points of the compass although those to the east predominated, accounting for 15 out of 26 for which the direction was stated. Parties of three occurred on three occasions while groups of four were noted moving west along Portsdown Hill on Sep. 30th 1982 and at Pennington Marsh on Aug. 31st 1983 (flying out to sea) and Aug. 17th 1988.

## Rough-legged Buzzard                                    *Buteo lagopus*

A rare winter visitor and passage migrant.

K & M and Cohen listed a total of 11, mostly shot or trapped, for the period between 1881 and 1945.

Subsequently, single birds were seen at Brockley Warren on Jan. 30th 1955, Titchfield Haven on Nov. 15th 1959, Rockford on Apr. 7th 1962, Beacon Hill, Highclere on Apr. 26th 1963 and near Beaulieu on Jan. 13th and 18th 1964.

In the 1966/67 winter, an influx into Britain was the largest for 50 years; at least 57 birds were present, mostly in south-eastern England (Scott 1968). In Hampshire, single birds were at Cheesefoot Head from Dec. 26th-Feb. 26th and at Boveridge on Feb. 15th. Another bird wintered at Cheesefoot Head in 1971/72, being recorded from Dec. 15th-Feb. 15th. A further influx in 1973/74 resulted in birds staying for several weeks at Great Litchfield Down and Cheesefoot Head and on one date only at Selborne Common, Bishop's Dyke, Harewood Forest and Old Winchester Hill. A third influx in 1974/75 was the largest yet recorded in Britain, with around 100 birds wintering (Scott 1978). Possibly 16 were present in Hampshire, with two at Great Litchfield Down (and three or four there on Dec. 15th), up to three at Faccombe (possibly the same birds), two at Cheesefoot Head and Tufton Warren Farm (Whitchurch), and single birds, mostly on one date only, at Old Winchester Hill, Titchfield Haven, Bishop's Dyke, Ashley Walk and Hampton Ridge.

In 1980/81, one or two were in the Combe/Inkpen area between Dec. 2nd and Mar. 20th, but since then the only records have been of single birds at Combe on Dec. 6th 1981, flying north over Southampton on Dec. 12th 1981, at Harvest Slade Bottom (New Forest) on Apr. 20th 1988 and moving north-east over Old Winchester Hill on Nov. 2nd 1981.

The cumulative monthly totals for 1955-92 are shown below.

| Oct | Nov | Dec | Jan | Feb | Mar | Apr |
|-----|-----|-----|-----|-----|-----|-----|
| 8 | 9 | 16 | 13 | 8 | 7 | 4 |

The extreme dates were Oct. 21st (1973, Great Litchfield Down) and Apr. 26th (1963, Beacon Hill, Highclere).

Due to the possibility of confusion with pale Buzzards, several other records, some of which have been published in *Hampshire Bird Reports*, are now considered to be insufficiently documented and are not included.

The Rough-legged Buzzard has a circumpolar breeding distribution; most of those occurring in Britain probably originate from Fenno-Scandia.

## Osprey *Pandion haliaetus*

A scarce passage migrant.

K & M and Cohen gave details of 13 seen between 1872 and 1949. Since 1951, Ospreys have been recorded in every year except two (fig. 30).

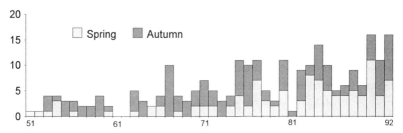

*Figure 30. Spring and autumn totals of Ospreys, 1951-92.*

In spring, the main passage occurs between mid-April and mid-May (fig. 31). During this period, most are seen flying over the observation point or pausing for a few hours, but one stayed in the Meon valley between Wickham and Mislingford from Apr. 23rd-27th 1972. Between mid-May and mid-June, birds have lingered for up to a week on five occasions; they may well have been immatures or non-breeding adults.

A few have been seen in July and early August; as in late spring these were probably non-breeders or early returning adults which failed to breed successfully. The main autumn passage is from late August until mid-October (fig. 31), when, in contrast to the spring, Ospreys often stay in areas with a plentiful supply of fish for several weeks.

Between 1951 and 1992, some 245 Ospreys were recorded, 107 in spring and 138 in autumn. About half of these were at coastal sites, including 36 between Lymington and Hurst, 33 around Langstone Harbour and Hayling Island, 23 at Titchfield Haven, 21 in Southampton Water and 13 at the Beaulieu Estuary. Inland, there were widespread sightings including 29 in the Avon valley, 22 in the Test valley, 18 in the New Forest, 15 in the Itchen valley, 12 at Frensham Great Pond and ten at Fleet Pond. Virtually all sightings involved single birds but two have been seen together on six occasions (five times in the Avon valley) and three were together at the Beaulieu Estuary on Oct. 7th 1967 and again on Sep. 28th 1969. Most occurred between Apr. 4th and Nov. 7th, the only exceptions being in the Avon valley near Fordingbridge on Mar. 6th 1954, at Lower Test Marshes on Mar. 20th 1991, Langstone Harbour on Mar. 23rd 1974, Marchwood on Nov. 24th 1988, Alresford Pond from Dec. 3rd-6th 1967 and Needs Ore on Dec. 7th 1953.

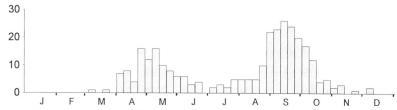

*Figure 31. Cumulative weekly totals of Ospreys, 1951-92.*

The Osprey is a conspicuous species and so the increase in sightings since the 1960s is no doubt real; it is presumably connected with the re-establishment and expansion of the Scottish breeding population, which winters in tropical West Africa. Ringing recoveries from elsewhere in Britain have confirmed that Scandinavian birds are also involved (BWP).

# Kestrel                                             *Falco tinnunculus*

A common resident, passage migrant and winter visitor.

Most observers agree that the Kestrel is the commonest raptor in Hampshire although in some areas it may be outnumbered by the Sparrowhawk. It inhabits urban areas, farmland, heaths and chalk downland; nest sites are varied and include disused nests (Carrion Crows, Magpies etc), holes in trees and quarries, church towers, electricity pylons and other structures and even window ledges on buildings.

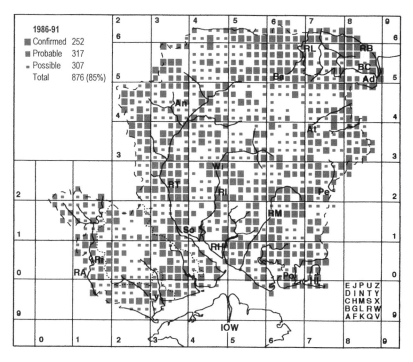

169

The Atlas Map shows a widespread distribution but indicates that some areas in the south-west and centre of the county may be thinly populated; this is probably indicative of birds being overlooked rather than a lack of Kestrels. In the absence of quantitative data, estimation of the Hampshire population is difficult. Assuming an average of two pairs per tetrad where breeding was confirmed or probable and one in those where it was possible indicates a figure of around 1500 pairs. The latest estimate of the British population is 50,000 pairs (New Atlas).

Large concentrations are sometimes reported, presumably where there is an abundance of food. Such gatherings have included 15 at Ashley Walk on Mar. 22nd 1975, ten at Old Winchester Hill on Aug. 22nd 1975, at least nine along the summit of Portsdown Hill overlooking Portsmouth on Oct. 15th 1975 and ten at Ashley Walk on Aug. 28th 1978.

Between 1971 and 1992, there have been several sightings at coastal sites suggesting passage. In spring, 16 were recorded between Mar. 28th and Apr. 27th, 14 flying in off the sea and moving inland and two leaving the coast to the south and south-west. In autumn, one was seen moving north on Aug. 11th and a further 13 were noted between Sep. 15th and Oct. 24th, seven flying in off the sea and six leaving the county in directions between south-east and west.

Ringing data also provide evidence of movements in and out of the county. Of 52 ringed in Hampshire and recovered or controlled, five moved in excess of 100 km. One ringed at Sway on Dec. 1st 1957 was found at Loir-et-Chor, France, 447 km south-east, on Feb. 27th 1959, and another, ringed as a pullus at Winchester on June 14th 1961, was also recovered in France, at Côtes-du-Nord, 315 km SSW, on Sep. 24th 1961. The latter record, and the other long distance recoveries in Oxfordshire, Somerset and Suffolk, show dispersal of juveniles. 27 ringed outside Hampshire have been recovered within it. These include 16 movements of over 100 km, mostly involving birds ringed as pulli, from England (11), Wales (3) and Scotland (2).

## Red-footed Falcon                                   *Falco vespertinus*

A rare non-breeding summer visitor and passage migrant.

K & M gave details of a female shot by Mr. Leggatt of Titchfield in October

1875, but do not give the actual locality, and of another shot at Fordingbridge on the highly unlikely date of January 1877.

The first this century was a male at Martin on Aug. 24th 1937 (*South Eastern Bird Report*). Between 1959 and 1992, there were records for 16 years with a total of 40 individuals involved, of which 24 were in the New Forest.

The first New Forest record involved a party of five, consisting of an adult male, an adult female, a first-summer male and two first-summer females, at Bishop's Dyke on May 16th 1959. Up to four remained until May 24th and the last sighting was of the adult male on June 6th. Subsequently, birds were seen in 1964, 1965, 1970, 1973 (2), 1976†, 1978 (3), 1979, 1982 (3), 1987 (2), 1990 and 1992 (3). Two have occurred together once only, in the Broomy Walk area in 1973, when a male was present from May 25th-June 23rd and a female from June 7th-16th. Most other records were from the Bishop's Dyke area. The extreme dates were Apr. 28th and July 5th, but most were present in the period from mid-May to mid-June.

Records from other localities were as follows:

| | |
|---|---|
| 1960: | first-summer male flying north-west, Farlington Marshes, May 29th; |
| 1964: | first-summer male, Nursling, May 30th-June 9th; |
| | adult female, Nursling, June 9th; |
| | male, Milford-on-Sea, Oct. 2nd; |
| 1973: | female, Farlington Marshes, June 5th and 6th; |
| 1974: | male, Bickton, May 5th; |
| 1977: | male, Winnall Moors, June 2nd and 3rd; |
| 1979: | adult female, Salterns (Lymington), June 4th; |
| | male, Cole Henley (Whitchurch), July 30th; |
| 1989: | first-summer female, Shipton Bellinger, June 2nd-14th; |
| | adult male, Mortimer West End, June 4th; |
| 1990: | female, flying west, Farlington Marshes, June 4th; |
| 1992: | adult male over Southampton City Centre, May 19th; |
| | adult male, Horsebridge, May 24th and 25th; |
| | second-summer male, Horsebridge, May 24th; |
| | first-summer male, John O'Gaunt's Lake (Kings Somborne), June 19th-21st†; |
| 1993: | female, Lower Test Marshes, June 21st†. |

The seven recorded in 1992 were part of an unprecedented influx into north-western Europe which involved over 700 in the Netherlands and at least 129 in Britain (Evans 1993).

The Red-footed Falcon breeds from eastern Europe to central Siberia and winters in southern Africa.


# Merlin                                          *Falco columbarius*

A scarce but regular winter visitor and passage migrant.

Evidence from Langstone Harbour, which has been consistently watched since the early 1950s, suggests considerable fluctuations in wintering numbers over the last 40 years. In the mid-1950s, one or two were present throughout each winter, but observations became less frequent in the early 1960s and only two were seen between 1963 and 1972. A recovery followed; since the 1980s, one or two have wintered in the area annually (Portsmouth Group 1991).

At Titchfield Haven, a different picture emerges, with six sightings during 1951-60, ten in 1961-70, 36 in 1971-80 and 52 in 1981-90 (Duffin 1991).

However, coverage improved during the period, especially following the appointment of a full-time warden in 1972.

The evidence from these two areas matches the trend in British breeding numbers, which fell to their lowest level in the mid-1960s following the widespread use of organochlorine pesticides (BWP).

The first normally arrive in late August or early September. Between 1970 and 1991, earliest dates covered the period Aug. 2nd-Sep. 18th with the average Aug. 26th. There was also one earlier record of a female or immature at Hamble on July 18th 1977. Most of the early autumn records were from coastal sites, especially the Lymington/Hurst area, where August birds have been seen in ten years since the first in 1973.

Autumn sightings reach a peak in late October. This is probably accounted for by passage through or into the county. Since 1971, six have been recorded apparently on migration: four leaving out to sea and two flying north off the sea. Records from inland sites where birds do not winter also peak at this time, e.g. at Fleet Pond, of five recorded since 1985, three were seen between Sep. 30th and Nov. 1st, all flying in southerly directions during diurnal passerine movements.

In winter, Merlins are most frequently observed at coastal sites and in the New Forest. As with the Hen Harrier, the latter area may be more important in providing secure roosts than as a hunting ground. Some of those feeding on nearby coastal marshes and farmland, where the density of prey is greater than on heathlands, are believed to fly into the Forest at dusk to roost. Several communal roosts are known; up to seven have been recorded roosting in small Scots pines at one site, although most counts are in the range one to three.

Merlins are also thinly scattered across the interior of the county, especially on the chalk. Reports during the 1980s have shown that they are regular on the chalk between Old Winchester Hill and Long Down, Greywell and Hillside and in the Great Litchfield Down area, and also in the Avon valley.

Wintering Merlins depart from February onwards, with little evidence of through passage. Between 1971 and 1992, last dates fell in the period Mar. 31st-May 9th with the average Apr. 20th. There have only been six May records, all since 1981, including those of one coming in off the sea at Hurst Beach on May 7th 1981 and another flying west at Black Point on May 9th 1992.

Most records involve single birds or two together, but one male and two females were seen circling and moving south over Bishop's Dyke on Jan. 11th 1972 and a similar group was seen over Pennington Marsh on Jan. 3rd 1976.

The cumulative monthly totals of all records for 1970/71-91/92 are shown below.

| Jul | Aug | Sep | Oct | Nov | Dec | Jan | Feb | Mar | Apr | May | Jun |
|-----|-----|-----|-----|-----|-----|-----|-----|-----|-----|-----|-----|
| 1 | 26 | 84 | 165 | 177 | 177 | 165 | 133 | 109 | 43 | 6 | 0 |

The origin of our wintering population is suggested by the recovery in Hampshire of three birds ringed as chicks in Northumberland, Durham and Tayside and an adult ringed in Powys.

# Hobby                                                   *Falco subbuteo*

A moderately common breeding summer visitor and passage migrant.

The Hobby is best known as a summer visitor to the lowland heaths of southern England, but in recent years it has become increasingly clear that it also occurs, albeit rather more sparingly, in a variety of farmland habitats (Parr 1985, Fuller *et al* 1985, Fiuczynski & Nethersole-Thompson 1980). Hobbies usually breed in old Carrion Crow's nests situated on the edge of woodland or in an isolated clump or line of trees. Parr (1985), who located 51 occupied nests in 1981-82 in the New Forest and on nearby river valley and downland farmland (not necessarily all in Hampshire), found that 49 were crow's, one was a Magpie's and one was a Woodpigeon's. 46 nests (including all those in the New Forest) were in Scots pine, two in Corsican pine, two in oak and one in beech. Tubbs (1986a) located all his New Forest nests in Scots pine, but two other observers have found a total of three nests in other trees.

K & M described the Hobby as a "rare summer visitor to all wooded districts in the county", but considered it to be overlooked. It was well known in the New Forest, but had apparently become increasingly scarce there by the turn of the century, presumably due to the activities of egg and skin collectors. One oologist "working" the county in the early 1900s regarded the finding of a nest in the Forest as "rare and lucky". Other egg collectors subsequently operating between the wars and after were of the opinion that the species was more than holding its own!

The first available comprehensive data for the New Forest are for 1949-54. During this period, D Humphrey located 12 regularly used territories in a 250 km$^2$ study area, all being occupied by nesting pairs in 1954 (Parr 1985). Between 1957 and 1960, 12-15 pairs were located annually by contributors to the *Hampshire Bird Report*. Since 1962, C R Tubbs has monitored a 465 km$^2$ study area, which extends beyond the New Forest boundary. Within this, 25 regularly used sites have been identified, although the most occupied in any one year was 19. Parr (1985), who covered an area of 290 km$^2$, found 11 breeding pairs and one other in 1981 and 14 breeding pairs and two others a year later. The 14 pairs were at a density of 4.9 pairs per 100 km$^2$ with a minimum distance between nests of 3.8 km. This shows little change from Humphrey's study in 1954 (4.8 pairs per 100 km$^2$) and suggests that numbers have remained stable. Eight of Humphrey's 12 sites were still in use in at least five years between 1977 and 1982.

Away from the New Forest, it is only in recent years that the likely size of the population has been realised. Between 1960 and 1966, up to eight pairs were reported annually although the actual number of territories involved was presumably greater than this. Cohen stated that "between five and ten pairs nest on the chalk and greensand in the west and north, but in the east it appears to be scarce". Improved coverage of the north-east from 1971 onwards has shown that six territories have been occupied almost annually and a further six (not always checked) have been used intermittently. In 1981 and 1982, Parr covered 580 km$^2$ of downland farmland and 250 km$^2$ of river valley farmland. In the latter year, he found nine breeding pairs on the downland (at a density of 1.6 pairs per 100 km$^2$) and seven in the river valley (at a density of 2.8 pairs per 100 km$^2$) (Parr 1985).

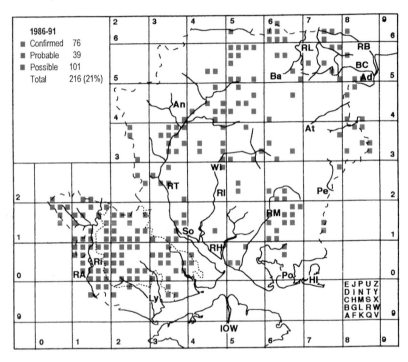

The Atlas Map shows the distribution recorded during 1986-91, with all registrations shown at the same level for security reasons. The Atlas Survey confirmed the tentative view that Hobbies were far more numerous in Hampshire than previously realised, although they were presumably overlooked in the north-west and east central regions of the county. In 1978, the population had been estimated at possibly 40-50 pairs (Sharrock *et al* 1980), while between 1982 and 1987 the records submitted for the *Hampshire Bird Report* referred to 42-52 sites annually. Although breeding was not confirmed at the majority of these, the records did not include complete New Forest data or information from several other traditional sites. On the basis of all the available information the county population is estimated at 75-100 pairs. This range is well supported if the combined density found in Parr's two farmland study areas (1.9 pairs per 100 km$^2$) is applied to Hampshire's 2160 km$^2$ of agricultural land. This gives a total of 41 pairs. Assuming 20 pairs in the New Forest and a further 20 pairs in other non-agricultural sites gives a total of 81 pairs. The British population was estimated at 500-900 pairs in 1988-91 (New Atlas).

Hobbies usually begin to arrive in the third week of April. Between 1971-92 first dates were in the period Apr. 12th-27th with the average Apr. 19th. However, the earliest ever was one at Moon Hill (New Forest) on Mar. 31st 1961. Spring migration is often protracted, with individuals continuing to arrive until early June. Analysis of the records from coastal sites shows a peak in the first week of May. Birds are often seen arriving off the sea, e.g. on May 3rd 1980, eight were recorded including four at Hurst Beach.

After arrival, groups of up to five are often seen feeding or displaying over suitable breeding habitat. There have been two records of larger groups hawking insects. 11 were in the Avon valley between Sopley and Avon Causeway on Apr. 28th 1988 and up to 12 were at Bishop's Dyke in late May 1989.

In autumn, Hobbies are likely to turn up anywhere in the county. They are frequent at dusk at hirundine roosts, e.g. at Farlington Marshes, Fleet Pond and Titchfield Haven, and have also been recorded hunting small waders and passerines over saltmarsh and reclaimed land in Southampton Water. Most depart in late September and early October. During 1971-92, only two were seen after Oct. 11th, the latest being at Old Winchester Hill on Oct. 26th 1974. However, the latest ever was one seen over Portsmouth Docks on Nov. 5th 1963.

There have been two ringing recoveries involving Hampshire birds. An adult ringed in the county on June 2nd 1967 was found locally on July 9th 1967, while one ringed as a chick in Warwickshire on Aug. 3rd 1976 was recovered in Hampshire on Aug. 23rd 1977. British birds winter in Africa south of the Sahara although as yet there are no ringing recoveries to confirm this.

## Gyr Falcon                                   *Falco rusticolus*

One record. A white-morph individual was seen by Meinertzhagen at Mottisfont on Jan. 18th 1896. Cohen quotes Meinertzhagen's diaries, which reveal that it "descended on to a large white Aylesbury duck, carried it 20 yards and ate almost the whole of it".

The Gyr Falcon has a circumpolar breeding distribution. It is a rare visitor to Britain, mostly occurring in the north of the country.

## Peregrine                                    *Falco peregrinus*

A scarce, but increasing, non-breeding visitor; has bred.

The fortunes of this species are closely tied to its success as a breeding species in adjoining counties. In the 1920s and 1930s, up to 15 pairs bred regularly in Dorset, 12 in East Sussex, four in the Isle of Wight and one on Salisbury Cathedral in Wiltshire (Ratcliffe 1980). There is also an exceptional record of a pair nesting in heather at the base of a Scots pine on a west Hampshire heath in 1928 (*Brit. Birds* 22: 190), although unfortunately the eggs were taken.

During the Second World War, the 1940 Destruction of Peregrine Falcons Order permitted their killing in certain parts of the country, but not in those adjacent to Hampshire. However, it is certain that some were killed on the coast of south-east England (Ratcliffe 1980). Although showing some recovery after the war, populations were unable to return to their 1930s level before the advent of organochlorine pesticides caused a further more serious decline. Between 1956 and 1961, Peregrines deserted all the previously occupied territories close to Hampshire.

Breeding birds did not return to Dorset until the early 1980s; from then on there has been a progressive re-occupation of old nesting sites which has coincided with a marked increase in sightings in Hampshire, especially from 1987 onwards. Table 27 shows the cumulative monthly totals for each decade in the period 1951-90.

| | Jan | Feb | Mar | Apr | May | Jun | Jul | Aug | Sep | Oct | Nov | Dec | Totals |
|---|---|---|---|---|---|---|---|---|---|---|---|---|---|
| 1951-60 | 10 | 13 | 14 | 7 | 2 | 1 | 1 | 4 | 11 | 11 | 13 | 16 | 103 |
| 1961-70 | 8 | 9 | 12 | 3 | 2 | 0 | 2 | 3 | 8 | 7 | 5 | 9 | 68 |
| 1971-80 | 14 | 11 | 11 | 3 | 2 | 0 | 1 | 3 | 9 | 12 | 14 | 11 | 91 |
| 1981-90 | 41 | 37 | 29 | 13 | 15 | 9 | 8 | 26 | 42 | 47 | 48 | 47 | 362 |
| Totals | 73 | 70 | 66 | 26 | 21 | 10 | 12 | 36 | 70 | 77 | 80 | 83 | |

*Table 27. Cumulative monthly totals of Peregrines, 1951-90.*

Coverage was quite good in the second half of the 1950s, especially on the coast, although Peregrines were already declining by this time. The low total in the 1960s agrees with the period when the British population was at its lowest ebb. The figures for the 1970s, although partially influenced by improving observer coverage, suggest that birds originating from distant areas, where the recovery was already underway, were wintering in Hampshire. The massive increase in the final decade, including summer records, coincides with their return as a breeding species to adjoining counties.

At the present time, Peregrines are a regular sight along the coast between August and April and are not infrequent in the summer months, especially in the west Solent and Southampton Water. Although most records involve single birds, sightings of two together are quite common and three were seen at Pennington Marsh on Jan. 8th 1987 and Titchfield Haven on Jan. 24th 1988. At inland sites, records are sporadic and some no doubt refer to migrants. However, localities such as Cheesefoot Head, Long Down and Martin Down on the chalk, Ibsley in the Avon valley, Ashley Walk in the New Forest and Stratfield Saye Park have all had between five and ten sightings in the last five years and may well be regular wintering areas.

## Black Grouse                                          *Tetrao tetrix*

Formerly resident on the heathlands of the New Forest and north-east, but died out by the 1920s.

Gilpin, writing in 1834, described how the Black Grouse was formerly found in great abundance in the New Forest, but had become much scarcer. This decline, which was traced in some detail by Tubbs (1968), continued through the nineteenth century. Considerable numbers were killed by sporting licensees and keepers, and this certainly hastened the decrease of the species, perhaps significantly. By 1905, it had "not quite died out", but the surviving population included stock introduced by Lascelles, the Deputy Surveyor at the time. The species hung on until the 1930s; the last record appears to be of a grey-hen seen at Fernycroft on Oct. 26th 1936 (J H Branford per C R Tubbs).

In the north-east, Gilbert White described its disappearance from Woolmer Forest in the mid-18th century. It was subsequently reintroduced there, but had disappeared again by 1899 (K & M). Black Grouse also occurred on other heathlands in north-east Hampshire, although the only site for which Clark (1984) was able to trace records for the period between 1880 and 1900 was Yateley Common.

## Red-legged Partridge                                    *Alectoris rufa*

A common resident.

Red-legged Partridges were first introduced into Hampshire in the nineteenth century; releases have continued so that today the species is widespread, occurring mainly on farmland but also sparingly on some heathlands and waste ground.

C & T considered that Red-legs were generally much less common than Grey Partridges. In 1968, a survey of 15 km² of farmland in SU54 produced only two pairs of this species but 29 pairs of Greys. However, national CBC data show that, over the past two decades, Red-legs have increased while Grey Partridges have undergone a drastic decline (Marchant *et al* 1990). Today, this is

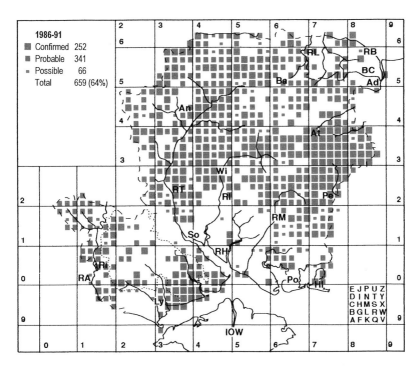

the more numerous of the two species in some parts of the county, but in some cases this is certainly due to the presence of released birds, e.g. in the Beaulieu/Sowley area. Since the 1970s, many releases have involved hybrids of this species and the Chukar *A. chukar*, known by shooters as "ogridges". These hybrids are very similar to pure Red-legs and there has been no attempt to distinguish between them on the Atlas Map.

During the Atlas Survey, there were registrations in 659 tetrads. On the basis of three to four pairs per occupied tetrad, this equates to a county population of 2000-2500 pairs, but any estimate is likely to be distorted by artificial stocking. It is clear that if releases were to stop the population of feral birds would be considerably lower than it is today. In 1988-91, the British population was estimated at 90,000 pairs (New Atlas).

## Grey Partridge                                    *Perdix perdix*

A common, but declining, resident.

K & M described the Grey Partridge as "resident and universally distributed in all districts in the county." A measure of its abundance is given by the fact that it formed 40% of Hawker's total bag: 7035 shot from 1802-53. Almost 70 years later, C & T wrote that "it breeds freely in all suitable localities, being especially numerous in some areas such as the chalklands around Winchester". They also warned that numbers had declined in some areas during the 1960s, but that it was too soon to say whether the decline was temporary or of a more serious nature.

In fact, the decline has proved to be very serious indeed. A continuous fall in the national population has been occurring throughout the century and has continued to the present day. The CBC index has fallen to a tenth of the level when it was first calculated in 1962 (Marchant *et al* 1990). Two main factors are involved in the decline (Potts 1980, 1984). The first is predation by corvids, small mammals and foxes, which increased because of reduced control by gamekeepers, and because changing farming practices led to loss of quality nesting habitat which made it easier for the predators to find their prey. The second is the effect of agricultural methods which reduced the densities of insects on which Grey Partridges and their chicks feed. The disappearance of sawfly larvae, a preferred food of chicks, as a result of decreased undersowing, has been a critical factor, while the more intensive use of herbicides and pesticides has reduced the food supply of adults (Thompson 1990).

In Hampshire, the Game Conservancy Trust has been monitoring Grey Partridge numbers for many years. Data from two estates in the centre of the county (Table 28) illustrate that the decline has been dramatic (Thompson 1990).

| Estate | Year | Number of broods | Brood size | Chick survival rate % | August population |
|--------|------|------------------|------------|-----------------------|-------------------|
| 1 | 1935 | 98 | 8.6 | 58.8 | 1247 |
|   | 1987 | 5 | 2.2 | 10.3 | 32 |
| 2 | 1935 | 83 | 9.2 | 64.9 | 1160 |
|   | 1987 | 5 | 3.0 | 15.7 | 23 |

*Table 28. Grey Partridges on two Hampshire Estates.*

The chick survival rates in the table are far too low to maintain a healthy population, yet, as the Atlas Map shows, it remains a widespread species. It is still found throughout the agricultural heartland of the county but is absent from much of the New Forest, the north-east heathlands and urban areas including the broad coastal zone from Portsmouth to Southampton. Counts in autumn and winter, e.g. in 1986, 80 between Middle Wallop and Danebury on Feb. 2nd, 35 in a single covey at Old Winchester Hill on Oct. 12th and 70 in the Greywell/Hillside area in December, show that populations remain healthy in some areas.

There are few estimates of breeding densities but it is clear that these can vary widely depending on local farming practices and gamekeeping activities. This is illustrated by the work of the Game Conservancy Trust which pioneered the use of "conservation headlands" on some Hampshire estates. To create a conservation headland, a farmer allows the outside six metres of his cereal crop - a border closest to the field boundary - to retain a scattering of weeds and higher densities of insects. Grey Partridges use the conservation headlands readily and chick survival rate increases markedly. In spring 1987, the Manydown Estate near Basingstoke, which has been using the technique, had 117 pairs on approximately 20 km$^2$, equivalent to almost six pairs per km$^2$. In 1989, nine Hampshire farms had some 100 km of conservation headland (Thompson 1990); this, coupled with increasing amounts of set-aside land, may offer the best chance of reversing the decline of this species in the county.

It is difficult to estimate the total population. During the Atlas Survey, there were registrations in 603 tetrads; since they are essentially sedentary, each

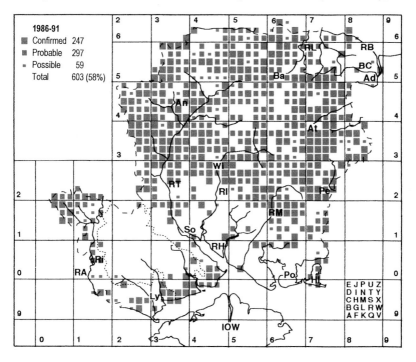

record is likely to refer to breeding birds. Although densities such as that quoted above are now unusual, most tetrads will hold more than one pair and some will hold considerably more. Assuming an average of four to five pairs per occupied tetrad indicates a Hampshire population of 2400-3000 pairs. In 1988-91, the British population was estimated at 140,000-150,000 pairs (New Atlas).

# Quail                                      *Coturnix coturnix*

A scarce and erratic summer visitor; formerly recorded occasionally in winter.

The Quail is recorded almost annually but numbers only occasionally reach double figures. Since 1951, the largest influxes have been in 1964 (47 calling males, including 40 in the Martin/Damerham area), 1976 (16), 1987 (16-22), 1989 (73) and 1990 (13). The Atlas Map incorporates records for 1951-85 as well as those from the Atlas Survey. Although the species is clearly under-recorded, the distribution shown presumably overstates the usual situation in any one year, since it includes records for 1989, an unprecedented "Quail year", and four other above average seasons.

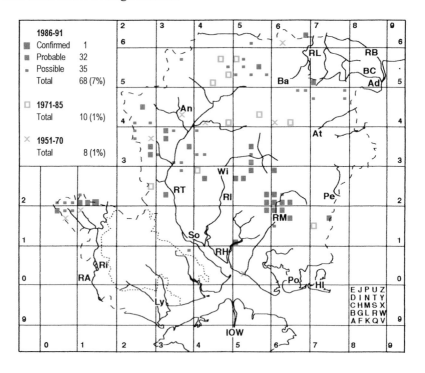

Because of the way numbers vary from year to year, it is not appropriate to give an estimate of the "normal" county population. The recorded average for the period 1970-92, excluding 1989, was six calling males. The reasons for the fluctuations are uncertain but influxes are generally associated with warm, dry springs and south-easterly winds – conditions which favour migration over-shoots. Other factors, such as high breeding success in the previous season and low mortality on the wintering grounds or during migration, may also play a part. 1989 was a remarkable year, not only in Hampshire, but throughout Britain, where the total number of calling males present was estimated at 2600 (New Atlas). In the other years of the New Atlas, the British population was estimated at 100-300 pairs.

The first males are usually heard in mid-May, although in 1976 and 1988 there were records for May 5th. There have been three earlier sightings of single birds at Hill Head on Mar. 5th 1950 (which had presumably wintered), Longwood Warren on Apr. 28th 1973 and Leigh Park on Apr. 9th 1991. Quails continue to arrive in June and possibly into July. Typically, they are heard calling from cereal fields, particularly barley, but also in other crops, including clover and oilseed rape, and unmown grass. As the Atlas Map shows, there are preferred areas where registrations are clustered. These are all on the chalk and include traditional sites such as Martin Down, Danebury, Farley Mount, Longwood Warren, Old Winchester Hill and Crondall. It is likely that many are missed in other, less-visited parts of the county. Males call regularly when they first arrive but much less frequently once they have acquired a mate, unless there are other males in territory nearby (Moreau 1951). A record of a lone calling male for more than a week is, therefore, more likely to refer to an unmated bird than to a breeding pair. Proof of breeding is very difficult to obtain; of the 68 Atlas Survey registrations the only one of confirmed breeding referred to a brood flushed during harvesting near Fordingbridge in 1989 (Stoate 1990).

Calling occasionally continues into August but there have been few records after the middle of that month. In recent years, the latest were of one at South Wonston Farm on Sep. 12th 1970, two near Andover on the same date in 1979 and four flushed from a track at Chilton Candover on Sep. 28th 1989. Between 1953 and 1959, there were several reports of birds flushed during winter shoots in the Damerham area on dates between Oct. 19th and Jan. 16th, and in 1961, one was flushed from kale during a Pheasant drive at nearby Whitsbury on Jan. 19th.

Quail breeding in western Europe are believed to winter in the northern Afrotropics (BWP).

# Pheasant                                    *Phasianus colchicus*

An abundant resident.

Cohen, quoting J S Ash, described the Pheasant as "widely and commonly distributed throughout the county except in the built-up areas; least numerous in the New Forest". This description remains valid today. The county's mix of agriculture and woodland suits the species well, while the coverts left on many estates for their protection are beneficial to several other species. During the Atlas Survey, there were registrations in 939 (91%) of tetrads, with breeding confirmed in 547, probable in 333 and possible in 59. They were scarce or absent only in the urban zones from Portsmouth to Southampton, in the north-east around Aldershot and in some heavily-wooded areas including the New Forest.

The national population has increased steadily throughout much of the present century although CBC data show that the upward trend has slowed markedly over the past two decades (Marchant *et al* 1990). Overall, the population is dominated by large scale releases of artificially-reared birds. A conservative estimate of the number released annually in Britain would be 10-15 million. However, since most are shot close to where they are released and many others do not survive the winter, relatively few remain to augment the breeding stock (Marchant *et al* 1990).

Rearing and releasing is widespread on Hampshire's many sporting estates. Typically 300 per km$^2$ are released annually (S C Tapper pers. comm.). Although the majority do not survive to the following breeding season, some dispersion occurs and it is likely that Pheasants have, by now, reached optimum densities in those habitats which are not shot and restocked. If releases were stopped the wild population would undoubtedly fall.

Territorial males are polygynous – they have a harem of two or more females. In Hampshire, it has been estimated that there are approximately 21,000 territorial males, 17,000 non-territorial males and 40,000 hens (Robertson *et al* 1989). The British population has been estimated in the order of 3 million territorial males, 2 million non-territorial males and 4.5 million hens (Marchant *et al* 1990).

# Golden Pheasant                              *Chrysolophus pictus*

# Lady Amherst's Pheasant                       *Chrysolophus amherstiae*

Very scarce introduced residents.

The first Golden Pheasants in Hampshire were probably in the Hinton Admiral estate. Edlin (1952) described how they arrived in the area after a fire destroyed the pine woods at Hurn Court (now in Dorset). He does not give a specific date, but since Hart shot a pair at Hurn in 1875, they presumably spread to Hinton Admiral at some time after that. They had died out by the mid-1960s (68-72 Atlas).

Golden Pheasants were also released on to the Beaulieu Manor Estate in 1925. These established themselves in the wild and in 1952 there were at least 12 pairs (Cohen). In 1958, or possibly earlier, Lady Amherst's Pheasants were released on the nearby Exbury Estate (J Rushen pers. comm.). In 1973, three cock and eight hen Lady Amherst's were seen at Exbury, but in 1977, four cocks in a group of 13 birds were clearly hybrids with Golden Pheasant. Subsequently, most reports from there have been of hybrids, although 16 pure Goldens, mainly males, were released in 1987 and occasional reports of pure Lady Amherst's continued until 1988. During the 1970s and 1980s, there were also reports of both species from the Stubbs Wood/Tantany Copse/Frame Wood area of the New Forest. Occasional sightings elsewhere in the Forest are probably the result of other introductions, e.g. 14 were put down in Manor Wood (Minstead) in October 1983.

Golden Pheasants are also present in the Queen Elizabeth Country Park area. They have been there since the early 1970s at least and are believed to have spread from West Sussex (M Wearing pers. comm.). In 1987, there were six pairs in Head Down Plantation and three on Oxenbourne Down. However, immediately following the great storm in October of that year, they disappeared from the latter site. Since then, they have been confined to Head Down, where a maximum of three pairs has been recorded.

During the Atlas Survey, Golden Pheasants were also reported at Noar Hill and Goleigh Wood, with up to six cocks present at each locality between 1988 and 1990. These are believed to have been released by shooting syndicates, despite the poor sport offered by the species (S H Carter pers. comm.).

Elsewhere, there have been occasional records of both species which are presumably escapes from ornamental collections.

Both species are usually found in woodland with little or no understorey. In the Exbury area, they occur in conifer plantations and in mixed woodland with clumps of rhododendron. At Queen Elizabeth Country Park, they inhabit extensive yew stands and beech and hazel plantations. The only nest ever found was in hazel coppice adjacent to a yew stand (M Wearing pers. comm.).

# Water Rail                                    *Rallus aquaticus*

A scarce resident; outside the breeding season the population is considerably augmented by immigrants.

In Hampshire, most breeding sites are in reed beds or thick sedges and rushes on the edges of rivers and lakes, although nesting has occurred in a few heathland bogs. Due to the nature of its habitat, and the tendency for it to remain largely silent by day during the breeding season, Water Rails were undoubtedly overlooked during the Atlas Survey. Breeding was confirmed or probable in 29 tetrads, and possible in a further 27. The Atlas Map also shows other breeding records for 1951-85, which involved a further 13 tetrads. Several of these, especially in the Avon valley, were not well covered during the Atlas Survey and probably still hold the species. The only sites where breeding has regularly been recorded since 1981 are Alresford Pond (1-2 pairs), Emer Bog (1), Fleet Pond (1-4), River Meon between West Meon and Exton (1-2), Titchfield Haven (max. 7 in 1985), Warsash (1-2), Wendleholme (1) and Woolmer Pond (1-2). Estimating a county population for this elusive species is extremely speculative, but it possibly lies in the range 25-100 pairs. It is also impossible to know of any long-term trends, although the population may have been hit by the five hard winters during the period 1978-87 (Marchant *et al* 1990). In 1988-91, the British population was estimated at 450-900 pairs (New Atlas).

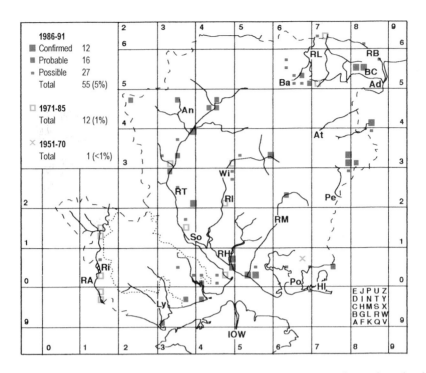

Outside the breeding season, Water Rails occur in a wider variety of wetland habitats, including gravel pit margins, overgrown streams and ditches, watercress beds and sewage farms. They are also present in some coastal reed beds which are apparently unoccupied during the summer. At Farlington Marshes, the first returns are usually noted in August or September, although there have been several in July including the earliest on 12th in 1986.

Peak numbers probably occur in November or December. It is impossible to count all the Water Rails present in a large area of reed beds, but estimates based on the numbers heard are regularly made at Titchfield Haven and Fleet Pond, where the maxima have been 70 in November and December 1989 and 40 in November 1988 respectively. Other localities with counts over five during 1971-92 include Alresford Pond (max. 15), Farlington Marshes (6), Greywell (20+), Keyhaven Marsh (6), Lower Test Marshes (10), Needs Ore (10), Stratfield Saye (8), Shepherds Spring (19) and Warsash (8). While some of these counts are exceptional for the localities concerned, others such as Alresford Pond, Keyhaven, Lower Test Marshes and Warsash may hold greater numbers on a regular basis. In severe weather, Water Rails become more conspicuous as they are forced out into the open to feed in ice-free areas. Notable concentrations are sometimes recorded, e.g. 19, including a group of nine together, along the edges of gravel pits and watercress beds at Shepherds Spring on Feb. 1st 1976 and 12 along a muddy ditch at Fleet Pond on Feb. 12th 1986. Most wintering birds leave between mid-March and early April.

National ringing data show that some Water Rails wintering in Britain originate from as far afield as Sweden, Poland and Czechoslovakia (Flegg &

Glue 1973). The only bird to be recovered in Hampshire was ringed as a juvenile in Neubrandenburg, eastern Germany on July 19th 1982 and picked up when it "dropped from the sky" at Farlington, 1050 km WSW, on Nov. 1st 1982. The only recovery of a Hampshire-ringed bird is also of note: an adult ringed at Twyford on Oct. 17th 1976 and found dead in Sudbaden, western Germany, 729 km ESE, in October 1977.

## Spotted Crake                        *Porzana porzana*

A very scarce passage migrant and winter visitor; has bred.

None was recorded in the first half of this century, but since 1951 Spotted Crakes have been noted in every year except five (fig. 32).

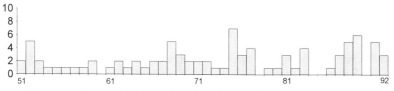

*Figure 32. Annual totals of Spotted Crakes, 1951-92.*

Most have occurred in autumn, with records in 32 years accounting for 67 individuals (fig. 33). Early birds were at Warsash on July 20th 1992 and Farlington Marshes on Aug. 3rd 1988, but the period when most have been recorded is from late August to mid-September. Some birds may have remained to winter; between December and February, there have been records in 13 years involving 15 birds, with the latest at Fleet Pond on Feb. 2nd 1972. Most of the winter birds were seen in mild weather.

Records for July-February have come from Farlington Marshes (41 birds), Titchfield Haven (11), Pennington and Keyhaven Marshes (8), Fleet Pond (5), Warsash (4), Alresford Pond, Lisle Court Lagoon and Paulsgrove Reclamation (2 each), and Bedhampton, Browndown, Cadland, Frensham Great Pond, Greywell, Mottisfont and Portsmouth town centre (1 each).

There have been eight spring records, of single birds at Farlington Marshes on Mar. 20th 1955, Mar. 29th 1964 (found dead), Mar. 27th 1965, Mar. 24th-31st 1968 and Apr. 5th 1986, Lower Test Marshes on Apr. 21st 1976, Fleet Pond on Apr. 12th 1989 and Titchfield Haven on Apr. 11th and 12th 1991.

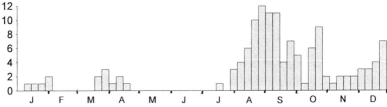

*Figure 33. Cumulative weekly totals of Spotted Crakes, 1951-92.*

K & M described the species as "a very local resident", although their only reports of confirmed breeding were from Hart, who collected mainly in the Christchurch area, outside the present day county boundary. In recent years, birds were present at Titchfield Haven during two summers and bred successfully on one occasion (Duffin 1991).

In Britain, the Spotted Crake is on the western edge of its breeding range, which extends east to Kazakhstan and Siberia. The main wintering areas are in tropical Africa and the Indian sub-continent.

## Little Crake                                         *Porzana parva*

One record. A male was at Farlington Marshes from Sep. 14th-20th 1959.

The nearest breeding grounds of the Little Crake are in France and the Netherlands. Its winter quarters are poorly known; although some have been reported in Europe in winter, most probably migrate to sub-Saharan Africa.

## Baillon's Crake                                    *Porzana pusilla*

One record. An adult was caught by a cat and released unharmed at Normandy Marsh (Lymington) on Mar. 17th 1990†.

This is one of only ten Baillon's Crakes recorded in Britain since 1958. The nearest breeding grounds are in France and the Netherlands. Most of the European population probably winters in sub-Saharan Africa.

## Corncrake                                            *Crex crex*

Formerly a breeding summer visitor, but now an increasingly rare passage migrant.

K & M described the Corncrake as a common summer visitor to all parts of the county, occasionally remaining for the winter. However, they noted an unusual scarcity in 1904, which appears to be the earliest reference to declining numbers in Hampshire. Cohen cited several examples of local declines in the first two decades of this century, and also quotes H G Alexander's report of the Land-rail Enquiry in 1913/14, which said that there were very few in the county, and to the east and west of the New Forest the "decrease had reached vanishing point" and that "it seems to have started at least 20 years ago".

186

By 1930, it was evidently very local, although observer coverage was poor at this time. Between 1935 and 1938, there were several reports from Ashmansworth, Highclere and Ecchinswell, although it had already become scarce in that area. At the latter site, an adult and three young were destroyed by a mowing machine in a hay field on June 14th 1938 (Summers-Smith 1950). No doubt the increased use of machinery during the first half of the 20th century was a major contributory factor in its decline. Subsequently, the only records for that area were of single birds at Burghclere on Sep. 1st 1943 and Ashmansworth on Oct. 3rd 1953.

Other areas where the species was reported during the 1930s include Leckford, the Anton valley, Petersfield, West Tytherley and West Dean, where a pair and six young were recorded in 1938 (*South Eastern Bird Reports*).

In the late 1940s, it was still present at Rockbourne and Damerham in summer. Although it continued to be recorded almost annually in that area up to 1960, most records were for August-October and may have involved migrants. Since 1950, the only confirmed cases of breeding have been at Fawley in 1951 and Park Gate in 1957. A male held territory at St. Cross from late April until July 12th 1957 but was apparently unmated.

Breeding records aside, a total of 51 was recorded between 1951 and 1992, with 26 in 1951-60, 13 in 1961-70, ten in 1971-80 and three in 1981-92. The marked reduction, despite greatly increased observer activity, parallels the national picture, where the breeding population has declined rapidly and is now largely confined to the Inner and Outer Hebrides (Hudson *et al* 1990). The cumulative monthly totals for 1951-92 are shown below.

| Jan | Feb | Mar | Apr | May | Jun | Jul | Aug | Sep | Oct | Nov | Dec |
|-----|-----|-----|-----|-----|-----|-----|-----|-----|-----|-----|-----|
| 0 | 2 | 1 | 5 | 6 | 0 | 3 | 10 | 16 | 5 | 3 | 2 |

Apart from the Damerham records already mentioned, which account for 11 birds, six were seen at Farlington Marshes and the rest were widely spread around the county, with 17 at coastal sites and 18 inland. Winter records were of single birds at Bedhampton on Feb. 11th 1951, Overton in December 1951 and February 1952, Middle Wallop on Mar. 16th 1967 and Needs Ore in December 1987, the latter being found freshly dead.

The Corncrake is primarily a summer visitor to Europe. The main wintering area is believed to be in tropical East Africa.

# Moorhen                                    *Gallinula chloropus*

A numerous resident and winter visitor.

Moorhens nest in virtually all freshwater habitats provided that suitable vegetation is available for nest building. In Hampshire, the largest concentrations occur in the river valleys, at lakes and ponds and in coastal marshes and reclamation areas. They also breed on the chalk at isolated village and farm ponds, often several kilometres from other suitable habitat. Few systematic counts of breeding pairs have been made. At Farlington Marshes, the population in a 30 ha CBC plot varied between six and 18 pairs during 1981-90, while in two plots totalling 108 ha at Titchfield Haven, totals in the same period were in the range 24-39 pairs. Surveys of the complete Hampshire section of the Basingstoke Canal between Greywell and Ash Vale (45.5 km) produced 111 pairs in 1978 (2.44 pairs per km) and 34 in 1991 (0.75 pairs per km). The reduction is attributed to the dredging and re-opening of the canal to motorised craft (G J S Rowland 1993). The Atlas Survey produced registrations of probable or confirmed breeding in 604 tetrads. Although a few will have held one or two pairs only, most probably held considerably more. Assuming 8-12 territories per occupied tetrad indicates a Hampshire population of 5000-7500 pairs. In 1988-91, the British population was estimated at 240,000 territories (New Atlas).

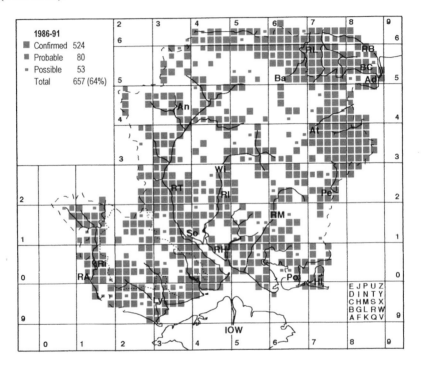

During the winter months, concentrations in excess of 50 are widespread. Since 1972, counts in the range 100-120 have been made at Allington Gravel Pit, Elvetham Lake, Needs Ore and Tundry Pond. At Titchfield Haven, where a regular winter census is carried out, the maximum count was of 179 in February 1984. The highest ever site count was of 268 at Farlington Marshes on Dec. 13th 1967.

Ringing data confirm that some of our wintering population is of continental origin. Of 40 recoveries and controls involving Hampshire birds, continental movements were to or from Belgium (1), Denmark (1), France (3), Germany (2), and the Netherlands (6). The longest movements involved one ringed as a juvenile at Nahskow, Denmark on Aug. 27th 1961 and controlled at Stockbridge, 941 km WSW, on Oct. 29th 1961, and another ringed as a juvenile at Leipzig, eastern Germany on Oct. 9th 1970 and shot at Timsbury, 956 km west, on Jan. 6th 1971.

# Coot                                    *Fulica atra*

A common resident with numbers much augmented by immigrants outside the breeding season.

The breeding population has increased considerably during the present century, due largely to the expansion of the gravel extraction industry which has created extensive new habitat. The largest concentrations are on gravel pit complexes at Blashford (81 pairs in 1986) and Eversley/Yateley (60 pairs in 1988), although several other lakes and ponds hold in excess of ten pairs. Coots also breed on rivers, canals and small ponds provided that sufficient emergent vegetation is available for nest building.

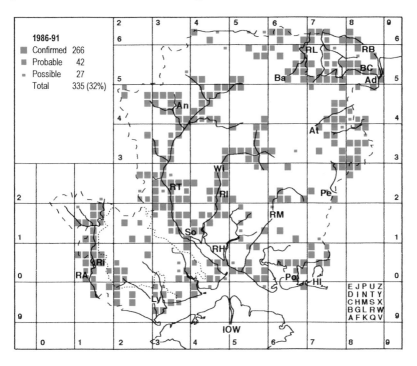

Estimating the total population for the county is difficult because of the wide variations in density between tetrads. Recent counts from ten localities (including Blashford and Eversley/Yateley) total 282 pairs in 35 tetrads. It is estimated that at the end of the Atlas Survey these held a minimum of 250 pairs. Taking a density of two to five pairs in the remaining tetrads where breeding was confirmed or probable, a population in the range 800-1600 pairs is suggested. In 1988-91, the British population was estimated at 46,000 individuals (New Atlas).

Outside the breeding season, the numbers and distribution have varied considerably since the early 1950s when systematic recording began. At the start of that period, the largest flock was found on salt water at Bedhampton Creek in Langstone Harbour, where the maximum was 450 in November 1952. Numbers then declined and none was seen there after the 1962/63 winter apart from 145 in December 1973. During the 1950s and 1960s, other important localities included Alresford Pond (max. 266, October 1964), Lower Test and Eling Great Marshes (max. 750 in severe weather, January 1963), Sowley Pond (max. 500+, January 1958), Titchfield Haven (max. 450 in severe weather, January 1962) and Winnall Moors (max. 220, February 1955).

In the last 20 years, the gravel pit complexes at Blashford and Eversley/Yateley have emerged as the main wintering sites for Coot, large concentrations being attracted by the profuse growth of Canadian pondweed which quickly establishes itself in newly-created lakes. Five-year means of maxima for these sites are shown below.

|  | 1970-75 | 1975-80 | 1980-85 | 1985-90 |
|---|---|---|---|---|
| Blashford Lakes | 262^ | 349^ | 1003 | 1143 |
| Eversley/Yateley Gravel Pits | 189 | 299 | 562 | 463 |

Numbers appear to have fallen recently at Eversley/Yateley although the highest count there was of 660 in November 1989. At Blashford, the flock continues to grow and reached 1635 in November 1990 and 1698 in January 1992. Maxima at other sites where counts have exceeded 200 during 1970/71-91/92 are shown below.

| Locality | Maximum counts | No. of winters with counts of 100+ |
|---|---|---|
| Alresford Pond | 273, October 1979 | 17 |
| Broadlands Lake | 342, December 1983 | 11 |
| Dogmersfield Lake | 249, January 1986 | 9 |
| Farlington Marshes | 238, December 1981 | 5 |
| Lower Test/Eling | 600, January 1982 | 15 |
| Paulsgrove Reclamation | 589, January 1982 | 8 |
| Stratfield Saye | 240, January 1982 | 8 |
| Titchfield Haven | 301, January 1987 | 15 |
| Timsbury Gravel Pit | 210, November 1988 | 10 |

Counts in the range 100-200 have also been recorded at Allington Gravel Pit, in the Avon valley at Blashford, Hucklesbrook, between Avon and Bisterne and above Fordingbridge, Fleet Pond, IBM Lake, in the Test valley between Longstock and Leckford, Northington, Rooksbury Mill, Sinah Gravel Pit, Sowley Pond and Wellington Country Park, but at most of these, this level was reached in one or two years only.

At some localities, e.g. Alresford Pond and Dogmersfield Lake, peak numbers are usually recorded in early autumn, suggesting that mostly local birds are involved. At other inland waters, the winter's maximum normally occurs in November or December, with a gradual departure in January which accelerates in February and March. During severe weather, many move to rivers and coastal marshes where they often graze on ice-free meadows.

Brown (1955) analysed national ringing data and found that some Coots wintering in England originate from as far away as Russia. Unfortunately, there does not appear to have been any more recent analysis of the available information. There have been 12 recoveries/controls involving Hampshire birds. A young male was ringed in Gironde, France on Sep. 28th 1973 and found dead at Lower Test Marshes, 700 km north, on Jan. 31st 1975. The other movements were all within England. Those exceeding 100 km involved single birds ringed at Abberton Reservoir, Essex in July and November 1962 and recovered at Farlington Marshes in December 1962 and Milford-on-Sea in January 1963 respectively, one ringed at Shrawley, Worcestershire in February 1963 and controlled at Chilbolton three months later, and one ringed at St. James' Park, London in November 1982 and seen at Titchfield Haven in February 1984, where it subsequently bred.

# Crane                                                            *Grus grus*

A rare passage migrant.

The first record of the Crane for the county was of one at the Beaulieu Estuary from Nov. 5th-29th 1959, when it was found dead. The next were two seen at Eastleigh on June 2nd 1961.

In late autumn 1963, at least 50 occurred in the county as part of a large influx into southern England involving some 500 birds (Harber 1964). These were probably en route from Scandinavia or the south Baltic to wintering grounds in Iberia and were drifted westwards by east winds. On Oct. 30th, 25 flew south-east over Otterbourne and two east over Farlington Marshes. The following day, 25 were seen over Bishop's Dyke and *c.* 50 off Milford-on-Sea. On Nov. 1st, flocks of 25 and 19 were seen over Bishop's Dyke and the next day 17 moved east over Farlington Marshes.

There were no more until 1978, when an adult and a juvenile were at Fareham Creek and Brownwich on Dec. 3rd. The next were two adults at Titchfield Haven on Feb. 27th 1979. Between 1984 and 1991, there were records in every year, as follows:

1984:  3, Emsworth and Titchfield Haven, Apr. 7th and presumably the same flying north-east over Farlington Marshes, Apr. 8th;
       1 soaring over Titchfield Haven, Apr. 27th;
1985:  1 flying over Goodworth Clatford, Apr. 16th;
1986:  1 moving north-west over The Kench (Hayling Island), Oct. 12th; later seen on the ground at Titchfield Haven and then flying east over Farlington Marshes;
1987:  1 flew from Thorney Island (West Sussex) to Eastney Park Farm (Hayling), Sep. 27th;
1988:  3 flew south over Amberwood Inclosure (New Forest), Nov. 12th;
1989:  1 flew west into gale force winds over Hayling Bay, Oct. 28th;
1990:  1 flew over Bishop's Dyke, June 16th;
1991:  1 near Titchfield Haven, Apr. 15th.

# Little Bustard                                                  *Tetrax tetrax*

A rare vagrant. There have been six records, as follows:

1810:  female, shot, Broadlands Estate, September;
1873:  female, shot, Whitchurch, Jan. 4th;
1879:  1, shot, between Fareham and Gosport, Jan. 9th;
1935:  1, shot, Stockbridge, Dec. 14th;
1944:  1, Avington, early January, and presumably the same bird at Bighton and Chawton Park;
1988:  1, North Ripley, Jan. 1st. It was present in adjacent areas of Dorset from Dec. 30th 1987 until at least Jan. 5th.

The nearest breeding grounds of the Little Bustard are in central and western France. This population disperses in winter, with most probably moving to southern France and Iberia. The decrease in records in Hampshire, which parallels the national picture, reflects the decline in many parts of Europe.

# Great Bustard                                    *Otis tarda*

Formerly resident, but only recorded once this century.

K & M quote several interesting records, including flocks of 25 and 12 in the second half of the 18th century. Breeding had clearly ceased by the 19th century, for which they list only three records, the most recent of a female shot near Romsey on Jan. 10th 1891. Seven females were procured in various parts of England in that winter. The only record this century is of an adult female shot at St. Mary Bourne on Jan. 12th 1910.

The Great Bustard breeds on the steppes of Iberia and from eastern Europe to Siberia and Mongolia.


# Oystercatcher                          *Haematopus ostralegus*

A moderately common breeder, common passage migrant and winter visitor.

The Oystercatcher was first proved to breed in 1934 (Cohen); in the following two decades a few pairs probably nested regularly at the Beaulieu Estuary and in the Lymington/Hurst area. In 1954, breeding was suspected in Langstone Harbour and in the next year it was confirmed for the first time. By 1966, the county population had reached 21 pairs with 11 at the Beaulieu Estuary and ten between Lymington and Hurst. During the 1970s, there was a continuing build-up at west Solent sites, with maxima of 48 pairs between Pitts Deep and Hurst in 1977 (a longer stretch of coastline than was covered in 1966) and 25 at the Beaulieu Estuary in 1979. A few pairs bred intermittently at other sites including Langstone Harbour, where the first full census of the islands by the RSPB in 1979 produced 15 pairs.

Numbers continued to rise through the 1980s; during the Atlas Survey, peak numbers in the three main areas were 34 pairs in Langstone Harbour in 1986 and 1991, 37+ at the Beaulieu Estuary in 1988 and 90 between Pitts Deep and Hurst in 1990. Breeding was also confirmed at Fawley Power Station (2-4 pairs), Warsash (1-3 pairs), and Titchfield Haven, Curbridge, Eling Great Marsh, Cadland Creek and between Stanswood Bay and Lepe (single pairs). Complete surveys at the three main sites in 1992 located 41 pairs at Langstone, 67 at Beaulieu and 129 between Pitts Deep and Hurst. These data indicate a Hampshire population of around 250 pairs. The most recent estimate of the British population was 33,000-43,000 pairs in the mid-1980s (Piersma 1986).

The increase in the population is attributable, at least in part, to the extra protection afforded by the establishment of wardened nature reserves at the principal sites. Most breed on shingle or saltmarsh but in 1992, 27 pairs nested in fields at the Beaulieu Estuary and one pair did so at Pennington Marsh.

Since the 1970s, over 200 immatures and non-breeders have summered in Langstone Harbour in every year but one. Counts reached 534 in early June 1989 and 536 a year later. Elsewhere, such gatherings rarely reach three figures.

After the breeding season, flocks build up from July onwards. The pattern is highly variable from site to site and year to year. Maximum numbers may occur at any time between August and February, although at Langstone and Chichester Harbours, the two principal localities, they have usually been recorded between October and December. Numbers at these two sites have increased steadily since the early 1950s, when the first three-figure flocks were recorded. During the five winters from 1985/86-89/90, the proportion of the British wintering population in Hampshire (based on January counts) averaged 1.4%. High tide roost counts at various localities are summarised in tables 29 and 30.

| | 55-59 | 60-64 | 65-69 | 70-74 | 75-79 | 80-84 | 85-89 | Peak counts |
|---|---|---|---|---|---|---|---|---|
| Chichester Harbour | - | - | 1002 | 715 | 1152 | 1417 | 1311^ | 2002, Sep. 1980 |
| East Hayling | - | 150* | - | - | 23 | 3 | 7 | 150, Aug. 1962 |
| Langstone Harbour | 156^ | 325 | 511 | 782 | 1188 | 1404 | 1529 | 2300, Oct. 1988 |
| Portsmouth Harbour | - | - | 110* | 431 | 282 | 341 | 240 | 600, Sep. 1971 |
| Southampton Water | 70^ | 139^ | 195^ | 604 | 775 | 777 | 616 | 984, Sep. 1980 |
| Beaulieu Estuary | 118^ | 164 | 107 | 66 | 67 | 84 | 191 | 332, Sep. 1989 |
| Lymington/Hurst | 39* | 26^ | 125^ | 61^ | 64 | 59 | 70 | 250, Aug. 1969 |

*Table 29. High tide roost counts of Oystercatchers in autumn (July-October): five year means of maxima and peak counts, 1955-89.*

| | 55-60 | 60-65 | 65-70 | 70-75 | 75-80 | 80-85 | 85-90 | Peak counts |
|---|---|---|---|---|---|---|---|---|
| Chichester Harbour | - | - | 826 | 772 | 1243 | 1404 | 1032 | 1872, Nov. 1982 |
| East Hayling | 80* | - | - | - | 19 | 48 | 26 | 85, Dec. 1984 |
| Langstone Harbour | 99 | 281 | 532 | 906 | 1317 | 1390 | 1915 | 2440, Nov. 1988 |
| Portsmouth Harbour | - | - | 155^ | 505 | 434 | 469 | 324 | 688, Dec. 1974 |
| Southampton Water | 110^ | 125^ | 200* | 598 | 657 | 550 | 582 | 1062, Jan. 1974 |
| Beaulieu Estuary | 89^ | 190 | 124 | 84 | 85 | 102 | 186 | 455, Dec. 1989 |
| Lymington/Hurst | 79^ | 35 | 114 | 60 | 60 | 78 | 94 | 300, Dec. 1968 |

*Table 30. High tide roost counts of Oystercatchers in winter (November-March): five year means of maxima and peak counts, 1955/56-89/90.*

In spring, there is a gradual departure of wintering birds and a small eastward passage along The Solent coast which peaks in late April and early May. During the period 1971-92, the recorded annual totals of birds moving east varied between zero and 102 (in 1990) with an average of 36. The highest day total was of 40 at Hurst Beach on Apr. 29th 1976.

Spring passage is also indicated by birds heard at night over sites just inland from the coast, e.g. at Portsdown, Oystercatchers were noted moving in directions between north-west and east on six dates between Feb. 8th and Mar. 17th 1980 and on seven dates between Feb. 7th and Apr. 14th 1984. However, in contrast to several other wader species, they are rarely seen moving inland from Langstone Harbour on spring evenings, 25 off north-east on Apr. 25th 1974 and 56 off north-west on Mar. 5th 1982 being the only recent records.

Further inland, Oystercatchers were recorded in 11 years between 1954 and 1970 and annually thereafter. The cumulative monthly totals for 1954-92 are shown below.

| Jan | Feb | Mar | Apr | May | Jun | Jul | Aug | Sep | Oct | Nov | Dec |
|---|---|---|---|---|---|---|---|---|---|---|---|
| 10 | 9 | 10 | 21 | 15 | 12 | 14 | 20 | 10 | 12 | 5 | 3 |

These data show peaks in spring and autumn. The majority of records involved birds heard at night, moving over during the day or grounded during or after inclement weather. Most have been recorded at Eversley Gravel Pit (31, including 6 on Oct. 16th 1987, Apr. 9th 1988 and Sep. 11th 1992), Frensham Great Pond (22, including 3 on June 25th 1972) and Fleet Pond (13). However, the largest group seen was of eight at Bishop's Dyke on Jan. 1st 1984.

Ringing information shows that 42 Oystercatchers ringed in Hampshire have been recovered. Most of these were caught using a cannon-net; 26 were later found at distances greater than 100 km, in the Netherlands (10), France (5), mainland Scotland (4), Norway (3), the Faeroes, the Orkneys, Lincolnshire and Yorkshire (1 each), mostly between April and September. This gives some indication of the breeding grounds of our passage and wintering birds. Only nine ringed elsewhere have been found in Hampshire, including one ringed as a pullus at Blakeney Point, Norfolk, on July 27th 1953 and found dead at Netley on June 30th 1957, and another ringed as a pullus in Friesland, Netherlands, on June 13th 1973 and recovered at Hill Head, 543 km WSW, on Sep. 19th 1973. Three others, trapped in Lincolnshire (2) and Gwynedd, were over 100 km from the ringing site when controlled in Hampshire. There have been two distant recoveries of Hampshire-bred birds: one, ringed at the Beaulieu Estuary on June 20th 1949, was shot in Manche, France, 206 km south, on Aug. 8th 1952 and another, ringed at Keyhaven on July 3rd 1970, was found dead at Felixstowe, Suffolk on Aug. 19th 1979.

## Black-winged Stilt                                *Himantopus himantopus*

A rare vagrant. There have been 11 records involving 17 birds, as follows:

1923:   1, Beaulieu, Nov. 23rd-26th;
1945:   1-4, Warren Flats (Needs Ore), mid-May;
1962:   1, Badnam Creek (River Hamble), Oct. 3rd;
1965:   1 male and 2 immature males, Dibden Bay, Apr. 10th-13th;
1987:   pair, Pennington Marsh, May 3rd-7th;
        male, Farlington Marshes, May 10th-20th;
        adult, Winchester Sewage Farm, May 17th;
        first-summer, Farlington Marshes, June 16th;
        moulting adult, Farlington Marshes, July 11th-25th;
1989:   adult, Farlington Marshes, Nov. 8th;
1990:   male, Farlington Marshes, Apr. 30th-May 2nd†.

The six birds which appeared in 1987 were part of a large spring influx into southern England involving some 30 individuals (Rogers *et al* 1988). The Black-winged Stilt is a summer visitor to Europe which winters mainly in tropical Africa. The nearest breeding grounds are in north-eastern France.

# Avocet                                    *Recurvirostra avosetta*

A scarce passage migrant and winter visitor.

K & M described the Avocet as "a rare occasional visitor to the coast". They mention 31 birds, including 18 in Southampton Water in September 1880, 12 of which were shot. In the first half of this century, records involving 28 birds have been traced, with a maximum of five at Keyhaven on May 22nd 1947.

Since 1951, the number of Avocets recorded annually has fluctuated widely, although the overall trend appears to be upwards (fig. 34). This can be attributed to increases in both observer activity and the breeding populations of some north-west European countries (BWP).

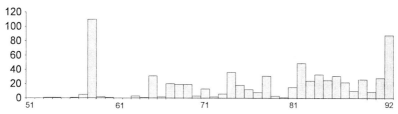

*Figure 34. Annual totals of Avocets, 1951-92.*

In spring, migrants have been reported throughout the period from mid-March to mid-June, with no real peak evident (fig. 35). Most sightings involve flocks moving east or pausing briefly, but occasionally groups of up to five have stayed for several days. Double-figure flocks have been recorded on eight occasions, including 25 moving east at Gilkicker Point on Mar. 14th 1965, 16 which flew east over Hurst Beach and paused briefly at Keyhaven on June 21st 1974, 13 seen at Warsash, Calshot and Langstone Harbour on June 3rd 1984, 14 at Langstone Harbour on May 2nd 1986 and 28 flying east off Sandy Point on Apr. 20th 1992.

Avocets are surprisingly scarce in early autumn, all the records for July to October being of one to three birds apart from those of six at Needs Ore on Aug. 14th 1983, seven flying west over Mill Rythe on Sep. 29th 1985 and 12 which left Keyhaven on Oct. 12th 1991; later that day 11 were at Titchfield Haven.

In some years, large flocks are seen in the closing two months of the year. In November 1958, 35 were in Langstone Harbour and 50 flew east at Sandy Point on 23rd and on the next two days, 23 were at Dibden Bay. Other notable records include those of nine which flew west over Chichester Harbour on Dec. 3rd 1982, 20 at Dibden Bay the next day, seven at Southampton Docks on Nov. 13th 1989 and 20 which left south-west from Frensham Great Pond on Nov. 9th 1992.

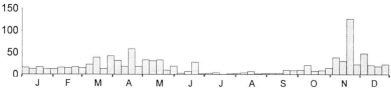

*Figure 35. Cumulative weekly totals of Avocets, 1951-92.*

One or two have wintered in Chichester Harbour annually since 1984/85, regularly being seen at East Hayling between October and March. There have also been occasional records from other coastal sites, individuals often remaining for several weeks.

In addition to the Frensham record above, there have been eight inland records. Two were at Shortheath Ponds (Oakhanger), on Aug. 25th 1908, one was found dead at Otterbourne on Jan. 28th 1942, one was at West Wellow from Mar. 30th-Apr. 4th 1969, six were at Holmsley Gravel Pit on Apr. 22nd 1976 (these presumably the same party seen at Hurst Beach on that date), and single birds were at Elvetham Park on May 11th 1978, Marsh Court on Dec. 29th and 30th 1978, Mockbeggar Lake on Nov. 17th 1984 and Eversley Gravel Pit on Apr. 26th 1992.

The Otterbourne bird had been ringed as a juvenile in Nyborg, Denmark in June 1941. More recently, one, colour-ringed as a pullus at Holme, Norfolk in August 1991, was seen at Farlington Marshes on Apr. 19th and 20th 1992 and at Stanpit, Dorset on May 1st 1992 (M Reed pers. comm.). These ringing returns indicate Avocets seen in Hampshire originate from breeding grounds along the coasts of the North Sea. Adults from these sites moult in the Waddenzee and adjacent areas in August and September, before departing in October and November to winter in south-western France, Iberia, Morocco and tropical West Africa (Prater 1981, BWP). This presumably accounts for the late autumn peak in Hampshire.

## Stone Curlew                                   *Burhinus oedicnemus*

A scarce summer visitor which has undergone a considerable decline during the last 50 years.

K & M described the Stone Curlew as "still plentiful on the bare downs and large fields of the Central Hill District". It traditionally bred on the short turf of the chalk downland, and may already have been declining when they wrote, due to the loss of such habitat to agriculture and afforestation.

Although the species adapted to nesting on fallow and sparsely vegetated arable land, nests and young were frequently destroyed by rolling and other farm operations. The agricultural recession between the two wars probably allowed some recovery, but this was only a temporary reprieve. The ploughing of downland resumed with the "Dig for Victory" campaign during the Second World War, and the decline was further exacerbated in the 1950s with a general reduction in grazing and the introduction of myxomatosis to control rabbits. This allowed much of the remaining downland to become covered in rank grass and scrub, and therefore unsuitable as breeding habitat.

Since then, numbers have continued to fall due to changes in agricultural practices. On farmland, the optimum nesting habitat consists of sparse or open-sown crops, e.g. kale, maize, broad beans, peas and game cover, mixed with open feeding areas, such as fallow, pasture or leys grazed by sheep, cattle or pigs. In Hampshire, this mosaic has largely disappeared, to be replaced by autumn-sown cereals and faster growing spring-sown crops. This results in much of the agricultural land being unsuitable for nesting because the crop is already too high and dense when Stone Curlews arrive. Increased mechanisation has also contributed; modern tractors and machinery carry out cultivations rapidly and give chicks little chance to escape (Green 1990).

Cooperation between farmers and those interested in protecting the birds can reduce the damage done by farm machinery. This was first achieved in the Martin area in 1963, when some farmers helped enthusiastically to prevent the destruction of nests marked by N W Orr. Since 1985, the RSPB has coordinated the monitoring and protection of Stone Curlews in Hampshire and adjoining counties. As a result, the decline has been arrested. Fledging success has begun to improve and the signs are that the population may now be holding its own (table 31).

At the beginning of the century, there were undoubtedly several hundred pairs breeding in Hampshire, and this was probably still the case in the 1930s. Few breeding records are available for this period, but reports of large autumn gatherings, such as 100 at Quarley Hill on Oct. 15th 1934 and Oct. 13th 1935, and 50 near Stockbridge on Oct. 5th 1935, indicate a sizeable population.

The HOS archives indicate that the species was still widespread during the 1950s and early 1960s. There were 15 pairs on a 16 $km^2$ estate at Damerham in 1951, while at Porton Down, on the Hampshire/Wiltshire border, the population was estimated at 20 pairs until the spread of myxomatosis resulted in a decline to around six pairs in the late 1950s (B C H Warren *in litt*). In 1955, pairs were found at eight sites within 10 km of Andover. Post-breeding gatherings noted include 30 at Sutton Scotney on Oct. 3rd 1958, 60 at Barton Stacey on Oct. 12th 1960 (which departed south-east in V-formation), 23 at Twyford on Oct. 14th 1961 and 32 at White Hill (Kingsclere) on Sep. 13th 1962. These figures suggest that the population still numbered considerably in excess of 100 pairs in the early 1960s.

Subsequently, a few observers reported declines. The species had disappeared from the Butser Hill area by the mid-1960s, while in the Whitchurch area, nine pairs were located in 1968 but considerably fewer in the early 1970s. In a partial survey in 1976, 16 pairs were located in the centre of the county, while there were at least 12 in the Martin/Damerham area and at least ten at Porton (about half of which were in Hampshire). Allowing for considerable areas which were not covered, the county population was probably around 50 pairs.

Declines continued to be recorded after the survey. In the Martin/Damerham area, which held 17 pairs in 1975, there had been a reduction to eight pairs in 1978 and six or seven by 1985 (N W Orr *in litt*). It has now disappeared from several sites in the east of the county, e.g. Abbotstone Down, Woodmancott and the Greywell/Tunworth/Winslade area.

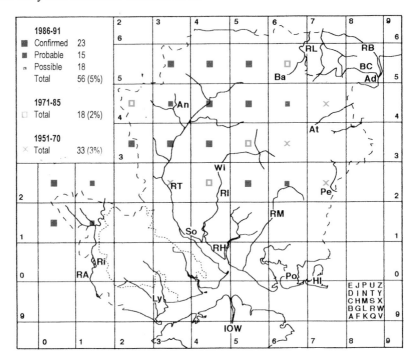

The Atlas Map shows the distribution recorded in 1986-91 on a 10 km square basis (for security reasons) and also incorporates earlier records. As mentioned above, the RSPB has been monitoring this species since 1985 and the results of their work are summarised in table 31.

| | Pairs located | Unmated individuals | Breeding confirmed | Young reared |
|---|---|---|---|---|
| 1987 | 16* | - | - | - |
| 1988 | 16/17* | - | - | - |
| 1989 | 21-23 | - | - | - |
| 1990 | 23 | - | 20 | 13-20 |
| 1991 | 20 | 5 | 16 | 17-19 |
| 1992 | 20-21 | 6-8 | 19 | 19 |

\* some known sites not covered

*Table 31. Breeding data for Stone Curlews in Hampshire, 1987-92.*

The bulk of the population occurs at Porton Down and in the surrounding area, where about 14 pairs bred annually between 1989 and 1992. The remainder is located in five outlying areas, each holding one or two pairs. At these sites, factors such as the continuation of livestock farming and provision of game coverts will be crucial to the survival of the species. Even allowing for a few pairs which may have been missed, the Hampshire total is probably no higher than 25 pairs. The most recent estimate of the British population was 148-158 pairs in 1990 (Spencer *et al* 1993).

The first returning Stone Curlews arrive in mid or late March, the earliest during 1971-92 being on Mar. 15th. However, older records include those of single birds at Chalton on Feb. 25th 1938 (Hudson 1973) and Danebury on Feb. 28th 1960, as well as several for the first week of March. In recent years, only one area has held a regular autumn gathering, with maximum counts of 24 on Oct. 8th 1979, 20 on Oct. 8th 1990 and 20 on Sep. 28th 1991. These usually disperse by the middle of October. The latest record is of four at Broughton on Nov. 6th 1966, apart from singles seen at Longwood Warren on Dec. 31st 1972 and at Farlington Marshes on Dec. 13th 1974.

They are occasionally seen away from breeding areas. The cumulative monthly totals of all coastal records for 1951-92 are shown below.

| Mar | Apr | May | Jun | Jul | Aug | Sep | Oct | Nov | Dec |
|-----|-----|-----|-----|-----|-----|-----|-----|-----|-----|
| 3 | 7 | 0 | 1 | 0 | 2 | 4 | 3 | 0 | 1 |

Of the 21 recorded, 13 were in Langstone Harbour, none of them after 1974. Recent records include those of single birds at Paulsgrove Reclamation on Mar. 27th 1982, Keyhaven on Oct. 14th 1989 and Warsash on Apr. 29th 1990. There have been a few inland records, including two of large flocks: 15 flying south-west over Woolmer on Sep. 30th 1972 (P F Le Brocq *in litt*) and 11 at Preshaw Down on Aug. 26th 1991.

There are a few ringing recoveries indicating passage through France and Spain. Birds ringed as pulli in Hampshire on July 24th 1951, June 19th 1983 and July 23rd 1987 were recovered at Durango, Spain, 870 km south, on Nov. 1st 1952, Irun, Spain, 870 km south, on Oct. 8th 1983 and Mirambeau, France, 632 km south, on Nov. 6th 1987 respectively. Some British Stone Curlews winter in Spain but most probably cross the Straits of Gibraltar to North Africa. Birds have also been recorded south of the Sahara but there are no ringing recoveries to indicate their origin (BWP).

## Cream-coloured Courser                    *Cursorius cursor*

One record. One was shot at Sopley Park in 1845 (K & M).

The nearest breeding grounds of the Cream-coloured Courser are in north-west Africa. Only six have been recorded in Britain since 1959.

## Collared Pratincole                    *Glareola pratincola*

Two records. One was watched in flight over Fleet Pond for ten minutes on May 28th 1974 and another was present all day in the Ibsley/Mockbeggar Lake area on May 6th 1987.

The Collared Pratincole is a summer visitor to southern Eurasia; the closest colony is in the Camargue, France.

## Pratincoles                    *Glareola sp*

There are three old records which are probably best assigned to this category:

one shot at Hurst Beach in May 1857, another seen at Stokes Bay in October 1864 and two seen for a week near Stockbridge in mid-May 1944.

Since then, there has been one record of a bird at Pennington Marsh on Aug. 6th 1983.

## Little Ringed Plover                                      *Charadrius dubius*

A scarce breeding summer visitor and passage migrant.

The Little Ringed Plover was not recorded until 1951, when one was at Fleet Pond on June 3rd. Two were there the next day and one was at Milford-on-Sea from July 26th-31st of the same year. In 1952, a pair bred successfully at a gravel pit near Sway. In the following year, a pair returned to the same site, and, over the next decade, one or two pairs bred intermittently on coastal flats at Ashlett and Dibden Bay and gravel pits at Lee and Nursling.

In 1964, a pair bred for the first time in the north-east at Bramshill, and in 1966, five pairs were located, three at what is now Wellington Country Park and one each at Bramshill and Yateley Gravel Pit. In the next four years, the only indication of breeding anywhere in the county was of a pair at Yateley Gravel Pit in 1969, but coverage of likely sites was not good.

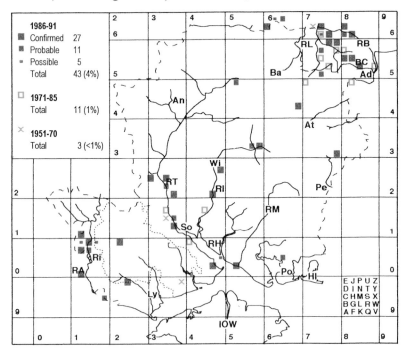

Breeding has been recorded annually since 1971. The Atlas Map shows the distribution revealed during the 1986-91 survey and also incorporates earlier records. In the early 1970s, expansion was slow, but there was a large increase in 1976, when 17 pairs were located at nine sites. In 1980, the population reached a peak of 33 pairs at ten sites.

Since then, reported numbers have fluctuated (table 32), partly due to incomplete coverage in some years, but also because some prime sites have become less attractive. In 1991, 19 or 20 pairs were located at ten sites, and the county total almost certainly did not exceed 25 pairs. During 1988-91, the British population was estimated to be in the range 825-1070 pairs (New Atlas).

| | 1971 | 1972 | 1973 | 1974 | 1975 | 1976 | 1977 | 1978 | 1979 | 1980 | 1981 |
|---|---|---|---|---|---|---|---|---|---|---|---|
| Yateley/Eversley | - | - | - | 1 | 1 | 7 | 8 | 10 | 8 | 7 | 4 |
| Bramshill area | 1 | 1 | 3 | 2 | 3 | 1 | 3 | 6 | 7 | 7 | 9 |
| Other N.E. sites | - | 1 | 1 | - | - | 1 | 2 | 1 | 3 | 1 | 6 |
| Avon valley | - | - | 1 | 1 | 3 | 5 | 3 | 2 | 11 | 13 | 6 |
| Test valley | - | - | - | - | - | 3 | 3 | 2 | 1 | 2 | 1 |
| Itchen valley | - | - | - | - | - | - | - | - | - | 2 | - |
| Coast | - | - | - | - | - | - | 2 | 1 | 2 | 1 | 1 |
| Totals | 1 | 2 | 5 | 4 | 7 | 17 | 21 | 22 | 32 | 33 | 27 |

| | 1982 | 1983 | 1984 | 1985 | 1986 | 1987 | 1988 | 1989 | 1990 | 1991 | 1992 |
|---|---|---|---|---|---|---|---|---|---|---|---|
| Yateley/Eversley | 4 | 3 | 4 | 9 | 7 | 5 | 4 | 3 | 5 | 5 | 3 |
| Bramshill area | 10 | 7 | 5 | 6 | 5 | 8 | 3 | 8 | 7 | 5 | 6 |
| Other N.E. sites | 2 | 1 | 2 | 1 | - | 2 | 1 | 3 | 2 | 1 | 1 |
| Avon valley sites | 6 | 2 | 3 | 5 | 4 | 6 | 3 | 4 | 3 | 3 | 3 |
| Test valley | 2 | 2 | 2 | 2 | 2 | 3 | 2 | 2 | 3 | 4 | 2 |
| Itchen valley | - | - | 4 | 2 | 2 | 2 | - | 1 | 1 | - | - |
| New Forest | - | 1 | 1 | 1 | 1 | 2 | 1 | 1 | 1 | - | 1 |
| Coast | 2 | 3 | 3 | 1 | 1 | 2 | 1 | - | 1 | 1 | - |
| Totals | 26 | 19 | 24 | 27 | 22 | 30 | 15 | 22 | 23 | 19 | 16 |

*Table 32. Reported totals of breeding pairs of Little Ringed Plovers, 1971-92.*

During the relatively short time that Little Ringed Plovers have been breeding in the county, about 47 separate sites have been utilised, many of them for one or two seasons only. This reflects the opportunistic nature of the species. It is quick to colonise a variety of unvegetated aquatic margins, but deserts them if they become too overgrown. About half the sites were gravel or sand pits, but several other habitats have also been used. These include coastal reclaimed land (e.g. at Paulsgrove and Southampton Docks), exposed shingle banks in the River Avon (used by two pairs in the hot summers of 1976 and 1990), a stony downland field (at Greywell in 1979), the dried beds of drained ponds (e.g. four pairs at Tundry Pond in 1980) and a recently cleared building plot (at Fleet in 1987 and 1988). Since most sites remain suitable for only a short time, the population is dependent on the continual generation of new habitat. In the three main areas, around Yateley, Bramshill and Ringwood, it is only the ongoing gravel

extraction which continues to provide new habitat and thus has enabled the sites to be continuously occupied since the early 1970s.

The first are usually back on breeding sites by mid or late March. The earliest ever were single birds at Bramshill on Mar. 10th 1986 and Timsbury on the same date in 1991. In other years during 1971-92, first arrivals were recorded up to Apr. 5th with the average Mar. 22nd. At the coast, a light passage is noted between mid-March and early June which peaks in April and the first two weeks of May (fig. 36). Occasional birds are seen coming in off the sea or moving east along the coast (e.g. 14 at Hurst Beach between 1971 and 1992).

Return passage occurs in July, August and early September with a clear peak between mid-July and early August (fig. 36). High counts recorded include seven at Farlington Marshes on Aug. 2nd 1977, 14 at Paulsgrove Reclamation on the same date in 1982 and nine at Farlington Marshes on July 16th 1983. The latest ever was one which remained at Titchfield Haven from Sep. 20th-Oct. 11th 1980. In other years during 1971-92, latest dates were recorded from Aug. 31st with the average Sep. 17th.

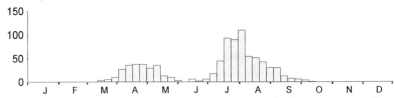

*Figure 36. Cumulative weekly totals of Little Ringed Plovers at coastal sites, 1971-92.*

Two birds, ringed as pulli in Hampshire in June 1975 and June 1976, have been controlled, the first at a breeding site in Surrey in July 1978 and the second at West Vlaanderen, Belgium, 330 km east, on Aug. 3rd 1976. British Little Ringed Plovers are believed to winter in tropical West Africa although there are no ringing recoveries to confirm this.

## Ringed Plover                                    *Charadrius hiaticula*

A moderately common breeder, common passage migrant and winter visitor.

K & M described the Ringed Plover as "a common resident on the coast .... increasing within our limits". Munn (1920) considered that it had increased further by then, but very little information is available for the period up to the 1950s except that it bred at Hatchet Pond from 1936-38 and possibly before (Cohen) and at Hurst Beach from 1946 onwards.

During the 1950s, there were a few breeding records from Needs Ore Point and Hurst Beach and in 1954 one pair nested on Long Island in Langstone Harbour. Improved coverage in the 1960s produced counts such as 11 pairs at Hurst Beach in 1961, 5-6 at Milton Reclamation (Langstone Harbour) in 1964, 15 at Needs Ore Point in 1966, and 12 between Pennington and Hurst, 9 at Calshot and 5 at Dibden Bay in 1969. In most years, a few pairs attempted breeding at other sites between Hayling and Warsash, while in 1965 single pairs bred in the New Forest at Stoney Cross and Janesmoor. By the end of the 1960s, the Hampshire population was probably around 50 pairs.

Surveys carried out in 1973 and 1984 as part of national censuses organised by the BTO produced totals of 70 and 165 territorial pairs respectively (table 33).

|  | 1973 | 1984 |  | 1973 | 1984 |
|---|---|---|---|---|---|
| East Hayling | 0 | 2 | Beaulieu Estuary area | 8 | 30 |
| Langstone Harbour | 4 | 40 | Pitts Deep/Oxey Creek | 6 | 10 |
| Paulsgrove Reclamation | 2 | 3 | Oxey Creek/Hurst | 23 | 40 |
| Gilkicker/Browndown | 7 | 5 | Hordle Beach | 1 | 0 |
| Hill Head/Warsash | 0 | 7 | Blashford Lakes | 1 | 3 |
| Southampton Docks | 0 | 3 | New Forest | 2 | 10 |
| Dibden Bay | 5 | 1 | Lakeside (Eastleigh) | 0 | 2 |
| Fawley/Calshot | 10 | 3 | Bramshill area | 1 | 1 |
| Cadland/Stone Point | 0 | 4 | Eversley Gravel Pit | 0 | 1 |
|  |  |  | Totals | 70 | 165 |

*Table 33. Territorial pairs of Ringed Plovers, 1973 and 1984.*

The increased numbers found in 1984 were due both to improved observer coverage and an expansion of the population, especially in protected areas. For example, in Langstone Harbour, a substantial increase since 1979 can be attributed both to the protection given to the islands by the establishment of the RSPB reserve and the coverage by the wardens which was not previously attempted (Steventon 1985).

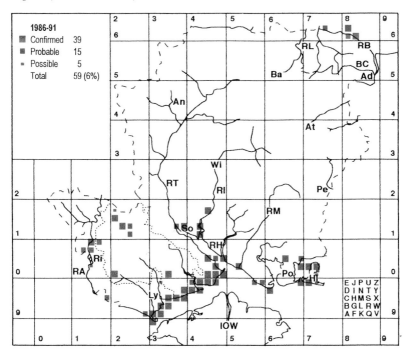

As the Atlas Map shows, the distribution recorded during 1986-91 was broadly similar to that revealed in 1984. Surveys at the three main sites in 1989 produced counts of 35 pairs at Langstone Harbour, 42 at the Beaulieu Estuary and 34 between Pitts Deep and Hurst. At other coastal localities, usually only one or two pairs are found, but there were at least four pairs between Fawley and Calshot in 1986 and six at Southampton Western Docks in 1987 and 1988. In the New Forest, between five and ten pairs continue to breed on various disused airfields and gravel pits, while elsewhere inland the main sites currently in use are Blashford Lakes (5-6 pairs in 1989) and Eversley Gravel Pit (3 pairs in 1990). A single pair bred successfully at Southampton Airport in 1989. The total population in 1991 was probably in the range 140-160 pairs, while the national total was estimated at 8600 pairs in 1984 (Prater 1989).

Outside the breeding season, counts usually show a peak in August or September and then decline through the winter months, although a secondary peak is sometimes recorded. Most wintering birds leave by early April. During the five winters from 1985/86-89/90, the proportion of the British wintering population in Hampshire (based on January counts) averaged 15.2%. High tide roost counts at various localities are summarised in tables 34 and 35.

| | 55-59 | 60-64 | 65-69 | 70-74 | 75-79 | 80-84 | 85-89 | Peak counts |
|---|---|---|---|---|---|---|---|---|
| Chichester Harbour | - | - | 412 | 301 | 500 | 493 | 879 | 1100, Aug. 1985 |
| East Hayling | 87^ | - | - | - | 105 | 58 | 4 | 310, Sep. 1978 |
| Langstone Harbour | 190 | 313^ | 442 | 380 | 368 | 461 | 746 | 928, Aug. 1986 |
| Portsmouth Harbour | - | - | 150* | 278 | 323 | 278 | 209 | 536, Aug. 1980 |
| Southampton Water | - | - | - | 956 | 858 | 605 | 503 | 1687, Aug. 1973 |
| Warsash | 237^ | 50* | - | 114^ | 93 | 204 | 219 | 400, Oct. 1959 |
| Dibden Bay | - | 115 | 152 | 438 | 127 | 158 | 0^ | 675, Aug. 1973 |
| Fawley/Calshot | 150* | - | 330* | 544 | 832 | 286 | 333 | 1200, Aug. 1977 |
| Beaulieu Estuary | 100* | 133 | 118 | 32 | 26 | 33 | 73^ | 300, Oct. 1965 |
| Lymington/Hurst | 25^ | 67 | 144 | 208 | 272 | 219 | 237 | 350, Sep. 1976 |

*Table 34. High tide roost counts of Ringed Plovers in autumn (July-October): five year means of maxima and peak counts, 1955-89.*

| | 55-60 | 60-65 | 65-70 | 70-75 | 75-80 | 80-85 | 85-90 | Peak counts |
|---|---|---|---|---|---|---|---|---|
| Chichester Harbour | - | - | 350 | 212 | 360 | 409 | 878 | 2083, Jan. 1990 |
| East Hayling | 66^ | - | 150* | - | 42 | 44 | 72 | 187, Dec. 1986 |
| Langstone Harbour | 316 | 125 | 213 | 218 | 402 | 399 | 526 | 1000, Dec. 1956 |
| Portsmouth Harbour | 88* | - | 150* | 146 | 60 | 147 | 212 | 375, Nov. 1988 |
| Southampton Water | - | - | - | 308 | 299 | 388 | 371 | 479, Jan. 1973 |
| Warsash | 150^ | - | - | 85^ | 125 | 142 | 167 | 230, Dec. 1989 |
| Dibden Bay | 300* | 97^ | 94 | 136 | 101 | 130 | 36 | 300, Jan. 1960 |
| Fawley/Calshot | 150^ | - | - | 167 | 140 | 145 | 141 | 274, Nov. 1970 |
| Beaulieu Estuary | 107^ | 52 | 34 | 17 | 20 | 28 | 63 | 200, Jan. 1956 |
| Lymington/Hurst | 20* | 59 | - | 128 | 190 | 245 | 197 | 310, Nov. 1981 |

*Table 35. High tide roost counts of Ringed Plovers in winter (November-March): five year means of maxima and peak counts, 1955/56-89/90.*

High tide roosts are also occasionally reported in areas not covered by BoEE counts, e.g. at Gilkicker Point (600 on Feb. 6th 1966 and 400+ on Dec. 24th 1983), Haslar sea wall (250 on Oct. 9th 1984) and between Eastney and Southsea (200+ on Jan. 31st 1988).

Small numbers of Ringed Plovers are usually involved in the eastward movements of seabirds and waders through The Solent in spring, peaking in early May. Between 1971 and 1992, the total recorded annually varied between zero and 102 (in 1980) with an average of 25. The highest day total was of 40 at Hurst Beach on May 3rd 1990.

This passage (presumably of a population wintering further south) is also shown by occasional influxes at high tide roosts, e.g. 230 at Fawley/Calshot on May 5th 1973 and 302 in Langstone Harbour on May 12th 1990. Small numbers have been recorded moving off inland (usually at dusk) from coastal sites. During the period 1953-83, a total of 116 was recorded leaving Langstone Harbour in directions between north-west and north-east on dates between Apr. 24th and June 6th.

The records from inland sites show distinct spring and autumn peaks, although the migration pattern is somewhat obscured by the presence of nesting birds, which may return from mid-February onwards. Cumulative monthly totals of all inland records away from breeding sites for 1952-92 are shown below.

| Jan | Feb | Mar | Apr | May | Jun | Jul | Aug | Sep | Oct | Nov | Dec |
|-----|-----|-----|-----|-----|-----|-----|-----|-----|-----|-----|-----|
| 1   | 9   | 5   | 39  | 54  | 7   | 13  | 70  | 29  | 4   | 1   | 0   |

Most of the early records were from Frensham Great Pond, where 42 were seen between 1956 and 1970 including six on Apr. 26th 1956 and nine on May 11th 1969. Sightings have become more frequent in the last two decades as the amount of suitable habitat provided by gravel pits has expanded and observer coverage has improved. Between 1971 and 1992, 174 were recorded including 30 at Fleet Pond, 25 at Timsbury Gravel Pit, 21 at Alresford Pond and 20 at Eversley Gravel Pit (before breeding started). Individual counts did not exceed four apart from that of five at Winchester Sewage Farm on Aug. 23rd 1991. Additional records from breeding sites, probably largely involving migrants, have included 11 at Eversley Gravel Pit on Aug. 26th 1990 and in the Mockbeggar Lake/Ibsley area, 16 on May 15th 1988, 22 on Apr. 8th 1989, 11 on Oct. 27th 1990 and 13 on Mar. 2nd 1991.

There have been 29 recoveries or controls of birds ringed in Hampshire. 12 were within the county, three each in France and western Germany, two each in eastern Germany and the Netherlands, and singles in Ghana, Greenland, Iceland, Morocco, Portugal, Cumbria and East Sussex. 38 ringed elsewhere have been found in Hampshire. Nine originated from southern England, five each from northern England and western Germany, four each from Denmark, eastern Germany, the Netherlands and Norway, and singles from Finland, Greenland and Poland.

Analysis of these and national data show that numbers are highest in autumn because birds originating from three areas are present. Those from Greenland, Iceland and north-western Britain move on to winter further south in Iberia and West Africa, whereas some or all Hampshire-bred birds and those from western Europe winter locally. These all belong to the nominate race, but four seen at Titchfield Haven on June 4th 1979 showed the characteristics of the race *C. h. tundrae*, which breeds along the coasts of Lapland and Russia. For further discussion of the movements and origins of Ringed Plovers in Hampshire and elsewhere see Insley and Young (1981), Steventon (1983) and BWP.

## Killdeer                                      *Charadrius vociferus*

One record. A first-winter bird was at Keyhaven Marsh on Sep. 28th and 29th 1980.

The Killdeer breeds in North America and the West Indies and winters south to central South America.

## Kentish Plover                           *Charadrius alexandrinus*

A rare passage migrant which has occurred less frequently since 1981; one winter record.

The first Kentish Plover for the county was at Titchfield Haven on Aug. 30th 1948. Another was seen there on June 23rd 1949. Between 1951 and 1992, 49 were recorded, but only seven since 1981 (fig. 37). The peak during the 1970s may have been because of the attractiveness of Dibden Bay at that time.

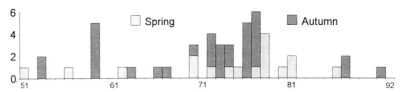

*Figure 37. Spring and autumn totals of Kentish Plovers, 1951-92.*

Spring records, all of single birds, covered the period between Apr. 5th and May 28th (fig. 38). Most sightings were on one date only, though single females were at Farlington Marshes from Apr. 16th-19th 1970 and Pennington Marsh from Apr. 5th-9th 1978.

Autumn records fell between July 5th and October 28th (fig. 38). Four were at Fawley Reclamation on Sep. 25th 1976, two staying until Oct. 3rd, and a female and three immatures were at Dibden Bay on Aug. 17th 1977, one remaining until Aug. 27th. All other records were of single birds on one date only except for two at Needs Ore on Aug. 28th 1953, two at Langstone Harbour on July 15th 1959 and one immature at Calshot from Oct. 18th-28th 1987.

There is one winter record of two at Black Point on Dec. 23rd 1959.

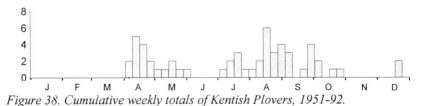

*Figure 38. Cumulative weekly totals of Kentish Plovers, 1951-92.*

Reports came from ten localities, principally Dibden Bay (14 birds), Pennington and Keyhaven Marshes (11) and Langstone Harbour/Farlington Marshes (10). All were coastal apart from a male at Eversley Gravel Pit on Apr. 11th 1986.

The Kentish Plover has a widespread world distribution but its nearest breeding grounds are on the north-west European coast. A decline in this area (BWP) probably accounts for the reduced numbers occurring in Hampshire.

# Dotterel                                    *Charadrius morinellus*

A rare spring and autumn passage migrant.

K & M cited two shot near Ovington on Sep. 30th 1893. Since then, there have been 18 records, as follows:

1934:   6 near Gorley, May 6th;
1955:   3, Farlington Marshes, Sep. 26th;
1969:   1, Keyhaven, Aug. 27th-29th;
1971:   1, Needs Ore, Aug. 24th;
1972:   1, Beaulieu Heath, May 13th;
1975:   1, Pennington Marsh, Aug. 17th and 18th;
1979:   3, Farlington Marshes, May 5th;
        17, Cheesefoot Head, May 6th;
        1, Warsash, May 19th;
1980:   14, Greywell, May 3rd;
1982:   1, Nether Wallop, Sep. 25th;
1985:   5, Roke Farm (Odiham), May 3rd;
1986:   7, Danebury, May 5th;
1987:   5, Snatchangers Farm (Odiham), May 3rd-6th;
1989:   2 near Brockenhurst, May 18th;
1991:   1 flew east over Old Winchester Hill, May 5th;
        2, Dibden Bay, May 17th;
        1 juvenile, Needs Ore, Aug. 23rd-26th.

Note that 58 of the 64 birds recorded in spring occurred between May 3rd and 6th.

Dotterels passing through Hampshire probably belong to the British or Scandinavian breeding populations, which winter in North Africa (BWP).

# Pacific Golden Plover                        *Pluvialis fulva*

One record. An adult in summer plumage was at Needs Ore on June 27th and 28th 1992.

The Pacific Golden Plover, which has recently been separated from the American (Lesser) Golden Plover, breeds in Siberia and Alaska and winters from East Africa to Australasia.

# Golden Plover                                *Pluvialis apricaria*

A common winter visitor and passage migrant, very scarce in summer.

Flocks of Golden Plovers winter in traditional areas, frequently being found in the same fields year after year. The preferred feeding habitat is permanent grassland, often on airfields, although winter-sown cereals and recently ploughed land may be utilised. Inter-tidal areas are sometimes used and assume greater importance in severe weather. Roosts, which may be used during the day or night, are most often on ploughed land, but flocks wintering near the coast may use saltmarsh or raised mud. In the Avon valley, birds regularly roost at Blashford Lakes when suitable islands and spits are exposed by low water levels. Counts from some regularly-used areas are summarised in table 36.

Noteworthy counts made since the period covered by table 36 include 1250 at Mockbeggar Lake (Blashford) on Dec. 29th 1990, 1200 at Middle Wallop Airfield on Jan. 20th 1991 and 925 at Hillside (Odiham) on Feb. 8th 1992.

| | 55-60 | 60-65 | 65-70 | 70-75 | 75-80 | 80-85 | 85-90 | Peak counts |
|---|---|---|---|---|---|---|---|---|
| Hayling Island | - | - | - | 188 | 377 | 271 | 284 | 787, Dec. 1977 |
| Titchfield Haven area | 382 | 292 | 344 | 465 | 476 | 638 | 581 | 900, Dec. 1973 |
| Warsash/Calshot | - | 300^ | 450^ | 386^ | 1145 | 1105 | 395 | 2000, Feb. 1984 |
| Needs Ore/Sowley | 193^ | 296 | 406 | 380 | 406 | 276 | 62 | 800, Feb. 1976 |
| Keyhaven area | - | 161* | 174 | 178 | 214 | 206 | 44 | 700, Feb. 1985 |
| Burton/Bisterne | - | 449^ | 160^ | 271^ | 650^ | 341^ | 470^ | 1200, Feb. 1990 |
| Ibsley/Blashford Lakes | 150* | 343^ | 117* | 300 | 244 | 364 | 388 | 830, Jan. 1990 |
| Danebury area | - | - | 300* | 504 | 919^ | 953 | 192 | 1700, Jan. 1978 |
| Eastleigh area | 401^ | 200* | - | 261^ | 460 | 268 | 258 | 1000, Feb. 1978 |
| Chilcomb/Morestead | 375^ | 375^ | 350* | 216 | 466 | 327 | 120^ | 600, Dec. 1979 |
| Harestock | - | - | - | 313^ | 668 | 80* | 805^ | 1300, Feb. 1989 |
| Easton | - | - | - | 311^ | 260 | 161 | 15* | 550, Jan. 1973 |
| Alresford/Ropley | - | - | 350* | 205^ | 256 | 104 | 245^ | 400, Dec. 1976 |
| Odiham/Crondall | - | - | - | - | 296^ | 300 | 474 | 850, Feb. 1990 |

*Table 36. Five year means and peak counts of Golden Plovers, 1955/56-89/90.*

Although coverage has been variable, the records suggest that the total wintering population is between 4000 and 8000 each season, with no evidence of any long term change. Coordinated counts on Jan. 9th 1977 and Jan. 1st 1978 produced totals of 5006 and 4771 respectively, although some flocks were undoubtedly missed on each occasion (Steventon 1981). These were part of the BTO Wintering Golden Plover Survey, which produced an estimated British population of 200,000 in both 1976/77 and 1977/78 (Fuller & Lloyd 1981). Severe weather may result in the desertion of inland sites, build-ups at coastal localities and cold weather movements through the county. The latter are small in comparison to those made by Lapwings, e.g. 192 moving west at Titchfield Haven on Dec. 31st 1978, 230 moving east there on Feb. 9th 1985, 180 moving south over Netley Shore on Feb. 5th 1986, and a total of 483 moving between south-east and south-west over four sites on Jan. 10th 1987.

Birds may arrive from their breeding grounds in late July or August, although numbers usually remain at a low level until mid-September. In some years, there has been evidence of passage at this time, e.g. in 1977, when 200 were at Roman Road (Basingstoke) on Aug. 25th and 300 were at Danebury on Sep. 4th; in 1978, when 57 were at East Hayling on Aug. 19th, 122 were at Needs Ore the next day and 70 moved west over Pennington Marsh on Aug. 28th; and in 1982, when 90 flew south over Titchfield Haven on Sep. 5th. The main influx occurs from mid-October onwards.

At most sites, numbers decline in March as the return to breeding grounds gets under way, but at others there may be an influx of passage birds in early April which have presumably wintered further south, e.g. 1000 at Enham Alamein on Apr. 5th 1975, 1500 at Danebury on Apr. 2nd 1978 and 1265 there on Apr. 11th 1982. Ringing data suggests that birds wintering in southern England are largely of continental rather than British origin, the latter only moving short distances to lowland habitat adjacent to their nesting grounds (BWP). Those present in April tend to consist largely of northern form birds, which are the dominant type breeding in Iceland, northern Fenno-Scandia and Russia (Marchant *et al* 1986). Most have left by mid-April but 750 were still at Danebury on Apr. 23rd 1977. Occasional birds have been recorded in spring coastal movements, but 33 flying east at Hurst Beach on May 10th 1980 and 90 flying north-east over Titchfield Haven on Apr. 28th 1984 were exceptional. Most other May records have been of five or less birds in the first half of the month, nearly all on the coast. Exceptions to this include 11 flying west at Gilkicker Point on May 25th 1968, nine at Fawley on May 5th 1974, 16 at Danebury on May 6th 1985 and 64 at Hurstbourne Tarrant on May 4th 1991.

The species is scarce between late May and mid-July; there have been ten June records, all of one or two birds at Langstone Harbour, in the Pennington/Keyhaven area or at Beaulieu.

Three Golden Plovers ringed in the Netherlands have been recovered in Hampshire. The birds were ringed in November 1956, April 1962 and November 1982 and recovered at Gosport in December 1962, Fareham in December 1963 and Beaulieu in June 1986.

## Grey Plover                              *Pluvialis squatarola*

A common winter visitor and passage migrant; moderate numbers summer.

The largest numbers occur in Langstone and Chichester Harbours, where there has been a steady increase since counting started in the 1950s. In most seasons, there are clear indications of passage peaks in September/October and/or March, but in others the maximum count is made in mid-winter. 100-200 non-breeders are usually present in Langstone Harbour through late May and June. Localities further west generally show a mid-winter peak. Overall, numbers at these sites have risen, although since the mid-1980s high tide roosts at Portsmouth Harbour and in Southampton Water have declined; some birds feeding in these areas now fly to roost in Langstone Harbour and the Beaulieu Estuary respectively. During the five winters from 1985/86-89/90, the proportion of the British wintering population in Hampshire (based on January counts) averaged 9.4%. The increase in numbers is in line with the position in the north-west European wintering population (Smit & Piersma 1989). High tide roost counts at the main localities are summarised in table 37.

| | 55-60 | 60-65 | 65-70 | 70-75 | 75-80 | 80-85 | 85-90 | Peak counts | |
|---|---|---|---|---|---|---|---|---|---|
| Chichester Harbour | 400* | - | 1269 | 1255 | 1804 | 2018 | 2341 | 3168, | Oct. 1986 |
| East Hayling | - | - | - | - | 1021 | 1087 | 765 | 1415, | Nov. 1979 |
| Langstone Harbour | 174 | 190 | 244 | 560 | 941 | 1379 | 1418 | 2161, | Mar. 1981 |
| Portsmouth Harbour | - | - | - | 139 | 234 | 490 | 213 | 640, | Mar. 1985 |
| Southampton Water | - | - | - | 277 | 405 | 577 | 371 | 860, | Feb. 1982 |
| Dibden Bay | - | - | - | 13 | 108 | 409 | 31 | 622, | Dec. 1981 |
| Fawley/Calshot | - | - | - | 274 | 395 | 416 | 388 | 570, | Jan. 1984 |
| Beaulieu Estuary | - | 53^ | 55 | 41 | 96 | 133 | 380 | 605, | Jan. 1989 |
| Lymington/Hurst | - | 125* | 63 | 231 | 353 | 357 | 332 | 500, | Nov. 1988 |

*Table 37. High tide roost counts of Grey Plovers: five year means of maxima and peak counts, 1955/56-89/90.*

Small numbers move east along the coast in spring. Passage has been recorded between Mar. 25th and May 31st with a peak in the first half of May. Between 1971 and 1992, annual totals logged varied between 12 and 292 (in 1980), with an average of 120. The highest day totals were of 140 at Hurst Beach on May 6th 1976, 100 there on May 7th 1981 and 102 at Lepe on Apr. 28th 1987. Birds are occasionally seen migrating inland, e.g. 36 flew north up the Meon Valley at Titchfield Haven on May 6th 1976 and 45 left north-east from Langstone

Harbour at 1300 hrs. on May 4th 1987. Single-figure flocks have also been recorded leaving north from Salterns Marsh (Lymington) and Langstone Harbour at dusk.

Inland, Grey Plovers are scarce. Between 1967 and 1992, there were 31 records involving 35 birds in 15 years. Most occurred in hard weather or in May or October, but there were sightings in every month. Records (all of single birds unless otherwise stated) came from Fleet Pond (10 birds), Frensham Great Pond (5), Avon Causeway (4 on Feb. 23rd 1986), Wellington Country Park (3 including 2 on Dec. 17th 1981), Alresford Pond, Blashford Lakes, Eversley Gravel Pit and Tunworth (2 each) and Allbrook, Broadlands Lake, Lower Brook, South Warnborough and Winnall Moors (1 each). Most were flying over the observation point or stayed for a few hours only, but two-day stays have been recorded twice, at Fleet Pond on May 22nd and 23rd 1970 and at Eversley Gravel Pit on Aug. 12th and 13th 1984.

Ringing has so far produced little to elucidate the movements of Hampshire birds. One ringed in Langstone Harbour in September 1972 was recovered locally a month later, another ringed in Portsmouth Harbour in February 1976 was found dead in western Germany in October of that year, and a third, ringed in Langstone Harbour in November 1988, was controlled in Norfolk in August 1989. Grey Plovers occurring in Britain breed on the coast of western Siberia; some winter south to tropical West Africa (BWP).

For a review of the population history of this species in The Solent, see Tubbs (1991b).

## Sociable Plover                                      *Chettusia gregaria*

One record. A juvenile was with Lapwings in the Titchfield Haven/ Brownwich/Chilling area from Oct. 17th-23rd 1986. It then moved to HMS Daedalus airfield at Lee-on-the-Solent, where it remained until Nov. 8th.

The Sociable Plover breeds on the steppes of Russia and Kazakhstan and winters principally in Sudan, Ethiopia, Iraq and Pakistan.

## Lapwing                                              *Vanellus vanellus*

A common but decreasing breeder and numerous winter visitor.

The Lapwing is widely distributed in the county, being absent only from built-up and heavily-wooded areas. The preferred breeding habitats are arable farmland, coastal and river valley grasslands and New Forest heaths, especially those previously used as airfields. Although quantitative data are lacking, the general impression is of a considerable decline in many areas over the last decade. On arable farmland, one of the most important habitats, the change from spring to autumn-sown cereals has rendered many fields unsuitable, as Lapwings will not nest where the crop is too high. In the river valleys, many meadows have dried out or the grass has become too lush, due to increased use of fertilizers or under-grazing.

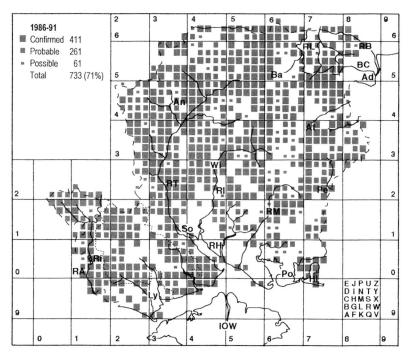

A survey of 35 randomly-selected tetrads was carried out in 1987 as part of a national survey organised by the BTO. 61 pairs of Lapwings were located, which, if scaled to the whole county, would equate to a total population of about 1800 pairs (Eyre 1988). However, this figure is almost certainly an underestimate because it does not give adequate weight to the coastal and river valley areas where densities are high. The 1990 Survey of Breeding Waders of the Avon Valley, organised by the RSPB, located 211 territories between Sopley and Downton. Annual counts at Farlington Marshes from 1975-90 were in the range 21-50 pairs, with 24 in 1990 (R A Billett *in litt*). Surveys and other records submitted to HOS during the 1980s suggest populations of about 90 pairs in the Test and Anton valleys and 60 pairs in the Itchen valley and its tributaries, while in 1992, there were 57 pairs at Needs Ore. In the New Forest, a partial survey carried out in 1981 produced an estimated population of 250-450 pairs (Tubbs 1986a). Assuming an average of 750 pairs in these areas, and three to four pairs in other tetrads where breeding was confirmed or probable during the Atlas Survey, suggests a Hampshire population in the range 2300-2900 pairs. The British total was estimated at 185,000-238,000 pairs in 1986-87 (New Atlas).

Post-breeding movements, mostly in directions between south-west and north-west, are observed from early June onwards. Numbers are generally small, the highest count being of 100 flying west over Fleet Pond on Sep. 11th 1976. Flocks of moulting birds build up in autumn, with gatherings between 300 and 500 recorded in most years and occasionally larger numbers, e.g. 2000 at Roman Road (Basingstoke) on Aug. 25th 1977, 1500 at Harestock (Winchester) three days later and 1400 at Ibsley on July 5th 1979.

The main winter influx occurs from October-December. Peak winter numbers are maintained through January but drop rapidly from mid-February onwards, with few flocks recorded after mid-March. Winter flocks occur in traditional areas, including all those occupied by Golden Plovers and others where that species is rarely recorded. Flocks have reached 2500 at Middle Wallop Airfield on Jan. 1st 1978, Hillside on Jan. 26th 1981 and Jan. 11th 1983 and Soberton Down on Dec. 16th 1985. Large numbers are attracted to floods in the Avon Valley, e.g. 5280 between Sopley and Ibsley on Jan. 29th 1984, following a thaw of lying snow, and 4790 (including 3000+ at Bisterne) on Feb. 4th 1990. At the coast, the highest numbers occur during severe weather (when frost-bound inland sites may be deserted) or when areas become flooded. Large counts include 3000 at Needs Ore on Jan. 16th 1972, 2200 in the Oxey/Keyhaven area on Feb. 5th 1977, 2900 at Farlington Marshes on Jan. 11th 1986 and 2800 in the Brownwich/Chilling area on Feb. 6th 1986.

Severe weather, especially heavy snowfall, often precipitates hard weather movements. On Jan. 30th 1972, 9000 moved south over Langstone Harbour during the day and 10,200 were counted passing south over Portsmouth Harbour between 1400 and 1630 hrs. At least 5000 were seen flying south over Fleet Pond and smaller movements were noted at many other sites in the county. Another large movement occurred on Dec. 31st 1978, when 5000+ moved south or south-west over the Keyhaven/Hurst area, 5940 moved south or south-east down Southampton Water in 4.75 hours and a further 3000 were seeking refuge at Titchfield Haven. During the severe winters in the 1980s, movements were less spectacular, the largest noted being of 3500 south over Netley on Feb. 5th 1986. However, in the Avon Valley, over 10,000 were estimated to be in frozen fields on Feb. 10th 1985 though most quickly moved on.

Return movements are occasionally noted in February or March. Generally small flocks are involved, counts such as 455 east over Bramshill on Feb. 14th 1979 and 670 north or north-east over Hambledon between Mar. 6th and 13th 1986 being exceptional.

Ringing studies have shown that some Hampshire-bred birds winter in France and Iberia; 18 ringed as pulli have been recovered in that region in their first or subsequent winters, some following cold-weather movements in southern England. Of 39 recoveries within Britain, only one involved a movement greater than 100 km: a bird ringed as a pullus at Farlington Marshes in 1978 and found dead in Tyne and Wear, where it was presumably breeding, on May 9th 1984. The origins of birds wintering in Hampshire are shown by the recovery of three birds ringed as pulli in Lancashire, western Germany and Norway. Two adults ringed in the county in winter were recovered in later winters in Spain and Bosnia Hercegovina, while another was found in the Netherlands in July.

# Knot                                               *Calidris canutus*

A common winter visitor to the eastern harbours. Elsewhere, a moderately common passage migrant and scarce winter visitor along the coast and rare inland.

After the breeding season, Knots arrive in Hampshire from mid-July onwards. There is a peak in late August and early September, when birds from both the north-central Siberian population (which moves on to winter in West Africa) and the Greenland and north-east Canadian population (which winters in north-west Europe) are present (BWP). In the 1960s and 1970s, counts at this time occasionally reached three figures, e.g. 100 at Langstone Harbour on Aug. 28th 1960, 230 in the Lymington/Hurst area on Sep. 16th 1962, 142 at Dibden Bay on Sep. 1st 1973 and 110 at Fawley Reclamation on Sep. 3rd 1978, but since then flocks in excess of 20 have become very scarce. During the 1980s, numbers in Langstone Harbour peaked at 260 on Sep. 14th 1985 and in the range 50-105 in four other autumns. Elsewhere, the only significant counts were of 80 in the Lymington/ Hurst area on Sep. 6th 1985 and 64 there on Sep. 5th 1987. Evidence for through passage was provided by a flock of 65 which moved west out to sea over Hurst Beach on Aug. 20th 1978 and three flocks totalling 91 which did the same on Aug. 28th of that year.

Wintering birds are largely confined to the eastern harbours, where the main arrival is in November. Peak counts may be recorded in any month up to February, after which there is a rapid departure in March. During the five winters from 1985/86-89/90, the proportion of the British wintering population in Hampshire (based on January counts) averaged 0.7%. High tide roost counts at the three main localities are summarised in table 38.

|  | 55-60 | 60-65 | 65-70 | 70-75 | 75-80 | 80-85 | 85-90 | Peak counts |
|---|---|---|---|---|---|---|---|---|
| Chichester Harbour | - | - | 297 | 995 | 1158 | 721 | 941 | 2000, Jan. 1980 |
| East Hayling | - | - | - | - | 536 | 443 | 402 | 1167, Dec. 1978 |
| Langstone Harbour | 264 | 400 | 280 | 560 | 1787 | 947 | 1928 | 2950, Feb. 1988 |
| Portsmouth Harbour | - | - | 815^ | 395 | 609 | 583 | 327 | 1260, Dec. 1975 |

*Table 38. High tide roost counts of Knot: five year means of winter maxima and peak counts.*

West of Portsmouth Harbour, Knots are very erratic in their appearance in winter, usually only occurring on isolated dates. Three-figure flocks were occasionally recorded in the 1960s and 1970s, e.g. 180 in the Lymington/Hurst area in severe weather on Jan. 27th 1963, 300 at the Beaulieu Estuary on Jan. 17th 1965 and 180 at Dibden Bay on Jan. 18th 1976; subsequently the only winter count of this magnitude was of 100 at Calshot on Nov. 24th 1985, and in some winters fewer than ten were recorded. Rarely, sizeable flocks have been noted in early spring, e.g. 65 at Fawley Reclamation on Apr. 4th 1978 and 100 at Warsash on Mar. 23rd 1984 and Mar. 27th 1985.

Later in spring, there is a passage of presumed West African wintering birds eastwards along the coast. Movement has been noted between Apr. 12th and May 24th and reaches a peak in the first two weeks of May. Numbers are small compared to most other species; between 1971 and 1992 the recorded annual total varied between zero and 120 (in 1978) with an average of 40. The largest day totals were of 80 moving north-east over Hill Head on Apr. 23rd 1978 and 102 flying east at Hurst Beach on May 7th 1981. Few have been recorded moving inland from Langstone Harbour in spring, the only recent record being of ten leaving high to the north-west on the evening of Apr. 30th 1978. The lack of such observations supports the conclusion that mostly Siberian breeders are involved in this movement. Some may pause briefly, but large flocks are unusual, the highest count being of 35 at Pennington Marsh on May 3rd 1990.

Passage may continue until early June, and in some years small flocks of non-breeders summer in Langstone Harbour, where the highest counts have been of 50 on July 1st 1961 and 33 on June 9th 1979.

There have been six inland records. Single individuals were on puddles at Barton Stacey barracks on Sep. 13th 1960 and at Alresford Pond on Mar. 27th 1962. Recent records have come from Eversley Gravel Pit (two on Sep. 6th 1987), Hillside Marsh (1 in severe weather on Feb. 7th and 8th 1988) and Mockbeggar Lake (two on May 31st 1991 and one on May 24th 1992).

There are only four ringing returns involving Hampshire birds. Three ringed in The Wash in September have been recovered or controlled in the Portsmouth area in winter, while one ringed in Portsmouth Harbour in winter was controlled in The Wash in September. These indicate that birds moulting on The Wash winter on the Hampshire coast.

## Sanderling                                                   *Calidris alba*

A moderately common passage migrant and winter visitor.

A flock of Sanderlings is present in Chichester Harbour in all but the summer months. In the 1980s, mid-winter counts were typically in the range 100-300 with a maximum of 376 in January 1983. In some years, larger flocks are recorded in autumn or spring, e.g. in 1988, when there were 540 on Mar. 19th, rising to 700 on Apr. 19th and then declining to 250 by May 17th.

The normal high tide roost site of these birds is at Pilsea Sands, off the southern tip of Thorney Island in West Sussex. However, in recent years, a large proportion of the flock has occasionally roosted at Black Point on the Hayling Shore, with peaks of 200 in January 1988, 280 in October 1988 and 370 in March 1989. Birds radiate out from the roosts to various feeding sites, eastward along the Sussex coast, across Spithead to Ryde Sands on the Isle of Wight, and westward into Hampshire, where the favoured areas are East Winner Bank (Hayling Bay), Sinah Sands (Langstone Harbour) and between Eastney Point and Southsea. The Hampshire sites are most frequently used in winter and spring, but rarely by more than 50 birds. Larger flocks in Hayling Bay include 200 in December 1954 and 180 in January 1974. Roosts of up to 60 occasionally form in these areas or on Haslar seawall and Gilkicker Point to the west. Exceptionally, a roost at Southsea held 319 on Dec. 5th 1990 and 246 on Dec. 7th 1991.

Elsewhere, Sanderlings are principally spring passage migrants. Eastward movements along the coast are recorded between mid-April and late May with a clear peak in the first half of May. Between 1971 and 1992, the total recorded each year varied between 54 and 374 (in 1973) with an average of 203. The highest day totals were of 104 off Hurst Beach on May 10th 1975 and 182 off Hurst and 102 off Hill Head on May 7th 1981. Birds may pause to feed or rest during their migration; such gatherings are usually of up to 30, but larger flocks recorded include 47 at Dibden Bay on May 10th 1968, 61 at Warsash on May 12th 1979 and 58 in Langstone Harbour on May 16th 1987. Passage occasionally continues into early June, e.g. 50 flew east off Needs Ore on June 1st 1963 and ten were at Pennington Marsh on June 10th 1979.

Autumn migrants appear from late July but numbers are very low, counts rarely exceeding five. Larger numbers recorded include 20 at Hurst Beach on Aug. 24th 1984, 13 there on Sep. 1st 1988, eight at Titchfield Haven on Sep. 10th 1987 and seven at Needs Ore on Sep. 27th 1975.

During the winter months sightings west of Gilkicker Point are exceptional, only one or two at most being recorded annually.

Inland, Sanderlings are very scarce. Between 1958 and 1992, there were 25 records in 17 years involving a total of 43 birds. Sightings were made at Frensham Great Pond (21, including 8 on May 11th 1969), Mockbeggar Lake (12, including 6 on May 25th 1983), Fleet Pond (3), Eversley Gravel Pit and Winnall Moors (2 each), and Lakeside (Eastleigh), Winchester Sewage Farm and Yateley Gravel Pit (1 each). All occurred in the period between May 2nd and 31st apart from three in August and one each in September and November.

Some evidence of the movements of Sanderlings has been provided by sightings of marked birds. One, colour-dyed on the Ribble Estuary in Lancashire in spring 1985, was in Chichester Harbour on July 21st of that year and another, colour-ringed in Iceland in late May 1989, was at the same locality on July 26th and Aug. 1st 1989. These birds almost certainly originate from the north-east Greenland breeding population. The sighting of a colour-dyed bird in Ghana indicates that some or all of this population winters in tropical West Africa. National ringing data suggest that those wintering in Hampshire may be of Siberian origin (BWP).

# Little Stint                                                   *Calidris minuta*

A passage migrant, scarce in autumn and very scarce in spring; in some years a few winter.

Little Stints are most numerous in autumn, although the number recorded varies considerably from year to year (fig. 39). At least four factors are likely to have influenced the numbers recorded: observer coverage, breeding success, incidence of favourable winds to drift birds westwards from their normal migration routes from arctic Scandinavia and Siberia to sub-Saharan Africa, and the availability of suitable habitat in Hampshire.

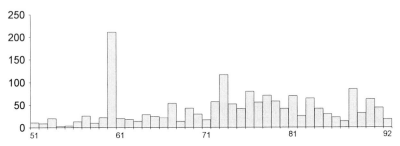

*Figure 39. Autumn totals of Little Stints, 1951-92.*

Returning adults may appear at the end of June although in most years none are recorded until late July or early August. The main arrival occurs from late August, with peak numbers at any time up to early October, after which a gradual reduction takes place. Virtually all the birds occurring during and after the peak period are juveniles. Records at the main sites for 1951-92 are summarised in table 39.

| | Period recorded | Years with records | Years with counts of 5+ | Peak counts | |
|---|---|---|---|---|---|
| Hayling Oyster Beds | 1987-92 | 5 | 2 | 8, | 11/9/90 |
| Farlington Marshes | 1952-92 | 40 | 21 | 30, | 9/10/60 |
| | | | | 19, | 25/9/73 |
| Paulsgrove Reclamation* | 1981-87 | 7 | 3 | 18, | 3/10/83 |
| Titchfield Haven | 1952-92 | 28 | 5 | 9, | 2 & 3/9/72 |
| Warsash | 1959-92 | 19 | 2 | 6, | 16/9/88 |
| Southampton Docks*/Eling | 1976-88 | 9 | 3 | 10, | 6 & 11/10/79 |
| Dibden Bay* | 1951-83 | 28 | 21 | 50, | 26/9/60 |
| | | | | 23, | 6/9/72 |
| | | | | 60, | 28 & 30/9/73 |
| | | | | 27, | 9/9/74 |
| Fawley Reclamation* | 1972-88 | 10 | 5 | 20, | 17/9/78 |
| Needs Ore | 1956-92 | 12 | 2 | 6, | 1/10/60 |
| | | | | 6, | 3/9/90 |
| Pennington/Keyhaven | 1954-92 | 36 | 20 | 56, | 4/10/60 |
| | | | | 19, | 18/9/90 |

* habitat now unsuitable

*Table 39. Summary of autumn counts of Little Stints, 1951-92.*

Records at other coastal sites are usually of one or two birds, but higher counts include seven at Northney (Hayling Island) on Sep. 27th 1957 and eight at Lisle Court Lagoon on Sep. 16th 1990. Inland records have come from Mockbeggar Lake (15 birds, including 4 on Oct. 2nd 1983 and 5 on Sep. 10th 1988),

216

Alresford Pond (4), Winchester Sewage Farm (2/3 on Aug. 24th 1966), Eversley Gravel Pit (2) and Frensham Great Pond, Timsbury Gravel Pit and Woolmer Pond (1 each).

In some years migrants continue to move through until late November or early December. Wintering birds (i.e. those present continuously from December to March or April) have been recorded at several localities, including Black Point (up to 10, 1958/59-64/65), Farlington Marshes (up to 3, 1972/73-77/78), Dibden Bay (up to 13, 1973/74-81/82) and Southampton Docks and Eling Great Marsh (up to 6, 1977/78-81/82). Since then, the only record has been of one at Eling on Mar. 6th 1986.

Between 1951 and 1992, there were spring sightings in 30 years involving about 135 birds, with a maximum of 14 in 1974. Few have been seen in April, apart from wintering birds; the peak movement is usually in mid-May. Most have been seen at Farlington Marshes, with 59 including five on May 15th 1985, and Pennington and Keyhaven Marshes, with 15 including four on May 7th 1961. Other records came from ten localities, all being of one to three birds apart from seven at Gilkicker Point on May 13th 1961, 11 at Dibden Bay on May 11th 1974, 11 at Southampton Docks on Apr. 18th 1979 and seven there on May 9th of that year, and five at Dibden Bay on May 3rd 1982. Single birds were inland at Lakeside (Eastleigh) on May 29th 1984 and at Eversley Gravel Pit on May 29th 1992.

A few have occurred in mid-summer, including three at Farlington Marshes from June 12th-July 22nd 1976 and two at Mockbeggar Lake on June 21st 1981.

Ringing has produced two controls in Hampshire. One involved an adult ringed at Cliffe, Kent on Sep. 13th 1975 and controlled at Fawley on Nov. 6th 1975, while the other referred to an adult ringed at Fawley on Oct. 7th 1976 and controlled at Southampton Docks on Jan. 13th 1979.

## Temminck's Stint                                      *Calidris temminckii*

A very scarce passage migrant.

The first Temminck's Stints for the county were five at Keyhaven Marsh on May 12th 1935. Another was seen there on May 25th of that year.

Between 1951 and 1992, there were sightings in 33 years, with a total of 92 recorded, 49 in spring and 43 in autumn (fig. 40).

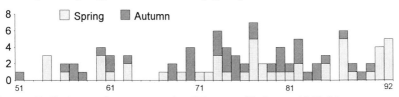

*Figure 40. Spring and autumn totals of Temminck's Stints, 1951-92*

Spring records covered the period May 1st (Farlington Marshes, 1960) to June 6th (Farlington Marshes, 1971), with the majority in mid-May (fig. 41). Records were for Farlington Marshes (26 birds), Pennington/Keyhaven Marshes (7), Mockbeggar Lake (4), Dibden Bay, Eversley Gravel Pit and Titchfield Haven (3 each), and Needs Ore, Paulsgrove Reclamation and Warsash (1 each). All sightings were of one or two birds apart from that of three at Farlington Marshes from May 16th-18th 1954. Most were present for one or two days only but some remained for up to five days. In 1977, two were at Farlington Marshes from May 17th-22nd and one was still present on May 24th.

Autumn records covered the period July 8th (Farlington Marshes, 1980) to Nov. 3rd (Dibden Bay, 1973), with most between mid-July and late August (fig. 41). Records were for Farlington Marshes (18 birds), Pennington/Keyhaven Marshes and Dibden Bay (7 each), Titchfield Haven (5), Milton Reclamation (2) and Ashlett, Eling, Lepe and Warsash (1 each). All records were of one or two birds. Stays of up to ten days were not infrequent, and single birds remained at Dibden Bay from Sep. 26th-Nov. 3rd 1973 and Farlington Marshes from July 20th-Aug. 11th 1974.

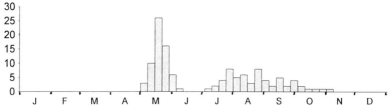

*Figure 41. Cumulative weekly totals of Temminck's Stints, 1951-92.*

The Temminck's Stint breeds in Fenno-Scandia and northern Russia and winters largely in tropical West and west-central Africa.

## Least Sandpiper                                    *Calidris minutilla*

One record. One spent the day at Farlington Marshes on May 22nd 1977.

The Least Sandpiper breeds in Alaska and Canada and winters from the Gulf of Mexico south to Peru and Brazil.

## White-rumped Sandpiper                             *Calidris fuscicollis*

A rare vagrant. There have been 11 records of single birds, all in autumn between Aug. 10th and Oct. 27th, as follows:

| | |
|---|---|
| 1963: | Titchfield Haven, Oct. 17th; |
| 1974: | Pennington Marsh, Aug. 10th; |
| 1981: | Warsash, Oct. 12th; |
| 1982: | juvenile, Eling Great Marsh, Oct. 25th-27th; |
| 1983: | adult, Warsash, Oct. 27th; |
| 1984: | adult, Farlington Marshes, Aug. 27th and 28th; |
| | juvenile, Warsash, Oct. 12th; |
| 1986: | adult, Farlington Marshes, Sep. 3rd; |
| | Eling Great Marsh, Sep. 29th; |
| 1987: | adult, Farlington Marshes, Aug. 10th-17th; |
| 1988: | juvenile, Titchfield Haven, Oct. 2nd-5th. |

The White-rumped Sandpiper breeds in arctic Canada and winters in southern South America.

## Baird's Sandpiper                                          *Calidris bairdii*

Three records. Single juveniles were recorded at Warsash on Oct. 7th 1986, Pennington Marsh from Sep. 7th-18th 1988 and Farlington Marshes from Sep. 19th-22nd 1989†.

The Baird's Sandpiper breeds in the Arctic from north-eastern Siberia, through Alaska and Canada to north-western Greenland; it winters in southern South America.

## Pectoral Sandpiper                                        *Calidris melanotos*

A very scarce passage migrant.

The first Pectoral Sandpiper for the county was one which flew from West Sussex across Emsworth Channel towards Hayling Island on Oct. 12th 1947.

Between 1951 and 1992, there were records in 27 years involving 53 birds, 44 of them since 1968. Annual totals varied between zero and three apart from 1970 and 1974, with five, and 1973, with four.

Three occurred in spring: single birds at Pennington Marsh on May 16th 1981 and May 29th 1983 and another at Warsash and Titchfield Haven from May 21st-23rd 1991.

Autumn records covered the period July 2nd (Farlington Marshes, 1977) to Oct. 30th (Keyhaven Marsh, 1976). The pattern is very similar to that shown nationally, with small numbers of adults in July and August, a peak in September when juveniles occur and very few after mid-October (fig. 42). The main localities were Pennington and Keyhaven Marshes (17 birds, including two on Sep. 1st and 2nd 1982 and up to five between Sep. 6th and 16th 1970), Farlington Marshes (14), Dibden Bay (7, including two on Sep. 20th 1968) and Paulsgrove Reclamation (4, including two from Sep. 1st-8th 1984). Other records, all of single birds, were from Eling Great Marsh (Oct. 6th-10th 1961), Warsash (Aug. 17th 1974 and Sep. 23rd-Oct. 2nd 1986), Calshot Reclamation (Aug. 24th-26th 1974), Mockbeggar Lake (Aug. 30th-Sep. 20th 1981), Titchfield Haven (Sep. 22nd 1983 and Oct. 2nd-6th 1987) and Needs Ore (Oct. 13th 1984).

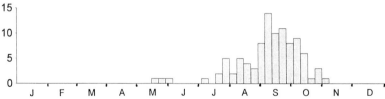

*Figure 42. Cumulative weekly totals of Pectoral Sandpipers, 1951-92.*

The Pectoral Sandpiper breeds in the Arctic from Siberia east to Canada and winters largely in southern South America.

## Curlew Sandpiper                                          *Calidris ferruginea*

A passage migrant, scarce in autumn and very scarce in spring; rarely winters.

Curlew Sandpipers returning from their breeding grounds on the Siberian tundra are recorded from early July, although single birds were at Fawley on June 21st 1975 and Titchfield Haven on June 22nd 1992. There is a peak in early August, consisting entirely of adults, then a short lull before the build up to the main passage period in early September, when most of those present are juveniles. Numbers decline rapidly through October with stragglers in November and December, some of which may winter. Between 1951 and 1992, numbers varied considerably from year to year (fig. 43), probably for the same reasons outlined above for Little Stint. Records at the main sites for 1951-92 are summarised in table 40.

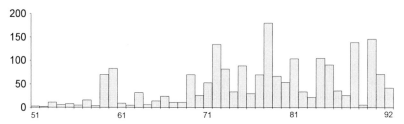

*Figure 43. Autumn totals of Curlew Sandpipers, 1951-92.*

| | Period recorded | Years with records | Years with counts of 5+ | Peak counts | |
|---|---|---|---|---|---|
| Hayling Oyster Beds | 1988-91 | 3 | 2 | 25, | 12/9/88 |
| | | | | 22, | 9/9/90 |
| Farlington Marshes | 1953-92 | 40 | 23 | 34, | 12/9/59 |
| | | | | 22, | 8/9/78 |
| | | | | 25, | 14 & 15/9/88 |
| | | | | 25, | 8/9/90 |
| Paulsgrove Reclamation* | 1975-86 | 8 | 2 | 19, | 10/9/78 |
| Titchfield Haven | 1969-92 | 17 | 9 | 28, | 24/8/84 |
| | | | | 18, | 11/9/92 |
| Warsash | 1955-92 | 19 | 5 | 21, | 13/9/90 |
| Dibden Bay* | 1951-83 | 24 | 9 | 19, | 8/9/59 |
| | | | | 18, | 30/8/60 |
| | | | | 37, | 5/8/71 |
| | | | | 36, | 3/9/73 |
| Fawley Reclamation* | 1968-88 | 10 | 7 | 25, | 6/9/75 |
| | | | | 83, | 5/9/78 |
| | | | | 33, | 9/9/79 |
| Needs Ore | 1958-92 | 14 | 2 | 6, | 6/9/81 |
| Pennington/Keyhaven | 1952-92 | 35 | 17 | 26, | 3/9/60 |
| | | | | 34, | 31/8/69 |
| | | | | 50, | 1/9/72 |
| | | | | 21, | 12/9/88 |

* habitat now unsuitable

*Table 40. Summary of autumn counts of Curlew Sandpipers, 1951-92.*

The only other significant record was of 34 at Northney (Hayling Island) on Sep. 19th 1959, which were probably from Farlington Marshes.

Curlew Sandpipers are rare inland. Single birds were recorded at Eastleigh Sewage Farm on Sep. 9th 1978, Mockbeggar Lake on July 29th 1980 and Alresford Pond on Aug 16th 1987 and Sep. 24th and 25th 1990. Up to seven were at Alresford Pond from Sep. 27th-Oct. 3rd 1991.

Wintering birds were present at Eling Great Marsh in 1979, 1980, 1982, 1983 (2) and 1989 and at Warsash in 1985. None were recorded after Mar. 6th. Usually, fewer than ten winter in Britain.

In spring, there were records in 30 years between 1951 and 1992 involving a total of 103 birds. There were 13 in 1971 and 11 in 1987, but in other years the maximum was eight. Single birds at Farlington Marshes on Mar. 27th and Apr. 10th 1960 and Apr. 5th 1966 may have been wintering; otherwise migrants occurred between mid-April and mid-June with the majority evenly-spread through May. The main localities were Farlington Marshes (53, including three on May 8th 1955, May 19th 1974 and June 2nd and 3rd 1992) and Pennington and Keyhaven Marshes (31, including ten on May 6th 1971 and four on May 7th 1981). Other records, all of one or two birds, were from ten coastal localities.

Three birds ringed at Farlington Marshes have been recovered or controlled. An adult caught in August 1977 was found dead in Calvados, France, 171 km SSE, on Aug. 26th 1987; another adult ringed at that time was retrapped on Aug. 11th 1990; and a juvenile ringed on Sep. 13th 1984 was controlled in Schleswig Holstein, western Germany, 759 km ENE, on July 29th 1992. The main wintering grounds of those passing through Hampshire are in tropical West Africa north of the Gulf of Guinea.

## Purple Sandpiper                                        *Calidris maritima*

A very scarce but regular winter visitor and passage migrant along the coast.

The first Purple Sandpiper recorded in the county was at Southsea Castle from Dec. 17th-29th 1939. During the 1950s, the only records from there were of two on Mar. 30th 1952 and four on Jan. 19th 1955, but regular observation from 1961 onwards revealed a small wintering population. Numbers increased to a maximum of 32 in 1981/82 but have since declined (fig. 44). The first normally arrive between mid-October and early November, the earliest records being of one on Oct. 10th 1984 and, exceptionally, two on Sep. 24th 1985. During the winter, numbers may peak at any time between November and March. In some years, none are recorded in April, but they reappear in early May, suggesting passage. The latest record is of four on May 14th 1973.

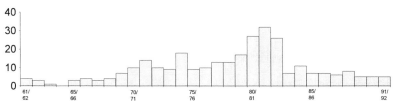

*Figure 44. Peak counts of Purple Sandpipers at Southsea Castle, 1961/62-91/92.*

Birds are most often found feeding around the rocky shore at Southsea Castle, especially as the tide falls. At low spring tides they can be found on the tank blocks just to the east of South Parade Pier or under the pier itself. There have also been occasional records from Eastney. At high water, they are usually absent, possibly roosting on the forts in The Solent or elsewhere. There may be some interchange with the Forelands/Bembridge Ledge area on the Isle of Wight, which would explain their rather irregular appearance at certain times and observations such as seven leaving towards Wight on Jan. 2nd 1975.

Away from Southsea, the species is rare, but numbers have increased recently, with 26 from 1953-80 and 55 from 1981-92. The cumulative monthly totals of these records are shown below.

| Jul | Aug | Sep | Oct | Nov | Dec | Jan | Feb | Mar | Apr | May |
|-----|-----|-----|-----|-----|-----|-----|-----|-----|-----|-----|
| 1 | 4 | 6 | 13 | 11 | 10 | 9 | 10 | 5 | 12 | 15 |

Most records were from the Hurst Castle/Milford-on-Sea coast, with 27 birds, some staying for several weeks at a time. Up to four were present there from Oct. 28th 1989-Feb. 26th 1990 and three on Jan. 4th 1991. At nearby Pennington and Keyhaven Marshes, 16 were recorded, all on one date only and all in the migration periods of March/April and July-November, often following gales. At Sandy Point, four flew east on Feb. 8th 1985; since 1987, up to four have roosted on an offshore structure there on dates between Mar. 25th and May 12th. The remaining records were from Hill Head (7 birds, including 3 E on May 9th 1986), Gilkicker Point (5, including 3 E on May 2nd 1986), Langstone Harbour (2) and Calshot, Dibden Bay, Hayling Bay, Hythe Pier, Needs Ore, Paulsgrove Reclamation and Portchester Castle (1 each).

The increase at Southsea in the late 1970s and 1980s and latterly elsewhere parallels the picture at other south coast localities such as Portland Bill. The nearest breeding grounds of the Purple Sandpiper are in Iceland and Fenno-Scandia.

## Dunlin                                                      *Calidris alpina*

An abundant winter visitor and common passage migrant. Small numbers summer.

The numbers of Dunlin wintering in The Solent increased dramatically from the mid-1950s onwards. Tubbs (1992), using information from the diaries of William Mudge, a punt gunner, and other sources, suggested that the increase was in response to the reduction of hunting pressure following the passing of the Protection of Birds Act in 1954. The population peaked at about 90,000 in 1974/75, and then fell, via three troughs with intervening periods of recovery, to 46,000 in 1986/87 (Kirby & Tubbs 1989). By 1989/90, it had recovered to 85,000, which represented about 18% of the total wintering in Britain (Kirby *et al* 1990). Numbers in high tide roosts in the Lymington/Hurst area, Southampton Water and Portsmouth Harbour are now less than in the 1970s, but counts at Langstone Harbour, the principal site, have continued to increase (table 40). Recent observations have shown that an increasing proportion of those feeding in Portsmouth Harbour move to Langstone to roost (Bill & Hollins 1989), presumably because of development and increased disturbance at the main roost site.

| | 55-60 | 60-65 | 65-70 | 70-75 | 75-80 | 80-85 | 85-90 | Peak counts | |
|---|-------|-------|-------|-------|-------|-------|-------|-------------|---|
| Chichester Harbour | - | - | 13165 | 24193 | 24697 | 26049 | 21193 | 30084, | Nov. 1982 |
| East Hayling | - | - | - | - | 12468 | 10048 | 10661 | 15000, | Oct. 1986 |
| Langstone Harbour | 13300 | 7600 | 17400 | 23720 | 29314 | 28057 | 31532 | 37660, | Jan. 1990 |
| Portsmouth Harbour | - | - | 14500* | 15512 | 9180 | 8601 | 7409 | 19650, | Dec. 1973 |
| Southampton Water | - | - | - | 7195 | 10130 | 6127 | 5326 | 14200, | Dec. 1978 |
| Beaulieu Estuary | - | - | 1240 | 558 | 1020 | 1520 | 1766 | 2700, | Jan. 1985 |
| Lymington/Hurst | - | 1250* | 2360 | 7200 | 4936 | 3778 | 3032 | 10000, | Jan. 1974 |

*Table 41. High tide roost counts of Dunlin: five year means of winter maxima and peak counts.*

Dunlin arrive in the Solent from late June onwards; counts may show autumn passage peaks, e.g. 3100 in Langstone Harbour on July 31st 1976 and 713 in the Lymington/Hurst area on Aug. 13th 1988. Numbers increase rapidly in October; they remain at a high level through the winter months except for occasional declines in periods of hard weather. Most depart in March but numbers may increase again as migrants pass through in spring, e.g. 1100 at Fawley on May 5th 1974, 1040 in the Lymington/Hurst area on May 4th 1985 and 4300 in Langstone Harbour on May 10th 1986. These counts coincide with the peak movement eastwards along the coast. Between 1971 and 1992, the total noted each spring averaged 507 but only twice reached four figures, with 1996 in 1973 and 1269 in 1974. The movement has been most noticeable off Hurst Beach, where day totals exceeded 100 on 18 occasions, including 561 on May 3rd 1973 and 388 on May 3rd 1980. Further east, the highest totals have been of 215 off Hill Head on May 7th 1981 and 211 in Hayling Bay on May 6th 1989. Small flocks are regularly recorded departing inland from coastal sites in spring, especially on fine, calm evenings. During the period 1953-72, a total of 3897 was seen to leave Langstone Harbour on dates between Apr. 3rd and June 3rd, 67% of them in the first two weeks of May. 90% left in directions between north-west and north, presumably heading for breeding grounds in Iceland (see below).

The numbers summering are low; counts in Langstone Harbour in early June have only twice exceeded 55 with a maximum of 230 in 1990.

Inland records largely coincide with the main passage periods (fig. 45), although some occur in winter during severe cold spells and considerable numbers are attracted to floods in the Avon Valley. Away from the Avon floods, some 731 were recorded inland between 1951 and 1992. The principal sites were Mockbeggar Lake (204 birds, including 34 probably from the Avon floods on Feb. 6th 1982, 22 on May 13th 1989 and nine or ten on six other occasions), Fleet Pond (106, max. 11, Sep. 14th 1975), Eversley Gravel Pit (102, max. 5, Apr. 29th 1985) and Winchester Sewage Farm (54, max. 7, July 29th 1988). Other records included 12 at Winnall Moors on May 7th 1962, 15 flying west over Frensham Great Pond in severe weather on Jan. 30th 1976 and eight moving south over Wellington Country Park in similar conditions on Dec. 17th 1981. In addition, a flock of 150 flew south-west over Millersford Plantation (New Forest) on Aug. 9th 1967.

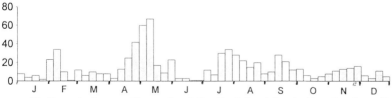

*Figure 45. Cumulative weekly totals of Dunlin inland (excluding the Avon flood plain), 1951-92.*

In the Avon valley, the largest numbers occur between Sopley and Bisterne. Flocks exceeding 100 were recorded in ten winters between 1976/77 and 1991/92, with records spanning the period between Dec. 15th and Mar. 10th.

The highest counts were of 400 at Avon Village on Jan. 16th 1977 and 700+ at Sopley on Feb. 10th 1979. Above Ringwood, counts reached 150 at Ibsley on Feb. 20th 1974 and between Dec. 31st 1976 and Jan. 29th 1977. Subsequently, there were 40 at nearby Blashford on Feb. 24th 1979, but since 1984, no more than eight has been recorded apart from flocks of 15 on Mar. 25th 1984 and 17 on Jan. 25th 1986.

Steventon (1977) used ringing and biometric data to show that birds wintering in the eastern harbours are of the race *C.a. alpina*, which breeds in northern Fenno-Scandia and arctic Russia and moults in the southern North Sea area in autumn, while those present in autumn and spring are of the race *C.a. schinzii*, which breeds in Iceland and north-west Britain; they moult at Langstone in autumn but move on to winter elsewhere.

Further recoveries have shown that autumn passage birds move to north-west Africa to winter. Of seven ringed in Hampshire in autumn and recovered or controlled, three were in Morocco, two in Spain, one in Portugal and one on the breeding grounds in Iceland. Three controlled in Hampshire in autumn had been ringed in Mauritania and Eire in April and France in May. Ringing studies also confirm the movement of the Hampshire wintering population through Scandinavia and northern Europe to breeding grounds in northern Russia. Of three recoveries there, the longest movement involved an adult ringed at Southampton Docks on Feb. 26th 1978 and found dead in Komi, Russia, 4076 km ENE, on June 2nd 1979.

## Broad-billed Sandpiper                              *Limicola falcinellus*

Three records. Single birds were at Farlington Marshes on Oct. 5th and 6th 1957, Paulsgrove Reclamation from May 22nd-25th 1982 and again at Farlington Marshes on June 4th and 5th 1988.

The Broad-billed Sandpiper breeds in Fenno-Scandia and Siberia and winters in East Africa, southern Asia and Australia.

## Buff-breasted Sandpiper                              *Tryngites subruficollis*

A rare vagrant. There have been nine records, one in spring and eight in autumn, as follows:

1975:    Keyhaven Marsh, Aug. 31st 1975;
1976:    Farlington Marshes, June 11th;
         Fawley Reclamation, Oct. 8th (caught and ringed);
         Fawley Reclamation, Oct. 9th and 10th (unringed);
1977:    Pennington Marsh, Sep. 4th;
1980:    Keyhaven Marsh, Sep. 12th-22nd;
1982:    Pennington Marsh, Sep. 25th-29th;
1983:    Sinah Common, Sep. 17th and 18th;
1991:    Pennington Marsh, Oct. 6th and 7th.

The Buff-breasted Sandpiper breeds in Alaska and north-western Canada and winters in central Argentina and Paraguay.

*ennis Bright*

Mature coniferous woodland, such as Slufters Inclosure, New Forest (*above*) provides suitable habitat for a variety of species including Crossbill. Clearings and young plantations are favoured by Nightjar (*over*).

*avid Kjaer*

*Jimmy Baldw*

Broomy Bottom, New Forest (*below*), a typical lowland heath which holds nationally scarce species such as Dartford Warbler and Nightjar.

*Dennis Brig*

*Dennis Bright*

Deadman Bottom, New Forest (*above*), a former breeding haunt of the Red-backed Shrike, which last bred in Hampshire in 1984.

*Norman Orr*

Craig Vince

Ludshott Common (*above*), a typical heathland in the north-east of the county, which, like the New Forest, provides habitat for species such as Dartford Warbler and Stonechat.

*Jason Groves*

*Dennis Brigh*

Craig Vincer

Occasional heath fires, such as the one at Ludshott in May 1980, create open habitat (*above*) which is colonised in the early stages of recovery by Woodlarks.

Norman Orr

Uncultivated downland at Martin (*above*). Recent survey work by the RSPB and HOS has shown that 20–25 pairs of Stone Curlew still breed in such habitat and also on arable farmland.

The Long-eared Owl is a scarce and elusive species which occurs in a variety of habitats including downland scrub and coniferous woodland. The Cirl Bunting, once common in many parts of the county, is now extinct as a breeding species.

*Dennis Bright*

Typical Hampshire farmland with copses at Morestead Down (*above*). While some species such as the Whitethroat have recovered from earlier setbacks, many others, particularly seed-eaters such as the Corn Bunting, have declined on the county's farmland.

*Dennis Bright*

*Roger Wilmshurst*

Gravel pits at Mockbeggar in the Avon Valley (*above*). During the extraction phase, the open gravel provides nest sites for Little Ringed Plover while Sand Martins occupy suitable exposed sand faces. As the pits mature, habitat for breeding waterfowl is created.

The Avon Valley meadows, such as those at Ibsley (*above*), are a regular wintering site for nationally important numbers of White-fronted Geese and Bewick's Swans.

The river Itchen at Ovington (*above*). The riverside meadows provide important inland breeding sites for waders such as the Lapwing.

Dennis Brigl

The Lower Test Marshes (*above*), which lie where the River Test enters Southampton Water, provide habitat for breeding Redshank and are a stronghold of Cetti's Warbler.

Norman Orr

Charles Mou

Coastal marshes, such as those at Titchfield Haven (*above*) and Keyhaven (*below*) are important sites for passage waders and wintering wildfowl and gulls.

*Dennis Brigh*

Nationally important colonies of Sandwich Terns, Common Terns and Black-headed Gulls are established at Needs Ore (*above*) on the Beaulieu Estuary.

*Norman O*

*Dennis Bright*

In winter Langstone Habour (*above*), supports internationally important populations of Brent Geese and several species of waders.

*Norman Orr*

*Dennis Brigh*

Ringing studies have established the origins and destinations of many species moving to and from Hampshire such as the Spoonbill and Roseate and Common Terns.

*Dennis Brigh*

# Ruff                                    *Philomachus pugnax*

A scarce but regular passage migrant and winter visitor.

The few records of Ruffs cited by K & M and Cohen for the period up to the mid-1950s indicate that the species was very scarce, occurring most often in autumn. In the late 1950s, numbers of passage and wintering birds started to increase, in common with other parts of Britain. This trend continued through the 1960s, with the wintering population peaking in the early and mid-1970s. Subsequently, a decline set in, and by the late 1980s, regular wintering was confined to only one locality and any count above five in autumn or spring was noteworthy.

In autumn, Ruffs may appear in late June though they are not usually recorded until the end of July. Numbers peak between late August and early October and then decline. In the Keyhaven area, counts reached double figures in 14 years between 1958 and 1981 with a peak of 47 on Sep. 21st 1980; since then no more than eight have been recorded. At Farlington Marshes, there were peaks in the range 11-27 in four years between 1958 and 1968, but subsequently the only counts above eight were of 14 on Sep. 21st 1980 (*cf.* Keyhaven) and 17-30 from Sep. 11th-14th 1987. At Dibden Bay, during the period from 1958-80 when the pans were attractive to many wader species, counts reached double figures in 16 years with a maximum of 40 on Oct. 6th 1973. Elsewhere, small numbers were regular at Titchfield Haven (up to 10) and occasional at other coastal sites (max. 11 at Paulsgrove Reclamation on Aug. 15th 1984) and inland.

The first indication of wintering was from the Keyhaven area, where nine were recorded in hard weather in February 1956. From 1958-61, up to 22 were recorded on isolated dates between January and March. In 1961/62, up to 17 were present continuously from December to March, and in the following years numbers increased rapidly to a maximum of 171 in February 1970. A similar pattern was observed at Titchfield Haven, although the numbers were lower, peaking at 40 in February 1969.

In most winters in the 1970s, numbers built up slowly in November and December to a peak in January or February, followed by a rapid departure in March. However, in 1975/76, only about 50 were in the county in January, but a large influx occurred in mid-February, when an estimated 350 were present including 225 in the Keyhaven/Sowley/Needs Ore area and 78 at Titchfield Haven. Most of these had moved on by the end of the month although 131 (possibly including some new arrivals) were in the former area in mid-March. In the late 1970s, numbers declined at Keyhaven but there was a corresponding increase in the Sowley/Needs Ore area to the east, with a peak count of 140 on Jan. 31st 1978.

In the early 1980s, numbers peaked at Keyhaven in November or December (maximum 43, December 1980) and Titchfield Haven between January and March (maximum 51, January 1984), while in the Sowley/Needs Ore area they were very erratic in appearance, with occasional isolated peaks such as 54 on Nov. 16th 1980, 68 on Dec. 5th 1982, 70 on Mar. 6th 1984 and 64 on Jan. 26th 1985. This suggests that there was considerable interchange between the three areas. By the end of the decade, wintering birds were virtually confined to Titchfield Haven; in 1991/92 only four wintered there.

Spring passage is characterised by generally low numbers with occasional large flocks, e.g. 33 at Keyhaven in early April 1957, 27 at Farlington Marshes on Mar. 29th 1968, 40 flying east over Hatchet Pond on May 12th 1979, 32 which flew in from the sea and high to the north-east over Hill Head on Apr. 18th 1981 and 18 at Dibden Bay on Apr. 21st 1992. Few have been seen after mid-May but birds have occasionally summered.

Inland, Ruffs are most frequent in the Avon valley, especially when suitable floods are available between late November and April. Since 1967, numbers have exceeded ten in six winters, including 35 at Ibsley on Mar. 25th 1967, up to 50 there from Dec. 25th 1976-Feb. 6th 1977 and 38 at Avon Causeway from Feb. 21st-24th 1985. Sightings in other months mostly refer to migrants seen at Mockbeggar Lake. At other inland localities, most occur during the passage periods, but in winter small flocks have occasionally taken up residence and a few birds have been caught up in cold weather movements.

Between 1956 and 1992, 112 were recorded in the Itchen valley, including 45 at Winchester Sewage Farm and 37 at Alresford Pond. Counts above six were of 11 at Winchester Sewage Farm on Sep. 3rd and 4th 1966, eight there from Sep. 1st-6th 1981, 15/16 at Alresford Pond from Feb. 28th-Mar. 28th 1976, and 10 at Lakeside (Eastleigh) on Mar. 31st 1987. Other records, which totalled 61 birds, were mostly from the Test valley and north-east of the county, the only counts to exceed five being of seven at Camp Farm Sewage Farm on Aug. 14th 1964, 11 flying south-west over Fleet Pond on Oct. 5th 1976 and six in pasture at Leigh Park on Feb. 17th 1985. The cumulative monthly totals of all inland records are shown below.

|  | Jan | Feb | Mar | Apr | May | Jun | Jul | Aug | Sep | Oct | Nov | Dec |
|---|---|---|---|---|---|---|---|---|---|---|---|---|
| Avon valley | 86 | 123 | 89 | 36 | 9 | 0 | 0 | 6 | 6 | 1 | 11 | 39 |
| Elsewhere | 11 | 27 | 34 | 20 | 3 | 1 | 4 | 39 | 43 | 17 | 2 | 9 |

The movements of Ruffs are not well understood. Ringing studies suggest that those occurring in autumn and spring, which include birds of both sexes, originate from Fenno-Scandia and Russia and winter further south, mostly in tropical West Africa. Those wintering in Britain are almost exclusively males. The influxes which occurred in late winter or early spring in some years may have been the result of hard weather in nearby wintering grounds on the continent (as in February 1976) or an early return of birds wintering further south. The only recovery involving a Hampshire bird involved one ringed at Farlington Marshes on July 16th 1977 and shot in Loire Atlantique, France, 395 km SSW, on Aug. 10th 1986.

## Jack Snipe                                          *Lymnocryptes minimus*

A moderately common winter visitor and passage migrant.

Jack Snipes are found in a variety of damp grassland and reed bed habitats, at both coastal and inland localities, and also on heathlands, often in quite dry situations. Due to their reluctance to fly until virtually trodden on, they are clearly overlooked.

The first usually arrive from their breeding grounds in Fenno-Scandia and Russia in the last ten days of September; the only earlier records are of single birds at Dibden Bay from Aug. 8th-Sep. 21st 1960 and Titchfield Haven on Sep.

5th 1990. Some of those recorded in the period until mid-November undoubtedly move on. This is confirmed by counts from important localities which show peaks at this time, e.g. at Farlington Marshes, 16 on Oct. 15th 1961 and 13 on Oct. 17th 1990, and at Titchfield Haven, ten on Oct. 29th 1966, and also by records from sites where they do not winter.

The main wintering population is present from mid-November until late March. The totals recorded in the winters from 1970/71-91/92 averaged 32, with peak counts of 57 in 1975/76 and 58 in 1981/82, both seasons when higher than normal numbers were found at inland localities during frosty conditions. The most favoured locality is Farlington Marshes, where counts regularly exceed five and the highest was of 17 in January 1967. Elsewhere, the only counts above five have been of ten at Basingstoke Old Sewage Farm in December 1960, six at Baddesley Common on Feb. 12th 1975, six at Winnall Moors on Nov. 24th 1975 and Jan. 20th 1976, seven at Sturt Pond on Jan. 24th 1982, six at Paulsgrove Reclamation on Jan. 29th 1983, eight at Darby Green on Dec. 27th 1988, seven at Dibden Bay on Mar. 18th 1989 and six at Lower Test Marshes on Feb. 24th 1992.

As in autumn, passage is indicated in spring by peaks such as 15 at Farlington Marshes on Apr. 6th 1956, 12 at Titchfield Haven on Mar. 15th 1957, and eight at Farlington on Apr. 9th 1974 where only one had been found ten days earlier. There have also been several records of up to four birds in late March and April at sites where they were not present during the previous winter. The latest were singles at Fawley Reclamation on May 4th 1974 and Farlington Marshes on May 9th 1977, apart from one which was flushed three times at Titchfield Haven on June 23rd 1957.

## Common Snipe                    *Gallinago gallinago*

A moderately common but declining breeder; common passage migrant and winter visitor.

K & M described the Snipe as "a local resident", with large colonies at sites such as Woolmer Forest and the New Forest. Munn (1920) reported an expansion of its breeding range in 1918 and 1919, and, according to Suffern, it abounded at Titchfield Haven in the 1920s and 1930s (Duffin 1991). Cohen noted a decline in several areas during the 1950s. Some indication of the range contraction is given by the Atlas Map, which shows those tetrads where the species was reported between 1951 and 1985 but not during the Atlas Survey. The real decline is undoubtedly greater than that shown as the available records for the earlier period are scant.

The main breeding habitats are wet, unimproved meadows and the valley mires and wet grasslands of the New Forest. The drainage and improvement of meadows in many areas has clearly contributed to the on-going reduction in numbers.

In the Avon valley, 32 territories were plotted between Ringwood and Bickton in 1982 (Steventon 1984), but a survey organised by the RSPB in 1990 located only six in this stretch. The main concentration in 1990 was of 19 territories between Sopley and Avon Causeway, with a further ten in other stretches of the valley, making a total of 35 between Sopley and Downton. In

227

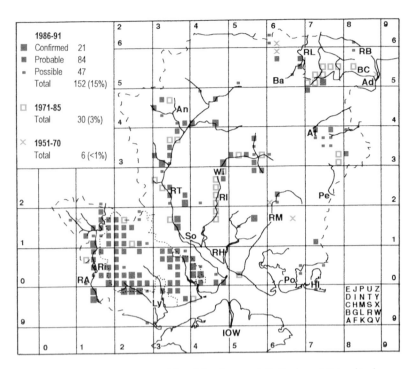

the Test valley between Lower Test Marshes and Fullerton, 16 territories were located and 23 estimated in 1978 (Evans 1981), but no recent counts have been made. However, Atlas fieldwork has shown that the species is now absent from some tetrads where it previously occurred. Surveys of the Itchen valley from Mansbridge to Cheriton, including the Alre and Candover streams, in 1976 and 1982 produced 26 and 14 territories respectively (Cloyne 1977, Steventon 1984). During the Atlas Survey, none was found south of Winchester. In the 1970s, Snipe were quite common in damp meadows in the Whitewater and Hart valleys. A survey in 1978 located 24 drumming birds in the Greywell/Hillside/Potbridge/Winchfield area, which covers eight tetrads, but during the Atlas Survey the only records were of single pairs breeding at Bidden Water and Hillside.

In the New Forest, numbers were small prior to the 1970s, but increased from 1975 onwards. The population was estimated at 120-200 pairs in 1981, this level being sustained until 1985 (Tubbs 1986a), but since then a decline has apparently occurred (C R Tubbs *in litt*).

Assuming figures of 35 pairs for the Avon Valley, two pairs per occupied tetrad in the New Forest and one pair per occupied tetrad elsewhere, suggests a county population of around 200 pairs in 1991. Although habitat destruction emerges as a major factor in the decline, this does not account for the decrease in the New Forest, and so it seems likely that other factors, such as the series of five cold winters between 1978/79 and 1986/87, also contributed. The most recent estimate of the British population was 30,000 pairs in the mid-1980s (New Atlas).

Birds appear at non-breeding localities from late June onwards, the margins of lakes, gravel pits and coastal lagoons being particularly favoured. Only small numbers occur until early August, a gathering of 40 at Paulsgrove Reclamation on July 29th 1983 being exceptional. Thereafter, double-figure counts become more frequent. Noteworthy records in early autumn include 50 at Camp Farm Sewage Farm on Aug. 21st 1966 and 82 at Winnall Moors on Sep. 18th 1971. Numbers continue to increase through October, the largest counts for that month being of 115 at Winchester Sewage Farm on 14th in 1972 and 153+ at Keyhaven Marsh on 26th in 1980.

Peak mid-winter counts may be made at any time between November and March. They are often associated with severe weather or heavy rainfall, when ice-free or flooded conditions may attract large concentrations. The highest numbers occur in the Avon valley. At least 750 were present between Sopley and Hucklesbrook on Mar. 4th 1984 and over 1000 were in the same stretch of the valley on Feb. 10th 1985. The most favoured area is between Ibsley and Hucklesbrook, where counts have regularly exceeded 200 and peaked at 400+ on Feb. 15th 1984 and 500 on Feb. 8th 1986. Flocks in the range 200-310 have also been recorded at Blashford, Sopley and in the Avon/Bisterne area.

The most comprehensive counts have been made at Farlington Marshes and Titchfield Haven. In the ten winters from 1970/71-1979/80, the peak winter counts averaged 185 and 218 with maxima of 300 in February 1974 and 500 in January 1975 respectively. In the following decade, counts at Farlington Marshes fell, with an average of 119 and a maximum of 173 in March 1981. However, at Titchfield Haven numbers were similar, with an average of 214 and a peak of 380 during severe weather in January 1982. Appreciable numbers also winter in the Eling/Lower Test and Keyhaven areas, but counting at these sites is particularly difficult as many birds occur in inaccessible areas. At Keyhaven, estimates of 200+ were made in January 1978, November 1981 and November 1989, but the true figure is undoubtedly higher at times, especially in severe weather. At Eling/Lower Test, there were 200+ in November and December 1987, 240+ in November 1988 and 200 in January 1990.

Elsewhere, the highest counts were of 210 at Paulsgrove Reclamation on Jan. 29th 1983 and 200+ at Bishopstoke on Jan. 6th 1985. Counts have exceeded 100 at a further 13 sites, including sewage farms, watercress beds, drained gravel pits and wet meadows and lagoons. At most of these, the large numbers were attracted by the presence of ice-free areas during severe weather, and were far in excess of the normal winter populations.

The departure of wintering birds takes place in March and early April. Passage peaks are sometimes recorded, e.g. 200 at Timsbury on Mar. 29th 1984 and 79 at Fleet Pond on Mar. 20th 1990. Nine flew off high to the north-east from Farlington Marshes on Mar. 30th 1974.

Nine birds ringed in Hampshire have been recovered outside the county. Seven of these were ringed in winter and subsequently shot, five in autumn in Finland, France, the Netherlands, Russia and Scotland and two in winter in France and Suffolk. Two ringed in July were shot in September in France and November in Ireland. Of seven recovered in Hampshire in winter, six were ringed in autumn in Finland (2), the Netherlands, Sweden, Cambridgeshire and Somerset, and the other was ringed in February in Essex. These data are consistent with the national picture, which indicates that many birds arriving in Britain in autumn originate from countries around the Baltic; some remain to winter while others move to Ireland or France (Winter Atlas).

## Great Snipe                                                    *Gallinago media*

Three records. Single birds were shot at Mottisfont in late September 1897, near Newton Stacey in late September 1905 and near Fordingbridge on Sep. 3rd 1934.

The lack of recent records parallels a decrease nationally, which may partly reflect the decline in snipe shooting (Dymond *et al* 1989).

The Great Snipe breeds in Scandinavia and from Poland to west Siberia and winters in tropical Africa.

## Long-billed Dowitcher                         *Limnodromus scolopaceus*

A rare vagrant, with four in autumn, one of which subsequently wintered, and four in spring, all since 1975. The records are as follows:

| | |
|---|---|
| 1975: | Pennington Marsh, Sep. 20th-29th; |
| 1978: | Pennington/Keyhaven Marshes, Apr. 5th-24th; |
| 1979: | Farlington Marshes, May 5th-12th; |
| 1981: | Pennington/Keyhaven Marshes, Oct. 3rd-May 11th 1982; |
| 1982: | Titchfield Haven, Nov. 4th; |
| 1986: | Curbridge, Mar. 10th-Apr. 16th; |
| 1988: | Curbridge, Apr. 4th-21st; |
| 1989: | Keyhaven Marsh, Sep. 5th-12th†. |

The Long-billed Dowitcher breeds in Alaska and north-eastern Siberia and winters in the southern USA and south to Guatemala.

## Dowitchers                                                    *Limnodromus sp.*

There are two records of birds accepted by the *BBRC* as Dowitcher *sp.*: at Needs Ore from Oct. 5th-Nov. 2nd 1963 and Pennington Marsh on Sep. 13th and 14th 1970.

## Woodcock                                                    *Scolopax rusticola*

A common resident and winter visitor.

The Woodcock is widely distributed in Hampshire, being particularly common in the broadleaved and mixed woodlands of the New Forest and north-east. It is least frequent in woods on the higher sections of the chalk, possibly because of the lack of suitable damp areas for feeding. Due to its crepuscular habits, it was undoubtedly under-recorded during the Atlas Survey, especially in the less well-covered areas in the centre of the county. Earlier records for 1971-85 have been added to the map, and, as there is no indication of any decline in numbers, these have been used in estimating the total population.

Recent work by Hirons (1980, 1982) has shown that roding males do not defend exclusive territories, but may display over several separate woods in an area of up to 1 km$^2$ in their search for a receptive female. Several males may have overlapping home ranges, thus making accurate counts difficult to obtain.

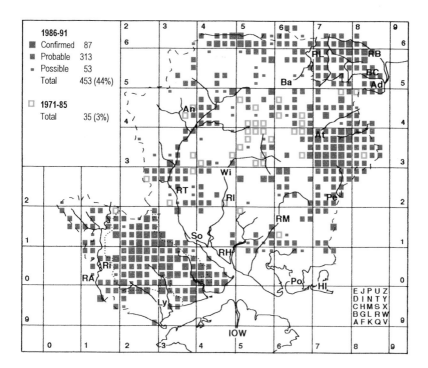

| 1986-91 | | | | |
|---|---|---|---|---|
| ■ Confirmed | 87 | | | |
| ■ Probable | 313 | | | |
| ▪ Possible | 53 | | | |
| Total | 453 (44%) | | | |
| □ 1971-85 | | | | |
| Total | 35 (3%) | | | |

Assuming an average of two males per occupied tetrad, the county population in 1991 was around 950. However, allowing for under-recording and the fact that many tetrads undoubtedly hold a higher density, the true total was probably in the range 950-1500 roding males. In 1988-91, the British population was estimated at 8500-21,500 pairs (New Atlas).

Outside the breeding season, Woodcocks are widespread in damp woodlands, but inconspicuous except when severe weather forces them into the open. The cumulative monthly totals of birds recorded at coastal sites during 1971-92 are shown below.

| Oct | Nov | Dec | Jan | Feb | Mar | Apr |
|---|---|---|---|---|---|---|
| 11 | 8 | 7 | 93 | 125 | 23 | 1 |

During mild winters the maximum total recorded was four, but the totals in seasons with hard spells were as follows: 1978/79, 11; 1981/82, 13; 1984/85, 71; 1985/86, 25; 1986/87, 13; 1990/91, 94. The largest numbers reported were 30 put up by a shooting party at the Wildgrounds, Gosport on Jan. 19th 1985 and 78+ at five sites on Hayling Island on Feb. 10th and 11th 1991. A few birds were seen moving, mostly to the south, in hard weather movements. Those recorded in autumn (earliest date Oct. 5th) and spring (latest date Apr. 2nd) were probably grounded migrants.

Ringing studies confirm that Hampshire birds are largely resident and are joined in winter by birds from further afield. Of 13 recovered in winter, seven were ringed as pulli, four in Hampshire and one each in the Czech Republic, Scotland and Sweden. The remainder were ringed as adults, one in June in

Finland and the others in autumn in the Netherlands (2) and Denmark, western Germany and Jersey (1 each). One ringed as a pullus in Hampshire was shot in the November of its first winter in Suffolk.

## Black-tailed Godwit                                   *Limosa limosa*

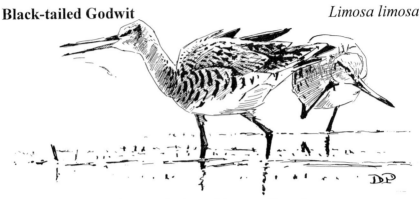

A common passage migrant and winter visitor; small numbers summer.

K & M described the Black-tailed Godwit as "an occasional visitor to our coast on the spring and autumn migration". In the 1940s, the species started to winter regularly; subsequently there was a steady increase until the 1970s, since when numbers have remained fairly constant. This change in status was shared with other parts of Britain and was attributed to a large expansion of the breeding population in Iceland during the period of climatic amelioration in the 1930s and 1940s (Prater 1975).

Birds start to arrive from their breeding grounds in late June, with a rapid build up from mid-July onwards. Numbers are highest in Langstone and Chichester Harbours, where flocks have occasionally exceeded 1000. Significant concentrations also occur between Hythe and Calshot and in other parts of Southampton Water, and in Portsmouth Harbour, although a large proportion of those feeding at the latter site now fly to Langstone to roost. Peak counts occur in September or October (table 42); numbers then fall in late autumn as some birds move on to winter elsewhere after completing their moult.

| | 55-59 | 60-64 | 65-69 | 70-74 | 75-79 | 80-84 | 85-89 | Peak counts | |
|---|---|---|---|---|---|---|---|---|---|
| Chichester Harbour | - | - | 721 | 857 | 773 | 824 | 620 | 1455, | Oct. 1973 |
| East Hayling | 383^ | 343^ | - | - | 210 | 222 | 414 | 700, | Sep. 1963 |
| Langstone Harbour | 385 | 378 | 542 | 460 | 647 | 659 | 999 | 1289, | Oct. 1989 |
| Portsmouth Harbour | 227* | - | 268* | 388 | 305 | 133 | 59 | 635, | Oct. 1971 |
| Titchfield Haven | 43 | 264 | 89 | 10 | 21 | 42 | 55 | 500, | Oct. 1960 |
| Hythe/Calshot | - | - | - | 151 | 239 | 190 | 197 | 290, | Oct. 1975 |
| Beaulieu Estuary | - | 63^ | 163 | 121 | 72 | 29 | 28 | 430, | Oct. 1966 |
| Lymington/Hurst | - | 10 | 15 | 32 | 60 | 130 | 77 | 212, | Sep. 1983 |

*Table 42. High tide roost counts of Black-tailed Godwits in autumn (July-October): five years means of maxima and peak counts, 1955-89.*

In winter, Langstone and Chichester Harbours normally hold the largest gatherings (table 43), although in severe weather many may leave. Since the mid-1970s, numbers have increased steadily at Titchfield Haven. In February 1988 and 1990, extensive floods attracted flocks in excess of 1000 and corresponding reductions were noted in the two eastern harbours. Sites in the west Solent usually have their highest counts in March; these probably include some birds which have wintered elsewhere. During the five winters from 1985/86-89/90, the proportion of the British wintering population in Hampshire (based on January counts) averaged 26.7%.

| | 55-60 | 60-65 | 65-70 | 70-75 | 75-80 | 80-85 | 85-90 | Peak counts | |
|---|---|---|---|---|---|---|---|---|---|
| Chichester Harbour | 228^ | - | 315 | 750 | 675 | 756 | 658 | 1400, | Dec. 1972 |
| East Hayling | - | 256* | 300* | - | 368 | 312 | 273 | 657, | Jan. 1990 |
| Langstone Harbour | 426 | 379 | 375 | 504 | 770 | 655 | 861 | 1037, | Dec. 1984 |
| Portsmouth Harbour | - | 105* | - | 266 | 337 | 149 | 74 | 809, | Nov. 1978 |
| Titchfield Haven | 179 | 313 | 134 | 54 | 205 | 283 | 683 | 1174, | Feb. 1990 |
| Fawley/Calshot | - | - | - | 100 | 257 | 201 | 178 | 320, | Dec. 1975 |
| Beaulieu Estuary | - | 253 | 220 | 210 | 206 | 163 | 251 | 500, | Mar. 1988 |
| Lymington/Hurst | - | 66 | 95 | 97 | 115 | 93 | 69 | 218, | Mar. 1976 |

*Table 43. High tide roost counts of Black-tailed Godwits in winter (November-March): five year means of maxima and peak counts, 1955/56-89/90.*

In April, numbers continue to build up, especially at west Solent localities. At the Beaulieu Estuary, counts exceed 200 in some years and as many as 500 were there on Apr. 20th 1975. The saltings between Tanners Lane and the Lymington River regularly hold 100-300, with peaks of 350 on Apr. 14th 1973 and 300 on Apr. 16th 1976; on the latter date a further 160 were counted at Oxey Creek, to the west of Lymington. Langstone Harbour may also have a peak at this time, e.g. 654 on Apr. 7th 1961 and 750+ on Apr. 19th 1965, although this has been less pronounced since wintering numbers increased from the mid-1970s onwards.

Spring floods in the Avon valley have also attracted large concentrations of Black-tailed Godwits in recent years. In 1980, numbers at Sopley rose from 14 on Mar. 14th to 390 by Apr. 10th. Such numbers did not recur until 1990, when there was a rapid build up in the Bisterne/Avon Causeway area from 85 on Mar. 3rd to 241 on Mar. 7th and 540 on Mar. 10th. These subsequently dispersed, presumably accounting for a flock of 283 at Ibsley on Mar. 19th and 152 still there on Mar. 25th. In late 1992, numbers appeared for the first time on winter floods, with 330 at Bisterne on the last day of the year. Other records for the Avon valley include 18 at Blashford on Mar. 12th 1978, nine at Mockbeggar Lake on Apr. 16th 1980 and seven at Sopley on Apr. 19th 1990.

The main departure from Hampshire in spring appears to be inland. On calm, clear evenings, large numbers leave Langstone Harbour in a north-west to north direction. Between 1953 and 1992, 5020 were recorded, mostly in the second half of April. The highest day totals were of 494 on Apr. 22nd 1962 and 232 on Apr. 22nd 1987. These observations, combined with the scarcity of the species in eastward coastal movements in spring (only 62 recorded at Hurst Beach in the same period), support the conclusion that the Hampshire (and British) wintering population belongs to the Icelandic race *L.l. islandica*.

Small numbers remain through the summer; in recent years, flocks of 20-60 have summered at the Beaulieu Estuary, Titchfield Haven and Langstone Harbour. In 1981, a pair defended a territory at one site. The male sang and displayed in May and the female was missing for a period, suggesting incubation, but there was no further evidence of breeding. In 1981, a displaying male was present for some time but no female was seen, and in 1990, a pair was seen displaying on May 31st.

Inland away from the Avon valley, Black-tailed Godwits were reported in four years between 1952 and 1966 and then in 15 years between 1970 and 1992. Records were confined to the periods Apr. 3rd-May 18th and June 20th-Oct. 16th. The cumulative monthly totals for 1952-92 are shown below.

| Apr | May | Jun | Jul | Aug | Sep | Oct |
|-----|-----|-----|-----|-----|-----|-----|
| 14 | 39 | 1 | 8 | 30 | 12 | 4 |

Most occurred at Alresford Pond, with 23 including five on Apr. 3rd 1989 and up to five from Aug. 29th-Sep. 11th 1991. Other records came from Purbrook (27 flying north-east, May 1st 1988), Frensham Great Pond (11 flying north-east, May 3rd 1980), Bitterne (7 flying south, Aug. 21st 1981), Broadlands Lake (7, Aug. 21st 1981), Eversley/Yateley Gravel Pits (6), Fleet Pond (5), Winnall Moors (4, Apr. 4th-9th 1959), Camp Farm Sewage Farm (3), Marsh Court, Winchester Sewage Farm and Sherborne St. John (2 each), and Brockenhurst, Eastleigh Sewage Farm, Polhampton and Swaythling (1 each).

Relatively few have been ringed in Hampshire; of three recoveries, two were within the county and one was in Kent. One ringed in Dorset was controlled at Farlington Marshes.

## Bar-tailed Godwit                                              *Limosa lapponica*

A common winter visitor and passage migrant; small numbers summer.

This species is principally a winter visitor to Langstone and Chichester Harbours. In some years a passage peak is recorded in August or September but the highest counts are usually between December and February (table 44). In the five winters from 1985/86-89/90, the proportion of the British wintering population at these two sites (based on January counts) averaged 1.9%. A rapid departure occurs in March, which coincides with an increase on the Waddenzee in the Netherlands, where birds gather to fatten up before leaving for their breeding grounds in northern Fenno-Scandia and Siberia (Prater 1981). At Langstone, influxes are sometimes recorded in April or early May but passage at this time is chiefly indicated by diurnal movement east along the coast. A summering population of non-breeders, normally numbering 50-100, is present in May and June; higher counts such as 300 on June 4th 1966 and 175 on June 8th 1975 may have included late migrants.

| | 55-60 | 60-65 | 65-70 | 70-75 | 75-80 | 80-85 | 85-90 | Peak counts |
|--|-------|-------|-------|-------|-------|-------|-------|-------------|
| Chichester Harbour | 213^ | 320* | 901 | 1129 | 1157 | 940 | 1271 | 2400, Dec. 1988 |
| East Hayling | 253* | 238^ | 445* | 872^ | 731 | 379 | 658 | 1500, Jan. 1973 |
| Langstone Harbour | 206 | 243 | 374 | 278 | 857 | 739 | 635 | 1212, Feb. 1977 |

*Table 44. High tide roost counts of Bar-tailed Godwits: five years means and peak counts, 1955/56-89/90.*

To the west of Langstone Harbour, flocks on the ground occur erratically and rarely reach 50. The only counts in excess of 100 have been of 200+ roosting at Dibden Bay on Jan. 19th 1980, 130 at Pitts Deep on Apr. 28th 1974 and 105 at Keyhaven Marsh on Apr. 25th 1975. The Pitts Deep and Keyhaven records referred to grounded spring migrants.

The Bar-tailed Godwit is one of the most numerous species in the eastward movements of birds along the coast in spring. The birds involved are believed to be en route from winter quarters in Mauritania and Morocco to the staging post in the Waddenzee. The highest numbers occur in years with persistent south-easterly winds, and in such conditions large flocks continue to move all day. Between 1971 and 1992, the average total recorded per year was 2686. In five years there were less than 500, while the highest totals were of 10,071 in 1973 and 10,862 in 1984. At Hurst Beach, day totals exceeding 1000 were recorded on 13 occasions, including 3090 on Apr. 21st 1974, 2261 on Apr. 26th 1975, 2725 on May 3rd 1980, 2186 on Apr. 28th 1984 and 5511 the next day. Totals at Hill Head rarely exceeded those at Hurst when both were watched simultaneously, four figures having been reached on only four occasions with a maximum of 3689 on Apr. 29th 1984. On this date, only 395 were logged in four hours watching at Hayling Bay and 962 in 14 hours at Selsey Bill, West Sussex (Newnham 1985), but 570 flew east over Farlington Marshes, which indicates that some birds take a more direct easterly route which misses Hayling and the Selsey Peninsula. Although movement has been recorded between late March and early June, it is concentrated in the three week period from Apr. 16th-May 6th, with 22.3%, 50.9% and 21.0% of the total for 1971-92, in each of those weeks.

Inland, the species was not recorded until 1972, since when there have been 18 records in 14 years up to 1992. The cumulative monthly totals are shown below.

| Apr | May | Jun | Jul | Aug | Sep | Oct |
|-----|-----|-----|-----|-----|-----|-----|
| 10  | 6   | 0   | 1   | 18  | 75  | 2   |

Records were confined to the periods Apr. 27th-May 14th and July 27th-Oct. 23rd and came from Fleet Pond (10 flying south-west with Whimbrels, Aug. 30th 1985; 45 flying north-west, Sep. 14th 1988), South Warnborough (15 flying west, Sep. 13th 1981), Tundry Pond (8 flying SSE, Aug. 22nd 1983), Enham Alamein (7 flying south-east, Apr. 29th 1977), Sopley (4, Sep. 12th 1982), Mockbeggar Lake (4 birds), Old Winchester Hill (3), Alresford Pond (2, including 1 from Sep. 9th-14th 1991) and Eversley Gravel Pit, Frensham Great Pond, Frimley Gravel Pit, Pinglestone Watercress Bed and Wellington Country Park (1 each). Unless otherwise stated, all records were of one or two birds pausing briefly or flying over the observation point.

The only ringing recovery involved one ringed in Rogaland, Norway on Sep. 7th 1937 and found in Langstone Harbour, 970 km SSW, on Feb. 11th 1939.

# Whimbrel                                    *Numenius phaeopus*

A moderately common passage migrant. A few remain through the summer but it is rare in winter.

The first normally arrive in late March or early April. Earlier birds, such as those at Keyhaven on Mar. 4th 1976, Langstone Harbour on Mar. 13th 1971 and at Pylewell on the same date in 1977 may have wintered locally. Easterly movement through The Solent may peak at any time between mid-April and mid-May. Between 1971 and 1993, the total recorded annually averaged 422 with peaks of 1225 in 1978 and 1045 in 1984. At Hurst Beach, day totals exceeded 100 ten times during that period, with a maximum of 198 on Apr.

exceeded 100 ten times during that period, with a maximum of 198 on Apr. 22nd 1976. At Hill Head, there have been seven such counts, with maxima of 185 on May 6th 1983 and 350 on May 9th 1984.

Many stop over for several days in Hampshire during their migration. The largest numbers occur in Langstone Harbour (table 45), but three-figure counts have also been made at Dibden Bay in six springs since 1966 (always at dusk, with a maximum of 131 on May 5th 1973) and twice at Pennington and Keyhaven Marshes (160 which arrived from inland at dusk on May 1st 1981 and 108 on Apr. 25th 1982). Other regularly-used sites with maxima in the range 40-54 include Pylewell, the Beaulieu Estuary, the Fawley/Calshot area and Portsmouth Harbour.

| 56-60 | 61-65 | 66-70 | 71-75 | 76-80 | 80-85 | 86-90 | Peak count |
|-------|-------|-------|-------|-------|-------|-------|------------|
| 149 | 106^ | 61 | 37 | 66 | 64 | 38 | 200, 28/4/58 |

*Table 45. Spring counts of Whimbrels in Langstone Harbour: five year means of maxima and the peak count.*

The apparent decline in Langstone Harbour may be connected with an increase in the numbers feeding on inland pastures and returning to the coast to roost at dusk (*cf.* Curlew), thus being missed on counts carried out during the day. The habit was first noted in 1977, when 25 were found at Creech Farm (Denmead) on May 1st. Later records include those of 103 at Purbrook Heath on Apr. 26th 1983, 130 at Havant Thicket on Apr. 29th of that year, 207 there on Apr. 28th 1984, 70 at Furzeley on May 3rd 1987 and 100 at Southwick on May 4th 1991.

Inland feeding has also been noted in other areas, e.g. 49 at Netley Marsh on May 11th 1982, 76 near Botley Wood on Apr. 24th 1984 and 120 at Dilton Farm (Brockenhurst) on Apr. 30th 1992. 130 flying south down the River Hamble at Curbridge at dusk on Apr. 30th 1990 probably originated from the Botley Wood area and were flying to roost at Dibden Bay or elsewhere in Southampton Water.

Small numbers are present in June in most years. At Langstone Harbour, up to eight are normal but 14 on June 30th 1973 indicates early return passage. In the Keyhaven area up to three are usually recorded but ten were counted on June 18th 1989.

Autumn passage is evident from late June onwards. The highest numbers are present between mid-July and mid-August. Langstone Harbour is the only site where counts have reached three figures, although numbers appear to have declined in the last 25 years (table 46). Elsewhere, the only count above 50 was of 94 at Calshot on Aug. 5th 1960, while counts in the range 20-50 have been made at Portsmouth Harbour, Warsash, the Beaulieu Estuary and in the Keyhaven area. Only in the last-named locality are such counts regular. Inland feeding is apparently infrequent at this time, the only records being of 20 at Botley Wood on July 28th 1984, eight there on Aug. 7th 1985 and three at Southwick from Aug. 5th-7th 1986. In contrast to the spring, little diurnal migration is recorded. Only seven sightings have been made at the coast involving a total of 171 birds moving in directions between south and west, with a maximum of 71 west over Langstone Harbour on Aug. 16th 1987. Usually, few remain in September. 200 were in Langstone Harbour on Sep. 6th 1958, but since then the highest count for that month has been of 20. Stragglers are recorded in October in most years and sometimes into November. Apart from wintering birds, the latest were four at Langstone Harbour on Nov. 21st 1976.

| 56-60 | 61-65 | 66-70 | 71-75 | 76-80 | 81-85 | 86-90 | Peak count |
|---|---|---|---|---|---|---|---|
| 177 | 144 | 76 | 109 | 63 | 71 | 62 | 300, 27/7/63 |

Table 46. Autumn counts of Whimbrels in Langstone Harbour: five year means of maxima and the peak count.

Since 1958/59, single birds (once two) have been recorded in December-February in 14 winters; most were in the Langstone Harbour and Keyhaven areas but one flew south over Broadlands Lake on Jan. 20th 1986.

Compared to the previous species, Whimbrels are far more frequently recorded migrating overland and are also regularly heard at night. The inland records for 1971-92, which covered the periods from Apr. 6th-May 30th and June 21st-Sep. 9th, are summarised in table 47. Birds which feed inland by day and return to the coast at dusk to roost have been excluded.

| | Heard at night | Total on ground | Total moving | | | | | | | |
|---|---|---|---|---|---|---|---|---|---|---|
| | | | W | NW | N | NE | E | SE | S | SW |
| Spring | 51 times | 164 | 22 | 81 | 159 | 137 | 29 | 4 | 2 | 7 |
| Autumn | 11 times | 32 | 11 | 21 | 3 | 3 | 21 | 11 | 48 | 73 |

Table 47. Summary of records of Whimbrels inland, 1971-92.

This shows the main direction of movement in spring to be between north-west and north-east. Departures at dusk from Langstone Harbour agree with this, e.g. 54 off north-west on Apr. 21st 1983 and 45 away north-east on May 6th 1984. Birds migrating along the coast also occasionally turn inland, e.g. 152 moving up the Meon valley at Titchfield Haven on May 9th 1980. The largest inland spring flock was of 44 moving north-east over Fleet Pond on Apr. 25th 1987. However, an unprecedented passage took place in 1989, when a minimum of 223 was recorded at 19 sites. High counts included 36 which left north from a meadow at Sway on Apr. 29th, 24 moving north at Tichborne and 24 near Damerham on May 6th, 20 at Crow and 28 flying north over Farley Mount on May 7th, and 20 moving north-west over Regent's Park (Southampton) at dusk on May 13th. In autumn, when numbers are much lower, movement is mainly to the south or south-west. The largest flocks recorded were all towards the end of the passage period, with 23 moving south-west at Fleet Pond on Aug. 22nd 1983, 20 south-west there with Bar-tailed Godwits on Aug. 30th 1985, 20 east at Fullerton on Sep. 4th 1985 and 17 north-west over Goodworth Clatford four days later.

The cumulative monthly totals of inland records for 1971-92 are shown below.

| Apr | May | Jun | Jul | Aug | Sep |
|---|---|---|---|---|---|
| 210 | 446 | 4 | 73 | 118 | 39 |

Most Whimbrels passing through southern England winter in tropical West Africa or further south (BWP). It is interesting to speculate on the destination of spring migrants: those moving north-west are possibly bound for Iceland while those moving north-east and east may be en route for staging posts in the Netherlands or breeding grounds in Fenno-Scandia or further east.

# Curlew                                    *Numenius arquata*

An uncommon breeder, confined largely to the New Forest, common passage migrant and winter visitor.

At the end of the 19th century, the Curlew was evidently a rare breeding species, with only one or two pairs nesting on the "wildest heaths" of the New Forest (K & M). The population in the New Forest increased considerably in subsequent years as 44 pairs were located in 75% of the suitable habitat in 1960, suggesting a total population approaching 60 pairs. Numbers were much reduced following the severe winter of 1962/63 but a further survey in 1966 indicated a total of 58 pairs. From the late 1960s onwards, a further expansion took place and during 1981-84 the population was estimated at 120 pairs (Tubbs 1986a).

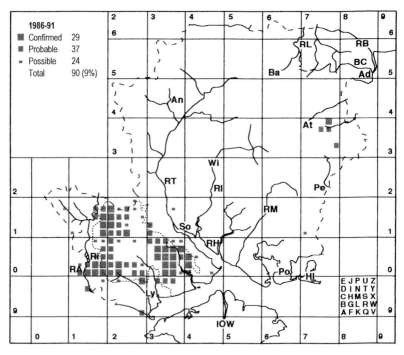

As the Atlas Map shows, Curlews are still widespread on the heaths of the New Forest; the population is thought to be at the same level as in the early 1980s. Elsewhere, one or two pairs have bred regularly on heathland in the Woolmer/Longmoor area since the 1950s or earlier, and pairs have occasionally held territory on other heaths in the north-east. In 1985, two pairs bred (one successfully) in cereals near Kingsley and in the following year (the first of the Atlas Survey) birds were recorded in three tetrads in that area with one pair confirmed breeding. In the Avon valley, several pairs were apparently breeding in water meadows at Breamore in 1954. Apart from occasional birds seen briefly in spring, there were no further records until 1990, when territorial behaviour was noted at four sites in the valley.

At the end of the Atlas Survey, the Hampshire population was probably between 100 and 140 pairs. The most recent estimate of the British population was of 33,000-38,000 pairs in the mid-1980s (Reed 1985).

By late June, flocks start to build up at the coast as adults arrive from continental breeding grounds. In Langstone and Chichester Harbours, four-figure gatherings are regularly recorded in July and August although in some years the peak count is made in the following three months, when large numbers of juveniles are also present. At Langstone, numbers reached 2000 in five autumns between 1959 and 1966 but since then the highest count has been of 1855 in September 1981. Counts elsewhere are usually much lower although gatherings in excess of 1000 were present at Dibden Bay and the Beaulieu Estuary in autumn 1960. Numbers apparently decline as the winter progresses, although isolated peaks are occasionally recorded, e.g. 1100 at the Beaulieu Estuary in February 1985. Most have left by mid-April, although 50-150 non-breeders usually remain through May and June in Langstone Harbour, with smaller numbers elsewhere. During the five winters from 1985/86-89/90, the proportion of the British wintering population in Hampshire (based on January counts) averaged 4.6%. High tide roost counts at the main localities are summarised in tables 48 and 49.

| | 55-59 | 60-64 | 65-69 | 70-74 | 75-79 | 80-84 | 85-89 | Peak counts | |
|---|---|---|---|---|---|---|---|---|---|
| Chichester Harbour | - | - | 1400 | 1167 | 1582 | 1881 | 1734 | 2652, | Sep. 1982 |
| East Hayling | 1610^ | 1432 | - | - | 917 | 937 | 729 | 2858, | Aug. 1962 |
| Langstone Harbour | 1500 | 1816 | 1446 | 1182 | 1111 | 1352 | 1432 | 2000, | Oct. 1966 |
| Portsmouth Harbour | - | - | 652^ | 798 | 644 | 446 | 289 | 950, | July 1971 |
| Southampton Water | - | - | - | 993 | 860 | 977 | 579 | 1159, | July 1982 |
| Dibden Bay | 650^ | 898^ | 713 | 640 | 424 | 409 | 63^ | 1300, | Aug. 1960 |
| Fawley/Calshot | 700* | - | - | 551 | 652 | 665 | 509^ | 960, | Aug. 1975 |
| Beaulieu Estuary | 250^ | 940 | 370 | 273 | 268 | 101 | 194 | 2000, | July 1960 |
| Lymington/Hurst | - | 367^ | 238^ | 300 | 343 | 358 | 298 | 600, | Sep. 1975 |

*Table 48. High tide roost counts of Curlews in autumn (July-October); five year means of maxima and peak counts, 1955-89.*

| | 55-60 | 60-65 | 65-70 | 70-75 | 75-80 | 80-85 | 85-90 | Peak counts | |
|---|---|---|---|---|---|---|---|---|---|
| Chichester Harbour | - | - | 1046 | 900 | 1272 | 1463 | 1441 | 2321, | Dec. 1985 |
| East Hayling | 600^ | 400* | 350* | - | 623 | 841 | 639 | 1094, | Jan. 1981 |
| Langstone Harbour | 1100 | 924 | 900 | 684 | 1045 | 969 | 769 | 2000, | Nov. 1966 |
| Portsmouth Harbour | - | - | 534^ | 501 | 426 | 420 | 400 | 620, | Nov. 1971 |
| Southampton Water | - | - | - | 795 | 725 | 775 | 654 | 1087, | Feb. 1975 |
| Dibden Bay | 500* | 500^ | 596 | 491 | 402 | 438 | 295 | 750, | Feb. 1970 |
| Fawley/Calshot | - | - | - | 202 | 186 | 225 | 213 | 397, | Feb. 1986 |
| Beaulieu Estuary | 750^ | 424 | 480 | 454 | 244 | 408 | 285 | 1100, | Feb. 1985 |
| Lymington/Hurst | 186^ | 418^ | 432^ | 328 | 305 | 278 | 325 | 800, | Feb. 1962 |

*Table 49. High tide roost counts of Curlews in winter (November-March); five year means of maxima and peak counts, 1955/56-89/90.*

Although Curlews feed mainly on mud-flats, during the winter months they also utilise pasture close to the shore (e.g. at Langstone and Chichester Harbours, Titchfield Haven, the upper Hamble, Needs Ore and Keyhaven) and in a number of areas which are several kilometres from the coast.

Evidence of inland feeding was first obtained in the mid-1960s in the lower Test valley, when 38 flew south over Nursling on Nov. 1st 1964 and 110 were at Testwood on Oct. 8th 1967. It is now established that there is a regular movement upstream soon after dawn, with flocks moving inland to Broadlands, Romsey and occasionally as far as Timsbury, and returning to the coast in late afternoon. Numbers are greatest between November and February although the movement begins in October (with occasional earlier birds) and continues until the first week of April. Over 100 are regularly involved, the highest counts being of 145 flying south over Lower Test Marshes on Jan. 22nd 1975 and 126 doing likewise on Nov. 15th 1987.

Curlews also move from Portsmouth and Langstone Harbours to feed inland. This was first indicated by a flock of 38 at Havant Thicket on Sep. 18th 1979. Subsequently, up to 150 were present in the Southwick area in January 1980 with reduced numbers until early April. Since then, Curlews have occurred on several farms to the north of Portsdown: in the Roche Court/White Dell Farm area to the north-east of Fareham (max. 104), around Lodge Farm and Mitchelland near Southwick (max. 175), at Closewood Farm near Denmead (max. 80+) and at Sheepwash Farm, Purbrook (max. 70). Few are recorded in autumn, when inter-tidal food supplies are good and the pastures are still dry. The highest counts occur between December and March, with birds continuing to move inland even in frosty weather. In contrast to the Test valley, flocks continue to use the area in April and early May, e.g. 38 at Vernon's Farm (Southwick) on Apr. 28th 1987. Inland feeding has also been noted at Sway (max. 50), Sopley (max. 7) and Bishopstoke (max. 4). This habit may be partially responsible for the reduced numbers recorded on mid-winter coastal counts compared to the autumn.

Further inland (away from breeding areas), most records of Curlew involve single birds or small parties flying over or grounded briefly. The cumulative monthly totals for 1971-92 shown below exhibit passage peaks in March/April and July-September and a further peak in December, which is largely accounted for by birds involved in hard weather movements.

| Jan | Feb | Mar | Apr | May | Jun | Jul | Aug | Sep | Oct | Nov | Dec |
|-----|-----|-----|-----|-----|-----|-----|-----|-----|-----|-----|-----|
| 13  | 27  | 45  | 133 | 18  | 24  | 46  | 49  | 45  | 23  | 4   | 34  |

Six counts reached double figures; those to exceed 20 were of 35 south-east over Tundry Pond on Apr. 16th 1977 and 22 north over Bishopstoke on Apr. 14th 1981.

At coastal sites, spring passage is evident from late February onwards. Analysis of the sea-watching records for 1971-92 shows that eastward movement through The Solent peaks in mid-April, although it is likely that many are missed in March when observer effort is much less. During the period analysed, the average annual total recorded was 183, with a peak of 496 in 1984. Day totals reached 100 on four occasions with a maximum of 150 at Hill Head on Apr. 19th 1974. Birds are also heard at night in spring (most frequently in late March), moving both east along the coast and north inland over Portsdown Hill. However, in contrast to several other wader species, few have been noted moving inland at dusk from Langstone Harbour.

There are relatively few ringing recoveries. Six ringed as pulli in Sweden (2), and Belgium, Finland, western Germany and the Netherlands (1 each), and recovered or controlled in Hampshire in July/August (2) and December-February (4) indicate the origin of our passage and wintering population. Other recoveries of foreign-ringed birds involved full-grown individuals ringed in the Netherlands in August and Belgium in March and found in Hampshire in January and October respectively. Of birds ringed in the county, two trapped at Fawley in October 1976 and July 1978 were both found breeding in western Germany in April 1982, while another, ringed at Portsmouth Harbour on Oct. 22nd 1972, was killed by a cat at Oulu, Finland, 2160 km north-east, on June 2nd 1975. Very few (if any) Hampshire-bred birds have been ringed. However, the few recoveries of birds ringed as pulli elsewhere in southern England indicate a movement to south-west England, France and Spain in winter (Bainbridge & Minton 1978).

## Spotted Redshank *Tringa erythropus*

A moderately common passage migrant and winter visitor.

K & M knew the Spotted Redshank only as a spring and autumn migrant, and this was still evidently the case in the 1930s as one which wintered at Needs Ore in 1936/37 was considered very unusual. The wintering numbers had increased by the early 1950s, in common with other parts of Britain (BWP). In 1953/54, four were at Needs Ore, three at Dibden Bay and one in Langstone Harbour. Subsequently, Needs Ore and later the Lymington/Hurst area regularly held wintering groups of ten or more, although numbers have been lower since the mid-1980s (table 50).

| | 55-60 | 60-65 | 65-70 | 70-75 | 75-80 | 80-85 | 85-90 | Peak counts |
|---|---|---|---|---|---|---|---|---|
| Needs Ore | 11* | 14 | 8 | 20 | 13 | 9 | 5 | 25, Dec. 1970 |
| Lymington/Hurst | 4* | 1 | 6 | 10 | 14 | 14 | 6 | 24, Jan. 1981 |

*Table 50. Winter (December-February) counts of Spotted Redshanks: five year means of maxima and peak counts, 1955/56-89/90.*

Elsewhere, one or two have wintered fairly regularly in the eastern harbours and at various sites in Southampton Water; higher counts have included five at East Hayling on Jan. 17th 1976, five at Calshot/Ashlett on Dec. 30th 1978 and five at Warsash on Dec. 12th 1981.

Numbers increase from mid-March as spring migrants arrive. Counts have occasionally exceeded ten in the two main wintering areas, e.g. at Needs Ore, 26 on Apr. 7th 1974 and 14 on May 5th 1990, and at Lymington/Hurst, 12 on Apr. 28th 1985. Small numbers are regularly recorded at other coastal localities although the only site to have held more than five is Farlington Marshes, where the maximum recorded was seven on May 6th 1987. Most have left by mid-May; then only occasional stragglers or summering birds are seen until the return from the breeding grounds begins in mid or late June.

At Needs Ore, 52 were present on June 16th 1978, while double-figure counts were made there in June in eight other years between 1963 and 1990. Similar counts elsewhere were of 14 at Pylewell on June 21st 1976 and the same number at Farlington Marshes on June 30th 1985. These flocks probably included failed breeders and post-breeding females, some of which leave the nesting grounds while the males complete incubation (BWP). Males and juveniles arrive from mid-August onwards and peak autumn counts may be recorded at any time until late September (table 51). There is a gradual departure through October, although in 1971, 50 were still at Needs Ore on Nov. 1st. By mid-November, only wintering birds remain.

| | 55-59 | 60-64 | 65-60 | 70-74 | 75-79 | 80-84 | 85-89 | Peak counts | |
|---|---|---|---|---|---|---|---|---|---|
| Langstone Harbour | 5 | 5 | 14 | 7 | 9 | 30 | 36 | 54 | 23/8/86 |
| Titchfield Haven | 1 | 2 | 1 | 2 | 3 | 5 | 6 | 14, | 27/9/86 |
| Dibden Bay | - | 8^ | 5 | 5 | 0 | 0 | 0 | 25, | 22/9/73 |
| Needs Ore | 21^ | 51 | 43 | 50 | 48 | 43 | 34^ | 75, | 16/9/75 |
| Sowley/Pylewell | - | - | - | 11 | 17 | 14 | 1 | 34, | 4/7/76 |
| Lymington/Hurst | - | 4 | 4 | 9 | 9 | 8 | 6 | 35, | 25/9/76 |

*Table 51. Autumn (June-November) counts of Spotted Redshanks: five year means of maxima and peak counts, 1955-89.*

The marked increase at Langstone Harbour has been attributed to the creation in the mid-1970s of the scrape at Farlington Marshes, which provides a safe high water roost site. The decline at Needs Ore is not fully understood but may be connected with changes in the water level or pollution of the favoured pools. No habitat changes are apparent in the Sowley/Pylewell area; the birds occurring there were probably part of the Needs Ore flock. During the five autumns from 1985-89, only three other British sites have held more than 50 birds: the Medway and Thames Estuaries and The Wash.

Elsewhere, counts have rarely reached double figures. At East Hayling, 55 flew across from the roost at Thorney Island, West Sussex as the tide fell on Aug. 24th 1967. Counts at Thorney often exceeded 30 in the 1960s and 1970s, but since 1982 the maximum there has been 14 and the highest count on the Hayling shore nine. In the Fawley/Calshot area, there were 16 on Aug. 29th 1973 and 12 on Oct. 18th 1981, but in recent years only occasional birds have been recorded. The only other notable record was of a flock of 33 flying west out to sea over Hurst Beach on Sep. 25th 1976.

Inland, Spotted Redshanks were first recorded in 1963, since when there have been records in 22 years up to 1992 involving 75 birds. All were in the periods from Mar. 27th-May 19th and June 25th-Oct. 27th. The cumulative monthly totals are shown below.

| Mar | Apr | May | Jun | Jul | Aug | Sep | Oct |
|---|---|---|---|---|---|---|---|
| 1 | 5 | 5 | 1 | 3 | 39 | 19 | 5 |

Records came from 23 localities, including Fleet Pond (16 birds), Winchester Sewage Farm (14), Basingstoke Old Sewage Farm (8), Eversley Gravel Pit (5), Mockbeggar Lake (4) and Timsbury Gravel Pit and Upton Grey (3). In spring, all sightings were of single birds on one date only apart from those of three at Upton Grey from May 8th-11th 1975 and one at Ibsley Flash from Mar. 27th-Apr. 26th 1988. In autumn, most records referred to one or two individuals, but there were three at Basingstoke Old Sewage Farm on Aug. 9th 1966 and up to four there from Sep. 4th-7th of that year, up to three at Winchester Sewage Farm from Aug. 22nd-28th 1964 and three at Fleet Pond on Oct. 3rd 1974. Birds often stayed for a few days or longer, e.g. one at Alresford Pond from Aug. 26th-Sep. 6th 1990.

The only ringing recovery was of an adult ringed at Braakman Polder, Netherlands, on Apr. 7th 1960 and found dead 335 km west at Hayling Island in severe weather on Jan. 6th 1963. National ringing studies have shed little light on the migration routes of birds passing through Britain, although most probably breed in arctic Fenno-Scandia and Russia and winter in the Afrotropics (BWP).

# Redshank                                         *Tringa totanus*

A moderately common but decreasing resident, common passage migrant and winter visitor.

In Hampshire, the three main habitats favoured by breeding Redshanks are the coastal marshes (where they nest on undisturbed islands, in saltmarsh and on rough pasture), the damp water meadows of the river valleys, and the valley bogs and heaths of the New Forest. They also nest around the margins of recently created gravel pits and occasionally in damp arable fields which may be some distance from water.

K & M described the Redshank as "a resident and increasing species", although at that time it apparently bred only along the coast and in the New Forest, which was colonised in the 1850s or early 1860s (Wise 1862). During the first half of the century it spread up the Avon, Test, Itchen and Meon valleys and along their tributaries, and also colonised the Loddon, Whitewater, Hart, Blackwater and Wey valleys in the north-east. This increase reflected a national trend which lasted until about 1940, and coincided with a period of deepening agricultural recession, in which arable farming declined and pastures became neglected and invaded by rushes (Marchant *et al* 1990). Hampshire information for the 1950s is scant but what there is indicates that Redshanks were still common and fairly widespread at that time. Successive hard winters in 1961/62 and 1962/63 caused a marked reduction in the breeding population though this recovered in most areas by 1967.

By the early 1980s, it had become evident that the species was decreasing in the river valleys, due to the progressive drainage and improvement of many of the meadows. This was probably exacerbated by other factors such as the increased use of chemicals on watercress beds (a favoured feeding habitat), the widespread change from mixed to intensive arable farming, the series of colder than average winters in the mid-1980s and the lowering of the water table caused by increased extraction and low rainfall in the drought years from 1988-91. The Atlas Map shows the distribution recorded during 1986-91 and also those tetrads in which Redshanks were found during 1951-85 but not during the Atlas Survey. The contraction of range does not appear to be too great, but densities are known to have decreased in many of the tetrads which are still

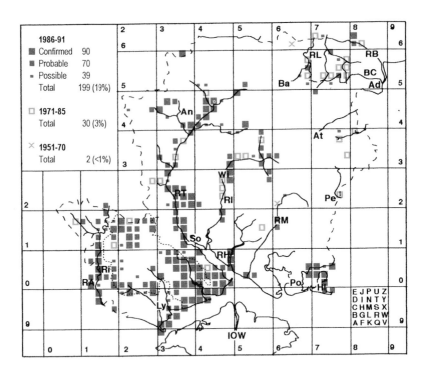

occupied. In contrast to the river valleys, the population in the New Forest expanded between 1961 and 1981, but it has since declined. Numbers at some coastal nature reserves increased during the 1980s but have fluctuated since. Systematic counts at various localities are shown in Table 52.

| | Counts | Reference |
|---|---|---|
| New Forest | 74 pairs, 1961/62; 20-30, 1963; 45 in 50% of habitat, 1966; 105-140, 1981. Probably <75, 1992. | Tubbs 1986a C R Tubbs *in litt* |
| Avon valley | 164 territories, Sopley-Breamore, 1990. No earlier data available, but believed to have declined. | M Clarke *in litt* |
| Test valley | 21 pairs located and 30 estimated, Lower Test Marshes-Fullerton, 1978. Declined since. | Evans 1981 |
| Itchen valley | 23-31 pairs upstream of Winchester, 1983. Declined since. | J M Cloyne *in litt* |
| Langstone Harbour islands | 60 pairs, 1986; 54, 1990; 35, 1992. | RSPB |
| Farlington Marshes | average 39 pairs, 1953-62; 17, 1963-72; no more than 12 since. | Portsmouth Group 1991 |
| Beaulieu Estuary | Gradual increase to 40 pairs, 1988; 29, 1992 | *HBR*, Hughes unpub. |
| Pitts Deep/Hurst | Gradual increase to 23 pairs, 1989; 51, 1992. | *HBR* |

*Table 52. Selected counts of breeding Redshanks.*

Taking the most recent figures for the New Forest, Avon valley and coastal sites from table 52, and assuming an average density of two pairs in other occupied tetrads where breeding was confirmed or probable, suggests a county total of 500-550 pairs in the early 1990s. The most recent estimate of the British population was 30,600-33,600 pairs in the mid-1980s (New Atlas).

Redshanks breeding in the river valleys and New Forest leave between mid-June and early August. A few migrants occur at inland sites such as gravel pits and sewage farms at this time, but a flock of 18 moving south-west over Shepherds Spring on June 22nd 1975 was exceptional. The species is rare inland in September and October. A flock of 80 which stayed at Mockbeggar Lake for an hour after dawn on Sep. 21st 1980 before leaving north was unprecedented and coincided with the arrival of 120 on the coast at Keyhaven which "appeared to drop out of the sky".

The build-up at coastal sites in July and August is rapid, with local breeders probably arriving first, to be followed by those from breeding populations elsewhere in Britain, on the near continent and in Iceland (Prater 1981). Counts normally show an autumn peak (table 53), and then decline as birds move on to winter further south. Winter numbers are usually highest in November and December (table 54). Lower counts later in some winters may be due to birds feeding inland on wet fields (cf. Curlew). However, the species is particularly susceptible to severe cold weather and in such conditions high mortality may occur. Overall, both autumn and winter numbers have fallen since the mid-1980s. This reflects the national trend and may well be connected with the increased incidence of cold winters in recent years. During the five winters from 1985/86-89/90, the proportion of the British wintering population in Hampshire (based on January counts) averaged 4.0%.

| | 55-59 | 60-64 | 65-69 | 70-74 | 75-79 | 80-84 | 85-89 | Peak counts | |
|---|---|---|---|---|---|---|---|---|---|
| Chichester Harbour | - | - | 2723 | 2808 | 2590 | 2234 | 1375 | 4110, | Sep. 1971 |
| East Hayling | 225^ | 600* | - | 900^ | 885 | 808 | 438 | 1270, | Oct. 1975 |
| Langstone Harbour | 2133 | 2500^ | 1560 | 1424 | 1978 | 1930 | 1231 | 3500, | July 1961 |
| Portsmouth Harbour | - | - | 1350^ | 1370 | 961 | 468 | 277 | 1900, | July 1971 |
| Southampton Water | - | - | - | 876 | 1055 | 1066 | 647 | 1397, | Sep. 1970 |
| Warsash | - | - | - | 458^ | 298 | 243 | 201 | 650, | Sep. 1972 |
| Fawley/Calshot | - | 460^ | - | 458 | 700 | 823 | 423 | 1250, | July 1982 |
| Beaulieu Estuary | - | 190 | 196 | 146 | 92 | 92 | 119^ | 400, | Aug. 1961 |
| Lymington/Hurst | - | 317 | 216 | 400 | 625 | 525 | 371 | 975, | Oct. 1976 |

Table 53. High tide roost counts of Redshanks in autumn (July-October): five years means of maxima and peak counts, 1955-89.

| | 55-60 | 60-65 | 65-70 | 70-75 | 75-80 | 80-85 | 85-90 | Peak counts | |
|---|---|---|---|---|---|---|---|---|---|
| Chichester Harbour | - | - | 1355 | 1361 | 1585 | 2179 | 1657 | 2516, | Jan. 1983 |
| East Hayling | 200* | - | 2000* | 720^ | 685 | 889 | 387 | 2000, | Dec. 1968 |
| Langstone Harbour | 1620 | 470 | 1260 | 670 | 987 | 694 | 698 | 3000, | Nov. 1966 |
| Portsmouth Harbour | - | - | 911^ | 631 | 453 | 512 | 377 | 1472, | Dec. 1969 |
| Southampton Water | - | - | - | 795 | 1033 | 693 | 736 | 1197, | Nov. 1974 |
| Warsash | - | - | - | 265^ | 198 | 182 | 172 | 450, | Nov. 1973 |
| Fawley/Calshot | - | - | - | 343^ | 703 | 559 | 420 | 800, | Jan. 1977 |
| Beaulieu Estuary | - | 83^ | 168 | 67 | 83 | 128 | 114^ | 280, | Dec. 1984 |
| Lymington/Hurst | 60* | 150^ | 337^ | 670 | 506 | 565 | 234 | 1000, | Nov. 1974 |

Table 54. High tide roost counts of Redshanks in winter (November-March): five year means of maxima and peak counts, 1955/56-89/90.

In Southampton Water, counts also exceeded 200 at Dibden Bay (500+, July 1960; 600+, October 1964; 350, September 1972) and Eling Great Marsh (300, December 1960; 277, December 1989).

Birds regularly winter inland in the upper Itchen and Avon valleys, but they rarely appear before November or December. Most of those in the upper Itchen feed by day on watercress beds and fly into Alresford Pond at dusk to roost. Between 1971/72 and 1983/84, over ten were regularly present with peaks of 22 in December 1973, 21 in January 1977 and 18 in January 1983. In recent years no more than seven have wintered. In the Avon valley, the highest numbers occur when there is extensive flooding, e.g. up to 27 at Blashford between mid-December 1976 and mid-February 1977 and 17 at Avon Causeway in January 1982. Later that year, 12 were at Ibsley by Nov. 26th. Most other mid-winter inland records involve occasional birds flying over or grounded in hard weather.

The return to inland breeding sites begins in mid-February and most are back on territory by late March. Spring flooding may attract noteworthy concentrations, especially in the Avon valley, e.g. 60 at Blashford on Mar. 12th 1978, 58 between Avon Causeway and Bisterne on Mar. 3rd 1990 and 70 at Ibsley on Mar. 15th 1990. 135 were counted between Sopley and Ibsley on Apr. 1st 1984. Counts elsewhere occasionally reach double figures, e.g. at Headbourne Worthy Watercress Beds and Winchester Sewage Farm, but a gathering of up to 40 at Alresford Pond in April 1973 and a flock of 49 flying over Enham Alamein on Apr. 4th 1974 were both exceptional.

In mid-April, flocks are frequently seen moving off inland from Langstone Harbour at dusk in directions between north and north-west, e.g. 70 on Apr. 23rd 1980 and 102 on Apr. 22nd 1987. These may well be en route to Icelandic breeding grounds. Very few are recorded moving through The Solent in spring, the highest day total involving a flock of 11 which flew east at Hill Head on May 7th 1981.

There have been 107 recoveries or controls of Hampshire birds within Britain. These confirm that at least a proportion of Hampshire breeding birds winters locally, and that many of those which arrive in the county in autumn remain for the winter and originate from northern England and Scotland. Two recoveries show that birds from further afield also occur. One involved an adult ringed in Denmark on May 2nd 1960 (when it was presumably breeding) and shot at Hayling Island, 1054 km WSW, on Jan. 24th 1963, and the other a bird ringed as a chick in Iceland on June 28th 1972 and shot at Pylewell, 2107 km south-east, on Sep. 2nd 1972. There have also been five foreign recoveries of birds ringed in Hampshire in autumn: four in France in January, May, July and December and one in the Netherlands in May.


## Marsh Sandpiper                                    *Tringa stagnatilis*

Three records. Single adults were at Farlington Marshes on June 27th and 28th 1976 and from July 5th-11th 1977, and at Pennington Marsh from July 28th-Aug. 4th 1983.

The Marsh Sandpiper breeds from eastern Europe through Kazakhstan to eastern Asia and winters in tropical Africa, southern Asia and Australia.

# Greenshank                                    *Tringa nebularia*

A moderately common passage migrant; small numbers winter.

K & M described the Greenshank as "a spring and autumn visitor .... either singly or in small numbers". Lack of observations in the eastern harbours in the 19th century may have masked its true status at that time, but improved coverage from the 1950s onwards showed increasing numbers in autumn and also the establishment of a small, but regular, wintering population.

As with many other wader species, by far the largest numbers occur in Langstone and Chichester Harbours. A heavy autumn passage occurs, which starts in late June and continues until early November. In Langstone Harbour, numbers showed a steady increase in the 1960s and 1970s. The maximum count exceeded 100 in 1962 and 1966, then in all but two years between 1977 and 1989 (table 55). Three-figure counts have been made between July 22nd and Oct. 1st; in some years, there was evidence of two peaks, one between mid-July and mid-August and another between late August and mid-September. Analysis of data concerning 430 caught by the Farlington Ringing Group from 1967-91 indicates that the two peaks correspond to the main passage periods of adults and juveniles respectively (P M Potts *in litt*). During the five autumns from 1985-1989, only three other British sites, the Medway and Swale Estuaries and The Wash, held similar numbers.

Autumn counts at other localities rarely reach 30 although numbers exceeding 50 have been recorded on single occasions at Fawley/Calshot, Needs Ore and Lymington/Hurst (table 55). Parties are occasionally seen leaving the county, notably 29 flying west over Hurst Beach on Sep. 25th 1976 (*cf.* Spotted Redshank), 14 doing likewise the following day and 21 flying high to the south-west over Langstone Harbour on Sep. 29th 1988.

| | 55-59 | 60-64 | 65-69 | 70-74 | 75-79 | 80-84 | 85-89 | Peak counts |
|---|---|---|---|---|---|---|---|---|
| Chichester Harbour | - | - | 95^ | 101 | 80 | 124 | 131 | 145, 8/8/87 |
| East Hayling | 20^ | - | - | 13^ | 14^ | 18 | 7^ | 37, 12/9/81 |
| Langstone Harbour | 30 | 69 | 78 | 71 | 97 | 149 | 126 | 182, 23/8/86 |
| Portsmouth Harbour | - | - | 3* | 14 | 10 | 21 | 7 | 30, 8/8/81 |
| Titchfield Haven | 2 | 5 | 1 | 3 | 10 | 9 | 8 | 28, 25/9/76 |
| Warsash | 4* | - | - | 10^ | 10 | 18 | 12 | 26, 21/9/84 |
| Dibden Bay | 26* | 21 | 19^ | 11 | 7 | 4 | 1 | 29, 17/8/77 |
| Fawley/Calshot | - | - | 6* | 10 | 20 | 33 | 11 | 70, 11/9/83 |
| Needs Ore | 18^ | 23 | 14 | 7 | 8 | 6 | 9 | 55, 24/9/61 |
| Lymington/Hurst | 17* | 17 | 17 | 21 | 27 | 31 | 20 | 65, 25/9/76 |

*Table 55. Autumn (June-November) counts of Greenshanks: five year means of maxima and peak counts, 1955-89.*

The principal wintering area is Southampton Water. In the late 1970s and early 1980s, the highest counts were made in the Calshot/Fawley area, with up to nine regularly during December-March period and maxima of 13 on Dec. 2nd 1979 and 19 on Dec. 5th 1982. In the late 1980s, the preferred area shifted to the River Hamble with up to nine recorded at Warsash and similar numbers upstream at Curbridge, where the maximum count was of 12 on Mar. 18th 1990. Greenshanks also winter in the Lymington/Hurst area, with a peak count of nine on three occasions. Single birds occur regularly in the three eastern harbours and at Needs Ore, with occasional higher numbers, e.g. 16 at Black Point on Dec. 30th 1984 and five in Portsmouth Harbour on Dec. 4th 1982.

Spring passage is evident from mid-April until late May. Counts occasionally reach double figures, e.g. 20 at Needs Ore on Apr. 23rd 1978, 18 at Farlington Marshes on Apr. 29th 1978 and May 7th 1984, 15 at Paulsgrove Reclamation (Portsmouth Harbour) on May 1st 1984, 20 in the Lymington/Hurst area on May 17th 1985 and May 5th 1986 and 17 at Curbridge on May 1st 1988. Birds may also be seen moving along the coast at this time; during 1971-92, a total of 116 was recorded, mostly moving east, on dates between Apr. 20th and May 21st. Usually, day totals were low, but three large flocks occurred at Hill Head: 18 on May 7th 1981, 19 on Apr. 28th 1987 and 14 on May 1st 1990. Between late May and June, occasional birds are noted; up to three have regularly summered in Langstone Harbour.

Since 1957, Greenshanks have been recorded inland annually, with 138 in spring between Apr. 13th and June 7th, 772 in autumn between June 22nd and Nov. 12th and three in winter. The autumn passage apparently shows two peaks, similar to the pattern observed at Langstone Harbour (fig. 46).

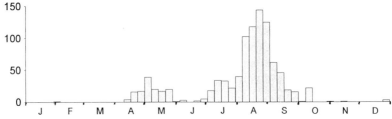

*Figure 46. Cumulative weekly totals of Greenshanks inland, 1957-92.*

In spring, most records refer to birds flying over the observation point or staying for a few hours only. The largest counts were of five moving north-east over Bramshill on May 22nd 1977, five at Eversley Gravel Pit on May 2nd 1989, and six, including four moving north-west, at Fleet Pond on May 3rd 1990. In autumn, several may be present for a week or more where there is suitable habitat. High counts have been made at Winchester Sewage Farm (9, Aug. 20th 1979; 10, Aug. 29th 1981), Mockbeggar Lake (9, Aug. 17th 1981) and Timsbury Gravel Pit (9, Sep. 10th 1989); counts have also reached five at Alresford Pond and Watercress Beds, Basingstoke Old Sewage Farm, Eversley Gravel Pit, Kingston Common, Winnall Moors and Woolmer Pond. A flock of 14 moved WSW over Fleet Pond on Oct. 11th 1976 and eight flew south over Lakeside (Eastleigh) on Aug. 23rd 1984. There have been three mid-winter records involving one on a watercress bed at Alresford on Jan. 31st 1965, two on floods at Sopley on Dec. 28th 1979 and one in a drained gravel pit at Eversley on Dec. 28th 1989.

Ringing at Farlington Marshes has indicated that the wintering area of most birds migrating through southern England is in tropical West Africa. An adult ringed there on July 20th 1985 was found freshly dead in a fishing net in Ghana on Jan. 28th 1992 and another adult, ringed on July 20th 1986, was recovered in Sierra Leone on Mar. 15th 1993. One ringed as a juvenile on Sep. 13th 1984 was found dead in Loire Atlantique, France on May 25th 1987, when presumably it had been on migration from Africa. Eight birds have been recovered abroad in subsequent autumns, six in France and one each in Denmark and Norway. The only control at Farlington Marshes involved an adult caught on Aug. 19th 1989 which had been ringed at Zeebrugge, Belgium on July 25th of that year. Those occurring in autumn are believed to breed in Fenno-Scandia. Circumstantial evidence suggests that some wintering birds originate from the Scottish population, although there are no ringing recoveries to substantiate this (BWP, Prater 1981).

## Lesser Yellowlegs                                  *Tringa flavipes*

A rare vagrant. There have been ten records, all of single birds, as follows:

| 1953: | Pennington/Keyhaven Marshes, Sep. 28th-Oct. 2nd; |
|---|---|
| 1954: | Keyhaven Marsh, Aug. 29th; |
|  | Farlington Marshes, Sep. 20th-28th; |
| 1962: | Farlington Marshes, July 19th-21st; |
| 1963: | Farlington Marshes, June 29th-Sep. 1st; |
| 1973: | Pennington Marsh, Sep. 18th; |
| 1974: | East Winner Bank (Hayling), Sep. 19th; |
| 1976: | Keyhaven Marsh, Oct. 9th; |
| 1977: | Dibden Bay, Aug. 29th-Sep. 9th; |
| 1986: | Farlington Marshes, Aug. 15th-27th. |

The Lesser Yellowlegs breeds in Alaska and Canada and winters in South America. The recent dearth of records in Hampshire parallels the national picture.

## Green Sandpiper                                    *Tringa ochropus*

A passage migrant, scarce in spring and moderately common in autumn. Small numbers winter.

K & M regarded the Green Sandpiper as a passage migrant but also mentioned that it had been seen "more than once in winter". Cohen wrote that "odd birds occasionally winter". Since the 1960s, it has been evident that there is a considerable wintering population, probably in excess of 50 birds in some years. On the watercress beds and ponds of the upper Itchen valley, up to ten were regularly present between 1965 and 1992 with peaks of 20 roosting at Alresford Pond on Feb. 13th 1972 and 21, possibly including some late migrants, at Old Alresford Watercress Bed on Oct. 30th 1976. Large concentrations have also been recorded on watercress beds at Mapledurwell, where there were 14 on Dec. 11th 1983 and 18 on Dec. 15th 1984. Elsewhere, parties of up to three are widespread, while occasionally larger groups gather when particularly attractive habitat is available, e.g. six on drained pools at Overton on Jan. 26th 1989 and six in similar habitat at Eversley Gravel Pit on Dec. 28th 1989.

Spring passage, indicated by the appearance of birds at sites where they have not wintered, occurs from mid-March. Records are usually of one to four birds, primarily at inland sites, with a total of 30-40 in most years. The largest number recorded at this time was 14 at Alresford Pond on Apr. 5th 1976, but this possibly included some wintering birds. Most have moved through by late April although stragglers are recorded in the first week of May in most years. The species is very scarce in the remainder of May and early June.

The greatest numbers occur on autumn passage, which begins in mid-June, reaches a peak between late July and late August and continues until the end of October. Between 1963 and 1975, the highest numbers occurred at Dibden Bay, where the many silt-filled ditches and areas of stagnant water created following reclamation proved extremely attractive (Glue 1971). Counts exceeded 20 in 11 autumns during that period and peaked at 32 on Aug. 4th 1968. At Alresford Pond, sizeable concentrations are attracted in years when the water level is low. From 1986-92, over ten were present each autumn with a maximum of 24 on Aug. 14th 1992. Currently, the other major site is Titchfield Haven, where the recently-created scrapes have held between seven and 16 annually since 1983. Records for 1951-92 at these and other sites are summarised in table 56.

| | Period recorded | Years with records | Years with counts of 5+ | Peak counts | |
|---|---|---|---|---|---|
| Farlington Marshes | 1951-92 | 42 | 19 | 18, | 18/8/58 |
| Titchfield Haven | 1951-92 | 41 | 20 | 16, | 15/7/89 |
| Warsash | 1954-92 | 26 | 11 | 12, | 19/8/86 |
| Dibden Bay | 1951-87 | 37 | 28 | 32, | 4/8/68 |
| Pennington/Keyhaven | 1960-92 | 33 | 10 | 15, | 29/8/69 |
| Blashford Lakes | 1973-92 | 18 | 14 | 13, | 7/8/90 |
| Winchester Sewage Farm | 1962-92 | 29 | 13 | 13, | 5/8/88 |
| Alresford Pond | 1957-92 | 31 | 23 | 24, | 14/8/92 |

*Table 56. Summary of autumn counts of Green Sandpipers, 1951-92.*

Counts of 8-17 have also been made at Old Alresford, Bighton Lane, Bishops Sutton, Western Court, Quidhampton, Southington and Mapledurwell Watercress Beds, Eversley and Timsbury Gravel Pits, Eastleigh Sewage Farm, Lower Test Marshes, Northington Lake, Paulsgrove Reclamation and Woolmer Pond.

The main breeding range of the Green Sandpiper is from Scandinavia to eastern Siberia. Those occurring in Hampshire probably originate from Scandinavia and winter largely in north-west and tropical West Africa (BWP).

# Wood Sandpiper                                        *Tringa glareola*

A passage migrant, very scarce in spring but regular in small numbers in autumn; recorded once in winter.

Between 1951 and 1992, Wood Sandpipers were recorded in spring in 30 years, with a maximum of ten birds in 1991 and 1992. Most occurred from late April to early June with a peak in the second half of May. Early sightings include those of single birds at Farlington Marshes on Apr. 11th and 12th 1966 and Ibsley from Apr. 4th-10th 1983. Of 105 recorded, 29 were at Farlington Marshes, 19 at Titchfield Haven and 13 at Pennington/Keyhaven Marshes, while 22 were inland. All records were of one or two birds apart from those of four at Titchfield Haven on May 16th 1961, three at Farlington Marshes from June 1st-3rd 1962, four at Needs Ore on May 7th 1989, three at Titchfield Haven on May 31st 1991, four at Lower Test Marshes from May 17th-19th 1992 and three at Mockbeggar Lake on May 23rd 1992. Most were recorded on one date only, but a few stayed for up to a week and one was at Needs Ore from Apr. 29th-May 9th 1990.

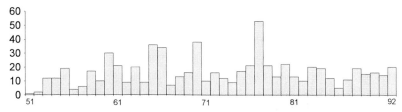

*Figure 47. Autumn totals of Wood Sandpipers, 1951-92.*

Small numbers of presumably non-breeding adults occur in the second half of June and July. The main autumn passage period is from late July until mid-September, reaching a peak in mid-August. Annual totals varied between five and 38, except in 1977, when 53 were recorded (fig. 47). Records for 1951-92 at the main coastal localities are summarised in table 57.

| | Period recorded | Years with records | Years with counts of 3+ | Peak counts | |
|---|---|---|---|---|---|
| Farlington Marshes | 1952-92 | 39 | 16 | 10, | 13/8/54 |
| | | | | 8, | 7/8/60 |
| | | | | 8, | 3/9/63 |
| | | | | 8, | 14-21/8/77 |
| Titchfield Haven | 1955-92 | 31 | 5 | 6, | 9/8/61 |
| | | | | 10, | 31/7/65 |
| Dibden Bay* | 1952-85 | 28 | 10 | 8, | 25/8/60 |
| | | | | 11, | 9/9/65 |
| | | | | 8, | 7/8/70 |
| | | | | 26, | 18/8/77 |
| Pennington/Keyhaven Marshes | 1960-92 | 31 | 16 | 12, | 24/8/66 |
| | | | | 11, | 12/8/69 |
| | | | | 6, | 7/8/70 |

\* habitat no longer suitable

*Table 57. Summary of autumn counts of Wood Sandpipers, 1951-92.*

Elsewhere, the other coastal records of more than three birds were of nine at Hook Lake (Warsash) on Aug. 24th 1955 and four at Paulsgrove Reclamation on Aug. 4th 1983. 89 of the 694 recorded were inland, the main sites being Woolmer Pond (19 birds), Winchester Sewage Farm (16), Alresford Pond (13), Eversley/Yateley Gravel Pits (7) and Mockbeggar Lake (5). All records were of one or two apart from 11 at Woolmer on Aug. 16th and 19th 1970 and three at Pinglestone Watercress Bed on Aug. 22nd 1976.

Few are recorded in October; after the middle of that month the only sightings have been of single birds at Keyhaven Marsh on Oct. 26th 1975 and Polhampton on Oct. 16th 1984.

The only winter record was of one on floods at Ibsley from Feb. 23rd-Apr. 6th 1984.

Although a few pairs nest in Scotland, the main breeding range of the Wood Sandpiper is from Fenno-Scandia to eastern Siberia; it winters in sub-Saharan Africa, southern Asia and Australia.

# Terek Sandpiper                                       *Xenus cinereus*

A rare vagrant. There have been five records, all of single birds, as follows:

1963:     Pennington Marsh, May 25th and 31st;
1983:     Langstone Harbour islands, July 9th-11th;
1984:     Langstone Harbour islands, May 23rd;
1986:     Oxey/Pennington saltmarsh, June 10th;
1990:     Farlington Marshes, May 13th, 23rd and 27th.

The Terek Sandpiper breeds from Finland to eastern Siberia and winters on the coasts of Africa south of the Sahara, southern Asia and Australia.

# Common Sandpiper                                     *Actitis hypoleucos*

A moderately common passage migrant; a few regularly winter; has attempted breeding at least once.

In spring, passage is evident from mid-April in some years and reaches a peak in the first half of May. Most records involve single birds or small parties, with the majority occurring inland at gravel pits, lakes, river margins and other similar habitats. The only counts to reach double figures were of 22 at Broadlands Lake on May 5th 1976, 14 at Wellington Country Park on Apr. 21st 1977, 14 at Keyhaven Marsh on Apr. 26th 1977, 13 at Shepherds Spring on May 24th 1977 and 13 at Curbridge on May 4th 1990. Between 1971 and 1992, a total of 21 was recorded moving east along the coast, including seven at Hurst Beach between Apr. 27th and May 5th 1984. The spring movement is usually complete by late May although a few stragglers occur in early June.

A pair attempted breeding at Timsbury Gravel Pit in 1978. Continuous display was observed in early May, and an adult was seen giving distraction display on June 10th. Unfortunately, no young were seen and the adults had left by the end of June. Display was also noted at Broadlands Lake in May and early June 1984, but there were no sightings after June 8th.

Return passage starts in mid-June and appears to show two peaks, in late July and early August and in the second half of August. This may reflect the peak movements of adults and juveniles. At this time by far the largest numbers occur on the coast (table 58).

| | 55-59 | 60-64 | 65-69 | 70-74 | 75-79 | 80-84 | 85-89 | Peak counts |
|---|---|---|---|---|---|---|---|---|
| Langstone Harbour | 27 | 26 | 25 | 25 | 23 | 27 | 17 | 48, 31/7/60 |
| Titchfield Haven | 7 | 10 | 8 | 12 | 7 | 15 | 10 | 21, 11/8/81 |
| Dibden Bay | 17^ | 31 | 30 | 27^ | 20 | 10 | 3 | 50, 6/8/73 |
| Lymington/Hurst | 16^ | 16 | 24 | 21 | 17 | 9 | 9 | 50, 15/8/69 |

*Table 58. Autumn (July-September) counts of Common Sandpipers: five year means of maxima and peak counts, 1955-89.*

Counts have also reached 20 at East Hayling (23, July 31st 1976), Paulsgrove Reclamation (in 4 years, max. 40, Aug. 4th 1984), the Hamble Estuary (23, Aug. 6th 1974; 29, July 27th 1986), Eling Great Marsh (23, Aug. 3rd 1969; 22, July 30th 1972) and Needs Ore (21, July 21st 1963). There have also been several records of flocks actually migrating, including ten arriving at Farlington Marshes from inland on July 22nd 1973, 45 moving along Milford-on-Sea Beach on July 13th 1982 and 34 flying high to the south-west over Sandy Point on Aug. 25th 1984. Inland, double-figure counts have been made at Blashford Lakes (in 6 years, max. 15, Aug. 29th 1977), Eversley Gravel Pit (in 3 years, max. 17, Aug. 13th 1986), Frensham Great Pond (25, Aug. 28th 1960; 19, July 14th 1992) and Winchester Sewage Farm (14, Aug. 17th and 20th 1965). Numbers of migrants gradually decline until by late October only wintering birds remain. The data in table 58 indicates a decline in the late 1980s, despite the provision of improved habitat at sites such as Titchfield Haven.

Wintering birds have been recorded at virtually all suitable tidal sites between East Hayling and Keyhaven. Most records have come from the Eling/Redbridge/Lower Test Marshes area, while other favoured localities include Beaulieu Mill Pond, the Itchen between Woolston and St. Deny's, the Hamble up to Curbridge, Fareham Creek, the Bedhampton/Langstone Village area and East Hayling. Usually, up to three are recorded but there were eight at East Hayling on Feb. 21st 1981 and seven in the Eling area in severe weather on Jan. 11th 1982. Inland records are rare. Most have come from Blashford Lakes, where one wintered in 1982/83 and 1984/85, three were present in December 1984 and five in February 1987. The larger numbers were attracted to lakes where the water level was low during conversion to storage reservoirs.

Ringing recoveries indicate that Scandinavian as well as British breeding birds pass through the county. One ringed as a juvenile at Farlington Marshes on July 30th 1969 was recovered in North Yorkshire on June 4th 1970, while an adult ringed at Titchfield Haven on Sep. 9th 1979 was found dead 1883 km north-east in Vasterbotten, Sweden on May 28th 1985. Another, ringed as a chick in Hordaland, Norway, on June 26th 1980 was controlled 1129 km south-west at Southampton Docks on Aug. 10th 1980. The fourth long-distance recovery involved one ringed at Farlington Marshes on Sep. 2nd 1962 and found 1446 km south-west in Ribatejo, Portugal only six days later. This bird had presumably been en route to wintering grounds in tropical West Africa.

# Spotted Sandpiper                                    *Actitis macularia*

One record. An adult was at Titchfield Haven from Oct. 4th 1986-Jan. 12th 1987. It disappeared during a spell of severe weather.

The Spotted Sandpiper breeds in most of North America and winters in Central and South America.

# Turnstone                                            *Arenaria interpres*

A moderately common passage migrant and winter visitor, with small numbers summering.

Turnstone numbers have increased since the 1950s, especially in Langstone Harbour. Adults begin to arrive from their breeding grounds in mid-July, while juveniles appear in strength from late August onwards. Counts usually peak between August and October (table 59) and then decline through November. Mid-winter counts, although generally lower than those in autumn, show great fluctuations (table 60); this may be partly connected with the difficulty in locating the many small roosts formed by this species. However, at Langstone Harbour especially, there is often a marked influx in March. Numbers decline in late March and April as wintering birds depart, but often rise again to a peak in early May. During the five winters from 1985/86-89/90, the proportion of the British wintering population in Hampshire (based on January counts) averaged 4.7%.

| | 55-59 | 60-64 | 65-69 | 70-74 | 75-79 | 80-84 | 85-89 | Peak counts |
|---|---|---|---|---|---|---|---|---|
| Chichester Harbour | - | - | 123 | 153 | 139 | 111 | 205 | 350, Oct. 1971 |
| East Hayling | - | - | - | - | 10 | 23 | 49 | 122, Oct. 1986 |
| Langstone Harbour | - | 45* | 29 | 96 | 112 | 264 | 412 | 512, Sep. 1984 |
| Portsmouth Harbour | - | - | - | 101 | 26 | 11 | 37 | 200, Sep. 1971 |
| Southampton Water | - | - | - | 306 | 383 | 350 | 334 | 457, Oct. 1976 |
| Warsash | 170* | 117* | - | 242^ | 266 | 243 | 204 | 332, Aug. 1977 |
| Fawley/Calshot | 231* | 105* | 185* | 204 | 167 | 164 | 135 | 282, Aug. 1971 |
| Lymington/Hurst | - | 35 | 65 | 110 | 59 | 100 | 121 | 279, Oct. 1986 |

*Table 59. High tide roost counts of Turnstones in autumn (July-October): five year means of maxima and peak counts, 1955-89.*

| | 55-60 | 60-65 | 65-70 | 70-75 | 75-80 | 80-85 | 85-90 | Peak counts |
|---|---|---|---|---|---|---|---|---|
| Chichester Harbour | - | - | 47 | 106 | 147 | 206 | 198 | 384, Nov. 1982 |
| East Hayling | - | - | - | - | 53 | 121 | 63 | 228, Nov. 1982 |
| Langstone Harbour | 136 | 43 | 65 | 77 | 118 | 339 | 318 | 492, Mar. 1981 |
| Portsmouth Harbour | - | - | - | 91 | 100 | 70 | 69 | 200, Mar. 1980 |
| Southampton Water | - | - | - | 263 | 383 | 381 | 337 | 490, Dec. 1976 |
| Warsash | - | 150* | - | 212^ | 214 | 236 | 151 | 350, Jan. 1981 |
| Fawley/Calshot | - | - | - | 89 | 104 | 133 | 163 | 192, Dec. 1985 |
| Lymington/Hurst | - | 55 | 52 | 156 | 132 | 153 | 163 | 260, Nov. 1984 |

*Table 60. High tide roost counts of Turnstones in winter (November-March): five year means of maxima and peak counts, 1955/56-89/90.*

In Southampton Water, the main feeding concentrations occur around Calshot Spit, off Dibden Bay and along the eastern shore between Weston and Hill Head (Unsworth 1991). In addition to the sites in tables 59 and 60, birds also regularly roost at Titchfield Haven (max. 110, apart from 154 in January 1977), Hythe (max. 155 on barges and nearby saltmarsh, Dec. 6th 1986), Weston Shore (118 on Dec. 16th 1967, but no more than 75 since) and Cracknore Hard (max. 68 on a buoy, Jan. 22nd 1989). Less regularly used sites are Dibden Bay (max. 90, apart from 214 on Jan. 17th 1971; very few since 1983) and Eling Great Marsh (max. 60+, Mar. 19th 1983). Away from Southampton Water, 100-120 are regularly present in Hayling Bay between November and February, with as many as 220 on Dec. 26th 1988. The disappearance of this flock in March may account for the increase recorded in nearby Langstone Harbour at that time in some years. Smaller roosts also occur in the west Solent at Pitts Deep (max. 35, Nov. 22nd 1987) and the Beaulieu Estuary (max. 90, Dec. 9th 1984). The latter move east as the tide drops to feed on the stony beach at Lepe, where the highest count was of 100 on Aug. 13th 1977.

In spring, easterly movement along the coast has been recorded between Mar. 26th and June 1st and reaches a peak in early May. Between 1971 and 1992, the total recorded annually varied between two and 258 (in 1980) with an average of 72. The only day total to reach three figures was of 140 off Hurst Beach on May 3rd 1980. Numbers at high tide roosts may peak at this time, e.g. 258 at Warsash on May 12th 1979 and, in early May 1989, 400 in Chichester Harbour, 383 in Langstone Harbour and 170 in Portsmouth Harbour. Flocks are regularly recorded at dusk moving inland in a north to north-west direction. At Langstone, such sightings have been made between May 11th and June 6th with a maximum of 87 north-west on May 19th 1984, while in the Lymington/Hurst area they occurred between May 7th and 19th with a maximum of 71 departing north over Salterns Marsh on May 18th 1976.

Small numbers of non-breeders summer in some years. Up to ten are regular in the Lymington/Hurst area and in Langstone Harbour; larger counts include 20 at Pennington Marsh on June 5th 1974, 83 in Langstone Harbour on June 16th 1983 and 86 there on June 7th 1986, but these probably involved some late spring migrants.

Turnstones are very scarce inland. Since 1962, there have been 23 records in 16 years, all in the periods Apr. 23rd-June 5th (38 birds) and July 27th-Sep. 10th (7). Birds were recorded at Mockbeggar Lake (22), Frensham Great Pond (12), Eversley Gravel Pit (5), Fleet Pond, Timsbury Gravel Pit and Winnall Moors (2 each) and Winchester Sewage Farm (1). All records were of one to four birds on one date only apart from 12 at Mockbeggar Lake on May 10th 1986 and single birds at Eversley Gravel Pit on May 4th and 5th 1990 and from Apr. 23rd-27th 1992.

Hampshire ringing data shed little light on the movements of Turnstones occurring in the county. An adult ringed in Iceland on Aug. 3rd 1972 was controlled 1917 km south-east in Portsmouth Harbour on Oct. 22nd of that year, another adult ringed at Farlington Marshes on Aug. 23rd 1978 was found dead near Portsmouth Cathedral on Mar. 15th 1985, while a colour-dyed bird seen in Langstone Harbour on June 9th 1985 had been ringed on May 4th 1985 at Wembury, Devon. National data indicate that the Greenland and north-east Canadian population winters in Britain, while that breeding in Fenno-Scandia and western Russia winters in Morocco and tropical West Africa (Branson *et al* 1978, BWP). Thus the autumn and spring peaks in Hampshire indicate when birds from both populations may be present. Some of those moving inland in spring may be heading for Greenland, while those moving east along the coast possibly belong to the northern European population.

## Wilson's Phalarope  *Phalaropus tricolor*

Four records. Single birds were at Dibden Bay from Aug. 14th-18th 1974 and on Oct. 9th and 10th 1977, an adult was at Paulsgrove Reclamation on Oct. 18th 1984 and a juvenile moulting into first-winter plumage was at Titchfield Haven on Sep. 14th and 15th 1989.

The Wilson's Phalarope breeds in western USA and Canada and winters in South America.

## Red-necked Phalarope  *Phalaropus lobatus*

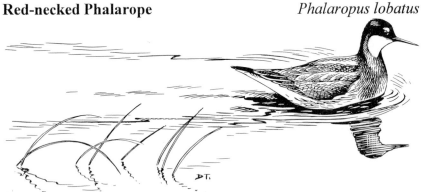

A rare passage migrant.

The first Red-necked Phalaropes for the county were two, one of which was shot, on the River Avon near Ringwood on Oct. 27th 1890. The next was not until 1950, since when there have been 32 records, some of which may have referred to the same individual, as follows:

1950:   Titchfield Haven, Oct. 14th;
1955:   Farlington Marshes, Sep. 10th-12th;
1957:   Stokes Bay, Sep. 10th-12th;
1958:   2, Dibden Bay, Oct 6th;
1964:   Dibden Bay, Aug. 19th;
1967:   Overton Paper Mill Lagoons, Sep. 20th;
1969:   juvenile, Pennington Marsh, Sep. 7th
        Dibden Bay, Sep. 14th;
1972:   Pennington/Keyhaven Marshes, May 27th-31st;
1973:   Dibden Bay, Sep. 28th-Oct. 1st;
1975:   Pennington/Keyhaven Marshes, July 10th-18th, Sep. 6th/7th and Sep. 23rd-28th;
1977:   female, Pennington Marsh, May 29th-June 1st;
        Needs Ore, June 19th;
        Dibden Bay, Aug. 7th/8th, Aug. 26th/27th, Aug. 31st-Sep. 7th and Oct. 2nd;
1979:   juvenile, Pennington Marsh, Aug. 25th;
1981:   Hurst/Pennington Marsh, Sep. 27th and Oct. 4th;
1982:   female, Titchfield Haven, June 9th;
1983:   female, Farlington Marshes, June 1st and 6th;
        juvenile, Titchfield Haven, Sep. 27th-Oct. 4th;
1984:   juvenile, Great Salterns Lake, Sep. 25th-Oct. 11th;
1987:   adult, Farlington Marshes, Oct. 11th-15th;
        juvenile, Hilsea Moat, Oct. 23rd and Farlington Marshes, Oct. 25th-28th;

The Red-necked Phalarope has a circumpolar breeding distribution with its nearest nesting sites in Scotland. It winters at sea in the tropics.

## Grey Phalarope                              *Phalaropus fulicarius*

A scarce autumn and early winter visitor, usually occurring after gales.

The status of the Grey Phalarope is evidently unchanged since K & M's time. They mentioned large invasions after autumn gales in 1866, 1886 and 1891 and several inland records. There are few records for the first half of this century but of interest are those of storm-driven birds on a pond at Hiltingbury on Oct. 6th 1935, on the River Avon near Fordingbridge on Nov. 7th 1936, at Ellingham Gravel Pit in late November 1943 and at Romsey on Oct. 20th 1949.

Between 1951 and 1992, there were records in 34 years involving some 203 birds. Most years produced a few birds but larger numbers occurred following severe gales, as in 1957 (20), 1960 (59), 1981 (12) and 1987 (25).

Records came from the Lymington/Hurst area (94 birds, including 18 on Oct. 9th 1960 and six on Sep. 27th 1981 and Oct. 19th 1987), Langstone Harbour/Farlington Marshes (36, including four on Sep. 24th 1983 and five on Oct. 18th 1987), Gilkicker Point/Browndown (21, including six on Oct. 3rd 1957 and seven flying west on Oct. 8th 1960), Hill Head/Brownwich (17, including three on Oct. 18th 1987), Dibden Bay (5), Needs Ore (4), Black Point, Portsmouth Harbour and Southsea (3 each), Lepe (2) and Calshot, Sowley Pond and Warsash (1 each). Inland, single birds occurred at Frensham Great Pond (6), Fleet Pond (2) and Alresford Pond, Exton, Kingston Common, Southampton Common and Winchester (1 each).

The earliest recorded in autumn was at Pennington Marsh on Sep. 1st 1988. Few were seen after mid-November; the latest was at Calshot on Jan. 30th and Feb. 20th 1972. The cumulative monthly totals for 1951-92 are shown below.

| Sep | Oct | Nov | Dec | Jan | Feb |
|-----|-----|-----|-----|-----|-----|
| 60  | 110 | 28  | 3   | 4   | 1   |

The Grey Phalarope has a similar distribution to the previous species although its nearest breeding grounds are in Iceland and Spitsbergen. It winters at sea; large concentrations have been discovered off Mauritania and Chile.

## Pomarine Skua                              *Stercorarius pomarinus*

A scarce passage migrant.

K & M described the Pomarine Skua as "an occasional visitor to the coast in autumn and winter". They cited four records, but only one, from Portsmouth in 1868, was within the present day county boundary. The next was not until 1957, when a pale phase adult was in Langstone Harbour on Oct. 10th. Subsequently, there have been records in every year but five.

The species has remained very scarce in autumn but increased considerably in spring (fig. 48). This increase, which appears to be genuine and not only the result of greater observer activity, has also been noted in other south coast counties.

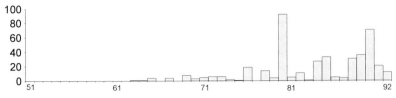

*Figure 48. Spring totals of Pomarine Skuas, 1951-92.*

The earliest was one flying east off Hill Head on Apr. 19th 1987. Most were recorded at the end of April and in the first two weeks of May, the largest numbers usually occurring in anticyclonic weather with light south-easterly winds. Of the 428 recorded between 1963 and 1992, 339 were seen from Hurst Beach. About 75% of these moved east through The Solent while the remainder returned south-west towards the Needles. The largest flock was of 55 on May 11th 1980, of which 37 moved through The Solent and 18 flew towards the Needles. Other double-figure counts include 20 on May 12th 1980, 15 on Apr. 29th 1984 and 24 on Apr. 30th 1990. Off Hill Head and Gilkicker Point, only 53 have been recorded, with a maximum of six flying east at Hill Head on May 7th 1978. At Hayling Bay, where regular sea-watching has only been undertaken since 1982, 35 have been recorded, with a peak count of 16 east, including a flock of 11, on May 1st 1988. One was seen inland, flying north-east over Beacon Hill (Warnford) on May 11th 1991. The latest in spring were two at Gilkicker Point on May 29th 1984 and one off Sandy Point on the same date in 1991.

There are two mid-summer records, of three flying east off Keyhaven on June 18th 1969 and one off Hurst Beach, which left east, on July 9th 1989.

Autumn birds, mostly moving west, occurred fairly evenly between Aug. 31st (Calshot, 1985) and Nov. 17th (Hurst Beach, 1963), often following south-westerly gales. Of 35 recorded between 1958 and 1992, 13 were seen in the Lymington/Hurst area and nine in the Hill Head/Gilkicker area. The remainder were at various coastal localities apart from an adult inland at Frensham Great Pond on Oct. 16th 1987, following the great storm.

There are three winter records, of one in Langstone Harbour on Dec. 25th 1960, another flying west off Hurst Beach on Dec. 7th 1964 and two in Hayling Bay on Dec. 1st 1987.

Most adults were pale phase, with fewer than 10% dark. However, there were six dark birds in a flock of seven which flew east at Hurst Beach on Apr. 29th 1986.

The Pomarine Skua breeds in the Arctic from Russia east to western Greenland. It winters at sea, largely in the tropics but also further south (BWP).

## Arctic Skua                                    *Stercorarius parasiticus*

A scarce passage migrant, recorded in every month except February.

The Arctic Skua was recorded infrequently during the period covered by K & M and in the first half of this century. This continued to be the case in the 1950s, despite the increased observer activity. In the autumn of 1960, 44 were recorded, many of them occurring in the aftermath of the gales on Oct. 8th/9th (*cf.* Grey Phalarope). Thereafter, autumn numbers fluctuated, but only once, in 1989, were fewer than ten recorded (fig. 49). The upsurge in spring sea-watching in the mid-1960s identified a regular eastward movement through The Solent which averaged 40 birds per year between 1965 and 1992 with a peak of 75 in 1985 (fig. 49).

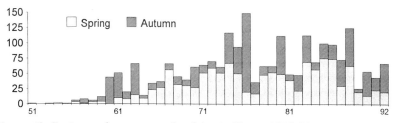

*Figure 49. Spring and autumn totals of Arctic Skuas, 1951-92.*

Early spring records were of an immature off Hill Head on Mar. 20th and 21st 1979 and one flying east at Gilkicker Point on Mar. 27th 1989. The main passage is in late April and early May (fig. 50). In April, day totals have reached double figures three times, the highest being of 18 at Hurst Beach on 25th in 1983. Such totals are more frequent in May, with 16 counts exceeding ten. The largest movements were of 20 at Hurst on May 4th 1973, 27 there on May 3rd 1974 (when 24 were seen at Gilkicker Point), 21 there on May 9th 1974, 25 at Hill Head on May 5th 1985 (when 23 were seen at Hurst and 15 at Hayling Bay) and 21 at Lepe on May 1st 1988. Large movements are normally observed on days with fresh to strong south-east to south-west winds and frequent squally showers; in such conditions birds may continue to move through until dusk. They occur in small parties of up to four, rarely six, but have never been seen in large flocks like the previous species. Occasionally, birds have been seen veering from their easterly course and moving inland, e.g. six moving north-east up the Meon valley at Titchfield Haven on May 27th 1984, four doing likewise on May 8th 1987 and one flying north-east over Langstone Harbour on May 6th 1989. Inland, two flew south-east over West Walk on May 9th 1972 and two flew north-east over Amberwood Inclosure on May 31st 1973. Movement continues until the end of May, with stragglers into June.

Dark phase birds predominate in spring movements. Of 421 at Hurst Beach for which phase was recorded, 274 (65.1%) were dark and 147 (34.9%) were pale (E J Wiseman *in litt*).

Occasional birds, possibly summering immatures, have been seen in June and July, including one which flew south over Portsdown Hill on June 23rd 1979.

Return passage starts in some years at the end of July. It can peak at any time between mid-August and early October (fig. 50), usually coinciding with south-westerly gales. Most are recorded in the west Solent area, where high counts (all of birds moving west) include 39 through Hurst Narrows on Sep. 24th 1974, 95 there on Sep. 2nd 1976, a flock of 25 off Pennington Marsh on Sep. 21st 1980, 25 off Lepe on Aug. 21st 1988 and 23 off the Lymington Estuary on Sep. 6th 1992. At other coastal localities, most records are of one to four, but higher counts include nine moving east at Gilkicker Point on Oct. 22nd 1961, eight south-west over Farlington Marshes on Aug. 21st 1982, seven south-west from Southampton Water across Hythe and the New Forest on Sep. 7th 1983 and ten west and four east at Hayling Bay on Sep 6th 1992.

There have been 14 inland records in autumn. At Fleet Pond, there were eight sightings totalling 29 birds on dates between Aug. 16th and Sep. 25th, including five moving north-west on Sep. 17th 1978 and 14 flying south-west on Sep. 13th 1980. Elsewhere, one flew south-west over Amberwood Inclosure on Aug. 19th 1961, one left north from Broadlands Lake on Oct. 3rd 1976, two flew east at Hillside on Aug. 24th 1979, three flew south-west over Bramshill on Oct. 12th 1981, one moved west over Broomy Plain on Oct. 24th 1982 and two flew south over North Waltham on Aug. 23rd 1987. In the north-east, most were recorded in late afternoon or evening, usually flying into a headwind, and on several occasions were known to coincide with westerly movements up the Thames Estuary.

Apart from mid-winter birds, the latest recorded were singles off Hurst Beach on Nov. 23rd 1975 and at Keyhaven on the same date in 1985.

There have been seven winter sightings of single birds: at Pennington Marsh on Dec. 16th 1973 and Jan. 18th 1986, Fawley on Jan. 2nd 1982, Dibden Bay on Jan. 23rd 1982, Southsea and Hayling Bay on Jan. 9th 1987 and Hurst Castle on Dec. 30th 1990.

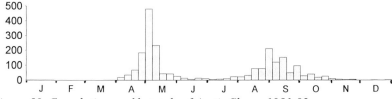

*Figure 50. Cumulative weekly totals of Arctic Skuas, 1951-92.*

The Arctic Skua breeds in Scotland, Iceland, Fenno-Scandia and throughout the Arctic. Most winter further south than the Pomarine Skua, particularly off the coasts of Argentina, Namibia and South Africa, and Australia (BWP).

# Long-tailed Skua                    *Stercorarius longicaudus*

A rare visitor. K & M cite a record of an immature shot at Crawley in autumn 1891. Since then, there have been 15 records, as follows:

1962:   adult flying east, Gilkicker Point, May 3rd;
1963:   adult, Hurst Beach, Oct. 5th;
1967:   adult flying east, Gilkicker Point, May 20th;
1982:   immature, Hurst Beach, Jan. 17th;
1983:   adult flying north, Hale (Avon valley), May 28th;
1985:   adult flying north-west, Dibden Bay, Nov. 4th;
1986:   adult flying east, Hayling Bay, May 11th;
1987:   sub-adult, Titchfield Haven, Jan. 29th;
1990:   adult, Dibden Bay, Aug. 21st;
1991:   adult flying east, Stokes Bay, June 21st;
        juvenile, Pennington Marsh, Aug. 19th;
        juvenile, Fleet Pond, Sep. 13th/14th;
1993:   adult flying east, Needs Ore, May 24th;
        adult, Normandy Marsh, June 30th;
        juvenile, Sturt Pond (Milford-on-Sea), Sep. 9th.

The Long-tailed Skua has a circumpolar distribution with the nearest breeding grounds in southern Norway. It winters at sea in the southern hemisphere; large numbers occur in the Benguela Current off Namibia (BWP). The increased numbers recorded in Hampshire reflect the national picture.

# Great Skua                    *Stercorarius skua*

A very scarce passage migrant, most frequent in spring and autumn but recorded in all months.

K & M described the Great Skua as "a rare occasional visitor to the coast in winter". They cited only one record from within the present day boundary, that of a bird found dead at Lainston (Winchester) in March 1904. The only other sighting in the first half of this century was also inland: two flying over Hazeley Down (Winchester) on Feb. 3rd 1918.

Since 1953, there have been records in every year but four (fig. 51).

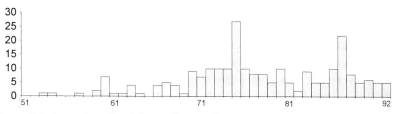

*Figure 51. Annual totals of Great Skuas, 1951-92.*

About 14 were recorded between January and early March. Six of these followed severe gales in early 1974, including one found exhausted inland at Enham Alamein on Feb. 12th.

Spring passage peaks in early May, although this is not so marked as in Pomarine and Arctic Skuas and sightings in late March and April form a greater proportion of the records than for those species (fig. 52). Numbers are always small, with none recorded in some years and a maximum of eight in 1972, including three flying east at Hurst Beach on May 6th and four there the next day. All other records were of one or two birds. Of some 80 recorded, 48 were off Hurst Beach (most of which moved east through The Solent), 18 between Hill Head and Gilkicker Point and ten in Hayling Bay.

There have been four records of single birds in summer: off Hill Head on July 12th 1959, Hurst on June 27th 1966, Browndown on June 6th 1972 and Hurst on July 8th 1990.

Autumn records spanned the period from early August to late October, with a few stragglers in the final two months of the year. Most sightings are of one to three birds but higher numbers may occur after gales, e.g. 19 off Hurst Beach on Sep. 14th 1975, six off Pennington Marsh on Sep. 5th 1976 and 15 off Hurst on Oct. 18th 1987. As these records suggest, the Lymington/Hurst area is the principal locality, with 97 out of 142 autumn birds recorded there. A further 20 were in the Hill Head/Gilkicker area and the rest were scattered along the coast or inland. Of the latter, one was on a rubbish dump at Shalden (Alton) in early October 1963 and, in the wake of the great storm, one flew over Worthy Down on Oct. 16th 1987 and two flew WNW over Fleet Pond three days later.

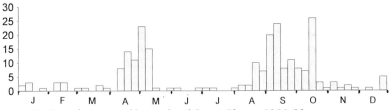

*Figure 52. Cumulative weekly totals of Great Skuas, 1951-92.*

The main breeding grounds of the Great Skua in the northern hemisphere are in Iceland, the Faeroe Islands and Scotland. This population winters at sea, mostly in the North Atlantic Ocean (BWP).

## Mediterranean Gull                              *Larus melanocephalus*

A scarce but regular visitor which has occasionally bred.

The first Mediterranean Gull for the county was an adult in winter plumage seen off Eastney Point on Apr. 27th 1954. Since then, numbers have increased considerably (fig. 53) and the species now occurs regularly in several coastal localities.

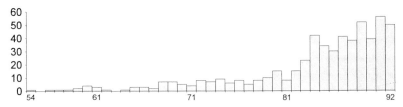

*Figure 53. Annual totals of Mediterranean Gulls, 1954-92.*

Between 1956 and 1965, 17 were seen in the Langstone Harbour area with sightings in every month except May, June and September. In the next three years there were reports from Gilkicker Point, Normandy Marsh, Titchfield Haven, Warsash and, most significantly, the Black-headed Gull colony at the Beaulieu Estuary.

At the last named site, single adults were present on July 18th 1966 and from Apr. 23rd-30th 1967. In 1968, an adult pair bred and raised two young, a second-summer paired with a Black-headed Gull and raised three young, and an adult bred with a Black-headed/Mediterranean Gull hybrid. In addition, one second-summer and one first-summer were seen in the gullery but did not stay. In subsequent years, one or two males, believed to be the 1968 chicks, held territory but failed to attract mates. The next breeding was in 1976, when a pair raised one young. Since then, single pairs have nested in 1979, 1980, 1982 and 1984 but all the nests were washed out by high spring tides. A pair was present in 1988 but a nest was not located. From 1971 onwards, single birds or pairs have been regularly seen in the Lymington area in summer, but there have been no indications of breeding there and they may be from Beaulieu.

The 1968 record was the first of breeding in Britain; full details of this and subsequent events are given by Taverner (1970, 1972). The species now holds a tenuous foothold in England, with 11 to 16 pairs present at ten localities in 1990 (Spencer *et al* 1993).

Outside the breeding season, between one and five were recorded annually from 1971-1977, with most seen in the Langstone Harbour and Lymington/Hurst areas. Numbers increased gradually from 1978 and rapidly in the early 1980s (fig. 53). Several wintering localities emerged, with one or two regularly recorded between August and March at Netley/Weston Shore and the nearby Newtown Rubbish Tip, Lee-on-the-Solent, Fareham Creek and Southsea.

However, the largest numbers now occur in the Langstone Harbour area. In the winter of 1981/82, an adult was present in December and January, and in the following year at least two adults and one first-winter were seen between November and February. Since then, the minimum total wintering in the area has varied between four and six. Most records have come from Sinah Gravel Pit, where birds bathe after feeding at Eastney Sewage Outfall on the falling tide. Some of the wintering totals are based solely on counts at Sinah, e.g. four adults and one first-winter on Nov. 26th 1988 and five adults and one first-winter on Nov. 25th 1989. Five adults seen later in the same winter at Eastney on Mar. 3rd 1990 may have included some additional birds.

During the 1980s, a small spring passage developed. This was indicated by the appearance of new individuals in wintering areas and easterly movement along the coast. At Titchfield Haven, where the species is irregular in winter, there is a clear spring peak. Of some 75 recorded there between 1968 and 1992, 20 have been in April and 12 in May. In the Langstone Harbour area, three adults were at Farlington Marshes on Mar. 26th and Apr. 4th 1981 and two adults were at Eastney Sewage Outfall on Apr. 5th and 8th 1981 where none had been seen during the previous winter. At Sinah Gravel Pit, five different adults and two first-winters were identified between Mar. 28th and Apr. 2nd 1986 of which at least two had not wintered in the area. Between 1984 and 1992, a total of 27 moved east along the coast on dates between Apr. 1st and May 23rd with a maximum of eight in 1989.

Small numbers, mostly first-years, have summered since 1983, most frequently in Langstone Harbour. Most records there are of one or two birds, but five first-summers were at Farlington Marshes on July 12th 1986 and two adults and three first-summers were there on June 30th 1992. Elsewhere, occasional birds are seen; three first-summers were at Paulsgrove Rubbish Tip on May 28th 1987.

Inland occurrences have increased since the first was seen at Bramshill Rubbish Tip on Dec. 17th 1978. In the north-east, 18 have been recorded at Eversley Gravel Pit (5), Bramshill (4), Fleet Pond and Queen's Parade, Aldershot (3 each), Wellington Country Park (2) and Frensham Great Pond (1). All occurred between Oct. 16th and Feb. 23rd apart from an adult flying west over Eversley Gravel Pit on July 24th 1992. In the south of the county, 26 have been discovered with sightings at Alresford Pond (10, including two on Mar. 29th 1988 and three different individuals between Mar. 14th and 29th 1992), Southampton Common (4, including one from Apr. 1st-May 11th 1984), Leigh Park and Eastleigh (3 each), Old Winchester Hill (2), and Beacon Hill, Heath Pond, Hedge End and Mockbeggar Lake (1 each). Birds were seen in every month except June, with peaks of five in December and nine in March.

The approximate cumulative monthly totals for 1954-92 (excluding breeding birds) are shown below.

|  | Jan | Feb | Mar | Apr | May | Jun | Jul | Aug | Sep | Oct | Nov | Dec |
|---|---|---|---|---|---|---|---|---|---|---|---|---|
| Adults | 68 | 76 | 73 | 57 | 28 | 15 | 31 | 28 | 36 | 37 | 49 | 64 |
| 2nd year | 15 | 9 | 16 | 17 | 10 | 1 | 10 | 13 | 11 | 10 | 13 | 19 |
| 1st year | 14 | 19 | 14 | 24 | 33 | 20 | 24 | 8 | 6 | 4 | 6 | 9 |
| Totals | 97 | 104 | 103 | 98 | 71 | 36 | 65 | 49 | 53 | 51 | 68 | 92 |

The increase in Hampshire forms part of a large expansion in north-western Europe. This is probably connected with increases in the Black Sea breeding colonies, which comprise the bulk of the world population. Since 1949, ringing has shown that some birds from the Black Sea (mostly immatures) migrate north-west in autumn to the Baltic Sea and thence to the English Channel. This presumably accounts for the regular breeding in eastern Germany from 1963 onwards (BWP). That birds from there colonised Hampshire is shown by the fact that the second-summer bird which bred at the Beaulieu Estuary in 1968 had been ringed as a chick on Riems Island, eastern Germany on June 7th 1966.

## Franklin's Gull                                                         *Larus pipixcan*

One record. An adult present in the Langstone Harbour area from Feb. 21st-May 16th 1970 was the first to be recorded in the Western Palearctic (Billett & Grant 1971).

The Franklin's Gull breeds in the prairies of Canada and the USA and winters on the Pacific coast from Guatemala to Peru.

## Little Gull                                                              *Larus minutus*

A scarce visitor which occurs in all months but is most numerous in spring.

K & M described the Little Gull as "a rare occasional visitor in winter". They cited five records from within the present day county boundary. During the first half of this century, only three were recorded: a first-winter shot at Newton

Stacey on Nov. 11th 1905 and two first-winters at Frensham Great Pond between Nov. 2nd and 20th 1948.

With the upsurge in birdwatching activity in the 1950s, the species was recorded annually. Between 1951 and 1955, no more than four were recorded per year and all occurred between Sep. 25th and Apr. 12th. In the next three years, sightings were made in all months, and by the late 1960s spring had emerged as the principal time of year for the species in Hampshire. Subsequently, the upward trend has continued (fig. 54).

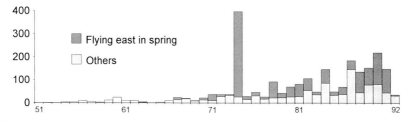

*Figure 54. Annual totals of Little Gulls, 1951-92.*

Spring passage, mostly indicated by eastward movement along the coast, extends from late March until late May with a clear peak between Apr. 20th and May 15th. By far the heaviest passage on record took place in 1974, when a minimum of 371 moved east. On May 3rd, 315, including at least 242 adults, flew over Hurst Beach in flocks of up to 40 between 0650 hrs. and dusk. 152 were seen off Hill Head on the same day. High day totals in other years included 30 at Hurst on May 8th 1981, 35 there on Apr. 29th 1988, 31 at Hill Head on Apr. 30th 1990 and 42 there the next day. Most of the large movements recorded occurred in anticyclonic weather with light south-easterly winds.

A total of 46 summering individuals has been noted in 11 years between 1973 and 1992. Records came from the Warsash/Titchfield Haven area (25, including 14 in 1991 and five in 1992), Langstone Harbour (13, including three in 1975 and five in 1982), Dibden Bay (6, including three in 1983), and Paulsgrove Reclamation (2).

265

Returning adults are occasionally noted from mid-July onwards, but the main autumn passage, indicated by the appearance of birds in juvenile and first-winter plumage, is in late August and September. Numbers at this time are much lower than in spring and the highest count so far has been of seven in the Keyhaven/Hurst area on Sep. 1st 1988. From October onwards, most appear following gales. In the aftermath of the great storm of Oct. 15th and 16th 1987, at least 100, possibly 130, passed through the county, including 40 off Hill Head, of which 20 left east, on 17th; 20 between Hayling Bay and Southsea on 18th; and 29, including ten flying west, at Hurst Castle the next day.

Between mid-November and mid-March, few are recorded, with some winters not producing any sightings. The only counts to exceed four were of 12 off Southsea Castle on Jan. 26th 1984 and eight in the Hurst/Milford-on-Sea area on Dec. 24th and 25th 1989, on both occasions following severe gales.

During the 1950s and 1960s, Little Gulls were rare inland, the only records being of single birds at Frensham Great Pond on Aug. 26th 1951 and Nov. 3rd 1968 and Winnall Moors on Apr. 16th 1967. Since 1972, there have been sightings in every year but one with a total of 100 recorded at Fleet Pond (44, including eight on May 1st 1990), Frensham Great Pond (22, including four on May 2nd 1990), Eversley Gravel Pits (15, including 10 flying south on Oct. 16th 1987), Alresford Pond (8), Blashford Lakes, Queen's Parade (Aldershot) and Wellington Country Park (2 each) and single birds at five other sites. The cumulative monthly totals of all inland records for 1951-92 are shown below.

| Jan | Feb | Mar | Apr | May | Jun | Jul | Aug | Sep | Oct | Nov | Dec |
|-----|-----|-----|-----|-----|-----|-----|-----|-----|-----|-----|-----|
| 1 | 1 | 1 | 12 | 24 | 0 | 4 | 12 | 21 | 24 | 4 | 2 |

Most sightings coincided with major movements or influxes at coastal localities.

Analysis of the records to date has shown that adults outnumber immatures (first- and second- years) by about 3:2 in spring but the position is reversed to 1:3 in autumn and 2:3 in winter. Some second-years are almost certainly aged as adults, especially in spring, so the preponderance of the latter at that season may not be as great as shown.

The change in status of this species since the 1960s has been noted in other parts of Britain and Ireland and is probably connected with the expansion of the breeding population around the Baltic Sea and in north-west Russia (Hutchinson & Neath 1978). These birds winter offshore in the English Channel and Irish Sea, off the Atlantic seaboard of France and Iberia and in the Mediterranean and Black Seas.

## Sabine's Gull                                          *Larus sabini*

A very scarce autumn passage migrant, usually occurring after gales.

In 1987, an amazing wreck of this species involving a minimum of 120 birds (about 95 adults and 25 juveniles), and probably in excess of 140, occurred as a result of the great storm of Oct. 15th and 16th. The first to be discovered on 16th were an adult and a juvenile among a flock of Black-headed Gulls on floods at Queen's Parade (Aldershot). They remained until dusk before flying off south-west. Also on this date, two adults were in Portsmouth Harbour and two adults flew south-east over Eversley Gravel Pits at dusk. The main influx occurred over the next two days. Coastal records for Oct. 17th-23rd are shown in table 61.

| | Oct. 17th | Oct. 18th | Oct. 19th | Oct. 20th | Oct. 21st | Oct. 22nd | Oct. 23rd |
|---|---|---|---|---|---|---|---|
| Hayling/Southsea | 8 (0) | 25 (0) | 4 (0) | 4 (0) | 2 (0) | 2 (0) | 1 (0) |
| Hill Head/Eling | 16 (4) | 5 (2) | 5 (1) | 1 (1) | 4 (1) | 2 (0) | - |
| Calshot/Needs Ore | 12 (1) | 31+ (4) | 24 (5) | 1 (0) | 4 (1) | - | - |
| Pennington/Hurst | 7 (2) | 50+ (-) | 36 (8) | - | - | - | - |

Numbers of juveniles are shown in brackets.

*Table 61. Numbers of Sabine's Gulls recorded at coastal sites, Oct. 17th-23rd 1987.*

On 17th and 18th, most were milling about just off shore, although ten of the 50 at Hurst moved off west. The main departure was the next day, when birds were seen moving at several sites and 33 flew west at Hurst Castle.

Following the records on 16th, there were further occurrences in the north-east of the county. A juvenile was at Queen's Parade and two adults flew west over Fleet Pond on 17th, a juvenile was feeding on a school playing field in Farnborough on 18th and an adult roosted at Frensham Great Pond on 20th.

Otherwise, there have been 18 records, as follows:

| | |
|---|---|
| 1891: | adult, Sturt Pond, Oct. 21st; |
| 1954: | adult, Hurst Castle, Nov. 28th; |
| 1960: | juvenile, Eastney, Dec. 4th; |
| 1965: | juvenile flying east, Gilkicker Point, Sep. 6th; |
| 1970: | juvenile, Hurst/Pennington Marsh, Sep. 12th-Oct. 11th; |
| 1975: | juvenile, Pennington Marsh, Sep. 28th; |
| 1976: | juvenile, Fleet Pond, Oct. 30th; |
| 1981: | juvenile, Sturt Pond, Sep. 25th; |
| | 2 juveniles, Pennington Marsh, Sep. 26th; |
| | juvenile, Hurst Castle, Sep. 27th; |
| 1987: | adult, Pennington Marsh, Nov. 14th; |
| 1988: | juvenile flying east, Hill Head and Lee-on-the-Solent, Sep. 2nd; |
| | juvenile, Hurst Castle, Oct. 8th; |
| 1989: | adult on flooded fields, Keyhaven, Dec. 20th; |
| 1990: | adult, Hurst, Aug. 19th; |
| | adult, Hill Head, Oct. 6th; |
| 1991: | juvenile, Hayling Bay, Nov. 12th. |

The Sabine's Gull has a circumpolar breeding distribution. Those seen in Britain are probably en route from nesting grounds in Greenland and north-eastern Canada to winter in the Benguela Current off Namibia and South Africa (BWP).

## Bonaparte's Gull                                          *Larus philadelphia*

Two records. A first-summer moulting into second-winter plumage was at
Farlington Marshes on July 15th 1980 and another first-summer was at
Gilkicker Point on Mar. 21st 1986.

The Bonaparte's Gull breeds in Alaska and Canada and winters in the USA,
northern Mexico and the West Indies.


## Black-headed Gull                                          *Larus ridibundus*

A numerous breeding resident, passage migrant and winter visitor.

The earliest known Hampshire breeding colony, which was mentioned as
being in existence during the reign of Charles I (1625-49), was on Pewit Island
in Portsmouth Harbour. However, in the late 19th century all the known
colonies were on wet heathland in the Bournemouth area (K & M), outside the
present county boundary.

Breeding colonies started to develop at Keyhaven and the Beaulieu Estuary
in the early 20th century. These two colonies expanded slowly until the late
1950s and early 1960s, when a massive increase took place. Numbers peaked
between 1971 and 1973 but then declined and stabilised at a lower level. The
increase up to the early 1970s is thought to be due largely to immigration from
colonies elsewhere, e.g. in Poole Harbour, although other factors including
greater legal protection and wardening of nature reserves are probably
responsible to a degree (Aspinall *et al* 1993). It is also probable that the *Spartina*
beds had come into optimum condition at that time and were thus able to
support large numbers.

At Keyhaven, breeding was first recorded on the saltmarsh between 1905
and 1913. The colony was still in existence in 1927 (Campbell 1979), supported
50 pairs in 1938 (Hollom 1940), and had become "large" by 1951. In 1958,
when there were 4000 pairs, it extended along 6 km of The Solent coast between
Keyhaven and Pitts Deep and was composed of several sub-colonies, some of
which moved, increased or decreased in later years. There were up to 5000 pairs
until 1966, 7000 pairs in 1968 and 6000-8000 pairs from 1969-72. Until that
time, numbers were fairly evenly split between the two sides of the Lymington
River, but in 1972 there was a crash in the Pennington/Keyhaven area west of
the river. In 1975, 5000-6000 pairs were counted, of which about 80% were east
of the river. Since then, the population west of the river has remained at around
1000 pairs. East of the river, there were around 5000 pairs from 1989-91.
Overall, the total numbers for the entire colony have possibly changed little
since the mid-1970s.

At the Beaulieu Estuary, breeding was first noted in 1909 and 16 pairs nested
a year later. There were 75 pairs in 1938 (Hollom 1940) and 274 in 1952. From
1957-62, between 900 and 1200 pairs bred, but in 1963 (the first time for some
years that eggs were not collected) there was an increase to 4700-5000 pairs. A
major expansion followed, with numbers peaking between 17,000 and 21,000
pairs from 1971-73. Subsequently, a decline set in. A low point was reached in
1989, when 6150 pairs were counted. Since then numbers have fluctuated, with
8726 pairs in 1991 and 7250 in 1992. The reduction at this site may be partly

due to the continuing erosion of Gull Island, which forms the core of the colony and yet lost 50% of its area between 1953 and 1992 (Aspinall *et al* 1993).

Black-headed Gulls have also bred in Southampton Water. A colony between Ashlett Creek and Dibden Bay was certainly in existence before 1939, although it was not covered during the first national census (Hollom 1940). There were 700 pairs in 1957, 500 in 1964, 800-1000 in the mid-1960s but only 58 (at Fawley Power Station) in 1969. A few pairs may have survived into the early 1970s but there have been no definite breeding records for at least 20 years.

A more recent site to be colonised is on islands in Langstone Harbour, where five pairs first bred in 1978. Between five and ten pairs attempted breeding in 1982, 83 in 1983 and 130 in 1984. This collapsed to two pairs in 1986, peaked at 184 pairs in 1988, then gradually declined to six pairs in 1992.

The Hampshire colonies, together with others on the south coast between Dorset and Kent, are significant in that collectively they support at least 1.5% of the world breeding population of this species. Hampshire, with about 14,750 pairs in 1991, contributes over 50% of that total, representing about 8% of the estimated British population of 167,000 pairs (Lloyd *et al* 1991). For a more detailed account of the Hampshire colonies, see Aspinall *et al* (1993).

The main dispersal from breeding colonies takes place in July. From then on, roosts build up at several places along the coast, the most important being in Southampton Water and Langstone and Portsmouth Harbours. In late summer and early autumn, several thousands fly inland up the main river valleys to feed, especially on recently-ploughed land. Large concentrations have included 5000 at Northfields Farm (Twyford) on Sep. 2nd 1981, a similar number in the Hambledon area on Aug. 24th 1984 and 3000+ between Alresford and Four Marks on Aug. 14th 1984. Between July and October, many of those feeding in the latter area roost at Alresford Pond rather than returning to the coast. Four-figure counts have been regular since the late 1970s with peaks of 2300 on Oct. 3rd 1983 and 2500 on Aug. 27th 1990. By November, roosting there has ceased and all return to the coast at night. Large numbers may also be found at rubbish tips near the coast, e.g. at Paulsgrove, where the highest count has been of 2000+ on July 21st 1974. An exceptional gathering, estimated at 6000, was hawking insects over Titchfield Haven, with a further 1800 in the marshes there, on July 27th 1975.

Black-headed Gull numbers build up steadily through the autumn, probably to a mid-winter peak. The vast numbers involved mean that few roost counts have been attempted, but the results of various coordinated surveys are shown in table 62.

| | Jan 72 | Dec 72 | Jan 77 | Jan 78 | Jan 83 | Jan 92 | Jan 93 |
|---|---|---|---|---|---|---|---|
| Lymington River | - | - | 817 | 3173 | 2264 | 850 | 5260 |
| Beaulieu Estuary | - | - | 5800 | 1300 | - | 375 | 176 |
| Southampton Water | - | 27300 | - | - | 15087 | 20000 | 18815 |
| Portsmouth Harbour | 8096 | - | 4259 | - | 9263 | 4825 | 15331 |
| Langstone Harbour | 12945 | 9028 | 9142 | 11576 | 10600 | 8500 | 6861 |

*Table 62. Counts of coastal roosts of Black-headed Gulls, 1972-93.*

The most recent count on Jan. 23rd 1993, carried out as part of the fifth BTO National Survey of Roosting Gulls, produced a total of 46,443 birds.

During the day, flocks of 1000-2000 are fairly common at rubbish tips, sewage outfalls and on playing fields, although birds are more dispersed at inland localities than in autumn. Larger counts have included 5000 at Bedhampton Rubbish Tip on Jan. 31st 1985, 4000 at Newtown Rubbish Tip on Feb. 26th 1985 and 4000 on playing fields at Eastleigh on Jan. 21st 1986.

Those feeding in the Avon valley and on the chalk to the north and west of Fordingbridge, and in the north-east of the county, do not normally roost on the Hampshire coast. In the former area, the main roost flight line is to and from Christchurch Harbour, Dorset. Counts have included 4650 moving north at dawn over Sopley on Jan. 29th 1984 and 7000+ along the length of the valley, which was heavily flooded, on Mar. 3rd 1990.

In the north-east, most fly in daily from roosts on the West London reservoirs, although presumed migratory and cold weather movements are also recorded. Between late June and early October, flocks are normally in single or double figures but in some years larger gatherings are recorded, e.g. 250 at Blackbushe Airfield on July 24th 1978 and 350 moving south over Woolmer on July 13th 1982. There is a rapid increase from October onwards, with the largest concentrations occurring at Bramshill Rubbish Tip, where up to 3000 are regular between December and February. Numbers there increase in severe weather, e.g. 5000 on Jan. 6th 1985 and 6000 on Feb. 26th 1986, presumably because the playing fields and farmlands used by some birds for feeding are frozen. In winter, some of the Bramshill birds may move north-west at dusk to roost on gravel pits in the Reading area, e.g. 2070 were seen moving in that direction over Wellington Country Park on Feb. 24th 1981. As many as 5000 were on floods near the latter site on Feb. 2nd 1990.

In most winters, a roost is established at Frensham Great Pond. Counts at dusk there have included 6000 on Feb. 24th 1978, 7500 on ice on Dec. 23rd 1982 (of which 4000 left SSW and 3500 apparently roosted), 10,000 on Feb. 18th 1983 (of which 5000 left south-west and 5000 roosted), 8000 on Feb. 23rd 1984 and Feb. 19th 1985, and 6000 on Nov. 20th 1985. If the pond is frozen over, many birds fly to Langstone Harbour to roost. This was shown by a movement of 6840 south over Woolmer at dusk on Feb. 13th 1985. Numbers have fallen since 1990 due to the closure of Wrecclesham Rubbish Tip, Surrey; 896 were counted in the roosting gulls survey on Jan. 23rd 1993.

There is a regular eastward movement through The Solent in spring. The largest total recorded was on Apr. 6th 1957, when at least 5250 (mostly adults) moved through Hurst Narrows in a force 5 north-easterly wind between 1245 and 1615 hrs. In recent years, recorded day totals have occasionally reached three figures with a maximum of 500+ east off Hayling Bay in three hours on Apr. 30th 1988. Passage is also recorded inland at this time, e.g. 100 moving north-east over Fleet Pond on May 6th 1976 and 103 over Winchester Sewage Farm on Apr. 23rd 1989. Unusual weather may induce movement at other times of the year, e.g. 1000+ west at Sandy Point in 2½ hours in cold weather on Feb. 10th 1985 and 1595 south and south-west over Fleet Pond between Oct. 16th and 18th 1987 following the great storm.

Analysis of the extensive ringing data for Hampshire sheds much light on the movements of Black-headed Gulls. Of 346 ringed in Hampshire and subsequently recovered or controlled, 194 were within the county, 114 elsewhere in southern England, six in northern England, five in Wales, three in Ireland and 24 in continental Europe. Most of those found in Britain were ringed as pulli in Hampshire colonies, which shows that the majority do not move far (254 less than 100 km). However, eleven pulli were found in winter in France (7), Spain (3) and Portugal (1). The remaining foreign recoveries involved 13 birds ringed in winter, eight at coastal sites and five at Bramshill, and found in Finland (4) and the Baltic States, Denmark and the Netherlands (3 each). All were found during the breeding season apart from one in Denmark in February.

169 ringed elsewhere have been recovered or controlled in Hampshire, 103 from southern England, ten from northern England, two from Wales and 54 from continental Europe. About 40% of the British birds were ringed as pulli; most of these were found in winter but some were breeding in Hampshire colonies. The continental birds involved 47 ringed as pulli in the Baltic States (13), Finland (10), Poland and Denmark (6 each), Sweden (4), Belgium, Germany and the Netherlands (2 each) and France and Norway (1 each). Most of these were found outside the breeding season but three first-years, one second-year and three adults were apparently summering in the county, while the French bird, ringed at St. Viatre on June 1st 1963, had been breeding in the Beaulieu Estuary colony when found dead in June 1966. The others were ringed in winter in Belgium and the Netherlands (3 each) and Germany (1) and found in Hampshire in subsequent winters.

To summarise, dispersal of juveniles from Hampshire colonies is largely within southern England, although some move south into France and Iberia for the winter. Chicks reared in Hampshire have later bred in colonies in other counties and vice versa. The adult breeding population is largely resident, but much augmented in winter by arrivals from further north in Britain and continental Europe.

# Ring-billed Gull                                       *Larus delawarensis*

A rare visitor. The first to be recorded was at Bedhampton Rubbish Tip from June 1st-Aug. 1st 1977, during which time it moulted from first-summer into second-winter plumage.

Between 1981 and 1993, a total of 17 has been recorded, as follows:

1981:   second-year, Eling Great Marsh, Mar. 28th and Apr. 5th;
1982:   adult, Dibden Bay, Mar. 17th and Apr. 10th;
1983:   first-winter, Titchfield Haven and Stubbington, Dec. 26th-Feb. 19th 1984;
1984:   adult, Stubbington, Feb. 4th and Hill Head, Feb. 17th;
1985:   adult, Titchfield Haven, Jan. 18th, 20th and 31st†;
        adult, Paulsgrove Reclamation, Apr. 4th;
1986:   adult, Bedhampton, Feb. 15th;
        second-summer, Sinah Gravel Pit and Eastney, Mar. 28th and 30th;
1987:   adult, The Kench, Langstone Harbour, Nov. 29th;
1988:   first-winter, Pennington Marsh, Apr. 9th;
        adult, Farlington Marshes, Dec. 26th;
1989:   first-summer, Hayling Oyster Beds, June 7th;
1990:   first-winter, Sinah Gravel Pit, Dec. 30th;
1992:   first-winter, Titchfield Haven/Hill Head, Feb. 28th;
        adult, Camber Dock (Old Portsmouth), Oct. 30th;
1993:   adult, Farlington Marshes; Jan. 9th-Mar. 19th;
        adult, Alresford Pond, Feb. 26th and Mar. 29th/30th.

The increase in Hampshire parallels the national picture. Although the Ring-billed Gull was not identified in Britain until 1973, between 30 and 100 were recorded annually between 1981 and 1992. The rush of records is probably partly due to greater awareness of the species' field characters, but a dramatic increase in eastern North America seems likely to be the main cause (Dymond *et al* 1989). It breeds in Canada and the USA and winters south to Venezuela.

## Common Gull                                                          *Larus canus*

A common winter visitor and passage migrant; small numbers (mostly immatures) summer and breeding was confirmed for the first time in 1991.

Numbers build up from mid-July onwards. In recent years, autumn counts have rarely exceeded 200 although 700 were night-roosting on flooded pans at Dibden Bay on Sep. 6th 1972.

In mid-winter, the largest concentrations occur in the eastern harbours. During the 1950s, up to 10,000 were regularly recorded roosting in Langstone Harbour. However, five counts made there between 1972 and 1983 were in the range 1604-3513, which suggests a considerable decline. The most recent count, carried out on Jan. 23rd 1993 as part of the BTO National Survey of Roosting Gulls, produced totals of 3941 in Langstone Harbour and 1013 in Portsmouth Harbour. During the day, many fly inland to feed on playing fields, downland pasture and recently ploughed land. From October to early April, flocks of 500 or more are widespread on the chalk between the Meon valley and the Sussex border. Larger counts have included 1800 at Old Winchester Hill on Feb. 6th 1984 and 1600 there on Nov. 2nd 1986. The decrease has been attributed to the reduced area of pasture, which this species prefers, and the change to autumn-sown cereals, which are unsuitable for feeding once the crop is too high (Portsmouth Group 1991, Aspinall & Tasker 1992).

Numbers roosting in Southampton Water are much lower. Six mid-winter coordinated counts between 1972 and 1993 produced a maximum of 276 on Jan. 23rd 1993. However, at least 1500 were estimated to be roosting off Fawley on Feb. 13th 1982. Some birds move inland to feed in the Itchen and Test valleys; concentrations are usually of less than 100 but higher counts include 548 at Alresford Pond on Jan. 9th 1992 and 300 at Casbrook Common Rubbish Tip in severe weather on Jan. 18th 1985.

Diurnal coastal gatherings rarely exceed 500 but may be larger in hard weather when inland feeding areas are frozen. Counts have reached four figures on five occasions with a maximum of 1800 at Black Point on Feb. 9th 1990.

Birds in the north-east originate from roosts on the West London reservoirs. The largest counts are made at Bramshill Rubbish Tip, where up to 200 are regularly present and higher numbers occur in hard weather, e.g. 400 on Feb. 18th 1985 and 850 on Feb. 26th 1986.

Numbers increase from mid-February onwards as birds which have wintered elsewhere pass through the county. At Langstone Harbour, there were 11,000 on Mar. 21st 1991, but numbers at other coastal sites are much lower. Visible movement may also be prominent. In 1962, 1000 flew east off Gilkicker Point on Feb. 27th and a further 683 between Apr. 13th and 17th. Since then, high totals have been of 562 east along the coast between Mar. 24th and May 19th 1984 and 612 east between mid-March and mid-May 1985.

Overland passage is lighter but movements or gatherings in excess of 200 are occasionally recorded, e.g. 220 flying north-east over Alresford Pond on Apr. 20th 1981 and 1300 at Tidpit Down on Feb. 23rd 1986. Adults predominate in the early movements but from late April onwards most are immatures.

Between late May and early July few are present, but groups of up to 30 immatures may summer in the eastern harbours. One or two adults have occasionally been seen around Black-headed Gull colonies in the west Solent, e.g. in 1975, 1980 and 1989. Single pairs bred at two sites in both 1991 and 1992; two of the attempts failed but the outcome of the others is not known. The nearest breeding colony is in Kent but only 34 pairs were found in English coastal colonies in 1985-87. The total British breeding population during this period was estimated at 67,800 pairs (Lloyd *et al* 1991).

Analysis of national ringing recoveries has shown that most wintering birds originate from colonies in Scandinavia and Germany (Hudson 1965a). Seven chicks ringed in Finland (3), Norway (2), Germany and Scotland have been found in Hampshire.

## Lesser Black-backed Gull                                    *Larus fuscus*

A common autumn passage migrant with reduced numbers in winter and spring.

The largest flocks occur in the north-east of the county but winter numbers in the south have increased since the mid-1980s.

The population roosting on the West London reservoirs builds up from mid-June onwards and there are daily flights into north-east Hampshire. The most consistently used site has been Bramshill Rubbish Tip. 120 (mostly immatures) were there as early as June 18th in 1976, but in most years three-figure flocks do not appear until July. Thereafter, gatherings of up to 500 may be recorded at any time until early November. Higher counts have included 1200 on Aug. 23rd 1975, 800 on Sep. 23rd 1976 and 600 on Oct. 13th 1981. Since the mid-1980s, a large pre-roost gathering has regularly formed on the tarmac at Blackbushe Airfield, especially on Sundays, when the rubbish left after the close of the market has proved attractive. 200-400 are usually present between July and November, with higher counts including 520 on Oct. 14th 1984 and 579 on July 29th 1990. Flocks of up to 100 also occur on ploughed land and as many as 300 were at Crondall on Sep. 20th 1981. At dusk, large flocks can be seen heading east or north-east to roost, e.g. 498 moving over Yateley on Sep. 13th 1988.

In winter, the gathering at Bramshill has occasionally exceeded 100, but counts such as 250 on Feb. 22nd 1977 and Feb. 23rd 1984 possibly included spring migrants. Birds feeding at Bramshill have occasionally been recorded flying north-west at dusk over Wellington Country Park, presumably to roost on gravel pits in the Reading area, e.g. 200 on Feb. 12th 1988.

In spring, sizeable flocks are occasionally recorded, e.g. 120 at Bramshill on Apr. 1st 1979, but most records at this time refer to small parties over-flying, generally in directions between north-west and east. 29 flew east over Fleet Pond on Apr. 20th 1983 but day totals are usually lower than this. Movements may continue until early June, then cease for a few days until the start of the daily feeding flights into the area later in the month.

The proportion of immatures in these flocks is surprisingly low; usually no more than 20% in late summer and early autumn and then falling below 10%. At first, most adults show the characteristics of the British race *graellsii*, but the proportion belonging to one or other of the darker-backed European races, now believed to be mostly *intermedius* (Grant 1986), increases as the autumn progresses. Of 285 adults at Blackbushe on Sep. 15th 1991, about half were *graellsii* and half *intermedius*. Winter flocks show a similar ratio.

The species can also be numerous in autumn across the chalk downland in the north of the county. Counts on the ground have generally been quite low, e.g. 189 at Kingsclere on Oct. 6th 1987 and 340 at Ewhurst Park on Sep. 3rd 1990, but large numbers have been seen moving north out of the county at dusk. On Oct. 9th 1986, 1039 flew over Kingsclere and two days later 1470 were counted. A similar movement seen from nearby White Hill on Aug. 23rd 1989 numbered 862. These are believed to roost at Farmoor Reservoir, Oxfordshire (J A Norton *in litt*). Very few are seen in this area in mid-winter, presumably because few feeding opportunities are available once autumn cultivation is complete.

Elsewhere, numbers are much lower but have increased since the mid-1980s. A wintering flock in the Test valley and Southampton Water reached at 50 in 1985/86 and has risen steadily since. On Feb. 11th 1991, 260 were counted in a pre-roost gathering at Eling Great Marsh, while in the following winter the maximum recorded was 275 at Timsbury Gravel Pit on Nov. 24th 1991. At other sites in the south of the county, winter counts have not exceeded 40 but higher numbers have occasionally been recorded in autumn, e.g. 103 flying south over Cheriton on Oct. 30th 1980, 52 in Portsmouth Harbour on Oct. 9th 1988 and 130 at Ibsley Water on Aug. 30th 1990.

In spring, movements occur along the coast and overland, while small flocks may pause for a few hours. Examples of coastal observations include 49 flying east off Hurst Beach on May 4th 1974 and 110 flying east off Hill Head between Mar. 25th and May 12th 1981. Grounded flocks rarely exceed ten, but larger gatherings have included 30 at Keyhaven Marsh on Apr. 13th 1970 and 70 at Timsbury on Apr. 7th 1983.

In 1990, a pair summered with nesting Herring Gulls in Southampton, but there have been no other suggestions of breeding.

The only ringing return involved a first-winter bird which was colour-ringed at Helensburgh, Strathclyde on Sep. 19th 1981 and seen at Bedhampton Rubbish Tip on July 15th 1984. Field observations confirm that both British and continental birds occur. Although wintering numbers have increased in Britain, most move south-west to Iberia, Morocco and tropical West Africa.

## Herring Gull                                    *Larus argentatus*

A common winter visitor and passage migrant; small numbers (mostly immatures) summer but a few pairs breed.

The first breeding record was of a pair which nested on the shingle at Needs Ore Point in 1938. Subsequently, a pair nested in *Spartina* at Pennington Marsh in 1950 and three pairs bred at Fawley Refinery in 1957. One pair attempted to breed at Needs Ore in 1966, and thereafter numbers built up to about 40 pairs in 1973, most breeding in the fields around Blackwater. In the following years, most nests were on shingle. About 30 pairs bred in 1977 and 1978 but during the 1980s the colony was wiped out by control measures. Between 1967 and 1981, one or two pairs occasionally bred on the saltings between Pylewell and Keyhaven. In 1977, one pair raised one young at Fawley Refinery and from 1981-83 a single pair attempted nesting at Marchwood Power Station.

During the Atlas Survey, breeding was confirmed in six tetrads. In Southampton, two pairs bred on the roofs of buildings in High Street in 1989, and at least seven pairs bred there and on buildings in the Eastern Docks in 1991 (R E Cooke *in litt*). At Fawley Refinery, a maximum of seven pairs bred on top of storage tanks and on pipes alongside the jetties in 1991. Additionally, single pairs bred at Needs Ore and Marchwood Power Station in 1986. These records indicate a Hampshire population of about 15 pairs in 1991. The latest estimate of the British population is 161,100 pairs in 1985-87 (Lloyd *et al* 1991).

Summering flocks, usually containing over 90% immatures, occur along the coast. The largest numbers have been recorded at Paulsgrove Rubbish Tip, where there were 1000 on June 11th 1972 and June 14th 1975. Since then, the maximum there has been of 562 on June 13th 1992. Counts elsewhere include 341 in the Hamble Estuary on May 25th 1974 and 880 in a nocturnal roost at Dibden Bay on June 2nd 1977.

Adults arrive from breeding colonies from July onwards. As in summer, the largest autumn counts have been made at Paulsgrove, e.g. 2500 on Oct. 15th 1971 and Sep. 14th 1974, and 1870 on Aug. 21st 1977. Large numbers have sometimes been recorded feeding on grassland and recently ploughed land on the high chalk between Winchester and Butser, particularly around Old Winchester Hill, where several counts of up to 500 have been made and as many as 1350 were present on Oct. 6th 1973 and 1044 on Sep. 23rd 1984.

Winter gatherings at coastal localities have occasionally reached four figures, e.g. 1600 at Browndown Rubbish Tip on Feb. 4th 1970, 2000+ at Hook Rubbish Tip and nearby Warsash on Nov. 25th 1977 and 1400 at Efford Rubbish Tip on Feb. 16th 1977. Counts of nocturnal roosts include 716 in Portsmouth Harbour on Jan. 30th 1972, 2000 in Southampton Water on Dec. 10th 1972, 290 at the Beaulieu Estuary on Jan. 29th 1977 and 643 on the Lymington River on Jan. 28th 1978. During the BTO National Survey of Roosting Gulls on Jan. 23rd 1993, a total of 1351 was counted, with 37 in Langstone Harbour, 816 in Portsmouth Harbour, 352 on Southampton Water, one at Beaulieu and 145 at Lymington. In contrast to the autumn, the numbers moving inland are rarely large, counts such as 400 at Buriton Rubbish Tip on Nov. 18th 1980 and 413 at Blashford Lakes on Feb. 23rd 1982 being exceptional.

In the north-east, counts at Bramshill Rubbish Tip reached 1000 in six winters between 1978/79 and 1987/88, usually during hard weather, and peaked at 1600 on Jan. 6th 1985. Other noteworthy counts in this area were of 850 at Fleet Pond on Dec. 29th 1977 and 1000 flying north-west over Wellington Country Park on Feb. 12th 1988, presumably to roost on the gravel pits in the Reading area. This was unusual in that the normal evening roost flight-line is towards the West London reservoirs.

The available records suggest that winter numbers reached a peak in the 1970s and have declined since, in line with the national breeding population (Lloyd *et al* 1991).

Spring passage is indicated by eastward movement along the coast between late March and mid-May. High counts include 450 off Hurst Beach on Apr. 20th 1963 and 604 there on Apr. 9th 1979, but generally such passage is poorly recorded. Small flocks may be seen inland, e.g. 30 moving north at Blashford on May 7th 1978, but a gathering of 700 at Meonstoke on Apr. 3rd 1986 was unprecedented.

There have been nine Hampshire recoveries of foreign-ringed birds, from northern France (3), the Channel Islands (3), Belgium, Denmark and Norway (1 each). The last involved one ringed as a chick at Vardo, Norway on July 12th 1968 and trapped at Bramshill Rubbish Tip on Jan. 13th 1977. Other movements to Hampshire involved seven chicks ringed in Wales, five in Scotland and one in Ireland. There have been only two foreign recoveries of Hampshire-ringed birds, both adults caught at Bramshill on Feb. 8th 1977. One was found at Heligoland, western Germany, on Sep. 19th 1983 and the other at Scheveningen, Netherlands, on Jan. 28th 1989.

Most seen on the Hampshire coast are pink-legged and probably belong to the race *argenteus* which breeds in Britain and between north-west France and the Netherlands. However, studies by Stanley *et al* (1981) have shown that those wintering in the London area are mostly of the race *argentatus* which breeds in Scandinavia and the Baltic. This is supported by the control of the Norwegian bird at Bramshill.

In recent years, increasing numbers of yellow-legged birds have been recorded. The first was an adult at Langstone Harbour on Apr. 26th 1957. Five were recorded between 1974 and 1977, then since 1980 some have been identified in every year. Numbers rose to 13 in 1983, 40 in 1984 and 60 in 1990. Most of these are of the race *michahellis*, which breeds in the Mediterranean and Iberia and undertakes a northerly or north-westerly post-breeding dispersal (Grant 1983). In Hampshire, they are usually present from mid-July, reach a peak in September and decline through the winter. The cumulative monthly totals for 1974-92 are shown below.

| Jul | Aug | Sep | Oct | Nov | Dec | Jan | Feb | Mar | Apr | May | Jun |
|-----|-----|-----|-----|-----|-----|-----|-----|-----|-----|-----|-----|
| 94  | 92  | 119 | 77  | 43  | 26  | 45  | 12  | 3   | 1   | 2   | 3   |

The largest numbers have been recorded at Eling Great Marsh, where high counts have included 18 on Sep. 17th 1987, 30 (21 adults, five second-years and four juveniles) on Sep. 12th 1990 and 15 (ten adults, four third-summers and one juvenile) on Oct. 17th 1990. Most other sightings have been made at coastal sites, particularly in the Langstone Harbour area, where there were 15 (mostly second- and third- summers, at Bedhampton Rubbish Tip on July 14th and 15th 1984 and ten (nine adults and one second-winter) at The Kench on Oct. 13th 1990. Inland, there have been records from Mockbeggar Lake, Timsbury Gravel Pit and five north-east sites, most regularly at Blackbushe Airfield where a maximum of five was recorded on July 29th 1990 and Oct. 18th 1991.

# Iceland Gull                                    *Larus glaucoides*

A rare visitor, usually in winter but recorded in all months except June.

K & M listed one obtained at Portsmouth in 1860, but the next was not until 1937, when one, almost adult, was at Beaulieu on Jan. 31st and possibly the same individual was at Langstone Harbour on Feb. 14th. There were no further reports until 1955, when a second-winter was inland at Damerham on Feb. 22nd.

Since then, there have been records in 21 winters totalling 48 birds, 29 of them between 1983 and 1992.

In early 1984, at least 12 were seen. These arrived in the wake of severe north-westerly gales which drove hundreds into Britain and Ireland from their usual wintering grounds in Iceland. The first was a second-winter at Wrecclesham Rubbish Tip (Surrey) on Jan. 6th which flew off west into Hampshire; this was followed by a first-winter at Sinah Gravel Pit on Jan. 17th and nearby at The Kench on Jan. 22nd. An unprecedented concentration was in the Hill Head/Calshot/Netley area, where probably three adults and seven first-winters were seen between Jan. 19th and Mar. 27th, with one first-winter staying at Newtown Rubbish Tip (Netley) until May 4th.

In other winters, totals did not exceed four. Records came from Langstone Harbour/Eastney (11 birds), Titchfield Haven/Southampton Water (9), Keyhaven/Hurst (5), Bramshill Rubbish Tip (2) and the Beaulieu Estuary, Black Point, Fleet Pond, Gilkicker Point, Gosport, Lee-on-the-Solent, Portsmouth Harbour, Rownhams, Tanners Lane and Wrecclesham. All records were of single birds apart from that of two adults flying east off Eastney on Sep. 18th 1960. Most were seen on one date only but longer stays included a first-winter at Eling Great Marsh from Feb. 8th-26th 1989, another first-winter at Weston Shore from Feb. 9th-16th 1991 and presumably the same individual at Walpole Park (Gosport) from Feb. 23rd-Mar. 16th of that year.

The extreme dates were July 17th (second-year, Fawley, 1977) and May 4th (immature flying east, Hurst Narrows, 1970). The cumulative monthly totals for 1937-92 are shown below.

| Jul | Aug | Sep | Oct | Nov | Dec | Jan | Feb | Mar | Apr | May |
|-----|-----|-----|-----|-----|-----|-----|-----|-----|-----|-----|
| 1 | 2 | 2 | 2 | 3 | 5 | 10 | 16 | 11 | 5 | 3 |

Of 50 individuals recorded, 18 were aged as adult or near adult, one as third-winter, six as second-winter, 20 as first-winter and five as immature.

## Glaucous Gull                                    *Larus hyperboreus*

A very scarce visitor; usually in winter but has been recorded in every month. Sightings have increased in frequency since the early 1980s.

Although K & M described it as "an occasional winter visitor to the coast", they did not cite any dated records within the present day county boundary. The first this century were two near Lymington on May 24th 1921, to be followed by an adult at Titchfield Haven on Oct. 16th 1948.

Since 1950/51, Glaucous Gulls have been seen in 28 winters, annually since 1978/79 (fig. 55).

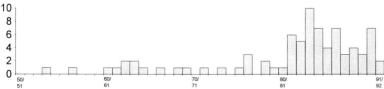

*Figure 55. Winter totals of Glaucous Gulls, 1950/51-91/92.*

Apart from a first-summer at Lepe on June 22nd 1983, all the records have been for five areas: Langstone and Portsmouth Harbours and the coast between Southsea and Black Point (20 birds), Titchfield Haven and the coast between Warsash and Gilkicker Point (18), between Lymington and Hurst (14), Southampton Water (13) and the north-east of the county at Bramshill (3), Eversley Gravel Pit (1) and Frensham Great Pond (1). During the 1980s, rubbish tipping was carried out at one or two sites in each of these areas, and provided an attractive food source for this and other gull species. Birds often stayed in one area for several days or even longer, e.g. a first-summer at Weston Shore from Apr. 4th-July 7th 1983, a first-year in the Langstone Harbour area from Jan. 22nd-July 14th 1984, a first-year in the Titchfield Haven area from Feb. 26th-July 12th 1984 and a second-winter there, possibly the same individual returning, from Mar. 13th-May 4th 1985. Three birds have returned several winters running. A third-year bird first seen in the Lymington/Hurst area on Apr. 23rd 1961 stayed until June 18th and returned in the next three winters, a fourth-winter at Browndown Rubbish Tip on Oct. 27th 1984 was seen there and at Titchfield Haven until Jan. 26th 1985 and returned in the next four winters, and another fourth-winter at Hardway (Portsmouth Harbour) was recorded between Nov. 14th 1984 and Feb. 14th 1985 and returned in the next eight winters, usually arriving in September (earliest date, Aug. 8th 1992) and departing in late February or March (latest date, Mar. 14th 1987). The cumulative monthly totals of all records for 1950/51-91/92 are shown below.

| Jul | Aug | Sep | Oct | Nov | Dec | Jan | Feb | Mar | Apr | May | Jun |
|-----|-----|-----|-----|-----|-----|-----|-----|-----|-----|-----|-----|
| 3   | 6   | 10  | 12  | 13  | 25  | 30  | 31  | 19  | 17  | 11  | 5   |

Of some 69 recorded, 12 were aged as adult, seven as third- or fourth- year, 12 as second-year, 30 as first-year and five as immatures. Three were not aged. Birds returning for several winters have been included only at their age when first seen, so sightings of adults are more frequent than indicated.

The Glaucous Gull has a circumpolar distribution, with its nearest breeding grounds in Iceland and Spitsbergen. Hampshire is at the southern limit of its normal wintering range.

## Great Black-backed Gull                                    *Larus marinus*

A moderately common winter visitor and passage migrant; small numbers (mostly immatures) summer; occasionally breeds.

The largest gatherings are recorded in mid-winter, usually at or near the coast, but birds also move inland to feed and return to the coast at dusk to roost. Those in the north-east of the county originate from roosts in the Thames valley.

In the Langstone Harbour area, 200-300 are regularly present. Higher counts include 514 flying to roost on Jan. 28th 1978, 570 on Sinah Sands at low tide on Dec. 28th 1978 and 650 at Bedhampton Rubbish Tip on Jan. 4th 1983. At nearby Portsmouth Harbour numbers are similar. Higher counts there include 550 on Jan. 16th 1972 and 359 on Dec. 30th 1978. In the BTO National Survey of Roosting Gulls on Jan. 23rd 1993, 310 were recorded in Portsmouth Harbour but only ten in Langstone Harbour.

In Southampton Water, the greatest numbers have been recorded roosting on barges at RAF Hythe. 445 were counted on Jan. 6th 1987, and in the following winter the roost built up from 579 on Jan. 3rd to 1001 on Jan. 6th. This coincided with high tides at dusk and very windy weather, which presumably forced birds from the open sea into the estuary to seek shelter. The survey on Jan. 23rd 1993 produced 346 in Southampton Water, including 254 at Hythe. Daytime counts in the area have included 320 at Newtown Rubbish Tip on Jan. 1st 1987, 360 at Hook Rubbish Tip on Jan. 6th 1988 and 217 at Hill Head on Jan. 4th 1990.

Numbers flying inland from the coast are usually low, e.g. 65 at Timsbury Gravel Pit on Jan. 5th 1984 appears to be the highest count for the Test valley. However, there is a regular movement from the eastern harbours to Buriton Rubbish Tip. This site regularly attracted over 100 in the early 1980s, with a maximum of 210 on Dec. 31st 1981. There is a daily movement up the Avon valley from the roost in Christchurch Harbour (Dorset), e.g. 133 flew north over Bisterne at dawn on Dec. 31st 1986. Most of these probably go to Somerley Rubbish Tip, but on Feb. 4th 1990, following heavy rain, 135 were on floods at Blashford. In the north-east, the largest numbers occur at Bramshill Rubbish Tip, where counts reached 100 in February 1977, February 1980 and January 1984. These normally fly east to roost at the West London reservoirs, but on Feb. 12th 1988, 150 moved north-west over Wellington Country Park at dusk, presumably to roost on one of the gravel pits in the Reading area.

Most adults have left the county by mid-March but through passage is occasionally noted, e.g. a total of 86 flew east off the Hampshire coast between Apr. 25th and May 12th 1984.

During the summer, flocks (usually containing about 90% immatures) occur along the coast. In the eastern harbours, up to 100 are regularly recorded; higher counts include those of 300 in Langstone Harbour on June 13th 1971 and 500 at Paulsgrove Rubbish Tip on July 21st 1974. The only other sites where three-figure counts have been made are Fawley/Calshot (max. 378, July 31st 1973), the Beaulieu Estuary (max. 125, May 31st 1991) and Keyhaven (100, June 30th 1984). Inland, the species is rare at this time, some years not producing any records during May-August.

The species has occasionally bred. Single pairs nested at Pennington Marsh in 1950 and 1951, the Beaulieu Estuary in 1972 and 1976, Langstone Harbour in 1988 and 1989, and on a wooden tower off Fawley in 1992. The most recent estimate of the British population is 18,900 pairs during 1985-87 (Lloyd et al 1991).

National ringing data indicate that the British breeding population is resident and locally dispersive, with movements over 300 km rare (Harris 1962). However, in winter, large numbers of Norwegian birds are present, especially in north-east England (Coulson et al 1984). That some of these reach Hampshire is confirmed by the movement of one ringed as a chick at Rogaland, Norway on June 17th 1984 to Emsworth, 1024 km SSW, where it was found dead on Nov. 30th 1984. Others, ringed as chicks or juveniles in the Scilly Isles, Steepholm (Avon) and Ross and Cromarty, have been found dead in Hampshire in winter, and another from Sark was found dead in Langstone Harbour in July during its second summer. There have been three recoveries of Hampshire-ringed birds: a first-winter caught at Farlington Marshes on Nov. 1st 1969 and found dead in Devon on July 2nd 1979, an adult caught at Bramshill Rubbish Tip on Feb. 8th

1977 and controlled at Troms, Norway, 2273 km NNE, on July 2nd 1978 and a first-winter ringed at Bedhampton Rubbish Tip on Dec. 12th 1977 and found dead at Zuid-Holland, Netherlands, 365 km ENE, on Feb. 11th 1979.

## Kittiwake                                          *Rissa tridactyla*

A passage migrant and winter visitor, usually scarce but sometimes occurring in large numbers following gales.

In mid-winter, Kittiwakes are infrequently recorded but influxes may occur during or after gales. In early 1984, some 600 were seen along the coast. Off Hill Head, 70 flew west on Jan. 16th and a total of 380 moved east between Jan. 10th and Feb. 6th with a peak of 223 on Jan. 26th. Other notable flocks at that time included 40 off Hurst Beach and 53 flying into Chichester Harbour on Jan. 16th and 48 off Southsea on Jan. 30th. Further large movements were seen on Jan. 19th 1986, when 259 flew east through Hurst Narrows, and on Feb. 24th 1990, when at least 100 were seen moving east through Hurst Narrows and off Lee-on-the-Solent.

In spring, easterly movements through The Solent have been recorded between mid-March and early June. The total recorded annually is usually low, only exceeding 100 three times between 1971 and 1992. The heaviest passage was in 1979, when 1379 were logged between Mar. 17th and May 20th, including 163 at Hill Head on Mar. 24th, 259 at Hurst Beach the next day, 553 at Hill Head on Apr. 7th and 203 there on Apr. 12th. In 1984, 165 were recorded including 103 at Hill Head on Apr. 14th, and in 1985, 246 including 108 at Hurst Beach on May 5th.

Between mid-June and early October, few are seen; since 1951 there have been only four double-figure counts in that period including 20 flying west off Hurst Beach on June 22nd 1968 and 15 flying east off Sandy Point on Aug. 11th 1985.

In late autumn, numbers are usually low but heavy movement may be recorded in rough weather. Day totals in excess of 100 have been recorded in the Hurst/Pennington area on six occasions with a maximum of 400 flying east on Oct. 15th 1971. Many of these were seen to move into or out of The Solent, so it is surprising that, apart from 153 flying east at Gilkicker Point on Nov. 16th 1963, only single-figures counts have been made further east.

Kittiwakes are rare inland. Between 1921 and 1957, single birds were seen at Frensham Great Pond on five occasions, six flew south-west there on Jan. 17th 1955 and three were "scavenging on the main road" at Swaythling on Dec. 21st 1928. Since 1973, there have been sightings in every year but four on dates between Nov. 3rd and May 31st. Those in winter were associated with gales and usually coincided with influxes at the coast. Most of the April birds appeared during persistent northerly winds. Such conditions resulted in the arrival of 13 at Fleet Pond on Apr. 12th 1982. 12 remained until Apr. 16th, four until Apr. 19th and one until Apr. 23rd. Other records came from Fleet Pond (15 birds), Frensham Great Pond (7), Mockbeggar Lake (2) and Avon Causeway, Bishopstoke, Dogmersfield Lake, Eversley Gravel Pit, Hatchet Pond, Ibsley, Wellington Country Park and Winchester Sewage Farm (1 each).

The approximate cumulative monthly totals of all records for 1951-92 are shown below.

|        | Jan | Feb | Mar | Apr  | May | Jun | Jul | Aug | Sep | Oct  | Nov | Dec |
|--------|-----|-----|-----|------|-----|-----|-----|-----|-----|------|-----|-----|
| Coast  | 930 | 400 | 660 | 1325 | 745 | 95  | 16  | 45  | 45  | 1170 | 815 | 150 |
| Inland | 3   | 7   | 4   | 25   | 1   | 0   | 0   | 0   | 0   | 0    | 4   | 2   |

An adult ringed on the Farne Islands on July 10th 1967 and found dead at Hythe on Apr. 20th 1982 is the only Hampshire recovery. Kittiwakes breed along much of the British, Irish and north-west European coasts and winter at sea in the North Atlantic.

## Gull-billed Tern                              *Gelochelidon nilotica*

A rare vagrant. There have been 11 records of 13 birds, as follows:

1958:   Hayling Island, May 18th;
1965:   2 flying east, Farlington Marshes, May 1st;
1966:   Hurst Beach, July 5th;
        flying west, Gilkicker Point, July 15th;
1967:   2, Farlington Marshes, Apr. 29th;
1968:   Langstone Harbour, June 9th;
1971:   Langstone Harbour, May 31st;
1972:   Pennington Marsh, May 27th;
1978:   Warsash, Apr. 29th;
1982:   Warsash, May 10th;
        Pennington Marsh and Oxey Creek, July 11th.

The absence of recent records, despite an increase in the number of observers, mirrors the pattern elsewhere in Britain and is probably connected with the decline of the breeding populations in northern Germany and Denmark (BWP).

## Caspian Tern                                        *Sterna caspia*

One record. One was off Milford-on-Sea on June 22nd 1974.
    The Caspian Tern breeds in many parts of the world. Those occurring in Britain may belong to the population which breeds in the Baltic Sea and winters in tropical West Africa.

## Sandwich Tern                                 *Sterna sandvicensis*

A moderately common summer visitor and passage migrant; rarely recorded in winter.

K & M described the Sandwich Tern as "an occasional visitor to the coast on spring and autumn migration". This remained the case until 1954, when the species bred for the first time.

Wintering birds apart, the first normally arrive in the second half of March. During 1971-92 first dates were between Mar. 13th and Apr. 5th with the average Mar. 22nd. Easterly movement along the coast peaks in the second half of April or early May. Between 1971 and 1992, the total recorded per year averaged 614, with peaks of 1219 in 1971 and 1414 in 1978. Day totals exceeding 200 have been recorded at Hayling Bay on five occasions (max. 354 on Apr. 22nd 1983), Hurst four times (max. 264 on Apr. 22nd 1983) and Gilkicker Point twice (max. 322 on Apr. 21st 1971).

The first recorded breeding in Hampshire was in 1954, when ten pairs bred between Lymington and Hurst. In 1955, 17 pairs nested there, in 1956 breeding was not confirmed and in 1957, 80 pairs reared approximately 50 young. In 1959, breeding was proved for the first time in the Beaulieu Estuary. From 1960, numbers increased steadily to a peak of 282 pairs in the two areas in 1971 and then fell back, with none breeding in 1980. Subsequently, the population has fluctuated, reaching an all-time high of 372 pairs in 1988 but decreasing thereafter (fig. 56).

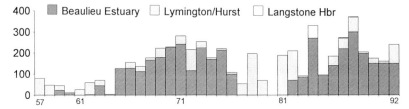

*Figure 56. Annual totals of breeding pairs of Sandwich Terns, 1957-92.*

The Beaulieu Estuary has been the favoured site, with annual breeding since 1959 apart from 1977-81. In most years, the colony held over 100 pairs with a maximum of 300 in 1988. In the Lymington/Hurst area, nesting has occurred in every year but eight since 1959. The highest numbers nested in 1978 (197 pairs) and 1981 (189 pairs), when none bred in the Beaulieu Estuary. The following year, 140 pairs bred, but since then the maximum has been 91 pairs (in 1992) and in four seasons none were present. A third site on islands in Langstone Harbour was first occupied in 1983, when six pairs attempted breeding. A year later, 60 pairs nested without success. In 1987-89, up to seven pairs were present but the species is yet to establish a firm foothold at this locality.

This and other breeding tern species have benefited from the designation of the principal Hampshire sites as reserves. However, while the resultant protection afforded by full-time wardening has reduced human interference (both unintentional and by egg collectors), the colonies are vulnerable to flooding during high spring tides and from fox and rat predation. Losses of nests and eggs from high tide "wash-outs" are sometimes severe but, if this occurs early in the breeding cycle, birds may move to other locations and re-lay.

During the Operation Seafarer census of nesting seabirds in 1969/70, Hampshire supported 2.3% of the British total of Sandwich Terns. Between 1985 and 1987, this figure had fallen to around 2%, reflecting an expansion of the British population from 9900 to 14,000 pairs (Lloyd *et al* 1991) rather than a reduction in the Hampshire total.

In contrast to some other tern species, autumn feeding flocks and movements are usually small. The only counts to reach 200 have been of 300 fishing off Pennington Marsh on Aug. 5th 1967, 462 moving west off Gilkicker Point on Sep. 1st 1968 and 200 moving west through Hurst Narrows on Sep. 21st 1980.

Prior to 1971, the species was rare inland, the only records coming from Frensham Great Pond, where singles were seen on Sep. 17th 1947 and Sep. 4th 1949 and four on Apr. 29th 1948. Between 1971 and 1992, there were records in every year except 1972 covering the periods Apr. 17th-June 22nd and Aug. 7th-Oct. 27th. The cumulative monthly totals for 1971-92 are shown below.

|         | Apr | May | Jun | Jul | Aug | Sep | Oct |
|---------|-----|-----|-----|-----|-----|-----|-----|
| Records | 2   | 4   | 3   | 0   | 12  | 25  | 6   |
| Birds   | 2   | 9   | 5   | 0   | 41  | 73  | 27  |

Of 157 recorded, most were seen at Fleet Pond, where there were 28 reports involving 90 birds, including ten flying SSW on Sep. 7th 1975, six on Sep. 8th 1977 and 13 on Aug. 22nd 1983. At Frensham Great Pond, there were eight reports of 19 birds including five flying south-west on Sep. 12th 1982 and five which left west on Sep. 4th 1992. Other sightings were made at a variety of sites including the Itchen and Test valleys and downland localities such as Dean Hill, Old Winchester Hill and Stockbridge Down. All were of one to three birds apart from those of seven flying south over Bishopstoke on Sep. 23rd 1976, 11 moving south over Frimley Gravel Pit (Surrey) into Hampshire on Oct. 6th 1985 and five flying south-west over Yateley Gravel Pit on May 15th 1990. Except for one at Frensham Great Pond on Apr. 17th and 18th 1971, all moved quickly through or paused for a few hours only.

The last are usually seen in October. During 1971-92, the latest dates recorded were between Sep. 17th and Nov. 10th with the average Oct. 18th. In recent years, there have been several records of presumed wintering birds which are listed below.

| | |
|---|---|
| 1976/77: | Warsash, Dec. 20th; |
| | Brownwich, Feb. 20th; |
| 1977/78: | Langstone Harbour, Dec. 27th-Jan. 7th; |
| 1979/80: | Langstone Harbour, Feb. 16th; |
| 1980/81: | 2, Black Point, Feb. 14th; |
| 1984/85: | Southsea and Hayling Bay, Jan. 10th-Feb. 10th; |
| 1989/90: | Chichester Harbour, Dec. 2nd; |
| | Langstone Harbour, Jan. 16th; |
| | Sandy Point, Mar. 10th (possibly an early migrant). |

The ringing of pulli at the Beaulieu Estuary colony has produced 19 distant recoveries. Ten were from the West African coast between Mauritania and Ivory Coast, all in the months September-April apart from a second-year bird found dead in Ghana in July 1971 which was presumably summering. Two, both ringed on June 18th 1966, moved even further. One was found in July 1970, or possibly earlier, in Angola, 7324 km south, and the other was found in Namibia,

8393 km south, on Dec. 22nd 1971. The other recoveries were from Devon (1), France (3), Portugal (1) and Spain (2), all in the months May-October. They included a 20 year old bird found dead in Lugo, Spain on May 5th 1990 and a second-year bird controlled in Bouches-du-Rhône, France in summer. Five ringed as pulli in other colonies in Northumberland (2), and Lancashire, eastern Germany and the Netherlands (1 each) have been recovered or controlled in Hampshire, one in June, one in July and three in August.

## Roseate Tern                                           *Sterna dougallii*

A very scarce summer visitor and passage migrant.

The Roseate Tern was not recorded in the county until 1955, when four flew north-east over Titchfield Haven on July 24th and five moved west over Hurst Beach on Sep. 4th. Since then, there have been reports in every year except 1956.

The first normally arrive in early May, but the earliest ever was one at Needs Ore on Apr. 27th 1975. Most spring records refer to birds moving through The Solent; in all, 64 have been recorded flying east between May 1st and 29th (fig. 57), with 14 in 1971 the most in one year. All sightings were of one to three birds apart from those of seven at Hurst Beach on May 3rd 1969, eight at Needs Ore on May 2nd 1971, five at Hurst on May 1st 1978 and five at Warsash on May 4th 1980.

Breeding was first recorded in 1957, when a pair laid eggs but the nest was destroyed by storms. Three sitting birds were located in 1958, when at least one chick was hatched but one or more of the nests was later flooded by high tides. Between 1959 and 1992, there have been at least 14 nesting attempts when birds have laid eggs. Fledging success rate, however, has been low; in only four years have young been seen. In many instances, the outcome has been unclear but it is almost certain that some of the failures are attributable to egg collectors. At least 20 other pairs have been present during the breeding seasons in this period.

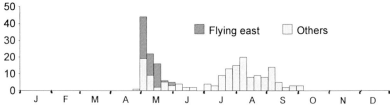

*Figure 57. Cumulative weekly totals of Roseate Terns (excluding breeding birds), 1955-92.*

Autumn records have become more frequent since 1984. This is largely due to an increase in sightings at Titchfield Haven, where Roseate Terns have been identified among large gatherings of Common Terns. Four adults were seen in 1984, at least four adults and two juveniles in 1987, four adults in 1990, four or five adults and one juvenile in 1991 and eight individuals in 1992 including five on July 25th. A colour-ringed adult seen on Aug. 5th 1990 had been ringed as a chick at an Irish Sea colony in 1988. Other autumn records were of one or two individuals apart from four flying west off Pennington Marsh on Aug. 4th 1978 and three, including two juveniles, moving west there on Aug. 16th 1978. The latest were an adult and juvenile moving west at Hurst Beach on Oct. 6th 1985.

Ringing has confirmed that Roseate Terns breeding in Britain and Ireland winter on the coast of Ghana and adjacent West African countries (BWP).

## Common Tern                                  *Sterna hirundo*

A moderately common summer visitor and common passage migrant.

The first are usually seen in the second week of April; during 1971-92 arrival dates were between Apr. 3rd and 20th apart from early birds at Needs Ore on Mar. 26th 1972, Hurst Beach on Mar. 27th 1989 (three, at least one of which may have been an Arctic Tern) and Frensham Great Pond the next day. The average arrival date during this period was Apr. 9th.

This is the most conspicuous of the species involved in easterly movements through The Solent in spring. Passage may extend from early or mid-April until late May or early June with a clear peak in the first week of May. Between 1971 and 1992, the total recorded per year averaged 2537, with peaks of 6118 in 1974 and 6517 in 1978. In five years, fewer than 1000 were recorded with a low of 427 in 1987. The heaviest movements occur in south-easterly winds, especially when associated with spells of rain. Day totals in excess of 1000 have been recorded nine times since 1965, all but two between May 1st and 4th. The two largest movements were on May 3rd 1974, when 3530 were seen at Hurst Beach and 2805 at Hill Head, and the early date of Apr. 20th 1983, when 2625 were recorded at Hurst, 2585 at Hill Head and 1043 at Hayling Bay.

Breeding was first recorded in the county in 1948, when 7-12 pairs nested in the Lymington/Hurst area. In 1951, 29 nests were seen in the same area. In 1952 and 1953, two nests were found in the Beaulieu Estuary, and in 1954 two pairs attempted nesting in Langstone Harbour. By 1957, Common Terns were well established on the west Solent coast with at least 78 pairs between Lymington and Hurst and 48 at Needs Ore Point.

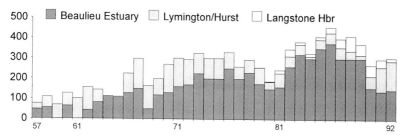

*Figure 58. Annual totals of breeding pairs of Common Terns in the three main colonies, 1957-92.*

Between 1958 and 1992, the population, although fluctuating, has gradually increased (fig. 58). At Needs Ore Point, the colony grew steadily and reached a peak of 375 pairs in 1986, although it was much smaller from 1990-92. In the Lymington/Hurst area, numbers peaked at 148 pairs in 1967 and exceeded 100

285

in every year but one until 1975. Subsequently, fewer were present, with only 11 pairs in 1984 and 18 in 1989; this low level coincided with the highest counts at Needs Ore. In 1991, there was a recovery to 120 pairs. A third significant colony is now established on islands in Langstone Harbour. From a beginning of two pairs which attempted breeding in 1979, numbers rose to a peak of 55 pairs in 1989.

Other coastal sites where breeding has taken place are Fawley, where a few pairs bred in the Black-headed Gull colony until the early 1960s, Titchfield Haven (a pair in 1977 and 1988), Eling Great Marsh (2 pairs in 1986) and Hamble Country Park (single pairs in 1986-88).

Common Terns first bred inland in 1967, when two pairs nested on duck rafts at Blashford Lakes. One or two pairs bred there in most years between 1978 and 1986, numbers then increasing to a maximum of five pairs in 1990. In the north-east, one pair bred successfully at Eversley Gravel Pit in 1991 and six pairs did so in 1992.

During Operation Seafarer in 1969/70, Hampshire held some 2.5% of the British total. In 1985-87, this figure had risen to 3.6%, when the British population was 12,900 pairs (Lloyd *et al* 1991).

In autumn, feeding flocks and roosts numbering several hundred are recorded between early August and mid-September. A nocturnal roost at Calshot peaked at 700 on Aug. 14th 1970, but numbers there have since dwindled, with 250 on Sep. 5th 1984 the only recent count of note. However, numbers at nearby Titchfield Haven have shown a corresponding increase, with large parties feeding offshore and roosting on the beach and in the reserve. Between 1975 and 1979, maxima between 250 and 280 were recorded in three years; since then, counts have included 650 on Sep. 12th 1981, 840 on Aug. 21st 1983 and 1200+ on Aug. 29th 1990. Maxima at other localities with regular autumn flocks include 1275 off Hurst Beach on Aug. 31st 1963, 400+ off Eastney on Aug. 9th 1980, 500 fishing in Hayling Bay on Aug. 26th 1985 and 475 in Langstone Harbour on Aug. 11th 1991.

Westerly movements occur at this time but in recent years have been under-recorded. In the mid-1960s, organised autumn sea-watching from Gilkicker Point produced totals of 2668 west in 1963, 2675 west in 1964 and 4518 west in 1965. The heaviest passage occurred between mid-August and mid-September with a maximum day total of 1426 on Sep. 3rd 1963. 2000+ moved through Hurst Narrows on Sep. 21st 1980. Since then, day totals have exceeded 200 four times with a maximum of 500 flying west off Hill Head on Aug. 31st 1990.

Although the main passage is over by mid-September, in most years some remain into October. In 1985, 83 were still at Hill Head on Oct. 2nd, 45 left west from there on Oct. 5th and 36 were off Hurst Beach the next day. In the wake of the great storm in 1987, an influx of 35 was recorded between Oct. 16th and 19th. The last are usually seen in late October, although there have been November records in 11 years since 1957. There are three December records of single birds: at Black Point on Dec. 15th 1957, Weston Shore on Dec. 5th 1981 and Langstone Harbour from Dec. 3rd-17th 1990. Only in the last case was the possibility of Arctic Tern ruled out.

Prior to 1971, few were recorded inland. Only four double-figure counts have been traced: 40 near Ringwood on Apr. 26th 1947, 14 at Frensham Great

Pond two days later, up to 30 at Frensham in early September 1956 and 12 at Fleet Pond on May 11th 1960. The cumulative monthly totals for 1971-92 are shown below.

|         | Mar | Apr | May | Jun | Jul | Aug | Sep | Oct |
|---------|-----|-----|-----|-----|-----|-----|-----|-----|
| 1971-80 | 0   | 38  | 323 | 24  | 29  | 292 | 266 | 1   |
| 1981-92 | 1   | 133 | 280 | 101 | 388 | 899 | 459 | 15  |

Most were seen in the north-east of the county. The increase in June-August in the second period was presumably due to feeding trips and post-breeding dispersal from nearby breeding colonies in the Thames valley, which expanded markedly during the 1980s. At Fleet Pond, 1621 were recorded, including 135 on Sep. 15th 1974 (*cf.* Black Tern), 40 on May 1st 1978 and 143 moving south-west on Sep. 5th 1982. At Frensham Great Pond, the total was 803, including 42 on May 1st 1979 and 26 moving south-west on Sep. 5th 1982. Elsewhere, totals reached three figures at Blashford Lakes (120, excluding breeding birds) and Eversley Gravel Pit (139), the maxima at these sites being 39 on Aug. 26th 1986 and 37 flying west on Aug. 11th 1987 respectively. Other records were from waters all over the county and also of flocks moving overland, e.g. 20 flying south over Polhampton on Sep. 16th 1977 and 36 flying south over Farley Mount on Aug. 29th 1990.

The winter quarters of Hampshire birds are indicated by the recovery of three (ringed as pulli in Solent colonies) in Gambia, Ghana and Senegal. Other recoveries of Hampshire-ringed pulli include one in Finistère, France, within six weeks of ringing and another in Kings Lynn, Norfolk after four years. An adult ringed at Teesmouth, Cleveland in July 1977 and found long dead in Langstone Harbour in February 1988 is the only distant movement to Hampshire.

Apart from breeding birds, many of the records analysed above referred to Common/Arctic rather than Common Terns. However, it is felt appropriate to review such records with those of definite Common Terns. As a result this account includes a proportion, probably small, of Arctic Terns.

# Arctic Tern                                        *Sterna paradisaea*

A scarce passage migrant.

The Arctic Tern is undoubtedly under-recorded. However, a better understanding of the diagnostic identification characteristics of summer, winter and juvenile plumages in recent years has not produced a significant increase in the number recorded.

Early arrivals were one in Langstone Harbour on Mar. 29th 1958 and one flying east at Hurst Beach on Apr. 4th 1987. Small numbers have been identified among the large flocks of Common/Arctic Terns which move east along the coast between mid-April and late May. 49 out of 281 which flew east over Farlington Marshes on May 1st 1965 were definitely this species and possibly they all were. There have been seven other double-figure counts at coastal sites including 27 flying east off Needs Ore on May 17th 1970 and 33 moving north up the Meon valley at Titchfield Haven on Apr. 27th 1991.

Among the few which have been reliably recorded between late May and early August were single first-summers at Hill Head on June 18th 1984 and July 25th 1992. Immatures usually remain on the wintering grounds in summer.

In autumn, four counts in the range 10-14 were made in the second half of August between 1956 and 1974 but since then no more than seven have been seen together. Many of the recent records have involved juveniles, e.g. six off Hurst Beach on Sep. 13th 1992. Most have left by mid-October but 15 were seen along the coast between Oct. 17th and 22nd 1987 following the great storm. The latest records were of single birds at Hurst Beach on Oct. 28th 1984, Canoe Lake (Southsea) on Nov. 4th 1952 and Langstone Harbour on Nov. 6th 1960.

Inland, Arctic Terns were recorded annually between 1970 and 1992 on dates in the periods Apr. 13th-June 27th and July 27th-Oct. 13th. The cumulative monthly totals are shown below.

|         | Apr | May | Jun | Jul | Aug | Sep | Oct |
|---------|-----|-----|-----|-----|-----|-----|-----|
| Records | 10  | 17  | 4   | 1   | 22  | 17  | 2   |
| Birds   | 28  | 42  | 6   | 4   | 37  | 20  | 2   |

Most were recorded at Fleet Pond (88 birds, including 14 on Apr. 28th 1973, 15 on May 1st 1990 and six on Aug. 20th 1977) and Frensham Great Pond (38, including seven on May 1st 1979). Others were seen at Blashford Lakes and Eversley/Yateley Gravel Pits (4 each), Broadlands Lake (3) and Tundry Pond and Wellington Country Park (1 each). Most were seen on one date only but juveniles have occasionally lingered for up to ten days in autumn.

Ringing activities have produced two movements to Hampshire, both involving birds ringed as pulli in the Farne Islands, Northumberland and recovered in September of their first winter. British Arctic Terns winter in the South Atlantic and off Antarctica.

## Sooty Tern                                          *Sterna fuscata*

Two records. An adult was at Keyhaven and off Hurst Beach on June 17th 1961 and another was found dead at Fawley Refinery on Aug. 18th 1969.

The Sooty Tern breeds on tropical and sub-tropical islands and disperses at sea in the same latitudes.

## Little Tern                                         *Sterna albifrons*

A scarce summer visitor which apparently first bred in 1930; recorded once in winter.

The first arrivals are usually noted in mid-April. During 1971-92, first dates were between Apr. 4th and 20th with the average of Apr. 12th. The earliest ever was one at Hurst Beach on Mar. 24th 1957. Spring passage east through The Solent peaks in the first week of May. During 1971-92, the total recorded each spring averaged 239, with peaks of 572 in 1976 and 600 in 1978. The only day totals to reach three figures were at Hurst Beach, with 145 on May 3rd 1973, 254 on Apr. 27th 1976, 139 on May 1st 1978 and 109 on May 9th 1981.

Since the early 1930s, Little Terns have bred at several sites along the west Solent coast between the Beaulieu Estuary and Hurst Beach. In 1932, there were 15 nests in the Beaulieu Estuary, and in the late 1930s, a flourishing colony on Hurst Beach numbered in excess of 50 pairs (N W Orr *in litt*). Little information is available for the war years but in 1947, 35-40 pairs nested between

Lymington and Hurst and in 1948, 16 pairs nested on Hurst Beach and at least 56 adults were at the Beaulieu Estuary. The Hurst colony was subject to constant disturbance in the 1950s and early 1960s with numbers slumping from 30 pairs in 1951 to around a dozen pairs in 1957-59. All nests there in 1961 failed but when, in 1962, the Hampshire Wildlife Trust erected a fence around the nesting area, 20 young were reared. The site was finally deserted in 1966. Despite the loss of the Hurst site, between 1960 and 1992 there has been a gradual increase in the total population (fig. 59).

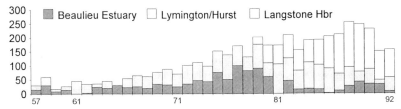

*Figure 59. Annual totals of breeding pairs of Little Terns in the three main colonies, 1957-92.*

In the Beaulieu Estuary, numbers peaked at 100 pairs in 1977 but have declined since, varying between two and 46 pairs from 1982-92. In the Lymington/Hurst area, the highest level was reached between 1975 and 1986, with over 70 pairs nesting in every year but three and a maximum of 105 in 1981. Subsequently, numbers have fallen. These fluctuations may be connected with changes in the availability of suitable nesting habitat. In the last three decades at least two important breeding sites in the Lymington/Hurst area have been lost to the effects of sea action but by the same token other localities have become attractive. For example, islands in a salt-water lagoon created and first flooded in November 1990 have already been used, young being reared in 1991.

The main reason for the overall increase has been the colonisation of the islands in Langstone Harbour after acquisition by the RSPB in the late 1970s. This colony held 27 pairs in 1979 and then grew steadily to a maximum of 171 pairs in 1989.

Little Terns are great opportunists. In 1971, 20 pairs raised 18 young on reclaimed land in Portsmouth Harbour, aided by protection from Portsmouth City Council and the site contractors. Breeding was also suspected in the Hamble Estuary in four years between 1982 and 1991. No nest was found but adults were seen feeding small young; these, however, may have been reared elsewhere.

During Operation Seafarer in 1969-70, Hampshire supported 4.9% of the British total. In 1985-87, this figure had increased to 9.2%, when the total British population was 2400 pairs (Lloyd *et al* 1991).

Following the breeding season, large gatherings form which presumably consist of both local birds and migrants. Three-figure counts have been made on eight occasions since 1955, including 250 in Langstone Harbour on Aug. 1st 1980, 210 in Hayling Bay on Aug. 2nd 1986 and 215 at Black Point on July 12th 1988. Such flocks normally disperse quickly and few remain by early September. In contrast to the spring, movements have been infrequently recorded. 230 moved west through Hayling Bay on Aug. 4th 1985 but otherwise day totals have not exceeded 40. Most have left by early October. The latest ever was one at Langstone Harbour on Oct. 22nd 1972. In other years during 1971-92, latest dates were between Sep. 18th and Oct. 21st with the average Oct. 7th. There is a single winter record of one seen at close range at Hardway (Portsmouth Harbour) on Jan. 17th 1990.

Inland, the Little Tern is rare, not being recorded annually. One was at Frensham Great Pond from Oct. 24th-26th 1932, which is the latest for the county. Between 1956 and 1992, there were 24 records involving 42 birds in 16 different years, covering the periods Apr. 21st-June 30th and Aug. 11th-Oct. 3rd. The cumulative monthly totals are shown below.

|         | Apr | May | Jun | Jul | Aug | Sep | Oct |
|---------|-----|-----|-----|-----|-----|-----|-----|
| Records | 4   | 11  | 3   | 0   | 3   | 2   | 2   |
| Birds   | 4   | 19  | 10  | 0   | 5   | 3   | 3   |

Records came from Fleet Pond (13 birds, including three on May 10th 1975), Broadlands Lake (8, including 7 on June 30th 1978), Frensham Great Pond (7), Wellington Country Park (3) and Winnall Moors (3 on May 1st 1958). Single records of one or two birds came from Hatchet Pond, John O'Gaunt's Lake (Kings Somborne), Mockbeggar and Morey's Lakes (Blashford) and Timsbury Gravel Pit. All were seen on one date only apart from one at Frensham on Sep. 29th 1956, which was joined by a second bird the next day, both remaining until Oct. 2nd.

There are only four ringing recoveries of Hampshire birds. One, ringed as a pullus at the Beaulieu Estuary on July 12th 1967, was controlled breeding on the North Friesian Islands, Germany, 717 km ENE, on May 21st 1973. Another, ringed in Clwyd on July 24th 1975, was found dead at Beaulieu on Sep. 3rd 1979. The other movements were both less than 20 km. Most British birds winter along the West African coast from Mauritania to the Gulf of Guinea.

## Whiskered Tern                                   *Chlidonias hybridus*

Five records. An adult was seen off Hurst Beach on May 12th 1970 and another flew east there on May 13th 1972. The next was an adult in the Hamble Estuary on Aug. 17th 1974, to be followed by one at nearby Warsash on May 20th 1978. Finally, two adults were at Mockbeggar Lake on May 14th 1988.

The nearest breeding grounds of the Whiskered Tern are in central France. European birds winter in sub-Saharan Africa.

## Black Tern                                        *Chlidonias niger*

A moderately common passage migrant.

The earliest ever were on Apr. 11th 1979, when two were at Frensham Great Pond and singles were seen at Hurst Beach, Titchfield Haven and Langstone Harbour. In 1980, one was at Titchfield Haven on Apr. 12th, but in other years during 1971-92 earliest dates were between Apr. 17th and 30th with the average Apr. 22nd.

The main feature of the spring passage is an easterly movement along the coast, which usually peaks in the first half of May. Between 1971 and 1992, the

annual total averaged 99, with peaks of 209 in 1980 and 212 in 1989 and lows
of 29 in 1983 and 28 in 1986. Optimum conditions appear to be anticyclonic
weather with light south-easterly winds, although any wind in the eastern quarter
may produce movements. At Titchfield Haven, flocks sometimes move north-
east up the Meon valley, especially in north-easterly winds. Most of these
presumably turn east and move across the north shores of Portsmouth,
Langstone and Chichester Harbours and on through Chichester Gravel Pits
(West Sussex). This route by-passes Gilkicker Point, Hayling Bay and Selsey
Bill and is regularly taken by other migrants, especially Bar-tailed Godwits. The
largest movement witnessed was on May 1st 1965, when 400+ flew east off
Hurst Beach, 439 flew east over Farlington Marshes and 204 were seen from
Gilkicker Point, i.e. a minimum of 643. The only other three-figure day totals
were of 120 at Hurst Beach on May 3rd 1974 (cf. Little Gull) and 107 at Hill
Head on May 12th 1982. In most other years, peak counts are in the range 20-
70, and frequently only one day in the spring produces such a movement.
Passage may continue until early June, but thereafter few are seen until the
return migration commences in late July.

In autumn, some years produce a peak in late July and early August which
largely involves adults, e.g. 22 moving west off Pennington Marsh on Aug. 5th
1979, 100 at Titchfield Haven on Aug. 2nd 1990 during hot anticyclonic
weather with light south-easterly winds, and 80 there on Aug. 7th 1992. The
main movement, in which juveniles usually predominate, occurs between late
August and mid-September. Typically, numbers are small, any flock in excess
of 20 being noteworthy. Larger counts have included 102 moving south off
Dibden Bay on Sep. 1st 1974, 60 at Titchfield Haven in a south-easterly gale on
Aug. 24th 1977, 50 off Pennington Marsh on Aug. 17th 1980, 64 moving west
there on Sep. 1st 1987 and 90 flying west in Hayling Bay on Sep. 6th 1992. In
most years, a few are seen in early October, although a flock of 26 moving west
at Keyhaven on Oct. 1st 1982 was exceptional. During 1971-92, latest dates
were between Sep. 10th and Nov. 12th with the average Oct. 11th. Only three
were recorded in November, at Dibden Bay on Nov. 11th 1973 (which had been
present since Oct. 20th), again there on Nov. 12th 1977 and at Keyhaven on
Nov. 2nd 1984. The latest ever was one which stayed at Frensham Great Pond
from Nov. 7th-15th 1967.

Inland, numbers are usually low, with some springs and autumns not
producing any. Occurrences often coincide with large coastal movements.
Before 1971, several large flocks were recorded, including 50 at Frensham Great
Pond on May 21st 1948, 40-50 at Winnall Moors on May 14th 1950, 23 at
Tundry Pond on May 2nd 1958 and 30 at Fleet Pond on May 31st 1966. The
cumulative monthly totals for 1971-92 are shown below.

| Apr | May | Jun | Jul | Aug | Sep | Oct | Nov |
|-----|-----|-----|-----|-----|-----|-----|-----|
| 35 | 348 | 33 | 41 | 180 | 345 | 15 | 2 |

Most were recorded in the north-east; this probably reflects the good coverage
of that area compared to other likely sites such as Blashford Lakes in the Avon
valley. Waters with high totals were Fleet Pond (473, including 29 on May 3rd
1974, 190 on Sep. 15th 1974, when only 45 were recorded at coastal localities,
and 16 on Aug. 14th 1986), Frensham Great Pond (261 including 14 on July

31st 1971, 40 on May 3rd 1974, 21 on Aug. 3rd 1980 and 17 on May 2nd 1990) and Blashford Lakes (94, including 22 on Sep. 15th 1982 and 23 on Aug. 31st 1986). Records came from 17 other sites but totals did not exceed 42; the only double-figure counts were of 12 at Alresford Pond on May 15th 1974, ten at Eversley Gravel Pit and 15 at Wellington Country Park on May 11th 1980 and 12 flying south over Winnall Moors on Aug. 29th 1984.

Black Terns occurring in Hampshire probably belong to those populations breeding in the Netherlands, Denmark and further east in Europe. They winter along the West African coast, principally from the Gulf of Guinea southwards.

## White-winged Black Tern             *Chlidonias leucopterus*

A rare passage migrant. Some 25 have been recorded, as follows:

1959:   Langstone Harbour, Sep. 14th;
1960:   adult, Lee-on-the-Solent, May 11th;
1963:   Hurst Beach, Aug. 11th and 18th;
1964:   juvenile, South Hayling, Sep. 1st;
1967:   juvenile, Farlington Marshes, Oct. 22nd-Nov. 15th;
1970:   juvenile, Fleet Pond, Sep. 8th;
1971:   juvenile, Titchfield Haven, Aug. 18th;
        juvenile, Keyhaven, Sep. 28th and Oct. 4th;
1972:   adult, Pennington Marsh, May 29th;
1973:   adult flying east, Farlington Marshes, May 26th†;
        juvenile, Pennington Marsh, Aug. 12th and 13th;
1979:   juvenile, Pennington Marsh, Aug. 25th;
        juvenile, Calshot, Sep. 1st† (presumed same as Pennington bird);
1980:   2 adults flying south, Mockbeggar Lake (Blashford), May 3rd†;
        adult flying west, Pennington Marsh, Sep. 21st;
1984:   juvenile, Titchfield Haven, Aug. 22nd;
1988:   adult, Broadlands Lake, Lower Test Marshes, Eling Great Marsh, Titchfield Haven and Hythe, July 6th-Sep. 5th;
        adult, Winchester Sewage Farm, Aug. 10th†;
1991:   adult, Pennington Marsh, June 3rd†;
        juvenile, Spinnaker Lake (Blashford), Sep. 22nd-25th;
1992:   adult, Langstone Harbour, May 14th†;
        second-summer flying east, Pennington Marsh, and north, Titchfield Haven, May 18th†;
        juvenile, Fleet Pond, Aug. 22nd;
        adult, Alresford Pond, Sep. 3rd†
        juvenile flying west, Hurst Beach, Sep. 6th†.

The nearest breeding grounds of the White-winged Black Tern are in eastern Europe. Birds from that area winter on the coast and inland lakes of sub-Saharan Africa.

## Guillemot                                                 *Uria aalge*

A scarce winter visitor and passage migrant; the numbers recorded have increased since the early 1980s.

Between 1951 and 1980, it was unusual to see a healthy Guillemot in Hampshire in winter, most being storm-driven or oiled. However, since then, small numbers have appeared all along the coast, with the most regularly used area that between Black Point and Hayling Bay. Records have usually been of one to four birds but higher counts included those of six at Black Point on Nov. 17th 1985 and Nov. 26th 1988, nine off Gilkicker Point on Jan. 11th 1986 and ten flying west off Hurst Castle on Dec. 23rd 1990. The proportion of oiled birds has decreased, with 94 out of 229 (41.8%) between 1951 and 1980 and 72 out of 412 (18.0%) between 1981 and 1992. The cumulative monthly totals for 1951-92 (see below) suggest a small spring passage, although only 11 were actually seen moving east, including seven through Hurst Narrows on May 7th 1988. Summer records are very scarce; in recent years only occasional birds have been seen but earlier sightings included those of seven off Southsea on Aug. 3rd 1953 and six off Hurst Beach on July 22nd 1967.

| Jan | Feb | Mar | Apr | May | Jun | Jul | Aug | Sep | Oct | Nov | Dec |
|-----|-----|-----|-----|-----|-----|-----|-----|-----|-----|-----|-----|
| 165 | 79  | 38  | 26  | 46  | 9   | 19  | 18  | 33  | 73  | 91  | 130 |

In the 30 years up to 1980, the total reported annually averaged eight with a maximum of 28 in 1966. During 1981-92, the average was 34 with a peak of 56 in 1986. While better observer coverage, especially on Hayling Island, is partially responsible for the increase, the improving fortune of the national breeding population is probably also a contributory factor. This was estimated at 550,400 birds in Britain and Ireland during Operation Seafarer in 1969-70 and 1,203,100 birds during 1985-87 (Lloyd *et al* 1991). Ringing recoveries confirm that birds from a wide area occur in Hampshire. Of 18 found in the county, five were from colonies in Scotland, four from Ireland, three from south-west England and six from Dorset. The nearest breeding colonies are in the Isle of Wight and Dorset.

## Razorbill                                                 *Alca torda*

A scarce passage migrant and winter visitor; the numbers recorded have increased since the early 1980s.

As with the Guillemot, Razorbills have become more frequent in winter during the 1980s, although the numbers involved are lower compared to that species. Six were in the Black Point area on Dec. 12th 1992, 5 were there on Nov. 16th 1985 and at least four were off Hurst Beach on Dec. 21st 1985, but most records at this season have only involved one or two birds. The cumulative monthly totals for 1951-92 (see below) suggest a small spring passage and a larger one in autumn. In spring, five off Hurst on May 12th 1976 is the most seen on one day and only ten were actually seen moving east. Rather more have been recorded moving west in autumn, with a total of 47 including eight off Hurst on Oct. 3rd 1981, 17 there the next day and five off Pennington Marsh on Oct. 31st 1989. Very few are seen in summer, seven off Keyhaven on July 14th 1969 being the only number of note.

| Jan | Feb | Mar | Apr | May | Jun | Jul | Aug | Sep | Oct | Nov | Dec |
|-----|-----|-----|-----|-----|-----|-----|-----|-----|-----|-----|-----|
| 91 | 68 | 23 | 30 | 57 | 2 | 21 | 21 | 31 | 120 | 51 | 75 |

During 1951-80, the total reported annually averaged nine with maxima of 29 in 1957 and 39 in 1974. Of these, 87 out of 268 (32.5%) were oiled. Between 1981 and 1992, the average increased to 25 with a maximum of 38 in 1981, but the proportion of oiled birds decreased, only ten out of 296 (3.4%) being affected. The increase in numbers is presumably due to a combination of improved observer coverage, especially on Hayling Island, and the upturn in the national breeding population. This is difficult to quantify because of the different census methods used in 1969-70 and 1985-87, but the population in Britain and Ireland was estimated at 181,900 birds in the latter period (Lloyd *et al* 1991). The origin of Hampshire birds is suggested by the recovery of five ringed individuals; two were from Ireland, one from Wales and two from Dorset. Razorbills formerly bred in the Isle of Wight although this has not been confirmed in recent years.

## Black Guillemot                                   *Cepphus grylle*

One record. A first-winter was at Southsea on Jan. 31st 1986.

Most Black Guillemots remain close to their nesting sites throughout the year; the nearest colonies to Hampshire are in southern Ireland and Anglesey.

## Little Auk                                            *Alle alle*

A very scarce winter visitor, usually appearing following storms.

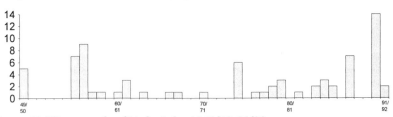

*Figure 60.Winter totals of Little Auks, 1949/50-91/92.*

Since 1949, birds have been seen in 23 winters with a total of approximately 75 involved (fig. 60). Records came from the Langstone Harbour/Hayling Island area (31 birds), between Warsash and Gilkicker Point (20), between Sowley and Milford-on-Sea (13) and inland at Fareham (2), Vales Moor (New Forest), Headley, Old Alresford, Kingsworthy and Havant (1 each). Four were found on the coast in the wreck of February 1950 but no further details can be traced (Sergeant 1952). Approximately 30 were found dead or dying, but the remainder were healthy. The cumulative monthly totals of all records for 1949/50-91/92 are shown below.

| Oct | Nov | Dec | Jan | Feb | Mar | Apr |
|-----|-----|-----|-----|-----|-----|-----|
| 2 | 24 | 22 | 14 | 12 | 0 | 1 |

The extreme dates for live birds were Oct. 23rd (1992, Southsea) and Feb. 9th (1988, Hill Head), but a long-dead corpse was found on Hurst Beach on Apr. 7th 1991. All records were of single birds apart from eight seen from a ferry between Portsmouth and Ryde, Isle of Wight on Dec. 1st 1956, two moving east off Hill Head on Jan. 6th 1988, Feb. 9th 1988 and Jan. 9th 1991, and two in Hayling Bay on Dec. 30th 1990. Most healthy birds were seen in flight offshore, but in 1985 a particularly obliging bird was at Black Point from Nov. 20th-23rd, then moving to Langstone Harbour entrance where it remained until Nov. 28th.

There are several older records, mostly for inland localities. White mentioned one seen at Alresford in spring 1771; subsequently specimens were obtained at Le Court (Greatham) on Nov. 19th 1861, Longwood Warren in November 1885 and the New Forest and Wield in January 1895.

The Little Auk is an abundant breeder in western Greenland and on islands in the Arctic Ocean from Spitsbergen to central Siberia. It winters in the North Atlantic.

## Puffin                                   *Fratercula arctica*

A rare visitor.

A flourishing colony on Freshwater Cliffs, Isle of Wight in the early years of the century had virtually died out by the 1950s. This presumably accounts for the increasing rarity of Puffins in Hampshire, only 22 having been recorded since 1949.

Between 1949 and 1955, storm-driven birds were found inland at Farringdon, Baughurst, Crondall and on the Basingstoke Canal near Fleet. Since then, all have been seen at the coast, with nine in the Pennington/Hurst area, six at Hill Head and singles at Calshot, Eling, Gilkicker Point, Hamble and Sandy Point. Six of these were dead, oiled or sick and the remainder were flying offshore. The cumulative monthly totals are shown below.

| Jan | Feb | Mar | Apr | May | Jun | Jul | Aug | Sep | Oct | Nov | Dec |
|-----|-----|-----|-----|-----|-----|-----|-----|-----|-----|-----|-----|
| 1 | 2 | 0 | 2 | 2 | 1 | 4 | 3 | 1 | 6 | 0 | 2 |

Small numbers of Puffins still breed in Dorset, the Channel Islands and the Isles of Scilly. The nearest large colonies are on Skomer and Skokholm islands off the Dyfed coast.

## Pallas's Sandgrouse                    *Syrrhaptes paradoxus*

A rare visitor, not recorded since 1908.

During the 1863 invasion, at least one was obtained at Aldershot. In 1888, one was near Itchen Abbas on May 5th and two were shot out of a flock of 20 at Itchen Stoke on May 15th. 30-40 flew over Broxhead Common on May 20th and two were obtained from a flock of 12 at Sinah Common a few days before May 31st. 17 flew over the River Avon near Ringwood on June 8th. Other records followed from Winchester, Overton, Hurstbourne and Stubbington in the period up to January 1889. Some remained in the neighbourhood of the New Forest until May 1889 (K & M). In 1908, five were near East Liss in mid-April, two flew over Havant on July 8th and five were at an unspecified locality in August (Cohen).

There have not been any recent invasions of this species, which breeds on the Asian steppes. This may be connected with a decline in the western part of its range (BWP).

## Feral Pigeon                          *Columba livia*

A common resident.

Rock Doves, the wild form of Feral Pigeons, could never have been common in Hampshire. In a county lacking high sea cliffs or inland crags, breeding sites would have been hard to find. In contrast, domesticated dovecote pigeons were probably an important part of the rural scene back into history and are thus the

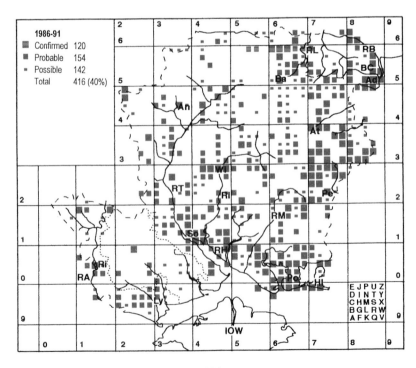

more likely immediate ancestors of today's feral birds. With the demise of the dovecote, Feral Pigeons have exploited niches in high buildings, church towers, factories and warehouses, continuing to live close to people in cities and towns. As the Atlas Map shows, their distribution in Hampshire matches the pattern of urbanisation with the main concentrations in Portsmouth, along the coast to Southampton and in the north and east in Basingstoke, Aldershot and Petersfield.

Feral Pigeons have received little attention in *Hampshire Bird Reports* and we have only scant information on their status or population trends. Comparing the results of the Tetrad Atlas with the 68-72 Atlas suggests that the range may have expanded over the past two decades. In the latter survey, birds were encountered in only 16 10 km squares with breeding confirmed in ten and possible in six. In the Tetrad Atlas, birds were recorded in 50 10 km squares with breeding confirmed in 33, probable in 15 and possible in four. Some of this apparent expansion is undoubtedly due to better coverage in the Tetrad Atlas, but it is also possible that Feral Pigeons have spread to more rural areas, aided by the same agricultural changes that have benefited Woodpigeons and Stock Doves over the past 20 years. Feral Pigeons breed prolifically, and this, coupled with their ability to travel long distances to feed, would favour rapid colonisation of new areas when conditions are suitable.

Given the lack of any quantitative information, one can do little more than guess the Hampshire population. It is likely that many of the tetrads with possible breeding records do not actually hold breeding pairs, but each of the 274 confirmed and probable registrations probably relates to colonies. On this basis, an estimate of 2000-3000 pairs seems reasonable. No attempt was made to estimate the British population in the New Atlas.

## Stock Dove                                    *Columba oenas*

A numerous resident and possible winter visitor.

As the Atlas Map shows, Stock Doves are widespread, but patchily distributed throughout the county. They are most common in parkland and open woodland, particularly where the timber is old and nest sites are plentiful. They also occur in woods and spinneys on farmland and increasingly in urban parks and large gardens. Where suitable timber is scarce, e.g. in the coastal belt east of Southampton Water, and in dense urban areas, they are less common.

Stock Doves feed chiefly on seeds and green leaves. They suffered badly during the 1950s when organochlorine pesticides were widely used as seed dressings, but following restrictions on their use in the early 1960s, numbers increased rapidly (O'Connor & Mead 1984). The growth continued until about 1980 when the population stabilised. Even so, the species remains sensitive to changes in farming practices. Widespread use of herbicides for weed control, elimination of stubble and fallows through autumn sowing of cereals, and general "tidying" of the countryside, may all adversely affect numbers.

In Hampshire, population densities vary widely from one part of the county to another. They are at their highest in the New Forest and other areas of ancient woodland. CBC data for Eyeworth Wood indicate densities of up to 20 pairs on 29.5 ha, equivalent to 68 pairs per $km^2$. Using national CBC data for 1989, the

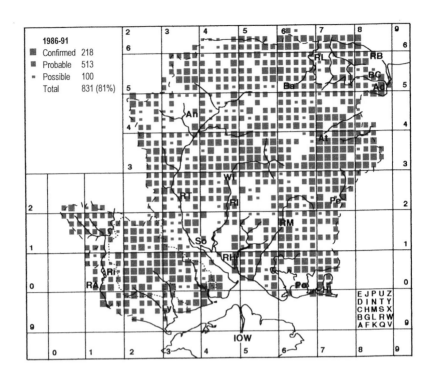

1986-91
■ Confirmed  218
■ Probable    513
▪ Possible    100
   Total      831 (81%)

New Atlas method indicates a county population of around 10,000 pairs. Allowing for the high densities in parts of the New Forest, a range of 10,000-12,000 is probably more appropriate. The British population was estimated at 240,000 pairs.

The breeding population is essentially sedentary. There have been 23 recoveries of birds ringed in Hampshire and all have been within the county or in neighbouring counties. Recently, however, due to systematic coverage at Fleet Pond, there has been evidence of regular diurnal movements in autumn and to a lesser extent in spring. In the six years 1987-92, 846 passed over Fleet Pond between Sep. 21st and Dec. 5th, mostly in directions between south and west. The maximum day total was of 80 south-east on Nov. 12th 1989.

In winter, some breeding areas, such as the New Forest, are abandoned, and feeding and roosting flocks assemble where food is available. Several flocks in excess of 100 are reported each year. The average size and number of flocks increased during the 1970s, consistent with the population growth during the period. Occasionally, larger gatherings are recorded, especially in spring, e.g. 550 at Sowley Farm on Apr. 27th 1986 and 500+ at Hillside on Mar. 29th 1987.

## Woodpigeon                              *Columba palumbus*

An abundant resident and winter visitor.

Woodpigeons occur in all suitable wooded habitats, both rural and urban. During the winter, despite attempts to control the population by shooting, their numbers can reach pest proportions on large areas of arable farmland. The species fortunes are strongly linked to changing agricultural practices. They feed on seeds and green leaves, rotating their diet throughout the year as different crops become available. In Britain, numbers have risen steadily since the mid-1970s, probably in response to an increasing availability of oilseed rape which provides food and aids survival through the winter (Marchant *et al* 1990). Also, the switch to autumn sowing of cereals has advanced the date when ripe grain is available and thereby extended the breeding season.

During the Atlas Survey, there were registrations in all but ten tetrads, with breeding confirmed in 746, probable in 267 and possible in eight. Using national CBC data for 1989, the New Atlas method indicates a county population of around 60,000 pairs and a national total of 2,100,000-2,550,000 pairs.

The local breeding population is essentially sedentary – 30 out of 31 recoveries of locally-ringed birds have been either in Hampshire or neighbouring counties – but numbers may be boosted in autumn by immigrants. Diurnal movements are noted most years in October and November, with the peak usually in the first half of November. The numbers recorded vary from year to year but are sometimes very large. In 1984, 30,240 were recorded between Oct. 15th and Nov. 29th, with the heaviest movement on Nov. 4th, when 8013 moved south in three hours at Camp Farm, 7570 south-west in five hours at Old Winchester Hill and a total of 4830 west or south-west at three other sites. In 1986, systematic watching at Tunworth produced a total of 23,050, mostly moving in directions between south and north-west, in 44.65 hours observation between Oct. 3rd and Nov. 20th.

Between 1987 and 1992, virtually daily coverage at Fleet Pond produced an average autumn total of 25,769. The heaviest passage was in 1989, when 65,196 were recorded between Oct. 23rd and Dec. 30th (61,568 in November) including 11,000 SSW in four hours on Nov. 5th, 7400 on Nov. 9th, 7900 on Nov. 12th and 8550 on Nov. 16th. Movement was again heavy in 1991, when 45,563 were logged between Oct. 7th and Dec. 7th (44,974 in November) with a peak of 12,720 east on Nov. 25th. In most years, the flight line each day was largely to the south-west or west until mid-November. After this, movements were usually to the north immediately after dawn but gradually turned south-east during the morning.

Movements at the coast are usually much smaller than at inland sites. Small parties have been recorded apparently heading towards the Isle of Wight but most follow the shore westwards, e.g. 2455 over Sinah Common in three hours on Oct. 31st 1992.

The origin of Woodpigeons involved in autumn movements is uncertain. There is a tendency for young birds to move south at this time of year, but an increase in the number of birds leaving local roosts due to the appearance of juveniles can be confused with migrant flocks (Murton & Ridpath 1962, Murton 1965). There is limited ringing evidence to indicate that non-local birds are involved. Two birds ringed in Norfolk in May and Cambridgeshire in March have been recovered in Hampshire in subsequent winters. However, there is little evidence of return movements in spring and there is one recovery which shows contrary northerly movement of a Hampshire-bred bird: one ringed as a pullus at Faccombe on Aug. 14th 1925 and recovered in North Yorkshire on Jan. 26th 1926.

Feeding and roosting flocks exceeding 1000 are recorded regularly from November-March and occasionally much larger gatherings are seen. In 1974, more than 20,000 were estimated to be in the Great Litchfield Down area on Dec. 15th, when "every tree seemed to be growing Woodpigeons". 10,500 were counted flying out of Islands Thorns Inclosure on Dec. 27th 1976 and there were 8000 there on Jan. 30th 1977. There were flocks of 5000 at Hen Wood (Tunworth) on Dec. 15th 1984 and at Chidden Down (Hambledon) on Dec. 12th 1985. 6000 were counted leaving a roost at Micheldever on Dec. 27th 1990. These large concentrations may gather in response to high mast or acorn crops.

## Collared Dove                                        *Streptopelia decaocto*

A numerous resident and passage migrant.

The spectacular spread of the Collared Dove in Britain, following its initial colonisation of Norfolk in 1955, has been well documented by Hudson (1965b, 1972). The first to be recorded in Hampshire was at Gosport on Aug. 30th 1957, and breeding occurred for the first time on Hayling Island in 1961. This was followed in 1962 by breeding at two sites close to the coast, Totton and Sway, and in 1963 by the first inland records from Andover, Stratfield Saye and Winchester. Over the following decade, very rapid colonisation of the county occurred, first in a wide coastal belt, followed quickly by penetration inland, particularly along the Test and Itchen valleys (C & T).

Ringing recoveries showed that the early immigrants were birds dispersing from breeding sites on the continent or in eastern England. An adult ringed in Gelderland, Holland on Jan. 2nd 1965 was killed at Marchwood on Aug. 31st 1968 and one, ringed as a juvenile in Kent on Sep. 30th 1967, was killed at Petersfield on Apr. 10th 1968.

By 1966, the species was already being described as a garden pest in Totton and in 1970, a flock at Lainston (Winchester) reached 250 on Feb. 25th. By the end of the 68-72 Atlas, breeding had been confirmed or was probable in all but four of Hampshire's 10 km squares.

Consolidation continued through the 1970s and early 1980s. During this period, post-breeding flocks exceeding 250 were recorded annually. In December 1975, 350+ were at Northfields Farm (Twyford) and during 1978, 584 were ringed there. The largest flock recorded to date was of 490 at Peak Lane (Stubbington) on Sep. 25th 1983. Thereafter, some local declines in breeding numbers were noted; this is consistent with national CBC data which show that the population peaked in 1982 (Marchant *et al* 1990). A contributory factor may have been the increasing level of protection afforded by farmers to their grain stores, e.g. in 1984, 200 were shot out of a flock of 250 on one Havant farm.

In the 1970s and early 1980s, ringing returns showed continuing long distance movements of birds into the county and dispersal of Hampshire-bred birds with a predominantly northerly bias. Between 1972 and 1985, there were 12 recoveries of birds ringed in Hampshire at distances in excess of 100 km from the ringing sites. These included five ringed as juveniles at Northfields Farm and recovered in Cambridgeshire, Cleveland, Glamorgan, Gloucestershire and Northamptonshire and seven adults recovered in France (3, with a maximum movement of 366 km SSE), Antrim, Morayshire, Powys and Somerset. Recently, national ringing data have indicated that the amount of long distance movement declined as Collared Dove densities levelled off (Marchant *et al* 1990).

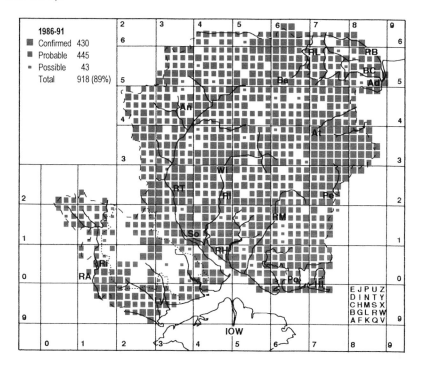

During the Atlas Survey, Collared Doves were recorded in 918 (89%) tetrads, with breeding confirmed in 430, probable in 445 and possible in 43. They are widespread and common; the highest densities occur around villages and farms, especially where grain supplies are plentiful and ornamental evergreens, a favoured nest site, are available. They are only absent from parts of the New Forest; this reflects both the lack of agriculture and the low human population density in that area. Using national CBC data for 1989, the New Atlas method indicates a county population of around 6000 pairs. However, many tetrads in Hampshire hold 20 or more pairs and so a range of 9000-15,000 pairs is considered more appropriate. The national population was estimated at 200,000 pairs (New Atlas).

It seems that most adults now remain close to their nesting sites and some continue to breed through most of the year, whenever the weather is favourable. However, recently there have been several records of diurnal movement in both spring and autumn. In spring 1990, singles arrived at Sandy Point from far out to sea on Apr. 30th and May 7th, and at Fleet Pond, four flew NNW on Mar. 21st and four north-east on Apr. 11th. In the autumn of that year, 42 passed over Fleet Pond, mostly moving west, between Sep. 29th and Dec. 12th.

# Turtle Dove                                    *Streptopelia turtur*

A moderately common, but declining, summer visitor and passage migrant.

C & T described the Turtle Dove as "a common summer resident .... breeding in all parts (of the county)". 20 years later, as the Atlas Map shows, the species is still widely distributed but can no longer be described as common. The national CBC population trend was one of a steady increase during the 1960s and most of the 1970s but since then the index has fallen markedly and today stands at well below its peak. In Hampshire, there are insufficient data to show whether the same pattern has occurred, but the general impression is one of increasing scarcity.

Several factors are possibly contributing to its decline. These include the hunting which it suffers on migration through Mediterranean countries and changes in agricultural practices in this country. They feed mainly on weed seeds, so modern farming methods aimed at reducing weeds, such as the use of selective herbicides and fertilizers, may be implicated.

The first are usually recorded in the second half of April. Between 1971 and 1992, first dates were between Apr. 2nd and 27th with the average Apr. 17th. Arrivals continues through May and into June. In 1973, two flocks, one of 58 and the second of 14, arrived at Gilkicker Point from the south on May 3rd, and in 1982, 16 flew north over Wellington Country Park on May 14th and 18 moved north-east over Park Corner Farm (Odiham) on May 27th.

The preferred nesting sites are typically in hawthorn, gorse or other scrub, overgrown hedges, copses and developing conifer plantations close to uncultivated grasslands or arable fields. They are thinly spread throughout agricultural areas and still relatively common at some sites on rough downland (e.g. at Martin Down, nine pairs on a 54 ha CBC plot in 1986 and at Old Winchester Hill, seven pairs on a 37.2 ha CBC plot in 1982, 1985 and 1986) and in thicket-stage conifer plantations in the north-east (e.g. at Alice Holt Forest, six pairs in 1986 and at Warren Heath, four pairs in 1989). They are uncommon in the New Forest and on the coast except in the west Solent and Titchfield Haven areas. At the latter site, there were 11 pairs on two CBC plots totalling 107.7 ha in 1983 but only five in 1990.

The Atlas Map probably overstates the distribution in any one year, particularly since only 13% of the registrations are of confirmed breeding and some may refer to migrants or unmated males. On the basis of two to four pairs per occupied tetrad the county population is estimated to be 1200-2400 pairs. The British population in 1989 was estimated at 75,000 pairs (New Atlas).

In the 1960s, flocks of 30-50 were regularly seen in late summer and occasionally reached 100 or more, e.g. 110+ at Winchester Sewage Farm on Aug. 10th and 11th 1964 and 110 in stubble at Keyhaven on Aug. 29th 1968. The most recent three-figure flock was of 100+ gathered on wires over corn at Bentworth on Aug. 25th 1980. Since then, the only counts to exceed 30 have been of 36 at Hillside on Aug. 7th 1981 and 35 at Liss on Aug. 12th 1984.

The last birds are generally seen in early October. Between 1971 and 1992, last dates were between Sep. 9th and Nov. 7th with the average Oct. 8th.

Records outside the dates quoted, possibly referring to wintering birds, include those of single birds at Titchfield Haven on Dec. 6th 1966, Weston from

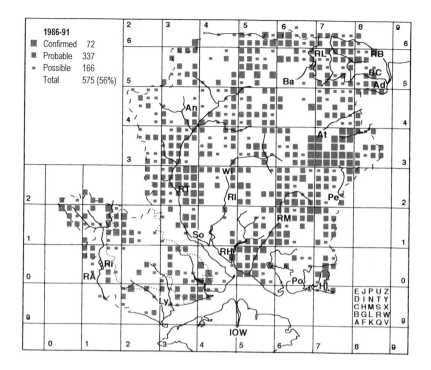

| 1986-91 | | |
|---|---|---|
| ■ Confirmed | 72 | |
| ■ Probable | 337 | |
| ■ Possible | 166 | |
| Total | 575 (56%) | |

Dec. 15th-26th 1969, Chandlers Ford on Mar. 25th 1970 and Lower Pennington on Feb. 8th and Mar. 8th 1975.

There have been five recoveries of Hampshire-ringed Turtle Doves. Four were shot in autumn in Portugal (3) and south-western France, when presumably they were en route to the wintering grounds in the Sahel and adjacent regions of West Africa. The other recovery involved one ringed as a pullus at Old Netley on July 30th 1987 and shot 2451 km east in Nikolayev, Ukraine on Aug. 24th 1988.

## Ring-necked Parakeet                           *Psittacula krameri*

A very scarce visitor, possibly resident.

The first for the county were two near Winchester Sewage Farm on Jan. 9th 1972. These were followed by one at Farlington Marshes on Nov. 26th 1972 and two at Fleet Pond on Oct. 1st 1974. Since then, there have been records in every year with a maximum of ten birds in 1984. Most sightings have been made in the east of the county and along the coastal strip, especially in the Fareham/Cosham/Havant area. Usually, one to three birds have been seen but five flew north-east over Tournerbury on Jan. 8th 1977. During the Atlas Survey, there was only one record suggestive of breeding which involved a pair in suitable habitat in square SU65X near Basingstoke in 1989.

Ring-necked Parakeets occurring in Hampshire possibly originate from the feral populations in Kent and London, although some may be local escapees.

# Cuckoo                                    *Cuculus canorus*

A common summer visitor.

During the Atlas Survey, the Cuckoo was found in most parts of the county. It was absent only from heavily built-up areas, but was rather thinly spread on the chalk in the centre and north-west. This probably reflects a combination of genuine scarcity on arable farmlands and some under-recording. Assuming a density of one to two pairs per tetrad where breeding was confirmed or probable indicates a county population in the range 700-1400 pairs. The British total was estimated at 13,000-26,000 pairs in 1988-91 (New Atlas).

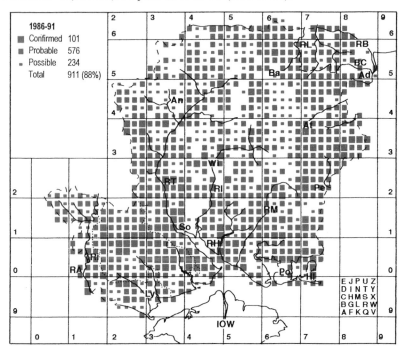

There are few quantitative data to enable any definite statements to be made about population trends in Hampshire. Over the last 30 years, many observers have reported declines, but there have also been increases. In the south-east of the county, numbers were unusually high between 1983 and 1986. This was attributed to the plentiful food supply provided by the abundance of caterpillars of the brown-tail moth *Euproctis chrysorrhea* in the area.

The first Cuckoos are normally heard in the first half of April. However, during 1971-92, there were March records in four years, with the earliest of a bird which flew in off the sea at Sinah on Mar. 15th 1989. Arrival dates in other years were in the period up to Apr. 19th with the average Apr. 5th. The main influx occurs in late April and May when concentrations of newly arrived migrants may be recorded. These are usually in single figures but higher counts have included 50 in an area of 600 m$^2$ at Woodfidley (New Forest) on May 11th 1971 (Christie 1979) and 15 at Timsbury on May 8th 1971. The last birds are usually seen in September. However, during 1971-92, there were October records in four years with the latest of one at Hamble Common on Oct. 11th 1986.

Females of the rufous phase were recorded in 11 years between 1971 and 1992 with a total of 15 in all.

British Cuckoos winter in sub-Saharan Africa, although there has only been one ringing recovery to confirm this, in Cameroon (BWP).

## Yellow-billed Cuckoo                                        *Coccyzus americanus*

Three records. One was shot near Avon Castle on Oct. 30th 1901. More recently, one was at Pennington Marsh on Nov. 6th 1976 and another was found freshly dead in a Woolston garden on Oct. 17th 1985.

The Yellow-billed Cuckoo breeds from southern Canada to central Mexico and winters south to Argentina.

## Barn Owl                                                           *Tyto alba*

A moderately common resident.

K & M described the Barn Owl as "generally distributed and not uncommon". National evidence suggests that it was common at the beginning of the 19th century, but by 1850, with the introduction of game-rearing, it suffered much persecution from keepers. This, together with a series of 15 severe winters between 1860 and 1900, produced a dramatic decline. However, the passing of the Wild Birds Protection Act in 1880 and the banning of the pole trap in 1904 reduced the number of Barn Owls which were killed (Shawyer 1987).

In the National Census of Barn Owls in 1932, the breeding population was reported as 351 pairs, with 150 in the south of Hampshire (Vice-county 11) and 201 in the north (Vice-county 12). The density of much of the north was put at 10-15 pairs per 10 km square (Blaker 1933).

A second National Census organised by the Hawk Trust during 1982-85 found a marked decline since 1932. The population was estimated at 144 pairs, with 104 pairs in Vice-county 11 and 40 pairs in Vice-county 12 (Shawyer 1987). This indicated a decline of 31% in the south and 80% in the north, with the breeding density in the latter area falling to 2.1 pairs per 10 km square. However, three areas, in parts of the Avon and Test valleys and coastal fringe south of the New Forest, were found to have a breeding density of 10-15 pairs per 10 km square, as high as anywhere in Britain. Following the census, the national population was estimated to be 4400 pairs (Shawyer 1987).

The results of the Atlas Survey indicate a slight increase since the Hawk Trust's census. Allowing for territories which overlap adjoining occupied tetrads and the fact that the Atlas Map probably exaggerates the picture in any one year, the current population is estimated to lie in the range 150-200 pairs. It is not certain whether the recent increase is part of an on-going recovery or just a short-term fluctuation reflecting the variable populations of its prey (field voles, wood mice and brown rats) and a series of mild winters. It is virtually absent from the New Forest, where the densities of small mammals are relatively low. It is also very scarce on the chalk in the north of the county, an area which has seen increased agricultural intensification since the 1950s. The loss of suitable

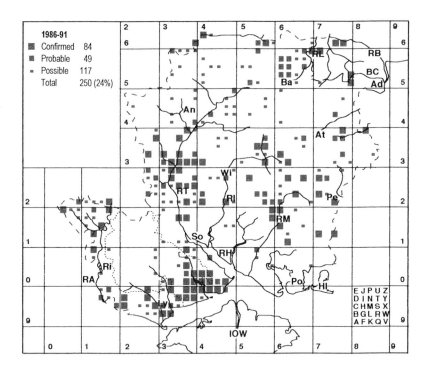

hunting habitat such as hedgerows and rank grassland; shortage of nest-sites due to the demolition of old buildings and loss of trees through Dutch elm disease and gale damage; reduction in food supply through the increased use of rodenticides; and increased road mortality are all thought to have contributed to the decline and are now limiting recovery.

Considerable efforts have been made to increase the Hampshire population. Since 1985, over 200 nest boxes have been erected by HOS and the Hampshire Wildlife Trust, concentrating mainly in the Avon, Test, Itchen and Meon valleys. Some of the boxes are now regularly occupied as nest sites while many are used as winter roosts. Unfortunately, the release of captive-bred birds has not proved successful in all areas. It has been estimated that over 200 captive-bred birds per year were introduced into the wild during the late 1980s but many of these were found dead and in an emaciated condition within six months of release (J Pain *in litt*). Recent legislation has made it illegal to release Barn Owls into the wild without a Department of Environment licence.

Hampshire ringing data indicate that Barn Owls are mostly sedentary but that young birds disperse from their natal areas. Of 34 ringed and subsequently recovered, 29 were found within the county and only one had moved further than 100 km: a bird ringed as a nestling at Bucklers Hard in June 1981 and found dead near Ramsgate, Kent in November of that year. 16 ringed elsewhere in Britain have been recovered in the county, including two ringed as nestlings in Devon and Dyfed and found dead in Hampshire in their first winter. The remainder originated from neighbouring counties.

# Scops Owl                                        *Otus scops*

A rare vagrant. K & M gave details of three specimens obtained at Wilverley Lodge in July 1866, Stokes Bay in June 1884 and near Holmsley in October of that year. One at Totton in 1950 had probably escaped after being brought in by a seaman (Cohen). Subsequently, one was found dead at Highclere on May 11th 1968 and a male held territory in Dummer from May 12th-July 20th 1980. Evidence has recently come to light that the Dummer bird had escaped from captivity.

The Scops Owl is a summer visitor to Europe which breeds as near to England as north-central France. It winters in the northern Afrotropics.

# Snowy Owl                                        *Nyctea scandiaca*

Three records. K & M admitted one which was shot at Burley Wood in the winter of 1848. The next was one seen near Southampton on Jan. 22nd 1946 and finally one was at Pennington Marsh on Mar. 14th 1965. Several seen in southern England in that year were considered suspect as a number were imported for sale (Harber *et al* 1966).

The Snowy Owl has a circumpolar distribution with the nearest regularly-used breeding sites in eastern Greenland and Scandinavia.

# Little Owl                                        *Athene noctua*

A common resident.

K & M mentioned several attempted introductions of the Little Owl prior to 1888 and the discovery of a nest at Holmsley in 1899. It was widespread by the 1920s, although the peak population was probably not reached until some ten years later (Cohen). Nationally, there were decreases in the 1940s, possibly connected with a run of severe winters, and between 1955 and 1963, a period which coincided with the organochlorine pesticide era and included the cold winters of 1961/62 and 1962/63 (Parslow 1973, 68-72 Atlas). Since that time, there has been an ongoing increase in the number reported in Hampshire. While this may be connected with the expansion in birdwatching activity, several observers have reported increases in their local areas. It is probable that the Little Owl is now as numerous in the county as it ever has been.

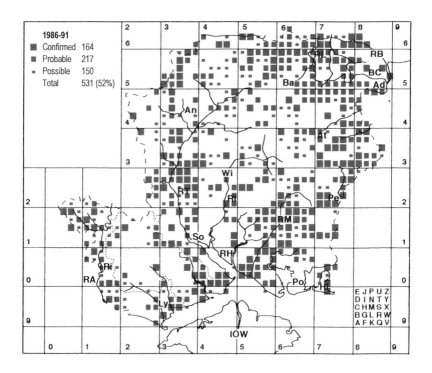

The Atlas Map shows its widespread distribution. It is largely absent from built-up areas and the centre of the New Forest, although it does occur around its perimeter. Its preferred habitats are lightly wooded farmlands and parkland. Most nests are in holes in trees, but they have also been found in straw stacks, sand pits, rabbit burrows, railway embankments and drainage pipes.

There are few quantitative data available. Thorough coverage of 60 km² of suitable habitat in the Crondall/Odiham area between 1979 and 1983 gave an average density of two pairs per tetrad, and a similar density was found in the rural parts of SU60 and SU61 in 1984. Assuming an average density of two pairs per occupied tetrad, this indicates a total population of just over 1000 pairs. However, being a largely nocturnal species, it has clearly been overlooked during the Atlas Survey, especially in those tetrads in the centre and north-west of the county to which relatively few visits were made. Thus the true figure may be nearer 1200 pairs. This indicates that Hampshire holds a significant proportion of the national population, which was estimated at 6000-12,000 pairs in 1988-91 (New Atlas).

Little Owls are usually regarded as sedentary, although ringing has produced evidence for the dispersal of juveniles. Seven ringed in Hampshire were recovered or controlled within 10 km of the ringing site, but there have been six longer distance movements including three of over 100 km. These involved three ringed as pulli, two of which had moved from Oxfordshire to Hampshire and the third in the opposite direction, all within one year of ringing.

# Tawny Owl                                                 *Strix aluco*

A common resident.

Tawny Owls are found at their greatest density in broadleaved woodland, but also occur in coniferous plantations, lightly wooded farmland and urban and suburban areas. Pairs have been reported in many Hampshire cities, towns and villages, breeding in gardens, parks and churchyards and often utilising nest boxes.

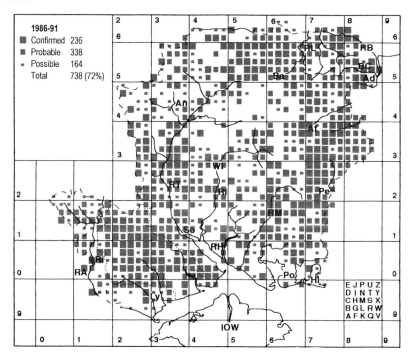

The Atlas Survey shows the species to be widespread, but thinly distributed on the farmlands in the centre and north-west. It is probably genuinely scarce in these areas, although, being a nocturnal species, it will undoubtedly have been overlooked in some tetrads which were poorly covered. This probably accounts for some of the gaps in other areas, e.g. around New Milton, but in Portsmouth it has virtually disappeared. This is attributed to the removal of many large elms following their death due to Dutch elm disease (Portsmouth Group 1991). This, and the spread of residential development, are also blamed for a decline in the Titchfield Haven area (Duffin 1991). Overall, there are insufficient data to be sure of population trends in the county as a whole, but national CBC data show a marked decline since a peak was reached in 1972 (Marchant *et al* 1990). Survey work in the rural parts of SU60 and SU61 in 1984 indicated an average density of four pairs per tetrad. This is probably too high for some areas of Hampshire, although in the extensive woodlands in the New Forest and elsewhere the true figure may be above this level. It is extremely difficult to make an estimate of the total county population, but with registrations in 736 tetrads a figure in excess of 2000 pairs seems possible. The national population in 1988-91 was estimated to be at least 20,000 pairs (New Atlas).

Tawny Owls are largely sedentary. Of 26 ringed in Hampshire and recovered or controlled, 20 moved less than 10 km and only one left the county, moving 137 km north-east to Hampstead Heath, London. These movements largely involved juveniles dispersing from their natal areas.

## Long-eared Owl                                         *Asio otus*

A scarce resident, passage migrant and winter visitor.

The Long-eared Owl is one of Hampshire's most enigmatic species – rarely encountered because of its secretive habits, and thus overlooked to an unknown degree. The available information suggests that it has declined as a breeding species since the early years of the century. This is possibly due in part to competition with Tawny Owls, which have increased during the same period (68-72 Atlas) and are known to kill this species (Mikkola 1983).

K & M described it as "a local resident .... common in suitable districts of the woods of the central district, being particularly numerous in large plantations of larch and fir". They also described it as common in some parts of the New Forest, and quoted Corbin, who found it to be particularly abundant in the Avon valley in the summer of 1902, when specimens in all stages of growth were brought to him.

In 1934, it was said to be common in the New Forest and around West Tytherley. In 1936, three nests were found in the north-east, in the following year two nests were found to the north of Andover, and in 1940 young were heard at Ampfield (*South Eastern Bird Reports*).

The Atlas Map, which includes all the available records since 1951, indicates that a considerable decline has taken place. During the 1960s, breeding was confirmed on several occasions, mostly in the New Forest, but since then the only recorded breeding there was in 1984 (N W Orr *in litt*). Elsewhere during the 1970s, there were a few summer records but only one of successful breeding, at Hinton in 1978. Between 1982 and 1992, breeding was confirmed at ten sites and probable at a further two. These records involved a total of 24 pairs, of which 16 raised a minimum total of 28 young. The maximum in one year was four pairs in 1988. At most sites, owls were present for one or two years only, the exceptions being at Porton Down, where up to three were present in 1984 and 1987-89 but breeding was not confirmed, and at a site near Southampton, where birds were present annually from 1983-90 with young certainly reared in 1986-90. Some Atlas registrations have been moved by up to two tetrads for security reasons.

Pairs have been found in a variety of habitats but are often associated with small groups of conifers, e.g. shelter belts and copses on farmland and in suburban areas. They also occur in large plantations, often containing broadleaved as well as coniferous trees, and may use islands of trees where those all around have been clear-felled. Nests have also been found in beech, hawthorn and blackthorn scrub on downland and in the Test valley.

The Long-eared Owl is clearly overlooked, but it nests sporadically, apparently deserting sites where it has successfully reared young. The

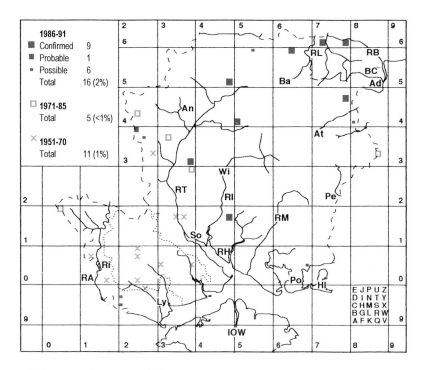

| | | 2 | 3 | 4 | 5 | 6 | 7 | 8 | 9 | |
|---|---|---|---|---|---|---|---|---|---|---|
| **1986-91** | | 6 | | | | | | | | 6 |
| ■ Confirmed | 9 | | | | | | RL | RB | | |
| ■ Probable | 1 | | | | | | | BC | | |
| ▪ Possible | 6 | 5 | | | | Ba | | Ad | | 5 |
| Total | 16 (2%) | | | | | | | | | |
| □ **1971-85** | | 4 | An | | | | | | | 4 |
| Total | 5 (<1%) | | | | | At | | | | |
| × **1951-70** | | | | | | | | | | |
| Total | 11 (1%) | 3 | | | Wi | | | | | 3 |
| | | | RT | RI | | Pe | | | | |
| | | 2 | | | RM | | | | | 2 |
| | | 1 | So | | | | | | | 1 |
| | | | RH | | | | | | | |
| | | 0 | Ri | | Po HI | | | | | 0 |
| | | | RA × | | | | E J P U Z | | | |
| | | | | | | | D I N T Y | | | |
| | | 9 | Ly | | | | C H M S X | | | 9 |
| | | | | | IOW | | B G L R W | | | |
| | | | | | | | A F K Q V | | | |
| | | 0 | 1 | 2 | 3 | 4 | 5 | 6 | 7 | 8 | 9 |

population may be greater following winter invasions (see below), although this is not evident from the limited Hampshire data. In recent years, several observers have made special efforts to locate this species, but without success, so it is clearly scarce. The county population may be as low as 10-20 pairs. In 1988-91, the national total was estimated to be in the range 1100-3600 pairs (New Atlas).

Winter records usually refer to roosting birds near the coast. The most consistently used site has been Farlington Marshes, where the first record was of four in blackthorn scrub on Dec. 2nd 1975. Numbers increased to eight in late December and the last was seen on Apr. 28th 1976. A large invasion into Britain occurred in that winter, which coincided with a crash of voles, the principal prey species, on the continental breeding grounds (Winter Atlas). Subsequently, one or two returned each winter until 1980/81. Another invasion in 1986/87 resulted in a roost being established at Farlington, with birds present from Nov. 22nd and peaking at seven on Dec. 31st. Two were present in April; one was found dead on Apr. 26th while the other summered. One or two were present in the following winter.

At Titchfield Haven, one or two were recorded in seven winters between 1975/76 and 1991/92, with extreme dates of Nov. 30th and Apr. 17th. Some were recorded for a few days only and were possibly migrants, although visits to the roost sites were restricted to minimise disturbance, so they may have been present for longer. Other coastal records have come from Sinah Common (6 birds including up to 3 from Feb. 4th-Mar. 15th 1992), Keyhaven (2, Dec. 31st 1991), Woolston (1, Sep. 4th 1981) and Salterns, Lymington (1, Oct. 1st 1990).

Inland, one or two are recorded in most winters in widely scattered localities, usually coinciding with coastal records.

Three ringed birds recovered in Hampshire give an indication of the origins of passage and wintering birds. One, ringed as a nestling at Overijssel, Netherlands on June 8th 1968 was found near Southampton on Dec. 29th 1968, another ringed as a nestling in Cambridgeshire on May 30th 1974 was killed by a car at Twyford on Aug. 4th 1975, and an adult trapped at Snodland Common, Kent on Jan. 30th 1987 was found dead on the road between Sutton Scotney and Winchester on Mar. 23rd 1988.

## Short-eared Owl
*Asio flammeus*

A regular winter visitor and passage migrant in variable numbers; has occasionally bred.

In Hampshire, most wintering Short-eared Owls occur at coastal marshes and on the downs. They also occur sparingly on the heaths of the New Forest. Away from these areas, records usually refer to migrants although birds sometimes winter elsewhere, e.g. in the lower Avon and lower Itchen valleys.

Numbers vary greatly from year to year, especially on the chalk. Early references to large concentrations include 16 at Bullington in the autumn and winter of 1904, 11 near Overton on Jan. 7th 1929, 26 hunting over 100 acres of stubble near Chilbolton on Nov. 22nd 1953 and up to 12 at Danebury in early March 1954. Fig. 61 shows the total recorded each winter from 1950/51-91/92.

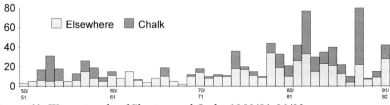

*Figure 61. Winter totals of Short-eared Owls, 1950/51-91/92.*

The fluctuations are probably due to a number of factors in addition to variations in observer coverage. Numbers arriving in Hampshire are likely to be high in years when vole populations have crashed in Europe or severe weather there has forced them to search for more hospitable conditions elsewhere, as in 1978/79 (Davenport 1982). However, the species is known to be highly mobile and nomadic in winter (Winter Atlas), so occasional concentrations on the chalk may reflect high local prey densities. It is interesting to note that numbers vary much less at coastal locations such as Langstone Harbour, where avian prey, which is not subject to such marked populations variations, forms a significant part of the diet, especially in the latter part of the winter (Glue 1972, 1977).

Records from localities with wintering birds in five or more winters during 1950/51-91/92 are summarised in table 63.

| | Period with records | Winters present | Winters with counts of 3+ | Peak counts | |
|---|---|---|---|---|---|
| East Hayling | 1954-89 | 20 | 4 | 7, | 23/11/57 |
| Langstone Harbour | 1950-92 | 41 | 32 | 9, | 15/11/70 |
| | | | | 9, | 11/12/85 |
| Dibden Bay | 1969-92 | 8 | 2 | 6, | 4/1/70 |
| Calshot | 1979-89 | 7 | 2 | 4, | 1/1/82 |
| Lymington/Hurst | 1953-92 | 29 | 3 | 7, | 29/12/81 |
| Ashley Walk | 1957-92 | 19 | 1 | 3, | 24/1/76 |
| Cheesefoot Head | 1970-89 | 13 | 7 | 6, | 19/1/75 |
| | | | | 6, | 18/1/89 |
| Worthy Down | 1974-92 | 7 | 3 | 6, | 8/2/89 |
| Longparish | 1981-92 | 8 | 3 | 8, | 27/12/88 |

*Table 63. Summary of winter records of Short-eared Owls, 1950/51-91/92.*

Counts have also reached five in the Woodcott Down/Ashley Warren area (up to 10 roosting in long grass, December 1985-February 1986; up to 12, December 1988-February 1989), Rushmore Down, Upton (9, Jan. 4th 1980; 7, Jan. 29th 1989) and Southampton Airport (5, Jan. 17th 1985). The species is also regular at Titchfield Haven. Although one or two birds have occasionally wintered, and six were present in severe weather on Feb. 24th 1963, it is principally a passage migrant there. Of 74 recorded between 1950 and 1992, 33 occurred between August and November (max. 4 on Oct. 25th 1982) and 21 in March and April.

The first autumn migrants are usually seen in late August or September, although there have been three records for the first week of August. Passage through the county peaks in late October and early November. At this time, birds apparently on migration are occasionally seen at coastal and inland localities. At regular wintering sites on the coast, birds are normally present continuously from mid-October (sometimes late September) until late March or April. However, at inland localities wintering birds are present in strength only from December-February with a rapid departure in March. Passage is again noted between late March and early May, with several records of birds seen arriving off the sea during this period.

Birds are occasionally recorded well into May. In 1979, one stayed at Ashley Walk until June 30th, and in the following year one was at Langstone Harbour from June 7th-18th and on July 29th. Other mid-summer records include those of single birds at Lower Woodcott Down on June 25th 1976, Winnall Moors on July 23rd 1977 and at John O'Gaunt's Lake (Kings Somborne) on June 1st 1984.

The cumulative monthly totals for 1950/51-91/92 are shown below.

| | Aug | Sep | Oct | Nov | Dec | Jan | Feb | Mar | Apr | May | Jun | Jul |
|---|---|---|---|---|---|---|---|---|---|---|---|---|
| Coast | 15 | 54 | 156 | 192 | 204 | 191 | 167 | 172 | 108 | 13 | 1 | 1 |
| Inland | 1 | 5 | 24 | 88 | 123 | 161 | 107 | 74 | 47 | 5 | 3 | 1 |

Short-eared Owls have bred on several occasions. Early records seem to have been associated with vole plagues. Single pairs nested near Ropley in 1882 and at Bransbury Common in 1892 and 1904 (K & M). Between 1928 and 1930, birds bred regularly and in some numbers in the Overton/Whitchurch/Micheldever area, including three pairs on the Laverstoke Estate in 1928 and seven pairs there in 1930 (Cohen). Recently, pairs were present at Porton Down in 1974, 1976, 1978 and 1980 with successful breeding recorded in the last year. Following the large influx in the winter of 1988/89, one pair nested in the Test valley and successfully reared two young.

The nearest breeding grounds of the Short-eared Owl are in northern Britain and the Netherlands. It is highly nomadic in winter; European birds regularly reach north-west Africa and some cross the Sahara (BWP).

# Nightjar                                     *Caprimulgus europaeus*

A moderately common summer visitor and passage migrant.

Nightjars breed on dry and wet heaths, in open broadleaved woodland, young conifer plantations and clear-felled areas, and in downland scrub. It would appear that in Hampshire they were formerly more widespread than today. K & M stated that the species was "a regular summer visitor to all parts of the county .... most plentiful in the heathy districts but also numerous in the oakwoods, where its eggs are laid in the open spaces amongst the undergrowth of hazel etc.".

Today, the main centres of distribution are on the sandy soils of the north-east and south-west, but it also occurs at various sites elsewhere. In many areas, favoured broadleaved woodlands have been felled and heathlands ploughed up, to be replaced by conifer plantations. In their early stages, these are attractive to Nightjars. Since the mid-1960s, plantations at sites such as Ampfield Wood, Botley Wood, Farley Mount, Lordswood and West Walk have held concentrations at various times, but they are now largely deserted, as the trees are too tall. However, in Ringwood Forest and in the Bramshill/Yateley area, mature conifers have been progressively clear-felled, thus producing a habitat which is once again attractive to the species.

In recent years, three surveys have been undertaken in Hampshire. The coverage achieved by the first, in 1979, was good in the centre of the county, moderate in the north-east and poor in the New Forest. This acted as a pilot for the BTO National Survey in 1981. On that occasion, coverage was considerably improved although still incomplete in the New Forest. The latest national survey, organised by the RSPB and BTO in 1992, achieved the best ever coverage of the county. Table 64 summarises the results of the latter two surveys.

The data suggest a considerable increase between the two surveys, but the estimate of 200-250 pairs in the New Forest in 1981 was clearly too low. More likely, numbers have changed little in the main sites, while gains in recently-felled areas such as Ringwood Forest have offset losses at sites where the habitat is no longer suitable.

|  | 1981 | 1992 |
|---|---|---|
| New Forest | 93 (est. 200-250) | 350 |
| Ringwood Forest | 7+ | 52 |
| Bramshill/Yateley area | 26 | 32 |
| Bricksbury/Long Valley | 20 | 21 |
| Woolmer/Longmoor Inclosure | 31 | 38 |
| Other north-east sites | 15 | 20 |
| Elsewhere | 35 | 17 |
| Totals | 227 (est. 350-400) | 530 |

*Table 64. Counts of churring male Nightjars in 1981 and 1992.*

The provisional results of the 1992 survey indicate a British population of at least 2700 churring males (Morris 1993), so the Hampshire total of 530 represents 19.6% of the total.

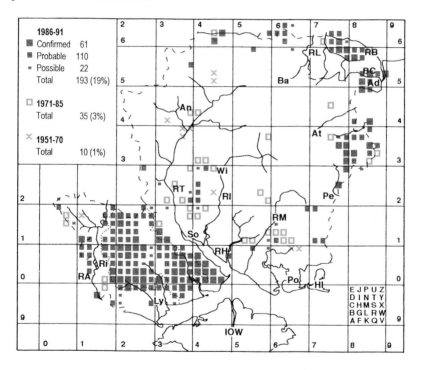

On the Atlas Map, the results of the 1992 survey have been incorporated with registrations from the 1986-91 Tetrad Atlas. Records for 1951-85 are shown separately.

The earliest recorded was one at Farley Mount on Apr. 30th 1977. However, arrivals do not usually start before the second week of May. Between 1971 and 1992, the first churring males were recorded on dates up to May 27th with the average May 10th. Research by Berry and Bibby (1981) has shown that males arrive approximately ten days ahead of females. Being predominantly night migrants, few are seen travelling by day. On the evening of May 22nd 1969, one was first seen far out to sea, before it flew over Hurst Beach and landed briefly on the saltings before flying inland. Another was watched flying in from the sea at Southsea on May 11th 1986.

In mid-summer, birds are occasionally recorded well away from known breeding areas. For example, there are three June records for Titchfield Haven and one was seen at the Nuffield Theatre (Southampton) on June 21st 1975.

Emigration commences during August. In autumn, Nightjars are occasionally recorded at coastal sites. There have been 15 such records since 1974, including seven for the Keyhaven/Pennington area, four for Titchfield Haven and one each for Lisle Court, Needs Ore, Portsmouth Dockyard and Sowley. Last dates for 1971-92 were in the period Aug. 27th-Sep. 26th, with the average Sep. 11th, although being nocturnal this species is no doubt overlooked at this time. There have been four later records of single birds at Farlington Marshes on Nov. 23rd 1958, Dur Hill Down on Oct. 13th 1974 and Titchfield Haven on Oct. 1st 1976 and Oct. 1st 1977.

There have been three ringing recoveries involving Hampshire birds. One ringed as a chick at Damerham in June 1953 was found dead at Nantes, France, 415 km south, on Sep. 8th 1954, another, ringed as a chick in Gloucestershire in July 1973, was found dead at Lordswood on Sep. 7th 1973 and a female, trapped in Wareham Forest, Dorset, in June 1981 was found dead at Ridge on May 15th 1982. European Nightjars winter in Africa south of the Sahara.

## Needle-tailed Swift                           *Hirundapus caudacutus*

One record. One was obtained by Corbin near Ringwood on July 26th or 27th 1879. Apparently it had been seen flying with another over the River Avon for a few days previously (K & M).

The Needle-tailed Swift breeds in the Eastern Palearctic and winters in Australia.

## Swift                                              *Apus apus*

A numerous summer visitor and passage migrant.

The Atlas Map shows a widespread distribution in the county. Although the largest colonies are found in our cities, towns and villages where there are plenty of old buildings to provide suitable cavities for nesting, small groups also occur in isolated buildings such as farms and country houses. There are no quantitative data available to help in the estimation of the county population. Some occupied tetrads will only hold one or two pairs whereas others in built-up areas may contain colonies of 20 or more pairs. Taking the 432 tetrads where breeding was confirmed or probable and assuming an average of 6-10 pairs in each suggests a total in the range 2500-5000 pairs. In 1988-91, the British population was estimated at 80,000 pairs (New Atlas).

The first Swifts are usually seen in mid or late April. The earliest ever were single birds at Calshot on Apr. 10th 1985 and at Bursledon on the same date in 1988. In other years between 1971 and 1992, first arrivals were noted in the period up to Apr. 28th with the average Apr. 18th. In some years flocks of up to 20 are seen before the end of April; in 1989 there was a notable influx on Apr.

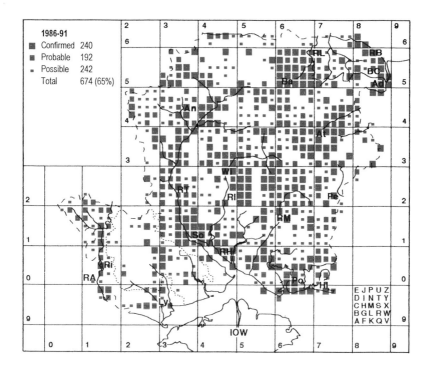

29th, when 100 were at Eversley Gravel Pits, 80 at Titchfield Haven and smaller numbers elsewhere. The main arrival takes place in May, when large numbers may be recorded coming in off the sea, flying north up the main river valleys or over large bodies of water during inclement weather. Counts of birds arriving at the coast and continuing inland have included 823 at Hurst Beach on May 13th 1978 and 1256 at Hill Head in six hours on May 7th 1981.

During the summer, gatherings of several hundreds are frequently recorded over water or areas of arable farmland, especially in adverse weather conditions when they are forced to feed at low levels. Substantial movements also occur, often ahead of advancing weather fronts. Prior to departure, large flocks also form in fine weather, usually building up to a peak in the evening and sometimes moving off in a southerly or south-westerly direction at dusk. Since 1971, four-figure flocks have been recorded on eight occasions, including 2000 in the Keyhaven/Pennington area after thundery showers on Aug. 1st 1972, 2100 feeding over oilseed rape at Old Winchester Hill on July 22nd 1975 and 1500 at Beacon Hill (Warnford) on Aug. 4th 1986.

Most have departed by late August, although a few are seen in September each year. Between 1971 and 1992, there were October records in 11 years with the latest at Liss on Oct. 28th 1990. Three have been seen in November: at Farlington Marshes on Nov. 11th 1969 and Nov. 17th 1974 and Romsey on Nov. 16th 1990.

National ringing data suggest that the main wintering zone of British Swifts is between Zaire and Malawi (BWP). There have been 62 recoveries involving

Hampshire birds, 49 of which were within the county. The remainder were all within Britain, the most distant involving two ringed in Hampshire moving to Yorkshire and one from Yorkshire moving in the opposite direction.

## Pallid Swift                                                    *Apus pallidus*

One record. One flew south-east over Farlington Marshes on May 20th 1983.

The Pallid Swift breeds in the Mediterranean and the Middle East and winters in the northern Afrotropics.

## Alpine Swift                                                      *Apus melba*

A rare vagrant. K & M accepted a sighting of two seen hawking over a pond a mile to the east of Basingstoke on Apr. 28th 1886, although the details they gave are incomplete. They did not know of one that Meinertzhagen claimed at Mottisfont on Sep. 9th and 10th 1894 (Cohen). Since then, there have been six records, as follows:

1911:    Brockenhurst, May 28th;
1946:    Leckford, July 18th;
1964:    Kingsworthy, Apr. 30th-May 7th†;
1965:    Gilkicker Point, Oct. 4th;
1990:    Lymington, Mar. 21st†;
         Titchfield, Mar. 26th.

The last was found trapped in an office block and ringed and released later the same day at nearby Titchfield Haven. There have been several other recent records, almost certainly genuine, which unfortunately have not been sufficiently documented, and so are not included above.

The nearest breeding grounds of the Alpine Swift are in the Alps and southern France. Birds from those areas winter in sub-Saharan Africa.

## Kingfisher                                                      *Alcedo atthis*

A moderately common resident whose numbers may be severely depleted following harsh winters.

As would be expected, the Atlas Map shows a distribution which correlates closely with the main drainage network of the county. However, few nests are located on the principal rivers themselves, most being found along their tributaries, side streams and ditches where there are suitable vertical or overhanging banks. Their apparent absence from stretches of some rivers, e.g. the lower Itchen and parts of the Meon, may be due to a lack of nest sites. Kingfishers also breed in suitable banks at gravel pits, along the Basingstoke Canal and in New Forest inclosures, and occasionally some distance from water, e.g. among the Sand Martin colony at Casbrook Common, in a chalk pit near Alresford and in a bank supporting a bridge over the M3 near Fleet. Nests have also been found twice in the roots of fallen trees and once in a gate post. Although usually absent from the coast in summer, pairs have occasionally bred at sites such as Dibden Bay, Langstone Mill, Netley Shore, Pylewell Park and Titchfield Haven.

The species suffers heavy losses during hard winters, e.g. in 1962/63,

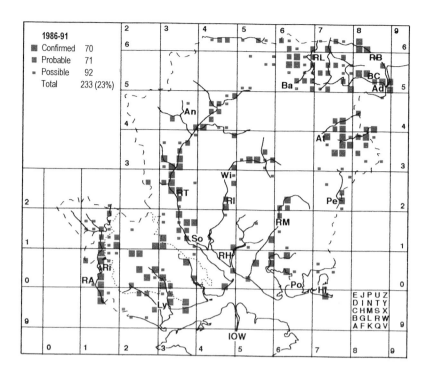

1978/79, four times during the early and mid-1980s and again in early 1991. Although the Atlas Map is a combination of six years fieldwork, it probably presents a fairly accurate picture of the species' distribution following a series of mild winters. Assuming one or two pairs per tetrad where breeding was confirmed or probable, an average of 0.5 pairs per tetrad where it was possible, and making a small allowance for overlooked pairs, suggests a county population in the range 200-350 pairs. In 1988-91, the British total was estimated at 3300-5500 pairs (New Atlas).

After the breeding season, many Kingfishers move to the coast, where returns may be noted as early as the end of June but more frequently from mid-July onwards. Their mobility makes it difficult to assess the total wintering at a particular site. Between Lymington and Hurst, a favoured area, five or six are regularly present when the population level is high. The species' scarcity following severe winters is all too evident, e.g. at Farlington Marshes there was only one sighting during 1985, on Sep. 28th. Ringing confirms that most of those occurring at the coast are juveniles which have dispersed from their natal areas (P M Potts *in litt*). Adults usually remain on their breeding territories throughout the year, only moving away at the onset of freezing conditions.

There have been 46 ringing recoveries or controls involving Hampshire birds. 22 had moved less than 10 km and 13 between 10 and 100 km, the furthest concerning one ringed as a juvenile at Ashurst on May 27th 1988 and controlled at Shoreham-by-Sea, West Sussex on June 22nd 1988. There has been one control of a foreign-ringed bird, which was ringed as a juvenile at Zuid

Flevoland, Netherlands on Sep. 21st 1983 and trapped at Southampton Docks, 494 km WSW, on Oct. 20th of that year. This was only the third British recovery of a foreign-ringed bird, which suggests that continental immigrants make up only a small proportion of our wintering population. However, there have been two records, both during hard weather, which indicate that some movement occurs. One was lost to sight as it flew high to the south from Pennington Marsh towards the Isle of Wight on Feb. 12th 1978 and another was first seen a long way out to sea as it flew in to Sandy Point on Jan. 13th 1985.

## Bee-eater                                   *Merops apiaster*

Two records. Single birds were seen in flight over Oliver's Battery (Winchester), on Aug. 19th 1979 and at Warsash on Aug. 29th 1981.

The Bee-eater breeds from Spain and Morocco to Kazakhstan (and also in South Africa) and winters from Senegal to Ghana and Kenya to South Africa.

## Roller                                      *Coracias garrulus*

A rare vagrant. There have been five records, as follows:

1904:   one near Ringwood, July;
1918:   female shot, New Milton, Sep. 23rd;
1947:   juvenile near Fareham, Sep. 15th-21st;
1955:   one, Butser Hill, May 30th;
1987:   one, Rowbarrow Pond (New Forest), May 30th and 31st.

The Roller breeds in much of the Mediterranean basin, eastern Europe and western Asia and winters in Africa south of the Sahara.

## Hoopoe                                      *Upupa epops*

A very scarce passage migrant; has bred.

Excluding breeding birds, between 1951 and 1992, a total of 147 Hoopoes has been recorded, with sightings in every year except 1992 (fig. 62).

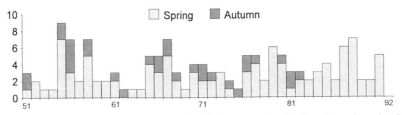

*Figure 62. Spring and autumn totals of Hoopoes (excluding breeding birds), 1951-92.*

The earliest was at Chalton from Feb. 24th-28th 1979. March birds were recorded in eleven years with the earliest at Yateley from 13th-20th in 1979. Most occurred in the following two months, with those in the first half of April mainly at the coast but inland sightings predominating thereafter. There was a scattering of birds in June, July and August, including a pair at Greywell on July 10th 1955, but the others were probably wandering unmated individuals. A slight peak was evident in September, with stragglers into October (fig. 63). The latest was at Sparsholt on Nov. 4th 1972.

Apart from those at Greywell, all records were of single birds, most staying for one or two days only. Long-staying birds included those at Keyhaven from July 15th-Aug. 3rd 1958, Upton Grey from Oct. 11th-24th 1976, Hedge End from Sep. 4th-11th 1981 and Penton Mewsey from May 16th-June 5th 1988.

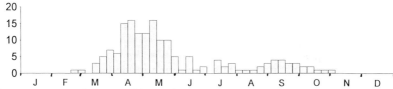

*Figure 63. Cumulative weekly totals of Hoopoes, 1951-92.*

K & M gave details of four breeding attempts, three of them successful, between 1897 and 1902. Since then, single pairs have bred near Sherfield-on-Loddon in 1953 and at Nether Wallop in 1956 (Cohen), at Southwick in 1954 and Knowle from 1956-59 (H E Woods *in litt*), and near Lyndhurst in 1959 (E J Wiseman *in litt*). Apart from the pair at Knowle in 1958, all were successful.

The only winter record is of one at Swanmore in early January 1940 which died during severe weather.

The nearest regularly-used breeding grounds of the Hoopoe are in France. Western European birds winter in small numbers in Iberia and North Africa, but most probably move to sub-Saharan Africa.

# Wryneck                                                    *Jynx torquilla*

A very scarce passage migrant; formerly bred.

K & M described the Wryneck as "a summer visitor to all parts of the county .... perhaps most plentiful along the coast". It bred on heathlands and in parkland, large gardens, orchards and other rural situations. In common with other parts of the country, a major decline took place in the first half of this century. In the 1950s, the only confirmed breeding was at Aldershot and Kingsley in 1950 and Drayton (Portsmouth) in 1954, with six other pairs possibly breeding between 1954 and 1958 (Monk 1963). Subsequently, one summered at Woolmer in 1966 and 1972 and pairs attempted breeding at Cranesmoor in 1968 and Four Marks in 1971. Finally, a pair was seen feeding young in a nest at Newnham in 1975 (C N Clayden *in litt*). Breeding was last confirmed in England in 1987 (*Brit. Birds* 82: 496).

Between 1951 and 1992, numbers of spring migrants showed little change, with never more than three in any year (fig. 64). However, observer coverage was much poorer in the first half of that period and so a decline has probably occurred. The earliest recorded were two at East Tytherley on Apr. 2nd 1961 and one at Shepherds Spring on Apr. 4th 1978, although, when the species bred commonly, it often arrived in the second half of March, with the earliest ever at Emsworth on Mar. 8th 1904. All other occurrences were of single birds on one date only apart from pairs at Stratfield Saye on May 27th 1956 and Rockbourne on May 6th 1972, one at Sinah Gravel Pit on Apr. 20th and 21st 1983 and one at Rowland's Castle from Apr. 13th-16th 1989. Of 23 recorded since 1971, four were on the coast, six were in the New Forest and the remainder were widely spread round the county. There have been no May records since 1981.

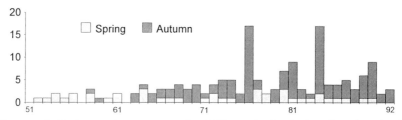

*Figure 64. Spring and autumn totals of Wrynecks (excluding breeding birds), 1951-92.*

Autumn totals during 1951-92 showed an increase in the second half of that period (fig. 64). In the 1950s, only two were seen, but since 1963 there have been sightings in every year except 1978, with peaks of 17 in 1976 and 15 in 1984. Birds were recorded from mid-July onwards, but most occurred between mid-August and late September (fig. 65). The increase reflects improved observer coverage but may be partly genuine. At Farlington Marshes, where coverage has been consistent since the early 1950s, singles occurred in 1959, 1967, 1969, 1973 and 1977 then in every year but two between 1981 and 1990. Other records were from all parts of the county with stays of up to a week not uncommon. In 1976, single birds were at Bishop's Dyke and Kingsworthy from Aug. 22nd-Sep. 4th. All sightings were of single birds apart from two at Nomansland from Aug. 15th-Sep. 7th 1981 and two at Calshot Reclamation on Sep. 2nd 1984. There were five October records, with the latest at Whitenap (Romsey) from Oct. 13th-18th 1990.

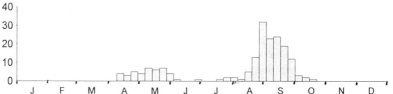

*Figure 65. Cumulative weekly totals of Wrynecks (excluding breeding birds), 1951-92.*

One ringed at Portland Bill on Aug. 25th 1990 was controlled eight days later at Southampton Western Docks. National ringing data indicate that most autumn birds originate from Scandinavia; these largely winter in the northern Afrotropics (BWP).

## Green Woodpecker                                    *Picus viridis*

A common resident.

The highest densities of Green Woodpeckers occur in the New Forest and parts of the north-east, where the mosaic of mature broadleaved woodland, heathland and pasture provides suitable nesting sites and open ground with a plentiful supply of ants, the principal item in the species' diet. In 1971, nine territories were mapped in 173 ha in the Bishop's Dyke area, a density of 5.2

pairs per km$^2$ (Glue 1973). It is also found in well-timbered parkland (even within towns and cities, e.g. at Southampton Common), river valleys and in farmland areas where livestock is reared.

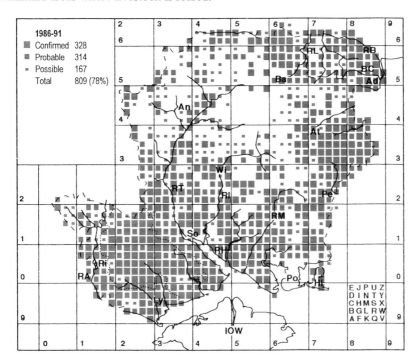

The principal gaps in its distribution are in heavily built-up areas and in some places on the chalk, especially in north central and north-west Hampshire and around Damerham. Although suitable timber is present in many of the chalkland tetrads where it was not recorded during the Atlas Survey, its absence may be explained by the intensive arable farming carried out in these areas, where a lack of well-grazed permanent pasture limits the establishment of ant colonies. However, it can be quite common at sites on the chalk which are undisturbed, such as Porton and Broughton Downs, where the feeding activities of the abundant rabbit population produce a short, dense turf which supports huge populations of the yellow hill ant *Lasius flavus*.

Assuming a density of three pairs per occupied tetrad in the New Forest and north-east, one pair per tetrad on the chalk and two pairs per tetrad elsewhere, a county population of around 1500 pairs is indicated. This suggests that Hampshire holds a significant proportion of the British total, which was estimated at 15,000 pairs in 1988-91 (New Atlas).

There is no evidence that the species is anything other than sedentary. Although few have been ringed, of four recoveries three were re-trapped at the original sites and one had moved 11 km. However, any coastal movement would be difficult to detect as it breeds on or very close to the coast in the Keyhaven area, at Needs Ore and Lepe, on both shores of Southampton Water and at East

Hayling. One was seen to fly from Needs Ore towards the Isle of Wight on Jan. 3rd 1982. At Farlington Marshes, where it does not breed, there were only four records between 1971 and 1992, including one of a bird which stayed from Jan. 26th-Mar. 9th 1986.

## Great Spotted Woodpecker                    *Dendrocopos major*

A common resident.

The Great Spotted Woodpecker occurs in both broadleaved and coniferous woodlands, timbered parkland, on farmland with well-wooded hedgerows and copses, along tree-lined watercourses and in suburban areas with parks and large gardens.

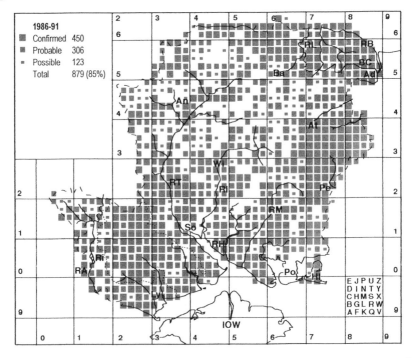

The Atlas Survey showed it to be widely distributed in the New Forest, south-east, east and north-east, but it appears to be rather more localised and less numerous elsewhere, especially on the chalk in the north-west and centre of the county. Assuming a density of two pairs per occupied tetrad on the chalk and four pairs per tetrad elsewhere, a county population of around 3000 pairs is indicated. The British total was estimated at 25,000-30,000 pairs in 1988-91 (New Atlas).

Ringing activities in Hampshire have produced 17 recoveries or controls, all within 13 km of the ringing site. This supports the belief that the species is largely sedentary. However, the occasional occurrence of high-flying birds at the coast in autumn indicates that movements in and out of the county may take place, e.g. one flying high to the north over Farlington Marshes and Portsdown

324

Hill on Oct. 18th 1975, one arriving off the sea from the south-west at Hill Head on Nov. 3rd 1980, two moving west over Titchfield Haven on Oct. 16th 1986 and one flying south from Keyhaven to the Isle of Wight on Sep. 27th 1987.

## Lesser Spotted Woodpecker *Dendrocopos minor*

A moderately common resident.

The Lesser Spotted is the scarcest of the breeding woodpeckers, but also the most easily overlooked. It occurs in various types of broadleaved woodland, including relatively small groups of trees, e.g. in farmland copses, parkland, orchards, and in gardens, cemeteries and parks, sometimes adjacent to built-up areas. It is often found in alders, willows and birches in damp woodland and alongside rivers.

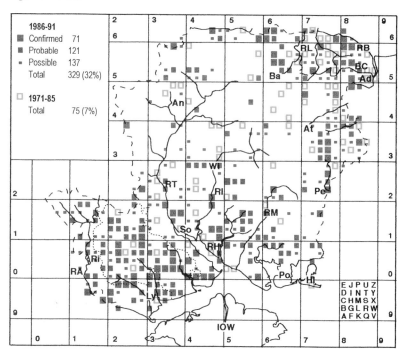

The species is probably most numerous in the New Forest, where Tubbs (*in litt*) estimated a density of 1-4 pairs per km$^2$ in the unenclosed woodland and those parts of the Inclosures which include old oak and beech. The other stronghold is in the north-east, where it is widely distributed and locally common, e.g. at Fleet Pond (2-3 pairs annually) and Stratfield Saye (4 pairs). There is also a concentration in the south-east, especially along the Hamble, Meon and Wallington valleys and in the woodlands to the north of Fareham and Portsmouth. On the Southwick Estate, 12 pairs were found in 3.5 km$^2$ of woodland in 1984 and in the following year 17 pairs occupied 5.0 km$^2$.

Assuming densities of four pairs per occupied tetrad in the New Forest, two pairs per tetrad in the north-east and south-east and one pair per tetrad elsewhere, a county population of around 600 pairs is indicated. However, the species was undoubtedly overlooked during the Atlas Survey. If some allowance is made for the 78 tetrads where it was recorded in 1971-85 but not during the Atlas Survey, then the true figure may be as high as 700 pairs. This represents a significant proportion of the British total, which was estimated at 3000-6000 pairs in 1988-91 (New Atlas).

Although there have not been any ringing recoveries, sight records offer little evidence to indicate that it is anything other than sedentary. The only record suggesting movement was of one which flew west just inland from the shore at Lepe on Sep. 9th 1987. It is very unusual at non-breeding coastal localities. At Needs Ore, the only record was of one on Aug. 27th 1978, while at Farlington Marshes there was one on Dec. 2nd 1974 and a total of ten sightings between March 1986 and November 1987, which suggests wanderings from a nearby breeding locality.

## Short-toed Lark                                   *Calandrella brachydactyla*

One record. One was present along the shingle shoreline between Calshot and Ower from Oct. 9th-19th 1983.

The Short-toed Lark breeds from Iberia and north-west Africa to Mongolia. Most European birds winter in the northern Afrotropics.

## Woodlark                                                 *Lullula arborea*

A moderately common but local resident and passage migrant.

The Woodlark's range has contracted considerably in the last 40 years. It is now confined principally to the heathlands of the New Forest and north-east with only occasional pairs found at other sites. The Atlas Map shows all records for 1951-85 as well as those obtained during the Atlas Survey. For security reasons, registrations in areas currently occupied are mapped on a 10 km square basis. Unfortunately, comparison with earlier years is difficult because of the lack of systematic data and because actual populations are known to fluctuate from year to year depending on the availability of habitat, breeding success and harshness of the winters.

The New Forest population has been monitored since the late 1950s but most counts have been incomplete. The available records suggest a total of possibly

150 pairs in the late 1950s and early 1960s, but then a sharp reduction after the severe winters of 1961/62 and 1962/63. In 1981, 56 pairs were located during the HOS Woodlark Survey and the total was estimated to be 90-100 pairs (Tubbs 1986a). The hard winter of 1981/82 caused a significant reduction and in 1982 the population was estimated to have fallen to 65 pairs. The Forest was again surveyed in 1990, when 51-54 pairs were located in 24 out of 48 tetrads searched. This was close to the 1981 count but the total population was estimated as unlikely to be substantially above 60 pairs (Burges 1991). However, the 1990 survey revealed a less widespread distribution than the Atlas fieldwork carried out in 1986-91, which located Woodlarks in 40 additional tetrads, mostly in the west of the Forest. It is possible that, because of the extended period of the Atlas Survey, the results give an optimistic impression of the range. On the other hand, the 1990 estimate may be too low. The Woodlark is a difficult species to survey because song can be infrequent where population density is low and several visits may be needed to ensure that a pair in territory is not overlooked. Even so, the differences between the two surveys give cause for concern by raising the possibility that the population is contracting in the Forest. This is supported by observations by N W Orr (*in litt*), who suggested that nests, often situated close to footpaths and tracks, were becoming increasingly vulnerable to accidental human destruction, e.g. due to horse-riders, and predation. Some recovery has evidently occurred since 1990; in two areas where a total of three pairs and three singing males was found by Burges in 1990, there were nine pairs and two singing males in 1991 and 13 pairs and two singing males in 1992. On the basis of the available data, the population could be anywhere between 60 and 100 pairs but is most likely to be in the range 70-80 pairs.

In the north-east, numbers rose in the late 1960s and 1970s, presumably due first to recovery from the 1962/63 winter and then in response to the additional habitat provided by heathland fires and the clear-felling of several conifer plantations in the 1970s. In 1981, 59 pairs were located and the population was estimated at 70 pairs. As in the New Forest, numbers were reduced by the 1981/82 winter and in 1982 the population was estimated to have fallen to only 35 pairs. The area was surveyed again in 1988 when 55 pairs were located and the population estimated to be 58 pairs (N Cowie *in litt*). Despite the severe weather of February 1991, data from several sites indicate that numbers have increased further since then.

During the Atlas Survey, none were proved to breed on the chalk where there was evidently a sizeable population until the early 1950s. Records indicate that the species was not uncommon at sites such as Butser Hill, Morestead and Fawley Down, Farley Mount, the Martin/Damerham area and Porton, Perham and Rushmore Downs in the north-west. Numbers declined rapidly following the myxomatosis epidemic of 1954/55, which depleted the rabbit population and allowed the habitat to become overgrown and unsuitable. This, coupled with the severe winters of 1961/62 and 1962/63, probably accounts for the demise of the Woodlark on the chalk, with the last recorded breeding at Farley Mount in 1964. After a gap of almost 20 years, two pairs were located at Porton Down in 1983 and 1984 and a single male held territory there in 1985, 1986 and 1989.

Woodlarks have occasionally bred in other areas. In the early 1980s, up to 11

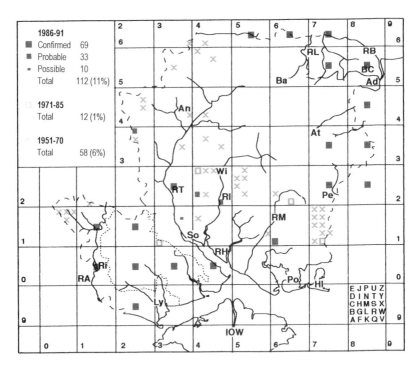

pairs were present in tree and shrub nurseries near Romsey. Numbers declined later in the decade, probably as a result of changes in horticultural practices, and no more than three pairs were recorded during the Atlas Survey. Other records in 1986-91 were of up to four pairs in a tree nursery in the east of the county, a single pair which attempted breeding in a clear-felled woodland near Southwick in 1988 and a male holding territory at Allbrook in the same year.

Based on the above, the total Hampshire population in the early 1990s is estimated to be 145-160 pairs, comprising 70-80 pairs in the New Forest, 65-70 pairs in the north-east and ten pairs elsewhere. The maximum number of pairs or singing males actually counted in a single year was *c.* 126 in 1981, when the total population probably exceeded 160 pairs. Hence, it would seem that the population today is at its highest level since 1981. In 1990, the British population was estimated at 400 pairs (Burges 1991), with about one third of these in Hampshire and a similar proportion in Suffolk.

The Woodlark requires dry, open countryside with short vegetation and bare, often broken, ground to feed. Scattered trees or alternatives such as electricity pylons are needed as song-posts. It nests in grass, heather or bracken, sometimes among low shrubs but often with very little cover and relying on its excellent camouflage for protection when sitting. In Hampshire, such habitat is only created and maintained in suitable condition either by accident or intervention. Heathland cleared of gorse and heather and regenerating after fire provides ideal habitat, but many of the sites are man made – military ranges, worked out gravel pits, golf courses, tree nurseries, forestry clearfells and restocks etc. In the New Forest, sites are created by stock close-cropping the heath. Woodlarks are opportunistic; they are quick to colonise new sites and continue to use them while the habitat remains suitable.

Post-breeding flocks of 15 or more are regular at favoured breeding locations, but they have usually left the heathlands by late October. Most probably winter on nearby farmlands, where recent records include those of ten on plough at Crondall on Nov. 8th 1982, up to nine at Home Farm (Beaulieu) from Feb. 4th-Mar. 18th 1988 and 17 on rough grassland at Hartley Wintney on Jan. 1st 1991. A record of ten in a tree nursery near Romsey on Jan. 3rd 1985 indicates that those breeding in that habitat remain through the winter.

There is evidence of movement, particularly in autumn, but also during hard winter weather and in spring. Between 1976 and 1992, a total of 143 was recorded. At Fleet Pond, where diurnal autumn passage was monitored annually during that period, 78 were noted on dates between Sep. 15th and Nov. 18th, mostly moving in directions between south-east and west. High counts included 11 flying south on Oct. 7th 1991, ten west on Oct. 16th 1992 and ten south-east on Oct. 19th 1992. Autumn records elsewhere included 16 at coastal localities with a maximum of five east at Needs Ore on Oct. 10th 1992. Those seen in winter included three which left south from Pennington Marsh towards the Isle of Wight in hard weather on Jan. 9th 1982 and four flying east with Skylarks at Hill Head in similar conditions on Feb. 6th 1986, while the spring sightings included one which arrived off the sea at Hurst Beach on May 9th 1988. The cumulative monthly totals for 1976-92 are shown below.

| | Aug | Sep | Oct | Nov | Dec | Jan | Feb | Mar | Apr | May |
|---|---|---|---|---|---|---|---|---|---|---|
| Fleet Pond | 0 | 17 | 52 | 9 | 0 | 0 | 0 | 3 | 1 | 0 |
| Elsewhere Inland | 0 | 1 | 16 | 8 | 1 | 1 | 0 | 1 | 0 | 2 |
| Coast | 1 | 0 | 16 | 0 | 1 | 5 | 4 | 0 | 3 | 1 |

Additionally, a further 25 grounded birds have been recorded at coastal sites. Most of these were seen in hard weather, often with Skylarks, but the largest number was ten at Chilling on Nov. 8th 1992. Most of the records probably refer to local birds, although some may involve individuals of East Anglian origin, since local observations and the limited national ringing data indicates that most of that population leaves the area in winter. The origin of those appearing in hard weather is uncertain but they are probably from the continent (Winter Atlas).

# Skylark                                                  *Alauda arvensis*

A numerous resident, passage migrant and winter visitor.

The Skylark breeds commonly throughout the county in most types of open country. The highest densities are recorded on arable farmland but it also occurs on pasture, uncultivated downland, heathland, commons, coastal marshes and wasteland. The main gaps in its distribution are in urban and heavily wooded areas. Apparent absences from a few tetrads on the chalk are probably due to under-recording rather than a genuine lack of birds.

CBC data show that the national Skylark population remained approximately constant from 1965-80 but declined significantly over the following decade (Marchant *et al* 1990). The hard winter of 1981/82 caused a marked reduction, but the continuing decline since has been linked to changes in farming practice,

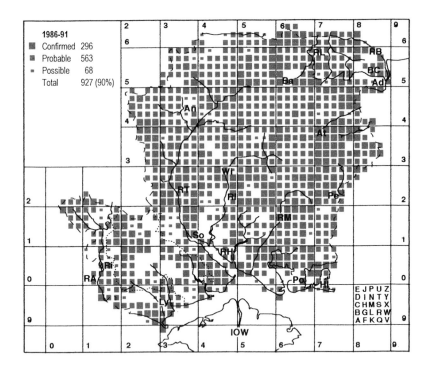

| 1986-91 | |
|---|---|
| ■ Confirmed | 296 |
| ■ Probable | 563 |
| ▪ Possible | 68 |
| Total | 927 (90%) |

particularly the reduction in area of temporary grassland which is the favoured habitat (O'Connor & Shrubb 1986). Data for Hampshire indicate a similar trend, with the county CBC index falling from 100 in 1981 to 78 in 1991. Using national CBC data for 1989, the New Atlas method indicates a county population of around 30,000 pairs and a British total of 2,000,000 pairs (New Atlas).

In autumn, Skylarks are often involved in diurnal passerine movements. Many of those involved may be continental immigrants, either en route to France and Iberia or arriving for the winter (BWP). Passage occurs from mid-September until late November with a peak in the second half of October. Movement at the coast is principally to the west or north-west but at inland sites the direction is rather more variable, with west, south-east and south-west headings favoured. Day totals rarely exceed 100, but larger movements recorded include 585 north-west over Keyhaven on Oct. 16th 1960, 272 west and north-west over Pennington on Oct. 24th 1981 and 292 west over Sinah Common in two hours on Oct. 20th 1983. Daily coverage at Fleet Pond during 1987-92 produced a total of 1547 moving over on dates between Sep. 17th and Nov. 27th. Annual totals varied between 180 and 492 (in 1989) with a peak of 140 south-east on Oct. 29th 1991. Grounded flocks rarely exceed 200 in autumn, there being only six such records during 1971-92 with the largest of 350 in a maize field at Bishopstoke on Nov. 2nd 1980.

Between December and early March, flocks of 300-500 are more frequent but much larger numbers occur during severe weather. Heavy snowfall may induce massive movement, as on Dec. 31st 1961, when 40,000 moved south-east at Gilkicker Point, 37,000 east at Titchfield Haven and 8400 west at Needs Ore. The next day, 7000 moved west at Gilkicker, this being the usual direction of movement in such conditions. Movement on such a large scale was not recorded again until the winter of 1978/79. Following heavy snowfall on Dec. 30th, passage was reported at several sites the next day with a maximum of 2760 west in two hours at Fleet Pond. On Jan. 1st, flocks were passing west on a broad front from the coast to the north of the county. In the Salterns/Hurst area, the movement was the largest ever witnessed, with birds moving from first light and reaching a rate of 5000 per hour at one time. Similar observations were made at several other localities and overall tens of thousands must have been involved. Several notable concentrations were located during the next few days with the largest of 2850 at Hamble Lane on Jan. 6th. Following further snowfall, a second heavy movement took place on Jan. 27th. This was largely noted at coastal sites, including Titchfield Haven, where an estimated 25,000 moved west between 1330 and 1700 hrs. A flock of 2000 was at Blashford, and the next day similar numbers were at Timsbury and Easton, but the latter birds had moved on within two hours. Another large movement took place on Dec. 12th 1981, again after heavy snow. This was principally recorded in the north-east, where a total of 8500 moved between south and west at four sites including 3000+ west at Hill Side. Smaller movements were recorded during most other cold spells. There has been little evidence of return movement with the onset of milder conditions.

Flocks are generally small in March and April, few reaching three figures. In contrast to the autumn, no diurnal movements of note have been recorded in spring.

There have been no recoveries of Hampshire-ringed pulli, but national data suggest that the British population is resident (BWP). There are two Hampshire ringing records which indicate that the winter population is augmented by continental immigrants: an adult trapped at Micheldever on Feb. 2nd 1954 which alighted on a boat 1788 km north-east in the Gulf of Bothnia, Finland on May 5th of that year, and one ringed in the Netherlands on Oct. 13th 1984 found dead at Winnall Moors, 395 km WSW, on Mar. 7th 1985.

# Shore Lark                           *Eremophila alpestris*

A rare late autumn passage migrant and winter visitor. There have been 15 records since 1955, as follows:

1955:    5, Pennington Marsh, Oct. 31st;
1955:    1, Warsash, Nov. 9th;
1959:    3, Black Point, Nov. 23rd;
1959:    3, Sinah Common, Dec. 29th;
1969:    3, Hurst Beach, Dec. 10th-Apr. 7th 1970, 1 remaining until Apr. 16th;
1971:    1, Black Point, Jan. 10th;
1972:    1, Farlington Marshes, Oct. 12th;
1975:    1, Farlington Marshes, Oct. 12th;
1977:    2, Needs Ore Point, Oct. 27th;
1978:    1, Ashley Walk, Nov. 4th;
1978:    1, Keyhaven, Dec. 14th;
1987:    1, Browndown, Jan. 15th;
1987:    1, Weston Shore, Jan. 21st;
1990:    1, Warsash, Dec. 10th and 19th.
1991:    1, Hayling Oyster Beds, Nov. 23rd and 24th.

The predominance of autumn and early winter sightings, and the species' increasing scarcity, are consistent with the pattern at its regular winter haunts elsewhere in Britain. Birds occurring in Britain probably originate from Scandinavia and western Russia, although there are no ringing recoveries to confirm this.

# Sand Martin                                           *Riparia riparia*

A common breeding summer visitor and numerous passage migrant.

The first normally arrive in the second half of March. Apart from an exceptionally early bird at Broadlands Lake on Feb. 27th 1990, the records for 1971-92 show first dates in the period Mar. 10th-Apr. 7th with the average Mar. 20th. The main period of arrival occurs between mid-April and the first week of May, although passage continues well into May in most years. During this time, concentrations of feeding birds are often found over open water or in sheltered river valley sites, particularly in cold or wet weather. Spring gatherings or roosts exceeding 200 have been recorded on at least 15 occasions, the largest being of 350 at Titchfield Haven on Apr. 21st 1977, and 350 at Fleet Pond on May 4th

1979 and Apr. 13th 1982. Spring roosts have been recorded at these two sites in most years, but rarely elsewhere in the county. Visible passage is usually light, three-figure day totals being unusual. High counts include 200 flying north at Blashford on May 7th 1978 and 270 north at Fleet Pond on Apr. 13th 1990. Ringing evidence indicates that Hampshire Sand Martins arrive on a broad front, as shown by spring recoveries from Tunisia, Malta, Italy, eastern and western France and the Channel Islands.

Sand Martins are distinctly local, being largely dependent on working or disused sand and gravel pits. Formerly there were coastal colonies in cliffs at Brownwich (deserted by 1961) and between Barton-on-Sea and Hordle (where breeding was last recorded in 1978). Small numbers have occasionally nested in other situations, although always near water: e.g. from 1961-67 up to 28 pairs nested in drainage pipes under a bridge over the River Itchen at Winchester, and from 1988-90 up to nine pairs bred in drainage holes over the moat at Fort Brockhurst (Gosport). The Atlas Map shows all known breeding sites occupied during 1951-85 as well as those in use during the Atlas Survey.

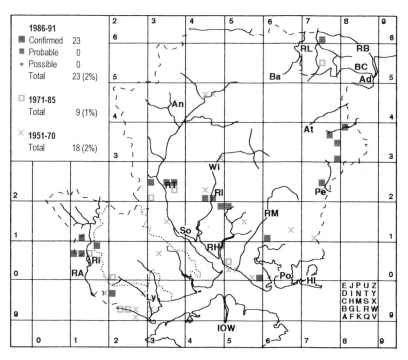

Prior to 1960, the Sand Martin was probably relatively common and widespread, breeding wherever there were suitable sand pits, river banks and coastal cliffs. However, the population has always fluctuated considerably. It reached a peak of over 5000 pairs during the mid-1960s, although it may have been even higher, as several colonies were not surveyed at that time. Numbers "crashed" spectacularly throughout Britain and western Europe in 1969, again in 1984 and more recently in 1991, and this is reflected in the recorded totals of the

Hampshire population (fig. 66). The main cause of these dramatic declines is considered to be the effect of severe and continuing drought in the species' key wintering area – the Sahel region of West Africa (cf. Whitethroat and Sedge Warbler).

From 1987 onwards, an annual survey of all breeding Sand Martins has been carried out by HOS. The results reveal the presence of between eight and 14 colonies, with the largest at Carter's Clay, Lockerley (800 pairs in 1988), Somerley Sand Pit, Ringwood Forest (600 pairs in 1990) and Fair Oak (449 pairs in 1990). The mean colony size (excluding single pairs) varied between 145 and 227 pairs. After the crash of 1984, when numbers fell to an all-time low of perhaps 300-400 pairs, the population steadily increased to reach a peak of around 3000 pairs in 1989, followed by a fall in 1990 and a further crash in 1991 to around 1350 pairs. Numbers recovered slightly in 1992, assisted by the opening of three large new quarries. From available information, the Hampshire total is believed to be significant in the context of southern England, but comparative data are sparse. The British population was estimated at 77,500-250,000 pairs during 1988-91 (New Atlas).

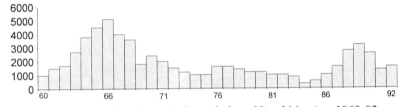

*Figure 66. Annual totals of occupied nest holes of Sand Martins, 1960-92.*

Following the destruction of a breeding colony at Sleaford in June 1986, and evident threats to other colonies, special efforts were made by a group of HOS members to help safeguard and provide suitable breeding cliffs at all known colonies, in cooperation with the owners and managers. As a result, nesting cliffs were specifically created or reserved for Sand Martins at many sites, notably at Bramshill, Casbrook Common (near Timsbury), Carter's Clay, Fair Oak and North Boarhunt. This timely action helped to maintain some colonies which would otherwise have certainly disappeared, and clearly demonstrated the potential importance of positive management techniques for this species. For example, a former breeding site at Allbrook, which had become completely overgrown, was restored in 1988, and over 90 pairs quickly returned to nest there after an absence of more than ten years.

By mid-June many of the first broods have fledged, and at least some of these juveniles are known to move quickly away from their natal colonies, to visit other colonies and form early autumn roosts. The results of ringing reveal that by early or mid July, other juveniles have also moved into Hampshire from colonies to the north and west. During late July and throughout August, passage is well under way, and most juveniles appear to move eastwards into Sussex and Kent, although there are several examples (from ringing) of northerly or westerly autumn movements. In recent years a large proportion of Hampshire-ringed Sand Martins (both adults and juveniles) have been controlled at

Icklesham in East Sussex, particularly between mid-August and mid-September, which indicates that south-eastern England is the major emigration point.

Visible autumn passage is recorded from about the third week of July to the second week of September, with the heaviest movement from mid to late August. Most coastal passage is in an easterly direction, although westerly and southerly movements also occur, e.g. 2000 flying south at Titchfield Haven on Sep. 3rd 1961. Numbers have fallen in line with the reduced breeding population; in the 1980s the largest day total recorded was of 200 moving east at Needs Ore on Aug. 3rd 1988. Roosts at coastal and inland reed beds reach a peak at this time. Counts have exceeded 2000 on five occasions with a maximum of 3500 at Titchfield Haven on Aug. 10th 1977. During the 1980s and early 1990s, such roosts have been significantly smaller, the largest being of 750 at Fleet Pond on Aug. 22nd 1983. Other exceptional autumn counts include 1500 at Needs Ore on Aug. 24th 1971 and 3000+ at Warsash on Aug. 18th 1977.

Departure is earlier than the other hirundines, most having left by early October. The records for 1971-92 show last dates between Sep. 28th and Nov. 12th with the average Oct. 14th. There are only three November records, with the latest at Langley (Fawley) on 12th in 1985. Hudson (1973) mentions one present near Havant from Nov. 29th 1906-Jan 23rd 1907.

Foreign recoveries of Hampshire-ringed birds have included 19 from the north and west coasts of France (14 in August – earliest Aug. 5th – and five in September) and seven from Spain (4 in September – earliest Aug. 30th). There are also eight records of birds ringed as juveniles in France on dates between July 14th and Sep. 3rd which were controlled at Hampshire colonies in later breeding seasons.

Finally, eight Sand Martins from Hampshire have recently been controlled at the Djoudj National Park in Senegal, an important wintering and passage site for British Sand Martins and other species. Four of these had been ringed at colonies (Kingsley and Timsbury) and the other four were trapped on passage at Titchfield Haven. All were found in Senegal between Jan. 13th and Apr. 2nd 1991.

# Swallow                                    *Hirundo rustica*

A numerous breeding summer visitor and abundant passage migrant.

The Swallow breeds commonly throughout the county, occurring in suburbia, country villages and farmland where a wide variety of buildings, out-houses, sheds and other man-made structures are utilised as nest sites. As the Atlas Map shows, it is absent only from areas where such artefacts are not available, e.g. in parts of the New Forest and in heavily built-up areas.

There is little information about breeding numbers or population trends in the county. CBC data show that the national population has fluctuated through the 1970s and 1980s, probably in response to conditions in the wintering areas of South Africa and on the migration routes across the Sahara (Marchant *et al* 1990). Using national CBC data for 1989, the New Atlas method indicates a county population of around 10,000 pairs. However, Swallows are common around Hampshire's many villages and numerous farms, and so a total in the

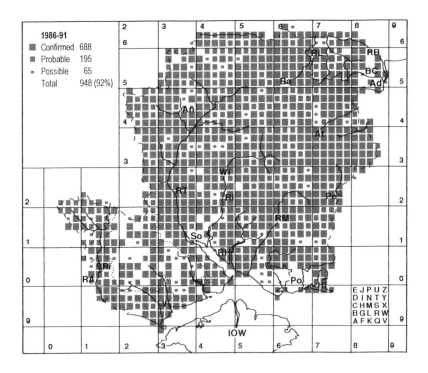

| 1986-91 | |
|---|---|
| ■ Confirmed | 688 |
| ■ Probable | 195 |
| ▪ Possible | 65 |
| Total | 948 (92%) |

range 12,000-15,000 pairs is considered more appropriate. The British population was estimated at 570,000 pairs.

The first birds usually arrive in late March. In 1971-92, first dates were between Mar. 11th and Apr. 1st with the average Mar. 25th. However, the earliest ever was one at Gosport on Mar. 10th 1960. Migration normally continues at a slow pace until late April and peaks in early May. At this time, northward movements of up to 300 per day are frequently recorded. Higher totals include 800 arriving from the south at Hill Head on May 3rd 1980 and 1852 doing likewise there on May 7th 1981. Small gatherings of up to 150 have been occasionally recorded roosting in *Phragmites* during the spring passage period.

The main period of emigration is from late August until early October, when large roosts form in *Phragmites*. Peak numbers normally occur in early September, although in warm autumns the highest counts have been made at the end of the month. At Titchfield Haven, counts exceeded 2000 in seven years between 1971 and 1981 with maxima of 5500 on Sep. 7th 1976 and Sep. 25th 1980. From 1982-87, numbers did not exceed 1000 but in the subsequent three years the peak counts were in the range 1800-2200. At Farlington Marshes, numbers exceeded 3000 in four years between 1971 and 1977 with peaks of 5000 on Sep. 1st 1972 and Sep. 12th 1973, but since then have only reached 1000 once. Four-figure counts have also been made at Lower Test Marshes (2000, 1978 and 1980), Fleet Pond (1500, 1980 and 1985), Shawford (4000, 1983 and 2000, 1984) and Timsbury (1200 in maize, 1987).

The heaviest movements occur in the second half of September. At inland localities, the direction is normally south, but on the coast most birds follow the shore, usually in an easterly direction. Movements of 1000-2000 per hour are regularly recorded, especially in light south-easterly winds. Exceptional records were of 30,000 moving west at Titchfield Haven on Sep. 25th 1958 and 14,000 east at Lepe in 1½ hours on Sep. 19th 1987. Passage continues into October although numbers are much lower, counts such as 1000+ NNW at Warsash on Oct. 13th 1976 and 1300 east at Titchfield Haven on Oct. 2nd 1987 being exceptional. Small numbers remain in late October and November. During 1971-92, last dates were between Nov. 11th and Dec. 22nd with the average Nov. 27th. This excludes records of possible wintering birds, which were of one at Stanmore Hotel (Winchester) and Winchester Sewage Farm throughout December 1974 until Jan. 3rd 1975, three at Alresford on Jan. 1st 1987 and two there on Jan. 1st 1991.

The wintering areas of birds ringed in Hampshire are indicated by recoveries between November and March in Cape Province (3), Transvaal (2), Natal and Zimbabwe (1 each). Two found dead in West Africa in October presumably had been en route to their wintering quarters. Recoveries in spring in Tunisia, Algeria and Morocco suggest the routes taken, while controls at autumn roosts at Titchfield Haven and Farlington Marshes show that most present in August are locally bred whereas in September birds from Scotland and northern England are also present.

## Red-rumped Swallow                                   *Hirundo daurica*

One record. One was at Farlington Marshes on Nov. 14th 1987. This was one of an influx of over 50 to Britain in the late autumn of that year (*Brit. Birds* 81: 572-577; 82: 537).

The nearest breeding grounds of the Red-rumped Swallow are in the Mediterranean basin. Birds from these areas are believed to winter in the northern Afrotropics.

# House Martin                                    *Delichon urbica*

A numerous breeding summer visitor and abundant passage migrant.

The distribution of the House Martin is very similar to the Swallow's, both species relying almost exclusively on buildings and other man-made structures for nest sites. House Martins appear to be more tolerant of dense urbanisation than the Swallow and penetrate further into built-up areas around Southampton, Gosport, Portsmouth and in the north-east. They are quick to occupy new sites and have almost certainly benefited from the rapid growth of modern housing and industrial estates in the county. In contrast, as the Atlas Map shows, they are less widespread in agricultural areas.

Nationally, CBC data show that the population, while fluctuating, has been fairly stable over the past 25 years. On the basis of limited survey data, Tatner (1978) estimated an average national density of 2 nests per km$^2$. This seems too low for Hampshire. Assuming a range of 3-4 pairs per km$^2$, a county population of 11,000-15,000 pairs is indicated. The British population was estimated at 250,000-500,000 pairs in 1988-91 (New Atlas).

The first birds are normally recorded in late March or early April. The records for 1971-92 show first dates between Mar. 20th and Apr. 10th with the average Apr. 2nd. This excludes two exceptionally early birds at Broadlands Lake on Mar. 11th 1981 and Mar. 2nd 1990. An unprecedented early influx occurred in 1989, with 12 at Eastleigh Sewage Farm on Mar. 27th and 105 at six localities, including 50+ moving north at Hale, on 29th. In most years, however, few are recorded before late April, with the peak passage in the first half of

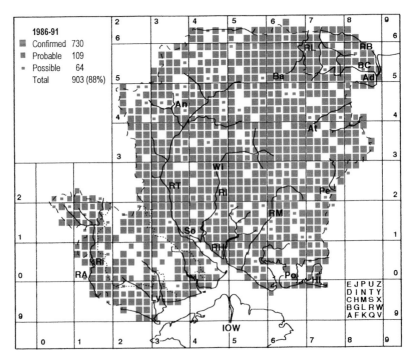

338

May. Spring gatherings have only three times exceeded 400 with a maximum of 700 at Eastleigh Sewage Farm on May 6th 1978. The largest movements recorded were of 300+ flying north over Blashford on May 7th 1978 and 300 arriving from the south at Titchfield Haven on the same date in 1981.

The main autumn passage takes place between mid-September and mid-October. The heaviest migration ever recorded took place in cold easterly winds and rain on the morning of Oct. 15th 1981, when a large westerly movement was noted at several coastal localities including an estimated 24,000 at Titchfield Haven. Other coastal movements recorded include 4800 west at Titchfield Haven in 30 minutes on Sep. 22nd 1979, 5000 north-east at Hamble Common in 30 minutes on Oct. 22nd 1983 and 4200 east at Warsash on Oct. 2nd 1987. 5000 were feeding over Titchfield Haven on Sep. 30th 1989. Movements at inland localities are generally in a southerly direction, e.g. 3000 south-east over Winchester in 45 minutes on Sep. 30th 1985 and 3700 south and south-west over Fleet Pond on Sep. 29th 1989. Few are seen after late October although 100 were around Calshot Spit on November 1st 1985. During 1971-92, last dates were between Oct. 31st and Dec. 22nd with the average Nov. 23rd. There were six December records in four years with the latest at Beaulieu Mill Pond on Dec. 22nd 1982 and Eling Tide Mill on Dec. 20th and 21st 1988.

The only wintering record is of one at Gilkicker Point in January and early February 1967.

In contrast to the Swallow, there have been no recoveries to indicate the wintering areas of birds ringed in Hampshire or indeed Britain. Sightings have been made over a wide area of tropical Africa but the major wintering area is yet to be discovered. The only long distance recoveries involving Hampshire birds were of one trapped in Malta on Apr. 12th 1979 and found moribund at Fawley, 2060 km north-west, on May 1st 1986, and a juvenile trapped in Strathclyde on Aug. 28th 1986 and controlled at Titchfield Haven on Sep. 25th 1986.

# Richard's Pipit                              *Anthus novaeseelandiae*

A rare passage migrant. Most Richard's Pipits have occurred in late autumn on coastal grassland or waste ground. However, among the 14 records, there have been two in spring, one in summer and one at an inland sewage farm. All except the first have involved single birds.

| | |
|---|---|
| 1955: | 2, Titchfield Haven, Apr. 16th; |
| 1960: | Needs Ore, Oct. 4th; |
| 1969: | Pennington Marsh, Nov. 1st; |
| 1970: | Keyhaven, Oct. 14th; |
| | Keyhaven, Nov. 15th and 21st; |
| 1973: | Warsash, July 21st (one of the few British records in that month); |
| 1974: | Needs Ore, Oct. 6th; |
| 1974: | Keyhaven, Nov. 3rd; |
| 1975: | Keyhaven, Oct. 1st; |
| 1980: | Keyhaven, Sep. 21st; |
| 1981: | Camp Farm Sewage Farm (Aldershot), Oct. 31st-Nov. 4th; |
| 1983: | Calshot Reclamation, Oct. 30th-Nov. 13th; |
| 1988: | Gilkicker Point, Nov. 5th; |
| 1992: | Brownwich, Apr. 29th. |

Richard's Pipits occurring in Britain probably belong to the race *richardi*, which breeds from western Siberia east to Mongolia. Most winter in the Indian sub-continent and south-east Asia, but small numbers have also been found in Spain and the Sahel region of Africa.

## Tawny Pipit                                            *Anthus campestris*

A rare autumn passage migrant. There have been 12 records of single birds, including three inland, as follows:

| | |
|---|---|
| 1963: | Needs Ore, Sep. 3rd; |
| 1965: | Gilkicker Point, Sep. 8th-11th; |
| 1967: | Gilkicker Point, Sep. 17th; |
| 1969: | Silchester, Sep. 13th-19th; |
| 1972: | Pennington Marsh, Sep. 3rd; |
| 1976: | Shepherds Spring (Andover), Oct. 16th; |
| 1977: | Dibden Bay, Sep. 4th-6th; |
| | Shepherds Spring (Andover), Sep. 11th; |
| 1982: | Sinah Common (Hayling Island), Oct. 9th; |
| 1985: | Farlington Marshes, Aug. 31st; |
| | Dibden Bay, Sep. 1st; |
| 1988: | Titchfield Haven, Oct. 2nd. |

The nearest breeding grounds of the Tawny Pipit are in France and the Low Countries, but it is declining in these areas. Western European birds winter in the Sahel region of Africa.

## Olive-backed Pipit                                      *Anthus hodgsoni*

One record. One was in a garden at Sway from Nov. 13th-26th 1987.

The Olive-backed Pipit breeds in much of the Eastern Palearctic and winters in the Indian sub-continent and south-east Asia.

## Tree Pipit                                               *Anthus trivialis*

A locally common summer visitor and passage migrant.

The Tree Pipit is common in parts of the New Forest, Ringwood Forest and the heaths in the Tadley area and the north-east, but is locally distributed elsewhere in the county. Heathland which is being invaded by birch or pine provides ideal conditions (*cf.* Meadow Pipit), but rough parkland, woodland edges, clearings and forestry plantations are also utilised provided there is sufficient ground cover for nesting and feeding and where trees or other suitable posts are available for song and display.

There has never been a coordinated survey of the county but counts for both the New Forest and the north-east heaths have been made. In the latter area, 137 pairs or singing males were located in 1971 with the main concentrations 23 at Longmoor Inclosure, 24 at Ludshott Common and 20 at Yateley Common. More recent counts include 24 pairs at Longmoor, 25 at Yateley and 28 in the Bricksbury Hill area in 1980, and 108 pairs at nine sites in 1987. The latter count excluded key sites such as Bricksbury and Longmoor as well as several others each holding a few pairs. When these are taken into account, the total for the north-east of the county is probably in the range 200-250 pairs.

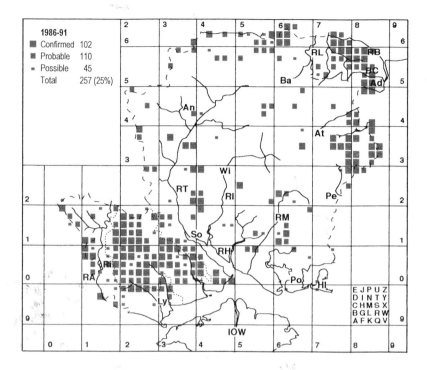

A survey of the New Forest in 1982 found the species to be widespread and generally associated with young birch woodland; the population was estimated at 300 pairs. Elsewhere, high concentrations can occur when conditions are suitable, e.g. ten pairs in Botley Wood in 1982 and 12 pairs in Ringwood Forest in 1988, but generally numbers are low. The total county population, based on 300 pairs in the Forest, 200-250 pairs in the north-east and 100-150 pairs elsewhere, is thus estimated to lie in the range 600-700 pairs. The British total was estimated at 120,000 pairs in 1989 (New Atlas).

The earliest ever was one at Bishop's Dyke on Mar. 16th 1992. In other years during 1971-92, first arrivals were recorded between Mar. 19th and Apr. 17th with the average Apr. 1st. Spring passage, indicated by records for non-breeding localities, is generally small and peaks in mid-April. The only double-figure counts have been of 19 flying north-west over Enham Alamein on Apr. 16th 1978, 18 at Old Winchester Hill on Apr. 22nd 1984 and 15 moving north over Dibden Bay on Apr. 18th 1985.

Autumn passage, which appears to involve much larger numbers than in spring, peaks in the second half of August. The highest counts have been made at or near the coast, e.g. 80 moving south and south-east over Keyhaven on Aug. 16th 1971, 200+ flying west at Warsash on Aug. 17th 1974, 48 moving west over Portsdown Hill and 60 at Sinah Common, some of which left west, on Sep. 6th 1983, and 40 moving west over Titchfield Haven on Aug. 28th 1987. Inland, the largest numbers recorded were 25 at Bramshill on Aug. 23rd 1983 and 36, including 28 flying over, at Old Winchester Hill on Aug. 26th 1984. Most have departed by late September. The latest ever was at Dibden Bay on Oct. 25th 1979; in other years during 1971-92, final sightings were made on dates between Sep. 12th and Oct. 22nd with the average Oct. 2nd.

Hampshire ringing activities have produced only two local recoveries. National data indicate that British Tree Pipits fly across the Bay of Biscay direct to Portugal in autumn, but there have been no recoveries in the presumed winter quarters in tropical West Africa north of the Gulf of Guinea (BWP).

## Meadow Pipit                                   *Anthus pratensis*

A locally common resident, numerous passage migrant and winter visitor.

The Meadow Pipit breeds commonly in the New Forest and on rough coastal grassland. It also occurs, though less commonly, on the north-east heathlands and on uncultivated downland but is only thinly scattered across the remaining intensively-farmed heart of the county. On heathland, there is some overlap with the Tree Pipit although the latter is more numerous where birch and pine invasion becomes significant (as on many of the north-east heaths).

The Meadow Pipit's preference for non-agricultural land means that, in the long term, numbers may have declined as marginal land has been brought into cultivation or urbanised (C & T). More recently, CBC data show that, for the country as a whole, numbers remained approximately constant through the 1970s but declined sharply during the first half of the 1980s. In Hampshire, the total recorded on five CBC plots shows a similar pattern, with a decline from 31 pairs in 1981 to ten in 1987 but then a rapid recovery to 29 in 1989.

Given the fluctuations in numbers and the preference for non-agricultural land, it is unlikely that the changes are related to farming or land-use practices. The pattern is consistent with population decreases following the hard winters of 1981/82 and 1985/86, but this would seem to be at odds with ringing evidence, which shows that most British Meadow Pipits winter further south in Europe (Winter Atlas). A possible explanation is that a significant proportion of the local breeding population does not move very far in winter. The only evidence from Hampshire ringing activities to support this is of one, ringed as a pullus in July 1967 and recovered in January 1971 in Calvados, France, 219 km south-east. Firmer evidence comes from birds ringed at Frensham, just across the county boundary in Surrey. Of ten ringed as pulli and recovered or controlled in winter, four were found in Iberia, one at Yarmouth, Isle of Wight and five within 20 km of the ringing site (P G Davis pers. comm.).

Estimation of the breeding population is difficult for two reasons: the species has never been surveyed in the New Forest or on the coast and breeding densities vary considerably from one part of the county to another. Using national CBC data for 1989, the New Atlas method indicates a county population of around 10,000 pairs. However, this is considered to be far too high. Assuming a density of 10-15 pairs per occupied tetrad in the New Forest and on the coast and 2-4 pairs per tetrad elsewhere suggests a population in the range 2500-4000 pairs. The British population was estimated at 1.9 million pairs in 1989 (New Atlas).

Outside the breeding season, by far the greatest numbers occur during the migration periods, when diurnal movements are often conspicuous. Spring

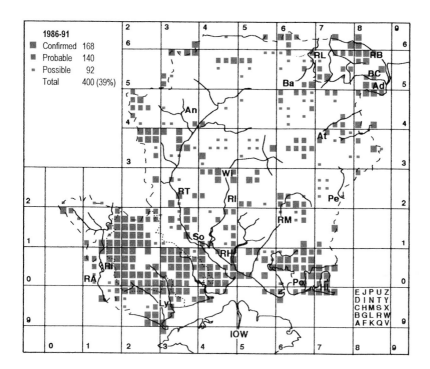

passage, which is principally to the north or north-west, peaks in late March and is particularly heavy in fair weather with light winds. Day totals of 300-500 are regularly recorded at individual sites; those to exceed this level have been of 1,461 moving north and north-west over Hayling Bay in 5½ hours on Mar. 24th 1985, 626 NNW at Tunworth in 2½ hours on Apr. 1st 1986, 815 north over Hill Head on Mar. 25th 1987 and 711 north over Hayling Bay in three hours on Mar. 26th 1988. Influxes are also recorded on the ground but counts have not exceeded 200.

In autumn, heavy diurnal movement may be observed at any time between late September and mid-October. At Fleet Pond, systematic daily watching during 1987-92 produced a total of 7628, mostly moving south or south-west, on dates between Sep. 4th and Nov. 30th. Day totals exceeded 300 on four occasions with a maximum of 389 south in two hours on Sep. 26th 1992. Similar counts at other inland sites include those of 350 south over Wellington Country Park on Oct. 3rd 1981, 384 south over Tunworth on Oct. 3rd 1986 and 338 south-east at Old Winchester Hill on Oct. 11th 1987. At coastal sites, movement is usually to the west or east, into the prevailing wind, with passage south out to sea rarely recorded. High day totals recorded include 390 moving south-east over Keyhaven on Oct. 2nd 1960, 530 south-east there and 625 ESE at Gilkicker Point on Sep. 23rd 1961 and 305 west at Hayling Bay on Sep. 25th 1986. As in spring, flocks on the ground are conspicuous, the largest gatherings recorded being of 500 at Farlington Marshes on Oct. 4th 1961, 500 at Keyhaven on Sep. 29th 1974 and 350 at Sinah Common on Sep. 30th 1983.

Between mid-November and early March, wintering flocks occur in a variety of habitats, including heathland, damp grassland, sedge and rush beds, recently-ploughed land, root crops on which livestock is enclosed, sewage farms, watercress beds and along the seashore. These groups rarely exceed 100, although 200 were at Vales Moor on Jan. 30th 1972. In severe weather, large concentrations may occur in ice-free areas. On Dec. 12th 1981, there were 400 at Dibden Bay and 200 at Camp Farm Sewage Farm, while at the latter site there was another large gathering of 260 on Feb. 15th 1986.

The origins and migration routes of wintering and passage birds are indicated by several ringing recoveries. Two trapped in autumn were recovered in Spain in November and in the Netherlands in April, while one ringed in mid-winter was found in Grampian in July. One ringed at Dungeness in November 1962 was found dead at Fawley in severe weather in January 1963, and another, ringed on the Isle of Man in April 1980, was controlled in Hampshire in April 1982.

## Red-throated Pipit                                          *Anthus cervinus*

One record. One was with Meadow Pipits at Titchfield Haven on Oct. 29th 1989.

The Red-throated Pipit breeds in the tundra zone from Lapland to eastern Siberia. European birds largely winter in the Sahel region, Sudan, Ethiopia and Kenya.

## Rock Pipit                                                  *Anthus petrosus*

A very scarce resident, moderately common passage migrant and winter visitor.

Rock Pipits require cliffs or a rocky shoreline for breeding, but there is little suitable habitat in Hampshire. The most regularly used site is Hurst Castle, where nests are built in gaps in the walls. Five to seven pairs bred annually between 1971 and 1983 but since then no more than three pairs have been found. One or two pairs also breed along Hurst Beach in most years. Occasional pairs breed on the cliffs at Hordle and Barton-on-Sea but these sites have been poorly covered. Nesting has also occurred at Calshot Spit, where two pairs bred in 1974 and one in 1985. Small numbers are fairly regular in the Pennington/ Keyhaven area from July onwards, which are presumably Hurst birds dispersing. The only other locality with summer records is Langstone Harbour, where singles were recorded on May 22nd 1977, Aug. 10th 1983 and May 8th and July 31st 1988.

Wintering birds, which are widely distributed along the coast, arrive from late September or early October and leave by late March or early April. Records from some sites indicate a passage peak in late October and early November. There is also a suggestion of a temporary exodus during severe winter weather. The largest concentration occurs in Langstone Harbour, but few complete counts have been made. On Dec. 18th 1984, 50+ were counted on North Binness and Long Islands and the total harbour population was estimated at 100+. On Jan. 3rd 1986, 98 were counted on the islands but only 51 were present during severe weather on Feb. 21st of that year. Other high counts include 37+ in the Pennington/Keyhaven area on Dec. 11th 1977, 22+ between Hook Spit and

Bunny Meadows on Nov. 13th 1982, 18 at Dibden Bay on Mar. 9th 1985 and 32 between Hurst Castle and Sturt Pond on Dec. 19th 1987. Recent counts at other sites have not exceeded ten although it is likely that greater numbers occur in Portsmouth Harbour and along the Hayling Shore of Chichester Harbour.

Inland records have been confined to the passage periods. In 1961, up to three were at Fleet Pond from Oct. 21st-Nov. 25th. Between 1979 and 1989, six were noted in autumn between Oct. 9th and Nov. 9th while in spring there were singles on Mar. 13th and 24th. Sightings were made at Eversley Gravel Pit (3 birds), Camp Farm Sewage Farm (2) and Bighton Lane Watercress Bed, Kingston Common and Wellington Country Park (1 each).

There have been several spring records of birds showing the characteristics of the Fenno-Scandian race, *A. p. littoralis*. By this time, such birds are assuming summer plumage, when they may be fairly easy to distinguish from the resident nominate race. However, ringing data suggest that, apart from resident birds, most of our wintering population are *littoralis*. Three ringed in Sweden and one in Finland during the breeding season have been controlled in Hampshire in subsequent winters; one of these returned to Farlington Marshes in three consecutive years.

# Water Pipit                                  *Anthus spinoletta*

A scarce winter visitor and passage migrant.

The Water Pipit was not identified in the county until 1951, when one was at Pennington Marsh on Nov. 14th. Between 1953 and 1962, there were annual sightings, all of which were coastal. Of 78 recorded, 53 occurred in March, suggesting passage. Most were at Farlington Marshes, including ten on Mar. 16th 1958 and Mar. 4th 1961. None were recorded in 1963.

Wintering birds were first recorded in 1964/65, when up to six were present on wet grassland at Lower Test Marshes. Counts there reached 20 in the five winters from 1972/73-76/77 but fewer were recorded in the early 1980s (possibly due to poor coverage). In recent years, it has emerged as the principal site in the county with over 30 regularly recorded.

In the early 1970s, Water Pipits were discovered on watercress beds, with those in the upper Itchen valley at Headbourne Worthy and in the Alresford area being particularly favoured. Between 20 and 35 wintered on the county's cress beds until the mid-1980s, but since then numbers have been much reduced. In a survey of 21 watercress beds in 1989/90, only one was found, at Alresford. The decline is possibly connected with the use of pesticides and other changes in cress growing and harvesting practices (Pain 1990).

Birds have also been recorded with some regularity at other wet grassland sites (Titchfield Haven, Dibden Bay, Bickerley Common in the Avon valley, Winnall Moors and Darby Green near Yateley) and sewage farms (Budds Farm, Camp Farm, Eastleigh and Winchester), although numbers have recently declined at some of these localities.

Counts at the main localities are summarised in Table 65.

| | Period recorded | Winters present | Winters with counts of 5+ | Peak counts | |
|---|---|---|---|---|---|
| Lower Test Marshes | 1964-92 | 27 | 19 | 38, | 25/1/91 |
| Dibden Bay | 1966-90 | 17 | 7 | 17, | 28/8/81 |
| Alresford area watercress beds | 1966-92 | 24 | 12 | 17, | 15/12/79 |
| Headbourne Worthy | 1968-92 | 24 | 17 | 15, | 27/12/76 |
| Titchfield Haven | 1976-92 | 13 | 8 | 13, | 20/2/92 |
| Bickerley Common | 1976-89 | 10 | 4 | 11, | 20/3/82 |
| Camp Farm | 1979-92 | 13 | 5 | 11, | 5/4/85 |

*Table 65. Summary of Water Pipit counts.*

The only other sites where counts have exceeded five are Nursling (max. 20, Nov. 27th 1976), Eling Great Marsh (max. 16, Jan. 14th 1979), Budds Farm (max. 8, Mar. 10th 1984) and Ibsley (8, Mar. 14th 1991). Records at the first two sites probably referred to Lower Test birds.

Water Pipits normally arrive in mid-October, although there have been several earlier records including those of single birds at Winnall Moors on Oct. 4th 1977 and Warsash on Sep. 28th 1984. There is a noticeable passage in the second half of October and November, when occasional birds occur at a wide variety of sites, often flying over during passerine movements.

In spring, passage is suggested by increases at wintering sites in late March and early April. Migrants also appear elsewhere, especially at coastal sites such as the Pennington/Keyhaven area, where the highest count has been of five on Apr. 5th 1974. Most leave by mid-April, but later records include those of single birds at Woolmer from Apr. 22nd-24th 1978 and Titchfield Haven on May 4th 1983.

Since the true status of the Water Pipit was appreciated in the early 1970s, the total recorded per winter, including passage birds, has usually been in the range 45-70 with a maximum of 80 in 1990/91. Those wintering in Britain almost certainly originate from the mountains of central and southern Europe, but there are no ringing recoveries to give a more precise indication. Several birds which were colour-ringed in the upper Itchen valley returned to the same watercress beds in subsequent winters.

# Yellow Wagtail                                      *Motacilla flava*

A scarce and declining summer visitor and common passage migrant.

Although quantitative data are lacking, it is clear that the Yellow Wagtail has declined considerably since the turn of the century, when K & M described it as "local in its distribution .... but especially plentiful in the larger river valleys". A decline has also occurred in other counties in southern England (Smith 1950, Parslow 1973). The main breeding habitats are damp meadows (especially in the Avon, Test and Itchen valleys), coastal grassland (principally at Farlington Marshes) and reclaimed land (as at Portsmouth Harbour and Southampton Water). Occasional pairs have nested around the margins of gravel pits and on farmland.

P E Brown, contributing to Cohen, described it as plentiful between the two world wars in parts of the Test valley and tributaries, especially between Whitchurch and Stockbridge. It was still numerous in this area in the late 1950s and early 1960s, with nine pairs at Chilbolton Common in 1958 and seven at Bransbury Common in 1960. However, it was apparently absent from much of the Test in the 1970s, although difficulties in accessing the many private areas may account for the lack of records. Since then, the decline has continued and during the Atlas Survey breeding was confirmed in only two tetrads.

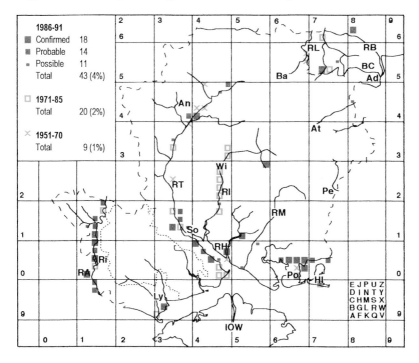

In the Itchen valley, a similar decline has occurred, although rather later. A survey of the valley in 1976 produced 27 pairs, with 22 between Mansbridge and Bishopstoke and the remainder upstream to Winnall Moors (Cloyne 1977). In 1982, only two pairs were located at Bishopstoke and breeding has not been recorded since apart from a pair at Cheriton in 1989, where they were not found in 1976.

In the Avon valley, breeding took place in most tetrads during the Atlas Survey but densities have undoubtedly declined. Quantitative data are lacking for the 1970s, but in 1982 there were an estimated 50 pairs on the Hampshire stretch of the river, including 18 between Blashford and Bickton. In 1990, only five pairs were located during the course of an RSPB survey (C G Bealey *in litt*).

Reasons for the decline in the river valleys can only be guessed at, but the increased use of agrochemicals, more intensive grazing, frequent rolling and the drying out of the meadows due to improved drainage and reduced rainfall may well be contributory factors. There is no good evidence to show that it has suffered from the effects of drought in its African winter quarters (Marchant *et al* 1990).

At Farlington Marshes, the breeding population was in the range four to ten pairs between 1957 and 1979, but during the 1980s, 12 to 15 pairs were recorded annually. This increase has been attributed to a reduction in cattle grazing. Numbers on the Langstone Harbour islands peaked at ten pairs in 1981 but have not exceeded four since. At other coastal sites with apparently suitable habitat, breeding is rarely recorded. At Pennington Marsh, a pair which bred in 1987 was the first since 1966, while at Titchfield Haven, single pairs which probably bred in 1979 and 1980 were the first since regular breeding ceased in 1967. Breeding has never been recorded in the Needs Ore area.

Waste ground created by reclamation schemes has proved to be an attractive, but temporary, habitat for the species. Breeding has been recorded at Horsea Island/Paulsgrove Reclamation (max. 4 pairs in 1983), Southampton Docks (3+ pairs in 1981), Dibden Bay (21 pairs found in a full survey in 1970 (Glue 1971); 9 in 1982) and Fawley/Calshot (11 pairs in 1972; 10 in 1982). However, during the Atlas Survey no more than two pairs bred at these sites. At Dibden Bay, one of the favoured areas has been developed into a yacht marina.

The Atlas Map, which incorporates all records for 1951-91, shows the range contraction which has occurred. During the Atlas Survey, breeding was confirmed or probable in 32 tetrads, but this undoubtedly exaggerates the current distribution. In 1991, the county population was probably no more than 30 pairs. The British population was estimated to be 50,000 pairs in 1988-91 (New Atlas).

The first normally arrive in late March or early April. The records for 1971-92 show first dates between Mar. 23rd and Apr. 11th with the average Apr. 2nd. However, in 1966 and 1968, there was a total of four records before Mar. 23rd, the earliest being of two flying north over Gilkicker Point on Mar. 10th 1968. Spring passage reaches a peak in late April and is virtually over by mid-May. Usually between 100 and 300 are recorded annually. The highest day totals were on May 3rd 1980, when 97 arrived from the south at Titchfield Haven and 32 flew north at Hurst Beach. Other large counts at coastal localities have included 35 roosting at Fawley Refinery on Apr. 21st 1977, 38 at Farlington Marshes on Apr. 23rd 1981 and 60 at Titchfield Haven on Apr. 29th 1989. Inland, flocks are smaller, gatherings of 40 at Eastleigh Sewage Farm on Apr. 28th 1978 and 30 at Eversley Gravel Pit on Apr. 23rd 1989 being exceptional.

Autumn migrants may appear in July but the main movement starts in mid-August, peaks later in that month or in early September, and continues until early October. Numbers are much higher than in spring, and include records of roosts (usually in *Phragmites*), grounded flocks (often associating with cattle) and diurnal movements.

A roost at Titchfield Haven has been monitored since the early 1970s. Between 1971 and 1980, the annual maximum averaged 286 with a high of 555 on Sep. 6th 1973. During the next decade, the average was 234 with a high of 460 on Sep. 8th 1981, but in 1992, the peak count was of 53 on Sep. 3rd. Coverage of the roost at Farlington Marshes has been less complete, but in most years the maximum was in the range 100-200. Higher counts were of 350 on Sep. 7th 1979, 300 on Sep. 6th 1986 and 250 on Sep. 16th 1990. Roosting has also been recorded sporadically at nearby Great Salterns Lake (100 in 1971, 120 in 1981) and Milton Reclamation (250+ in 1981, 150 in 1982).

Other than roosts, flocks in excess of 50 are regularly recorded and occasionally reach three figures. High counts include 200 at Pennington and Keyhaven Marshes on Sep. 3rd and 4th 1976, 150 there on Aug. 27th 1990, 300+ on Hayling Island on Aug. 31st 1985, 205 at Sinah Common on Sep. 6th 1986 and 150 there on Sep. 1st 1990. Diurnal movements may be in either direction along the coast or south out to sea. Day totals are usually of less than 50 but higher counts include 230 south over Keyhaven on Aug. 27th 1960, 100+ east at Sinah Common on Aug. 25th 1984 and 156 north-west over Titchfield Haven on Sep. 4th 1986.

Inland, few flocks have exceeded 30. A roost at Shepherds Spring in 1976 reached a peak of 242 on Sep. 4th. Other large gatherings were of 100 at Bishopstoke on Sep. 13th 1982, the same number at Soberton Down on Aug. 28th 1984 and 96 at Wide Lane playing fields (Eastleigh) on Sep. 22nd 1985.

Most have departed by early October. However, 45 were roosting at Farlington Marshes on 2nd in 1982 and inland, 40 moved south over South Warnborough on 6th in 1979 and 21 flew south at Longparish on the same date in 1987. During 1971-92, last dates were in the period Oct. 2nd-Nov. 9th with the average Oct. 20th.

There have been six records of possible wintering as follows: single birds at Titchfield Haven on Dec. 8th 1957 and from Nov. 13th-20th 1976, one in the Farlington Marshes/Budds Farm area from Nov. 28th 1983-Feb. 24th 1984, one with Meadows Pipits at Keyhaven Marsh in very cold weather on Jan. 16th 1985, two at Dibden Bay in January 1986 and two at North Hayling on Dec. 13th 1986.

Up to five individuals showing the characteristics of the continental race *M. f. flava*, the Blue-headed Wagtail, have been recorded annually. Most pass through in spring but males have bred with *flavissimma* females in at least seven years between 1971 and 1990. In addition, a pure pair bred at Farlington Marshes in 1979. Males showing the characteristics of the western Siberian race *M. f. beema*, Syke's Wagtail, were recorded in 1976-77 and 1980-84, and bred with *flavissimma* females at Farlington in 1983 and 1984. A male of the Scandinavian race, *M. f. thunbergi*, the Grey-headed Wagtail, was at Farlington Marshes on Apr. 8th and 9th 1977. It is likely that all the records of *beema* and the majority of those of *flava* refer to hybrids or variants of *flavissimma* (Williamson 1955, Milne 1959, BWP).

Ringing activities at autumn roosts have produced foreign recoveries in Portugal in October (2) and in the Canary Islands and Jersey in April, while one ringed in Jersey in September was controlled in Hampshire a year later. There have been 11 other recoveries or controls to or from English counties as far north as Greater Manchester. No British-ringed birds have been recovered in the wintering grounds in tropical West Africa, but field observations indicate that birds of the race *flavissimma* winter as far east as Liberia (BWP).

## Citrine Wagtail                          *Motacilla citreola*

Two records. A first-summer male was at Fleet Pond on May 15th and 16th 1993† and a first-winter was at Farlington Marshes from Aug. 30th-Sep. 3rd 1993†.

The Citrine Wagtail breeds in much of the CIS and winters in Iran, the Indian sub-continent and south-east Asia.

## Grey Wagtail                            *Motacilla cinerea*

A moderately common resident, passage migrant and winter visitor.

Most Grey Wagtails breed close to running water, utilising structures such as weirs, mills and bridges for nest sites. Pairs have also been found breeding in porches and sheds. Cohen suggested that a considerable increase occurred during the first half of the century which continued in the 1950s. This is a similar pattern to that observed in other southern and eastern counties (Parslow 1973). 28 pairs were located in the New Forest in 1960, but coverage elsewhere in the county was poor. A major decline occurred following the hard winters of 1961/62 and 1962/63, but it had fully recovered by 1969 when 32 pairs were found in the New Forest (Tyler 1970, C & T). Subsequent counts included 124 pairs in a partial survey of the county in 1972 (Thelwell 1973), 43 pairs in the Itchen valley in 1976 (Cloyne 1977) and 42 pairs in the north-east, including 16 along the Basingstoke Canal between Greywell and Ash Vale, in 1978. Complete surveys of the New Forest between 1980 and 1982 produced 57, 65 and 48 pairs respectively (T G Heathcote *in litt*), the decline in 1982 following a severe winter. A decline was also noted in the county following the 1984/85 winter, which mirrors the pattern shown by the national CBC and WBS indices (Marchant *et al* 1990).

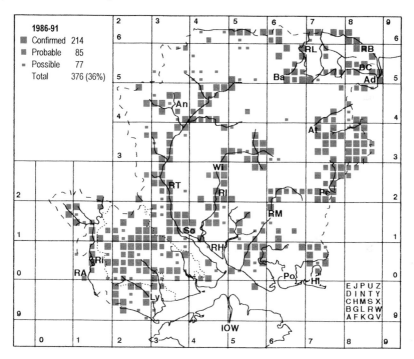

Allowing for some tetrads which hold more than one pair, the county population was probably between 300 and 400 pairs in 1990, following three mild winters. It is not known whether the short severe spell in February 1991 affected breeding numbers, but only one pair was found along the Basingstoke Canal. The reduction there since 1978 was attributed, at least in part, to the increased use of the canal by motorised boats (Rowland 1993).

Post-breeding dispersal is indicated by the appearance of birds at coastal localities from mid-June in some years. Diurnal movements are recorded between late August and late November. At coastal localities, passage peaks in September and is mostly to the west, but in October no direction is prominent although very few are seen to fly south out to sea. Day totals are usually small, the only counts to exceed ten being of 30 west at Warsash on Sep. 16th 1956, 25 south-east at Gilkicker Point on Oct. 18th 1969, 13 west at Sinah Common on Sep. 29th 1984 and 22 west there on Sep. 8th 1990. At inland localities, the direction of movement is usually between south and west. At Fleet Pond, systematic coverage during 1987-92 produced a total of 137 flying over between Aug. 21st and Nov. 24th with most in September and early October. Day totals did not exceed five.

In winter, the species is widely distributed at suitable coastal and inland localities, although most of the New Forest breeding territories are deserted (Tyler 1970). Sewage farms and watercress beds are particularly favoured. Gatherings do not usually exceed five, but at Eastleigh Sewage Farm there were 50 on Feb. 6th 1978, 60+ on Mar. 16th 1980 and 27 on Feb. 10th 1986. Elsewhere, the highest count was of 14 at Wickham Sewage Farm on Dec. 30th 1983. Roosts are rarely discovered, but 81 were counted into *Phragmites* at Lower Test Marshes on Jan. 5th 1967, 180+ were with 100+ Pied Wagtails in the same habitat at Fullerton on Jan. 28th 1978 and 12 were found in a reedy ditch at Keyhaven on Jan. 12th 1990.

Diurnal movement is occasionally detected between mid-March and early May, when single birds or flocks of up to four are recorded flying over, usually in a north or north-westerly direction. A flock of 15 with Meadows Pipits at Winchester Sewage Farm on Apr. 5th 1984 were presumably grounded migrants.

The dispersal of Hampshire-bred birds is illustrated by the movements of six ringed as pulli in the New Forest. Two were found in their first winters in Vienne, France (487 km SSE) and Kent, three were found in subsequent winters in Seine-Maritime, France (197 km south-east), East Sussex and Surrey and the other was recovered in London a year after ringing. The origins of some of the wintering population are indicated by the control in their first winter of three birds ringed as pulli: two from Powys and one from eastern Germany. The only other movement in excess of 100 km involved one ringed in Hampshire in September 1979 and controlled in Gwent in July 1983.


## Pied Wagtail                                              *Motacilla alba*

A numerous resident, abundant passage migrant and winter visitor.

During the Atlas Survey, the Pied Wagtail was found in 923 (90%) tetrads, with breeding confirmed in 645, probable in 191 and possible in 87. Most of the gaps in its distribution were in the New Forest and on the chalk (especially around Farley Mount and to the north and west of Andover). Absence from the chalk is presumably due to a combination of poor coverage and a lack of suitable habitat. Experience shows that it is often found close to water and generally relies on buildings or other man-made structures for nest sites. Favoured sites include farm buildings (particularly where there are animals), sewage farms, villages and a variety of urban situations.

The paucity of local data makes estimation of the county population very uncertain. Using national CBC data for 1989, the New Atlas method indicates a county population of around 4500 pairs. However, this undoubtedly underestimates numbers in urban and suburban areas and the true figure is probably in the range 6000-10,000 pairs. The British total was estimated at 300,000 pairs (New Atlas).

In some years, diurnal passage is quite heavy in autumn, usually peaking in the first half of October. At the coast, most passage is to the east or south-east, e.g. 167 south-east at Gilkicker Point and 215 south-east at Keyhaven on Oct. 7th 1962, and 91 east at Hayling Bay on Oct. 4th 1986, but westerly movements also occur. At inland sites, movement is usually to the south-west quarter, e.g. at Fleet Pond, daily coverage in autumn during 1987-92 produced a total of 961 moving over, mostly in directions between south and west. At this time, roosts frequently form in *Phragmites*. Since 1971, roosts of 400-600 have been found at Farlington Marshes, Fleet Pond, Longstock, Titchfield Haven and Winnall Moors. These, and other smaller gatherings, all had autumn peaks.

During the winter, roosts in *Phragmites* are usually much smaller. However, other sites, such as bushes in sheltered courtyards, factories and greenhouses, are used more frequently. Regular monthly counts of a roost on lagged steam pipes at a North Baddesley factory showed mid-winter peaks with a maximum of 1200 in January 1990. Other large counts have included 1000 at Queen Alexandra Hospital (Cosham) in December 1989 and 800 at the now demolished Eastleigh Carriage Works in January 1976. Feeding flocks of up to 200 are regular at sewage farms, higher counts being of 1000+ at Basingstoke on Nov. 12th 1961, 400 at Eastleigh on Nov. 8th 1981 and 350+ at Goodworth Clatford on Jan. 1st 1984. Smaller gatherings occur in a wide variety of habitats including flooded meadows, freshly-ploughed land and fields with stock.

Passage is not as prominent in spring as in autumn. Flocks of up to 50 occur on the coast and at inland sites such as gravel pits between mid-March and early May. Small numbers are occasionally noted moving over, e.g. 22 flying north over Winchester on Apr. 27th 1986 and a total of 26 moving north at Fleet Pond between Mar. 19th and Apr. 26th 1988.

Ringing activities confirm its status as a partial migrant. One Hampshire-bred bird was controlled in Portugal in November. Four ringed in Hampshire in autumn were recovered in France, Spain, Portugal and Morocco between November and January, while another ringed in March was found in Northern Ireland in August. Of 447 movements within Britain, 53 exceeded 100 km including seven to or from Scotland.

Birds showing the characteristics of the continental race, the White Wagtail *M. a. alba*, occur between early March and late May with the peak passage in the second half of April. Most occur on the coast, with the Pennington/Keyhaven area the main locality. Numbers there have reached double figures in seven years including 30 on Apr. 20th 1966, 21 on Apr. 17th 1983 and 22 on Apr. 23rd 1989. Similar counts have also been made at Farlington Marshes in four years (max. 13 on Apr. 22nd 1978) and at Eversley Gravel Pit once (13 on Apr. 17th 1988).

Outside the main spring passage period, there were sightings during 1969-92 of one in February, three in June and 12 between Aug. 26th and Oct. 18th. In autumn, the race is difficult to identify and many no doubt go undetected in flocks of Pied Wagtails.

# Waxwing
## *Bombycilla garrulus*

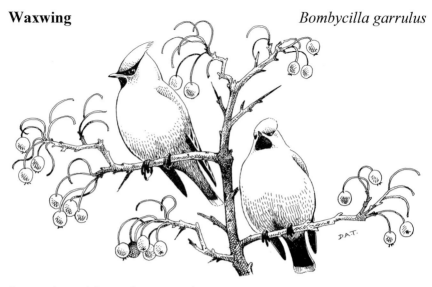

A rare winter visitor and passage migrant.

Between 1951 and 1992, Waxwings were seen in Hampshire in 22 winters. High numbers occurred in 1958/59 (33), 1965/66 (202), 1970/71 (134), 1981/82 (13) and 1988/89 (51)  In the remaining winters, a total of 42 was recorded, 25 of them in November and December, indicating passage. The cumulative monthly totals of all records are shown below.

| Nov | Dec | Jan | Feb | Mar | Apr |
|-----|-----|-----|-----|-----|-----|
| 17  | 163 | 205 | 104 | 109 | 26  |

The largest flocks recorded were of 47 at Farnborough in late December 1965, 40 at Aldershot in early January 1966, up to 36 at Southampton in January 1966, 23 flying west at Posbrook on Jan. 15th 1966, 20-30 in the Bedhampton/ Cosham area in March 1966, 26 at Portchester on Dec. 26th 1970, 20 at Farnborough in late January 1971, 25 at Millbrook from Mar. 20th-22nd 1971 and 20 at Calmore Road, Totton on Dec. 21st 1988. Flocks were recorded feeding on hawthorn, cotoneaster and rowan berries, and pears.

The extreme dates were Nov. 5th (1961, 2, Butser Hill) and Apr. 29th (1966, 1, Stanmore).

Waxwings occurring in Britain form part of eruptions from breeding grounds in northern Fenno-Scandia and further east in Siberia, which are probably initiated by food shortages (BWP).

# Dipper
## *Cinclus cinclus*

A rare visitor; occasionally breeds.

K & M described the Dipper as "an accidental visitor". It evidently extended its breeding range into Hampshire in the 1930s. In the Avon valley, a pair was near Breamore in 1934 while in the Allen valley, a pair bred between Fordingbridge and Martin in 1937. In the Test valley, single pairs were near Andover in 1934, at Andover, Fullerton and Leckford "as usual" in 1937, at

Leckford again in 1938 and at Compton Manor in 1942. In the Itchen valley, a pair bred at Brambridge in three years just prior to the Second World War. Other records at this time were of single birds at Alresford on Aug. 2nd and Oct. 18th 1942 and Testwood Mill in August 1942, and two at Longparish on Jan. 15th 1945 (*South Eastern Bird Reports*, Cohen).

In 1953, one was at Winchester on June 3rd, and in the following year a pair bred at Breamore Mill (N W Orr *in litt*). In the next 25 years, the only records were of single birds at Brambridge from January-March 1963, Broughton on Apr. 18th 1969, Winchester on Jan. 3rd 1970, Mislingford from Nov. 19th-24th 1972, Bere Mill (Whitchurch) on Apr. 17th 1978, Kingsclere in March 1980, Fordingbridge in late December 1983 and early January 1984 and Warnford on Jan. 28th 1989.

A pair was located in the Test valley on Nov. 3rd 1990, where they remained and bred successfully in 1991 and 1992, no doubt aided by the low water level in the river during that period. One was at Kimbridge on Dec. 16th 1990, from Nov. 3rd 1991-Jan. 5th 1992 and on May 17th and June 1st 1992, and another was at Tanners Brook on Nov. 26th and 27th 1992. In the Meon valley, a first-winter was in the Warnford/Meonstoke area on Dec. 21st and 22nd 1991 and had probably been present since late October.

# Wren                                    *Troglodytes troglodytes*

An abundant resident.

The Wren occurs at its highest density in woodland but is found in almost all habitats including farmland, heathland, villages and towns. During the Atlas Survey, there were registrations in 1023 (99%) tetrads, with breeding confirmed in 743, probable in 272 and possible in eight. It was absent only from eight tetrads in coastal areas where the main habitat was saltmarsh or shingle.

It is particularly susceptible to harsh winters, so that numbers breeding in the county fluctuate from year to year. This is illustrated for the period 1981-91 by the Hampshire CBC indices, which show falls of 30%, 10%, 15% and 25% after the hard winters of 1981/82, 1984/85, 1985/86 and 1990/91 respectively. More graphic evidence of the toll which severe weather can take was obtained when a tree containing a squirrel's drey was felled at Alton during a cold spell in January 1985 and found to contain 19 dead Wrens. Using national CBC data for 1989, the New Atlas method gives an estimated Hampshire population of 190,000 pairs and a national total of 7.1 million pairs.

Most local birds are sedentary, moving only short distances, sometimes in response to harsh weather, to the coast or to communal roosts in reed beds, old nests and nest boxes. Of 47 birds ringed in Hampshire and subsequently recovered, only seven were outside the county. One, ringed as a juvenile at Winchester on July 1st 1967, was found dead at Amiens, France, 293 km ESE, on Jan. 3rd 1968, and three others moved distances of greater than 100 km to Gwent and Gloucestershire (both ringed outside the breeding season and recovered in June) and Devon (found dead after cold weather). Of seven ringed outside Hampshire and recovered within the county, five had moved distances in excess of 100 km from Essex, East Sussex, Worcestershire, Lincolnshire and Northamptonshire. The last two were found dead during severe weather.

## Dunnock                                          *Prunella modularis*

An abundant resident.

The Dunnock occurs in a wide variety of habitats, ranging from open countryside to city wasteland, wherever there is low scrub and ground cover. In parts of the New Forest, where the ground flora is limited by intensive grazing, it is scarce or absent (Glue 1973, Irvine 1977). Similarly, in intensively farmed areas and grazed downland it is restricted by the lack of cover. It may be at its highest density in suburban gardens, parks and scrub. During the Atlas Survey, it was located in 1020 (99%) tetrads, with breeding confirmed in 695, probable in 307 and possible in 18. It was not recorded in nine on the coast (which contained saltmarsh) and two in the New Forest.

The Hampshire CBC indices show that the county population has fluctuated over the past decade, falling as a result of the hard winters in 1981/82, 1984/85, 1986/87 and 1990/91 and generally recovering in the following more favourable seasons. Overall, there may have been a slow decline, with the index falling from 100 in 1981 to 86 in 1990 despite three consecutive mild winters from 1987/88. This is consistent with the national picture which shows a downward trend from 1975 for reasons which are not fully understood, but may well be linked to changes in farming practices (Marchant *et al* 1990). Using national CBC data for 1989, the New Atlas method gives an estimated population for Hampshire of 50,000 pairs and a national total of 2.0 million pairs.

The breeding population is essentially sedentary. Of 160 recoveries of Hampshire-ringed Dunnocks, 158 have been within 9 km of the ringing site. However, there is some evidence of movement into the county. An adult ringed at Telemark, Norway, on Apr. 21st 1975 was controlled at Sway on Feb. 11th 1976, and another, ringed on the Isle of May on Oct. 6th 1976, was recovered at Northney on Mar. 11th 1977. Birds are occasionally noted in diurnal passerine movements, e.g. one flew high to the west over Widley on Oct. 12th 1980 and five flew high over Titchfield Haven on Oct. 5th 1987, of which three moved off east.

In winter, large gatherings are occasionally recorded. No fewer than 40 were ringed in a kale field at Sopley in the last week of February 1960. There were 50 in similar habitat at Needs Ore on Dec. 26th 1961. More recently, there were 80 at Eastleigh Sewage Farm on Oct. 24th 1976 and 60, again in kale, at Chawton on Nov. 12th 1980.

# Robin                                           *Erithacus rubecula*

An abundant resident, passage migrant and winter visitor.

The Robin is very catholic and adaptable in its choice of nest sites and tolerance of disturbance, and therefore occurs in a wide range of habitats. During the Atlas Survey, it was found in 1018 (99%) tetrads, with breeding confirmed in 882, probable in 134 and possible in two. It was absent only from 12 on the coast which contained little suitable habitat. It is susceptible to cold winters so that breeding numbers fluctuate from year to year. The CBC indices for Hampshire show marked reductions in 1982, 1985, 1986 and 1991 (following severe winters) and increases in 1988 and 1989 (after mild winters). Using 1989 national CBC data, the New Atlas method indicates a Hampshire population of around 130,000 pairs and a national total of 4.2 million pairs.

The local breeding population is largely sedentary. Although some post-breeding dispersal occurs, the distances moved are generally small. The only long distance movement of a bird that might have been locally bred involved one ringed as a juvenile at Sway on July 20th 1983 and found dead in Birmingham in October 1987. Two ringed as juveniles outside the county, in Sussex in September 1971 and Devon in September 1983, were recovered in Hampshire in later breeding seasons.

Passage through and into the county occurs in autumn. Ringing activities at Southampton Docks between 1982 and 1990 resulted in the capture of 27 adults and 179 juveniles on dates between July 23rd and Nov. 4th with a peak in September (B Dudley *in litt*). At Farlington Marshes, where usually only one pair breeds, there is a wintering population of 30-40 which arrives in September and October. One ringed there was recovered at Dungeness, Kent in June (P M Potts *in litt*). Influxes have occasionally been noted elsewhere, e.g. 33 at East Hayling on Sep. 25th 1985, 74 nearby at Sinah on Sep. 28th of that year and 75 at Fleet Pond on Dec. 1st 1989. Ringing recoveries show that most of the immigrants have a north-easterly origin. Birds from Denmark (2), Norway, Northumberland, Nottinghamshire and Suffolk have been found in Hampshire outside the breeding season, while three ringed in Hampshire in autumn had moved to Lincolnshire, Suffolk and Kent in subsequent breeding seasons.

# Nightingale                                      *Luscinia megarhynchos*

A moderately common summer visitor.

At the turn of the century, K & M described the Nightingale as "found in most parts of the county .... very plentiful in many localities, particularly in the hedgerows and coppices of the Central Hill district". In the 1940s and 1950s, it was still considered common, and in good seasons said to be "almost abundant in some parts of the county, notably in the upper Test valley and in the vale country running from Kingsclere to Eversley (P E Brown in Cohen). However, by 1961, N W Orr and J S Ash had detected a decline in the south-west which was subsequently noted by several observers in other parts of the county.

In 1976, a survey of the county, undertaken as part of a national census organised by the BTO, produced a total of 259 singing males in 93 different tetrads. The coverage was poor in some areas although the organiser doubted whether more than 300 singing males were present (Blindell 1977). A further

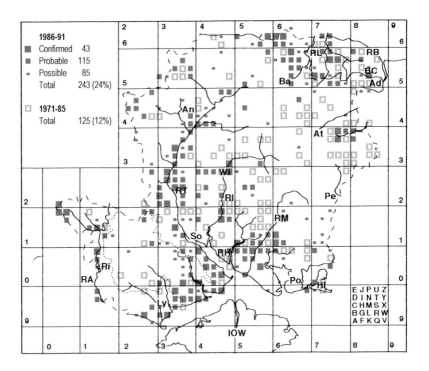

survey in 1980, when coverage was much improved, located 355 singing males
in 118 tetrads (Pain 1981). Finally, work for the Atlas Survey during 1986-91
produced registrations in 241 tetrads, of which 171 were not previously known
to be occupied. The Atlas Map shows all 368 tetrads where Nightingales were
detected between 1971 and 1991; only 22 of these held birds in 1976, 1980 and
during the Atlas Survey.

These data reflect the opportunism of the Nightingale, which is quick to
occupy habitats such as scrub, coppice and young coniferous plantations, and
then abandon them when they become too mature. Counts from a selection of
important localities are shown in Table 66.

Most of these sites have shown declines although unfortunately some of
them have not been surveyed since the early 1980s. In conifer plantations, the
reductions are due to the trees becoming too tall. Between Aldershot and Fleet, a
combination of the succession to climax oak woodland, scrub clearance and the
dumping of silt from dredging the Basingstoke Canal is thought to have
contributed to the decline. At other sites, such as Hazeley Heath and Martin
Down, the habitat is largely unchanged, although at the latter site rabbits may be
having an effect by overgrazing the scrub (P Toynton *in litt*).

Overall, the population has almost certainly fallen since the 1950s
(especially in the west of the county), no doubt accelerated by the decline in
coppicing and the clearance of scrub for development. However, habitat
availability is probably not the limiting factor since densities have fallen where
the habitat is unchanged and much apparently suitable ground is not occupied.

The population clearly fluctuates from year to year, the highest numbers usually coinciding with springs with warm, dry anticyclonic weather (Marchant *et al* 1990). Possibly the increased frequency of cool, late springs since the 1950s is having the greatest effect on the Nightingale, which is at the edge of its range in Britain.

| | Habitat | Counts |
|---|---|---|
| Ampfield Wood | Young conifer plantation | 1975, 19; 1976, 14; 1982, 8+ (in new areas) |
| Aldershot/Fleet military area including Basingstoke Canal | Scrub | 1961, 30/32; 1976, 17; 1980, 12; 1987, 4. |
| Bramley Camp | Blackthorn scrub | 1980, 21. |
| Botley Wood | Thorn/birch/sallow scrub/ young conifer plantation | 1976, 14; 1980, 9; 1981, 16; 1982, 29; 1983, 30; 1985, 19; 1992, 8. |
| Crab Wood/West Wood/Pitt Down | Hazel coppice/ young conifer plantation | 1975, 26; 1976, 14; 1980, 13. |
| Hazeley Heath | Scrub | 1981-86, 3-7; 1988, 8; 1990, 11; 1991, 3. |
| Martin Down CBC | Scrub | 1979, 11; 1980, 15; 1981, 16; 1982-89,7-12; 1990, 6; 1991, 3. |
| Martin Down NNR (including CBC) | Scrub | 1980, 24; 1987, c.20. |
| S.E. New Forest + coastal strip, Lymington-Lepe | Oak/willow | 1975, 13; 1976, 7; 1980, 36. |

*Table 66. Counts of singing male Nightingales in selected areas.*

Its predilection for the short-term occupation of many sites means that birds will be overlooked when they first occupy new areas. However, the distribution produced by the six-year Atlas Survey no doubt exaggerates the situation in any one year. If it is assumed that half the squares with registrations were occupied in any one year, with 2-3 pairs per occupied tetrad, then the county population would be in the range 240-360 pairs. The national survey in 1980 produced a total of 4770 singing males (Davis 1982), and in 1988-91 the British population was estimated at 5000-6000 pairs (New Atlas).

The first Nightingales normally arrive in mid-April. The earliest were recorded at Lepe on Apr. 3rd in both 1975 and 1988. Other first dates in 1971-92 fell in the period up to Apr. 29th with the average Apr. 16th. Most are in territory by late April or early May although a few have been recorded on passage at non-breeding coastal localities at this time.

Being single-brooded, most have left breeding localities by late July. Small numbers are recorded in autumn at coastal localities, with a peak in mid-August. The cumulative monthly totals of such records for 1971-92 are shown below.

| Jul | Aug | Sep | Oct |
|---|---|---|---|
| 13 | 77 | 14 | 2 |

During 1971-92, latest dates fell between Aug. 9th and Sep. 19th apart from two late birds at Fordingbridge on Oct. 5th 1983 and Titchfield Haven on Oct. 9th 1985. The average latest date was Aug. 27th.

There have been seven recoveries or controls involving Hampshire birds. All had moved less than 50 km apart from a juvenile ringed at Beachy Head, East Sussex, on Sep. 8th 1979 and controlled at Purbrook Heath on Aug. 24th 1984 and an adult trapped at Lewes, East Sussex, on June 30th 1984 and controlled at East Worldham on June 8th 1985. British Nightingales winter in tropical West Africa.

## Bluethroat                               *Luscinia svecica*

A rare passage migrant.

Apart from an undated record for Eastney in the 19th century, the first were in 1956, at Farlington Marshes on Sep. 9th and 10th, and Damerham on Oct. 11th. A total of 13 records followed in the period up to 1969, including annual appearances in the years 1961-65. One was at Southsea on Mar. 26th 1958, but the remainder occurred in the period between Aug. 30th and Oct. 27th. Sightings, all of single birds, were made at Farlington Marshes (5), Titchfield Haven and Keyhaven/Hurst (3 each) and Yateley Gravel Pit (Oct. 3rd 1965). Since 1970, there have been only six records, as follows:

| | |
|---|---|
| 1972: | Farlington Marshes, Aug. 20th; |
| | Old Winchester Hill, Sep. 15th-20th; |
| 1976: | trapped, Lower Test Marshes, Aug. 21st; |
| 1979: | Southsea, Oct. 24th; |
| 1981: | trapped, Lower Test Marshes, Aug. 25th; |
| | Farlington Marshes, Sep. 5th. |

The pattern of less frequent autumn occurrences since 1970, despite the greatly increased observer coverage, mirrors the national picture. It has been suggested that the decline is due to a change in the species' migration pattern (Dymond *et al* 1989). The Bluethroat has a widespread distribution in the Palearctic region, with the nearest breeding grounds in Scandinavia and from Germany to Spain. Most birds from these areas probably winter in the Sahel region of Africa and Arabia.

## Black Redstart                          *Phoenicurus ochruros*

A rare resident, scarce passage migrant and winter visitor.

K & M described the Black Redstart as "an uncommon winter visitor". They cited four records including one for early May. A further eight birds were recorded in the period up to 1940.

In 1942, a singing male was present on a bomb site in Southampton, and in the following year, three males were located, with two pairs confirmed breeding. A pair also bred successfully at Bartley. Two pairs again bred in Southampton in 1944 and 1945, while in the latter year a pair reared young in Portsmouth. The next record indicative of breeding was in 1958, when a juvenile with yellow gape-flanges, which "must have been reared nearby", was ringed at Latchmore Bottom on Aug. 29th.

In 1965, singing males were present in Portsmouth at the Naval Base, Southsea and Eastney (the latter with two females), but breeding was not confirmed. There were no further records in the Portsmouth area until 1972, when one was at Fort Purbrook on Mar. 25th and June 10th. A pair bred successfully there every year from 1973-77 and possibly in 1981. At nearby Fort Widley, a pair bred successfully in 1974, 1978 and 1985, and birds were present from 1986-88. Single pairs bred on the site of a new school at Buckland and in the Naval Base in 1974. Subsequently, singing males were heard in the Naval Base on one date only in 1983, 1984 and 1986, and a male held territory at Old Portsmouth from Mar. 12th-26th 1989.

Between 1973 and 1978, one or two pairs nested each year on the site of a new housing estate at Knight's Enham (Andover). Other recent records were of immature males holding territory at Eling Wharf from May 15th-June 14th 1975, Haslar Hospital (Gosport) from June 18th-July 6th 1984 and on a building site at Petersfield from Apr. 13th-July 3rd 1987, a female apparently carrying food into a barn at Lower Bordean Farm, near Petersfield, on July 9th 1987, a male at the same Petersfield building site from Apr. 3rd-May 2nd 1988, and a recently fledged juvenile at Northfields Farm (Twyford) from Aug. 13th-25th 1988.

Difficulties of access and poor coverage of likely breeding sites mean that some pairs will have been overlooked. However, it is doubtful whether Black Redstarts are breeding annually in Hampshire in the early 1990s. In Britain, the population fluctuates from year to year; from 1973-90 the total recorded was in the range 74-112 pairs, all in England (Batten *et al* 1990, Spencer *et al* 1993).

Records of non-breeding birds showed a steady rise from the 1950s until the mid-1980s, but then declined (fig. 67).

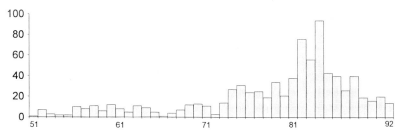

*Figure 67. Annual totals of Black Redstarts (excluding breeding birds), 1951-92.*

The highest numbers are recorded on autumn passage, which peaks between mid-October and mid-November. Inland, birds occur at a wide variety of sites; good coverage has produced regular records at Northfields Farm, Twyford (26 birds since 1975) and Dean Hill (24 since 1975, including five on Nov. 2nd 1982). At the coast, favoured areas include Hayling Island (39 birds, including four on Oct. 31st 1982 and Nov. 4th 1984), Pennington/Hurst (38), Eastney/Southsea (25), Hill Head/Chilling (21), Fawley/Calshot (19), Farlington Marshes (18) and Dibden Bay (16). Since the 1970s, autumn totals have usually been in the range 10-30, but 58 were recorded in 1982 and 68 in 1984.

In the late 1950s and 1960s, there were occasional winter records, especially for Hurst Castle. Wintering has been regular since 1974/75, when seven were present in the period December-February. Numbers subsequently fluctuated but peaked at 16 in 1982/83. Between 1987/88 and 1991/92, no more than four were recorded; this may be as much due to poor coverage of the likely sites as to a decline. Most occur on the coast; regularly-used sites include the north shore of Langstone Harbour, Eastney, various localities around Southampton City and Docks, Dibden Bay and Fawley/Calshot. Usually, one or two birds were involved but three were recorded at Langstone Harbour on Dec. 12th 1981, Dibden Bay on Dec. 16th 1981 and Southampton Docks on Dec. 19th 1982. Inland, wintering birds have been recorded at Eastleigh Sewage Farm, Farnborough Airfield, Hawkley, Northfields Farm, Overton Mill and Petersfield (in each case in one winter only), and also around the breeding sites at Portsdown Hill and Knight's Enham.

A light spring passage occurs from mid-March to early May, with most recorded at inland sites. The total for each spring is usually between five and 12, but there were 17 in 1983 and again in 1985. All reports have been of one or two birds, apart from those of four at Gilkicker Point on Mar. 22nd 1965 and three at Southsea Castle on May 4th 1984, West Hayling on Apr. 5th 1985 and Amery Farm Estate (Alton) on Apr. 24th 1985.

The cumulative monthly totals (excluding breeding birds) for 1951-92 are shown below.

| Aug | Sep | Oct | Nov | Dec | Jan | Feb | Mar | Apr | May | Jun | Jul |
|-----|-----|-----|-----|-----|-----|-----|-----|-----|-----|-----|-----|
| 8 | 20 | 223 | 202 | 89 | 60 | 58 | 103 | 101 | 17 | 3 | 3 |

There have been no recoveries or controls of Hampshire birds. National ringing data suggest that birds occurring on passage in southern England breed in central Europe and winter in Iberia (BWP).

## Redstart                    *Phoenicurus phoenicurus*

A locally common summer visitor and passage migrant.

The stronghold of the Redstart is the New Forest, where it favours the unenclosed ancient and ornamental woodlands. There, the pressure of grazing has produced an open structure lacking a dense undergrowth. This, combined with the abundance of natural nesting holes provided by mature and decaying trees, produces a habitat supporting high densities. It also occurs in small oak copses and single trees on the open heaths. There are no quantitative data for the

1960s or early 1970s, but information from two CBC plots at Eyeworth (29.5 ha) and Burley Old Inclosure (16.7 ha) surveyed since 1976 show a steady increase. At Eyeworth, there was an average of nine territories during 1976-78 and 18 during 1984-90; at Burley the figures were four and nine respectively. Extrapolation of this data, supported by other information, suggests a population of 400-500 pairs in 1976 and 1977 and around 1000-1100 pairs in the late 1980s and early 1990s (G C Evans, C R Tubbs *in litt*). This increase mirrors the national picture.

The other main area is the north-east of the county. There, Redstarts are most frequently found breeding in belts or clumps of Scots pine on heathlands or along the edges of cleared plantations, but they also occur in habitat similar to that used in the New Forest at Waggoners Wells. Maximum counts of pairs or singing males at the main sites are as follows: Bramshott Common/Waggoners Wells/Ludshott Common, 13 in 1981; Bricksbury Hill, 11 in 1980; Longmoor Inclosure/Weaver's Down, eight in 1990; Bramshill area, nine in 1989; Woolmer, 16 in 1985. The total population in this area is probably in the range 50-70 pairs. Earlier information suggests that numbers were at a similar level in the 1960s.

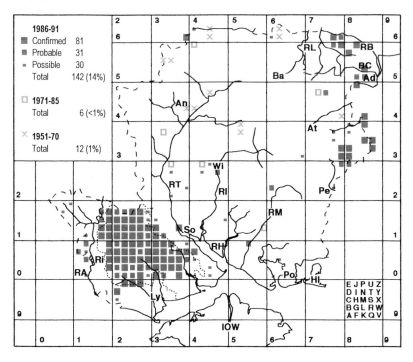

Elsewhere, Redstarts were formerly far more widespread, breeding sparingly in woodlands on the chalk. The Atlas Map shows 18 additional tetrads where they bred between 1951 and 1985, but since coverage of most of these areas was poor during that period, they were presumably more widespread. Only six of these tetrads were occupied after the crash in 1969. During the Atlas Survey, breeding was probable or confirmed in only nine tetrads outside the New Forest and north-east strongholds. The remaining records of possible breeding presumably refer mostly to passage birds.

The total Hampshire population in the early 1990s is probably between 1050 and 1200 pairs. In 1988-91, the British total was estimated to be in the range 90,000-330,000 pairs (New Atlas).

The first Redstarts are usually seen in early April. During 1971-92, arrivals were between Mar. 25th and Apr. 19th with the average Apr. 7th. However, there have been two earlier records, of a male in a Portsmouth garden on Mar. 5th 1989, which may have been wintering, and one at Farlington Marshes on Mar. 17th 1968. The main spring passage occurs in late April and continues in reduced numbers until the end of May. The total recorded in spring away from breeding sites rarely exceeds 50; individual site counts have all been in single figures apart from that of 22 on Hayling Island on Apr. 24th 1990.

A few are seen away from breeding sites in July, which probably indicates local dispersal. Autumn passage peaks in late August and the first half of September. Initially, a greater proportion occurs inland, but from mid-September onwards more are recorded at coastal sites. Notable concentrations have included 16 at Old Winchester Hill on Aug. 29th 1982, 15 at Sandy Point on Aug. 27th 1984 and 17 at Beacon Hill (Warnford) on Sep. 7th 1986. The number recorded per autumn increased from below 50 in the early and mid 1970s to 200-250 in 1986 and 1987. Although the increase in observer effort no doubt accounts for some of the rise, it does correlate with the increased breeding numbers described above. Most depart by mid-October. During 1971-92, last dates were in the period Sep. 25th-Nov. 4th with the average Oct. 16th. This excludes two exceptionally late birds at Morestead on Nov. 22nd 1975 and Pennington Marsh on Nov. 24th 1989.

Ringing activities have resulted in seven recoveries involving Hampshire birds. These include one ringed at Fordingbridge on June 4th 1968 and shot in Algeria on Apr. 7th 1969, one ringed on the North Sea coast of Germany on Aug. 25th 1973 and controlled at Farlington Marshes on Sep. 9th of that year, and one ringed at Hamble on Sep. 12th 1986 and shot in Morocco on about Apr. 24th 1987. British Redstarts winter in the scrub-savannah belt of the Sahel region of West Africa (BWP).

## Whinchat                                                         *Saxicola rubetra*

A scarce summer visitor and common passage migrant.

K & M described the Whinchat as "a summer visitor to all parts of the county, but nowhere plentiful". Today, as a breeding species, it is largely confined to the New Forest, where it prefers bracken-clad slopes with heather and/or grass and scattered gorse bushes. Partial surveys during the 1960s produced totals of 12+ pairs in 1961, 13 in 1965 and nine in 1966 in 50% of the suitable habitat. Few were reported during the 1970s, but annual counts for 1978-90 are shown below.

| 1978 | 1979 | 1980 | 1981 | 1982 | 1983 | 1984 | 1985 | 1986 | 1987 | 1988 | 1989 | 1990 |
|------|------|------|------|------|------|------|------|------|------|------|------|------|
| 2 | 6 | 20 | 20 | 13 | 13 | 9 | 20 | 10 | 19 | 10 | 11 | 1 |

These data were provided by M & P Cambridge and P Toye (*in litt*), who emphasised that they were not the result of complete surveys.

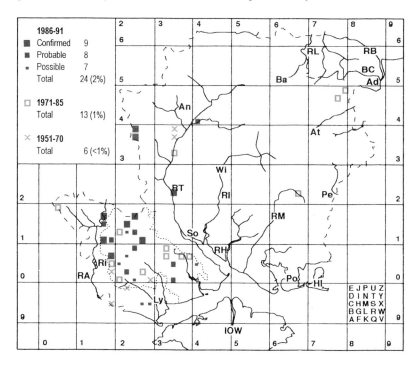

On the Atlas Map, earlier records for 1951-85 have been incorporated with those from the Atlas Survey. Some registrations have been moved by up to two tetrads for security reasons. Some contraction of range is evident, especially in the east of the Forest, although it has always been very scarce in that area. The Atlas results and the data above suggest a population normally in the range 15-25 pairs. However, there was apparently a decline from 1988 onwards and possibly fewer than five pairs bred in 1990-92.

Outside the New Forest, Whinchats are rare and erratic breeders. They formerly bred regularly at Martin Down but the only recent records were of single pairs in 1982 and 1983. At Porton Down, they have bred for at least 30

365

years, with up to six pairs present, about half of these on the Hampshire side of the county boundary (B C H Warren *in litt*). In the Test valley, single pairs bred at Chilbolton in 1957, Charity Down Farm in 1967, Longstock in 1969, Houghton in 1978 and Greatbridge in 1988 and a male held territory at Bransbury Common in 1989. Elsewhere, two pairs with young were seen near Crondall in 1980 and an adult and a juvenile were at East Meon in the same year. Most of these reports refer to family parties, which indicates that nesting may not always have taken place at the site where the birds were seen. In 1988-91, the British population was estimated at 14,000-28,000 pairs (New Atlas).

The first Whinchats normally arrive in late April, although the earliest ever was at Stockbridge on Mar. 21st 1968. During 1971-92, there were early birds at Braishfield on Apr. 2nd 1984 and at Old Winchester Hill on Mar. 31st 1985, and other first dates were between Apr. 7th and May 2nd with the average Apr. 18th. Spring passage peaks in early May but continues until the end of that month and occasionally into June. In the late 1980s, the recorded annual spring totals were usually in the range 50-80. Most sightings were of one to four birds but higher counts included those of eight at Shepherds Spring on Apr. 29th 1978, Dean Hill on May 3rd 1978, Lower Test Marshes on May 3rd 1980 and Hayling Island on Apr. 25th 1985, 14 at Hayling Island on May 14th 1988 and 30 at Keyhaven on May 1st 1990.

In autumn, a few are seen from early July onwards. The main movement starts in mid-August and reaches a peak in early September. The numbers involved are much greater than in spring; the recorded total exceeded 500 in four years during the 1980s with a maximum of 1132 in 1984. Regular watching has shown Farlington Marshes to be an important site; counts of 20+ were made there in six years during 1971-92 with a maximum of 40 on Sep. 22nd 1980. Counts of the same magnitude were also made at Hayling Island (in 3 years, max. 32, Aug. 27th 1984), Titchfield Haven (2 years, max. 33, Aug. 28th 1977), the Pennington/Keyhaven area (3 years, max. 40, Sep. 9th 1987), Martin Down (2 years, max. 38, Sep. 7th 1984), Portsdown Hill (2 years, max. 26, Aug. 26th 1983) and in one year only at Bishopstoke, Beaulieu Heath East, Calshot, Dibden Bay, Needs Ore, Southampton Docks, Twyford Down/Hockley Golf Course, West Tisted and Warsash. The numbers passing through decline sharply in the last week of September and few are seen after mid-October. Between 1971 and 1992, last dates were between Oct. 11th and Nov. 15th with the average Oct. 27th. This excludes one at IBM Lake (Cosham) on Dec. 1st 1984.

In early 1983, two were discovered wintering – at Hilsea Lines from Jan. 10th-30th and Wicor (Portchester) from Jan. 16th-23rd. Both were found in paddocks with rough grass and scattered bramble bushes. Subsequently, single birds were seen at Mengham (Hayling Island) on Feb. 28th and Beaulieu Heath on Mar. 10th. The only earlier record suggestive of wintering involved a male at Keyhaven on Mar. 9th 1938.

The only ringing recovery to involve a Hampshire bird was of a first-winter female trapped on Fair Isle on Sep. 6th 1956 and found dead near Petersfield on Oct. 10th 1956. British birds are believed to winter in the Sahel region of West Africa (BWP).

# Stonechat                                           *Saxicola torquata*

A moderately common but local resident and partial migrant.

The Stonechat's preferred habitat is lowland heath with scattered clumps of gorse. At times of high population level, young conifer plantations with heather ground cover and other sites with gorse, such as coastal heaths and commons, downland and wasteground in river valleys and around factories, docks and gravel pits, may be occupied.

The main population centre is the New Forest. Several surveys have been carried out, all of which relied on partial coverage of the available habitat, with extrapolation of the data to obtain an estimate of the total number of pairs. In 1961, there was an estimated 430 pairs, but following two successive severe winters the population fell to 83 pairs in 1962 and 58 in 1963. A further survey in 1966 located 162 pairs in 61.5 km$^2$ of heathland and bog, about 50% of the available suitable habitat. This indicated a total of 324 pairs (Tubbs 1968), showing a quick recovery from the effects of the 1962/63 winter. In 1974, there were 350 pairs, numbers then rising to over 400 pairs by 1977 (Tubbs 1986a). Severe weather presumably accounted for successive reductions to 320 pairs in 1978 and 290 pairs in 1979. In the early 1980s, the population again expanded, the 1981/82 hard winter apparently not depleting numbers. However, following the severe winter of 1984/85, there was a sharp decline, sample counts showing a reduction of 60% compared to 1984. Further cold spells in the succeeding two winters no doubt hindered recovery, but a survey in 1988 located 119 pairs in 66% of the suitable habitat, indicating a total population of 180 pairs (D V Westerhoff *in litt*). Numbers have increased since then although no further surveys have been attempted.

The other important area is the heathland in the north-east of the county, where winter weather tends to be harder than in the New Forest and the suitable habitat is fragmentary. In 1966, 33 pairs were located. Numbers reached a peak level between 1976 and 1978, with an estimated 75 pairs present. The series of five severe winters in the next nine years resulted in a considerable decline to 15 pairs in 1987. By 1992, numbers had increased to about 80 pairs. The four major sites are Yateley Common/Blackbushe Airfield (highest counts 10 pairs in 1980; 9 in 1990), Bricksbury Hill/Long Valley (15 in 1978 and 1991), Ludshott Common (13 in 1978; 17 in 1990) and Woolmer (14 in 1980, 1983 and 1984; 17 in 1991).

Elsewhere, numbers reached a peak during 1974-76, with an estimated 60-80 pairs breeding. Favoured sites included coastal scrub at Titchfield Haven (max. 8 pairs in 1974), Warsash (4 pairs in 1974), Hamble Common (4 pairs in 1974) and between Lymington and Milford-on-Sea (8 pairs in 1975, but no more than two in other years), Baddesley Common (6 pairs in 1975 and 1977), Porton Down (10-12 pairs during the 1970s) and Portsdown Hill (4 pairs in 1975). During the Atlas Survey, many of these sites were not occupied. In 1990, probably about 25 pairs bred at localities away from the New Forest and north-east. This is low compared to the mid-1970s, when many pairs were undoubtedly missed. This suggests that marginal habitats are not re-occupied in strength until saturation level is reached on the heathlands. However, habitat destruction, such as the ploughing up of parts of Baddesley and Copythorne

Commons, will also have contributed to the decline. In 1992 and 1993, breeding took place at several coastal sites where it was not recorded during the Atlas Survey, including a pair at Farlington Marshes in 1993, the first ever to nest there.

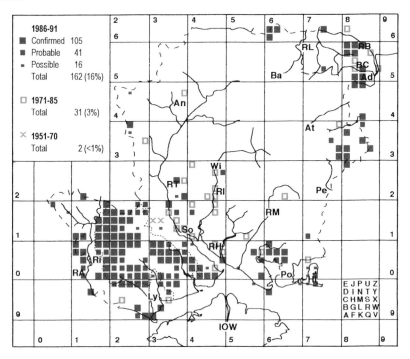

The Atlas Map incorporates all records for 1951-75 as well as those obtained during the Atlas Survey, and thus shows the likely distribution following a series of mild winters. On the basis of the available records, the county population was probably around 500 pairs in the mid-1970s but only 300 pairs in 1990. By 1993, it was probably approaching 500 pairs again. In 1988-91, the British total was estimated to be in the range 8500-21,500 pairs (New Atlas).

Post-breeding dispersal of first-brood juveniles takes place from June onwards, with higher numbers, often involving family parties, in August and early September. These sightings, presumably involving local breeding birds, are mostly at inland sites on the downs and in the river valleys. From mid-September to mid-October a marked passage occurs, with the majority recorded at coastal localities. Large counts have included 18 at Titchfield Haven on Sep. 30th 1973, 15 at Itchen Abbas on Sep. 20th 1974, 29 at Warsash on Oct. 13th 1976, 22 on Hayling Island on Sep. 29th 1984, 15 at Needs Ore on Sep. 30th 1989 and 23 at Hale Meadows on Sep. 30th 1990. As winter approaches, numbers gradually decline to a low point in February. The size of the autumn passage is no doubt influenced by the level of the local breeding population and breeding success in the previous summer; this is demonstrated by the fact that the 1990 movement was the best since the mid-1970s, with over 150 noted during the main passage period. This reflects the species' gradual recovery following the cold winters of the early and mid-1980s.

Varying numbers remain to winter, but most quickly disappear at the onset of a severe spell of weather. When the population level is high, pairs and singles may be found scattered along the coastal strip and in the main river valleys. The highest mid-winter counts made in recent years were of 14 at Alresford on Dec. 14th 1976 and nine at Titchfield Haven on Jan. 19th 1986. However, no comprehensive counts have been made around Langstone Harbour, which probably supports higher numbers in some winters. Small numbers are also present on the New Forest and north-east heaths in winter, numbers again depending on the severity of the winter. These may be mostly immigrants from elsewhere, as P G Davis (pers. comm.) has ringed hundreds of pulli in east Hampshire and west Surrey and yet never seen a ringed bird in winter. Few comprehensive counts have been made in the New Forest, but in mild winters 100 or more may be present. 11 on Ridley Plain on Dec. 29th 1974 gives an idea of the number which may be present on one heath. In the north-east, the total wintering may reach 30. Eight were around Yateley Common and Blackbushe Airfield on Dec. 5th 1981, but two weeks later, following severe blizzards, only one could be found, and there were no further sightings anywhere in the north-east until Feb. 13th 1982. The highest count was of 14 at Ludshott Common on Dec. 27th 1991.

Recoveries of seven pulli, ringed in Hampshire and just across the Surrey border, in their first winter, confirm the Stonechat's status as a partial migrant. Three were recovered abroad between December and February in north central France, near Barcelona, Spain and in Algeria. Another was found dead at Denmead in January, while the remainder were found near Alton in August, at Budds Farm in October and in Sussex in April, all at times when they may have been on migration. The marked declines in the breeding population which occur following hard winters suggest that many wintering in southern England perish. The recovery in France indicates that some do not move far enough to escape the rigours of the worst winter weather.

Dispersal from coastal and river valley wintering sites takes place from February onwards. A few are occasionally recorded on passage in late February or March, more rarely up to early May, at sites where they have not wintered, but ten at Dibden Bay on Feb. 21st 1990 was exceptional.

One showing the characteristics of one or other of the eastern races *S.t. maura* or *stejnegeri*, known as Siberian Stonechats, was at Titchfield Haven on Oct. 31st 1988.


## Wheatear                                    *Oenanthe oenanthe*

A scarce summer visitor and common passage migrant.

K & M described the Wheatear as "plentiful in most parts of the central hill district, and also found in suitable localities in the northern woodlands and in the New Forest". They described how its range extended: as the cultivated parts of the central hill district reverted to downland through neglect, so Wheatears appeared and increased abundantly.

The first indication of a reversal of this trend was in the late 1930s, when a marked decline was noted on the downs between Combe and Linkenholt (G Brown *in litt*). The few records available for the 1940s and early 1950s show that concentrations of four to six pairs still bred at Butser Hill, Longwood Warren, Farley Mount and Martin, Porton, Rushmore and Woodcott Downs, and no doubt elsewhere. However, a reduction in the area of suitable habitat, due to increased cultivation during and after the Second World War, led to a decline. This was exacerbated by the reduction in sheep farming and the loss of rabbits in the mid-1950s, due to myxomatosis. The resultant lack of grazing, and deterioration of rabbit burrows, a favoured nest site, made such areas unattractive to Wheatears. They had gone from most of the downs by the late 1950s, although two or three pairs survived at Martin Down until the early 1960s (N W Orr *in litt*).

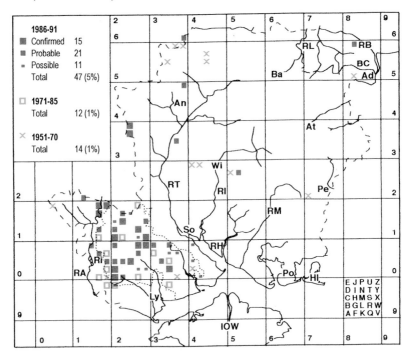

The Atlas Survey produced confirmed breeding in two tetrads at Porton Down. There, increased numbers of rabbits have produced a large area of suitable short turf on the Hampshire side of the county boundary. Breeding had certainly recommenced by the mid-1980s, and between 1988 and 1991, numbers there rose from four to eight pairs (B C H Warren *in litt*). At other localities on the chalk, the Atlas Survey produced three records of probable breeding. In 1988, a pair held territory at Longwood Warren but birds have not been seen there since. The remaining records are likely to refer to late spring migrants.

Today, the main breeding stronghold is in the New Forest. They nest where suitable holes are available, often on disused airfields and lawns where the turf is kept short by grazing, and in the vicinity of rabbit warrens. In 1957, 34 pairs were located, including 12 on the eastern half of Beaulieu Heath. Subsequently, a decline occurred, for only one pair bred on Beaulieu Heath in 1958 and 1959, and partial coverage of the whole area in 1966 and 1968 produced 11 and 12 pairs respectively. Few pairs were reported in the 1970s, but the Atlas Survey produced records for 39 tetrads in the New Forest, with breeding probable or confirmed in 29. The Atlas Map incorporates both Atlas Survey records and those for 1951-85; some have been moved by up to two tetrads for security reasons. The map suggests that the Wheatear's range has, like that of the Whinchat, contracted in the east of the Forest; this may partly be connected with the destruction of some of the old runways. Not every tetrad will have been occupied annually, and so the total population is probably now in the range 10-20 pairs.

In the north-east of the county, Wheatears have probably always been rare although they did attempt breeding at Tweseldown Racecourse in 1963. During the Atlas Survey, the only record was of one prospecting a suitable nest hole at Blackbushe Airfield in 1986. However, breeding is not thought to have occurred there, despite the presence of a juvenile on July 7th 1990.

The only other site where breeding may have occurred is Dibden Bay, where a single bird or pair was present in June in 1981-84 and 1986, and recently fledged young were observed in 1981 and 1982.

In 1988-91, the British population was estimated to be at least 55,000 pairs (New Atlas).

Wheatears are one of the earliest summer visitors to arrive, the first normally appearing by mid-March. During 1971-92, first dates were between Mar. 1st and 29th with the average Mar. 14th. This excludes two earlier records of birds at Lasham Airfield on Feb. 26th 1985 and Needs Ore on Feb. 6th 1989. Major arrivals may occur at any time between late March and early May, this being attributed by Williamson (1962) to variation in the timing of calm, anticyclonic weather with clear nights over Iberia and France. In some years, there are two waves of immigrants, in late March and early April and four or five weeks later. At coastal sites, falls of 40 or more occur at favoured localities. High counts include 80 at South Hayling on Apr. 14th 1983, 95 there on Apr. 10th 1984, 51 at IBM Lake/Paulsgrove Reclamation on Apr. 2nd 1985 and 100 at Southampton Docks on Mar. 23rd 1990. Occasionally, birds are seen making landfall, e.g. 13 flying in off the sea at Hurst Beach on May 3rd 1980 and 12 likewise on Apr. 14th 1981. Inland, numbers are lower, although flocks of 10-30 are regularly recorded at airfields and downland sites, e.g. 25 at Martin Down on May 8th 1979, 24 at Blackbushe Airfield on Mar. 31st 1988, 32 at Soberton Down on Apr. 25th 1989 and 30+ at Stoney Cross on Mar. 24th 1990.

Passage may continue until late May or early June. Many of the later birds are described as large and bright, i.e. showing the characteristics of the Greenland race *O. o. leucorhoa*, but only a few have been trapped to confirm this.

In autumn, as with several other migratory passerines, a few juveniles occur from early July onwards. The main passage starts in early August and the peak movement occurs at the end of that month. However, substantial numbers continue to pass through until mid-October, with stragglers into November in most years. As in spring, the later birds may well be from the most northerly breeding populations. Large counts are mostly made on the coast. On Hayling Island, 108 were counted on Aug. 26th 1984 and 106 on Aug. 26th 1985, while other concentrations included 72 between Brownwich and Warsash on Aug. 12th 1960, 50 at Farlington Marshes on Aug. 15th 1975 and 40 in the Pennington/Keyhaven area on Aug. 25th 1984 and Sep. 9th 1988. Inland, sizeable gatherings are frequently attracted to stubble fields and other suitable sites, e.g. 24 at Crondall and 22 at Martin Down on Aug. 26th 1980, 33 at Portsdown Hill on Sep. 14th 1982 and 26 at Beaulieu Heath on Aug. 27th 1986.

During 1971-92, last dates were between Oct. 27th and Nov. 21st with the average Nov. 7th. This excludes later birds at West Hayling on Dec. 8th and 9th 1979, Southsea Castle from Dec. 10th-15th 1982 and Warsash on Dec. 13th 1987.

The only ringing recoveries involving Hampshire birds are of one trapped at Gilkicker Point on Aug. 16th 1965 and controlled 2036 km SSW in Morocco on 20th September 1965, and two ringed as pulli and both found dead within 15 km of the nest. Most British Wheatears winter in tropical West Africa.

## Black-eared Wheatear  *Oenanthe hispanica*

Three records. Single males, all of the race *O. h. hispanica*, were at Farlington Marshes on Sep. 18th 1954 and June 5th 1987, and at Keyhaven on Apr. 25th 1992†.

The Black-eared Wheatear breeds from Spain and Morocco to Iran and winters in the Sahel region of Africa.

## Desert Wheatear  *Oenanthe deserti*

One record. A female was at Farlington Marshes from Nov. 4th-19th 1961.

The Desert Wheatear breeds from North Africa east to Mongolia and winters principally in the Sahara and Sahel regions of Africa, Arabia and Pakistan.

## Ring Ouzel  *Turdus torquatus*

A scarce passage migrant; recorded three times in winter.

Most Ring Ouzels are recorded inland, with localities on the downs and in the New Forest being particularly favoured. Good coverage at Beacon Hill

(Warnford) and Old Winchester Hill in the late 1980s produced virtually annual sightings in both spring and autumn. Although numbers fluctuate from year to year, the overall upward trend since the 1950s (fig. 68) reflects the improved observer coverage.

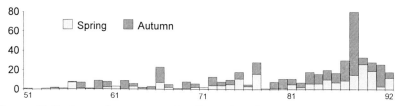

*Figure 68. Spring and autumn totals of Ring Ouzels, 1951-92.*

Spring passage reaches a peak in mid-April but there were March records in 16 years between 1951 and 1992. Several exceptionally early birds occurred in March 1990, with one at Sway on 8th, and six at Beacon Hill and one at Basingstoke on 14th. One was at Watership Down on Mar. 14th 1971, but otherwise the earliest date was Mar. 18th. The spring total exceeded ten in six years with a maximum of 26 in 1989. Most records involved up to four birds, sometimes pausing for a few days before moving on. Apart from the Beacon Hill record already mentioned, the only larger groups were of nine at Pilot Hill on Apr. 16th 1964 and seven at Martin Down on Apr. 13th 1989. Very few have been recorded after early May, the latest being at Old Winchester Hill on May 31st 1989.

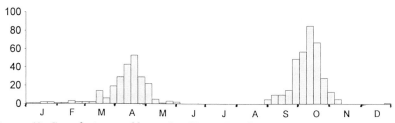

*Figure 69. Cumulative weekly totals of Ring Ouzels, 1951-90.*

Autumn passage normally begins in mid-September but earlier records include those of one at Beaulieu Heath on Aug. 27th 1957 and six at Ridley Wood (New Forest) on Sep. 6th 1969. The autumn total exceeded ten in six years with a maximum of 65 in 1988, although 23 in 1991 was the next highest. Most occur in early or mid October (fig. 69), often coinciding with falls of Redwings and Fieldfares, thus suggesting a Scandinavian origin. Large parties recorded include 15 at Godshill with other thrushes from Sep. 27th-Oct. 1st 1987, six at East Hayling on Oct. 15th 1988 and 15 at Old Winchester Hill and six at Beacon Hill on the following day. November birds were recorded in five years with the latest at Ashley Walk on 10th in 1984.

There have been three wintering records: a male at Yew Tree Bottom (New Forest) from Dec. 31st 1983-Apr. 4th 1984, a female at Winchester College water meadows from Jan. 23rd-Feb. 27th 1985 and a male in a Titchfield garden on Feb. 17th 1985.

British and Scandinavian birds winter in southern Spain and north-west Africa.

## Blackbird                                                    *Turdus merula*

An abundant resident, passage migrant and winter visitor.

The Blackbird occurs in all habitats where there are trees and bushes, particularly in suburban parks and gardens. During the Atlas Survey, it was found in 1027 (99%) tetrads, with breeding confirmed in 956, probable in 70 and possible in one. The only tetrads where it was not recorded were four which contained only saltmarsh.

Local CBC data suggest that the county population has been declining through the 1980s with a 26% fall between 1981 and 1990. This mirrors the national trend, which has been downward since the mid-1970s. The decline may be related to the lower average winter temperatures over the period (Marchant *et al* 1990), although changes in farming practices, such as the reduction in spring tillage and removal of hedgerows, may also be involved (O'Connor & Shrubb 1986).

Using national CBC data for 1989, the New Atlas method indicates a Hampshire population of 120,000 pairs. However, this does not give enough weight to suburban areas, where Batten (1973) estimated populations as high as 250 pairs/km$^2$ and Simms (1978) recorded even higher densities in ideal habitats such as overgrown gardens. Possibly a figure of 150,000 pairs is more appropriate. The national total was estimated at 4.4 million pairs (New Atlas).

From early October until early December, apparent influxes are recorded in all parts of the county. The two largest counts both involved gatherings attracted to haws: 150 at Timsbury on Nov. 13th 1971 and 195 at Fort Fareham Wood on Dec. 2nd 1981. As with other thrushes, diurnal and nocturnal movement is also detected at this time, although the numbers involved are surprisingly low. At Fleet Pond, regular coverage from 1987-92 produced a total of 227 flying over, with most moving in directions between south and west. Movement was noted between Oct. 1st and Nov. 25th, with the peak in late October and early November, rather later than other thrushes apart from Fieldfare.

In winter, resident birds remain on territory except in the most severe conditions, but immigrants live in loose flocks and forage socially (Winter Atlas). The largest gatherings recorded were feeding on fallen apples during hard weather: almost 100 near Titchfield Haven in early January 1979 and 100+ at Stoke Fruit Farm (Hayling) in mid-January 1987. Communal roosts often hold up to 100 birds, but exceptionally 500 were counted into mixed scrub, principally hawthorn, at Old Winchester Hill in cold, but not severe, weather on Dec. 20th 1979. Compared to other thrushes, there is little evidence of hard weather movements, the only such observation recently being of three flying west at Titchfield Haven on Jan. 1st 1979.

Analysis of the ringing data confirms that the Hampshire breeding population is largely sedentary. Only two adults ringed in summer have been recovered over 100 km away: in Essex and Kent in subsequent breeding seasons. There have been no foreign recoveries of Hampshire-bred birds, unlike Song and Mistle Thrushes. In contrast, the origin of birds trapped in Hampshire in autumn and winter is indicated by nine controls in later breeding seasons in western Germany (3) and Belgium, eastern Germany, north-east France, Finland, Norway and Sweden (1 each). Onward movement was shown by one ringed in September and shot in January of the same winter in Spain. Other recoveries outside the breeding season in subsequent years were in France and western Germany (4), Netherlands, Norway and Poland (2 each), and Belgium, Denmark and Sweden (1 each). One, ringed as a pullus in the Netherlands, was found dead in Hampshire in mid-winter.

# Fieldfare                                   *Turdus pilaris*

A numerous to abundant winter visitor and passage migrant.

The first Fieldfares are normally recorded in late September or early October, the average date during 1970-91 being Oct. 2nd. During that period the earliest was one at Hill Side on Sep. 6th 1981, but in 1968 there were seven at Hale Purlieu on Aug. 3rd, with two still there on 5th, and one at Andover Sewage Farm on Aug. 15th. There was a widespread early arrival throughout Britain in that year (*Brit. Birds* 61: 428, 474). Diurnal passage peaks in late October and early November. At this time, day totals of 100-200 are not uncommon, with most moving in directions between south-west and north-west. By far the heaviest passage ever recorded took place on Nov. 2nd and 3rd 1986, when movement took place on a broad front across southern England. At Tunworth, 4635 moved west in a total of six hours watching on the two days and lower numbers were recorded elsewhere in the county. At Fleet Pond, daily coverage in autumn during 1987-92 produced a total of 4496 on dates between Oct. 4th and Nov. 30th with peaks of 267 SSW on Oct. 13th 1990 and 299 west on Nov. 10th 1991. The variation in timing of the main autumn arrival may depend on weather conditions, sizeable early movements usually coinciding with anticyclonic conditions with clear skies and light east or north-easterly winds. However, studies in Scandinavia, the area of origin of our wintering population, have shown that the time of departure of Fieldfares depends on the abundance, and hence the time of depletion, of the rowan fruit crop (Tyrvainen 1975, Winter Atlas).

Even in years with heavy diurnal movement, recorded numbers on the ground are usually low until late November, gatherings such as 1000-1500 in the Cheesefoot Head area from Oct. 30th-Nov. 11th 1974 being exceptional. This is possibly explained by the fact that small flocks are widely distributed feeding on hedgerow berry crops, haw being the preferred fruit at this time (Snow & Snow 1988). As the winter proceeds, the exhaustion of this food source forces them on to fields, where large flocks form to feed on soil invertebrates. Counts of 500-1000 are made in most winters, those to exceed this level including 1500+ at Enham Cross Roads on Jan. 11th 1975 and 2000+ around Preston Candover on Dec. 9th 1979. Communal roosts of several hundred form in woodland scrub, often close to water, and also in mature heather and gorse. The largest recorded was in alder scrub at Fleet Pond, where 1435 flew in at dusk on Feb. 26th 1988.

During severe weather, large numbers may move into the county or pass through in search of milder conditions elsewhere. The heaviest movement ever recorded was on Dec. 31st 1961, when 30,000 moved south-east at Gilkicker Point. Recently, high numbers were noted in February 1985, when 10,200 coasted eastwards at Hill Head in 3.3 hours on 9th and 10,000+ were estimated to be in frost-covered fields in the Avon valley between Bickton and Sopley the next day, and in February 1986, when 14,114 moved east at Hill Head in six hours on 6th and an estimated 15,000 flew west at Milford-on-Sea on 7th. In hard weather, large numbers are attracted to frost-free areas such as watercress beds and sewage farms and to windfall apples and pears. Birds become tamer and are a frequent sight in gardens where they do not usually occur.

Return passage is evident from early March onwards. Diurnal movements usually involve flocks of up to 100 moving in directions between north and east. These reach a peak in late March and early April but may continue until the end of the latter month. The largest movement recorded was of 300 leaving north-east from Park Corner Farm (Odiham) on Apr. 1st 1983. In most years, large flocks form on the ground at this time, the maximum being 2010 in the Stratfield Saye area on Mar. 17th 1984. Numbers gradually decline through April although flocks of up to 300 may be present as late as 20th. At Park Corner Farm, a flock peaked at 111 on May 2nd 1980 and 130+ were still at Hartley Wespall on May 1st 1982. The last are normally recorded in late April or early May, the average date during 1971-92 being May 2nd with the latest at Martin Down on May 23rd 1980. This excludes one at Yew Tree Heath (New Forest) on June 10th 1977.

Ringing activities have resulted in 23 recoveries of Hampshire-ringed birds, 19 of them abroad. Seven were found in France in subsequent winters but one, ringed at Leckford on Jan. 7th 1985, was shot 291 km to the south in France eight days later. Of four recovered in Norway, one was found during the breeding season but the others were in January, September and October. The origin of our wintering population is confirmed by the recovery during the breeding season of four in Finland and three in Sweden.


## Song Thrush                                        *Turdus philomelos*

A numerous resident, passage migrant and winter visitor.

During the Atlas Survey, the Song Thrush was found in 1016 (99%) tetrads, with breeding confirmed in 761, probable in 223 and possible in 32. It was not recorded in 15, ten of which were coastal and contained little or no suitable habitat. It has similar habitat requirements to the Blackbird, but generally is outnumbered by that species. For example, a census of 281 ha of mixed woodland, grassland and scrub at Botley Wood in 1981 located 95 Blackbird territories but only 43 of Song Thrush, while a survey of 562 ha of farmland, woodland and habitations at Manydown Farm (Wootton St. Lawrence) in 1984 found 150 pairs of Blackbirds but only 15 of Song Thrush (Fuller 1984).

The national population has been in decline for at least 50 years (Marchant *et al* 1990) and CBC data show that the trend has been marked since the mid-1970s. The picture presented by Hampshire CBC data is unclear. In an area of 108 ha surveyed at Titchfield Haven, the number of territories mapped declined from 13 in 1974 to seven in 1990. However, at some other sites, numbers have remained fairly stable overall despite reductions after severe winters in 1981/82, 1984/85 and 1990/91. The national decline may be connected with the increased frequency of cold winters since the late 1970s. However, since Song Thrushes rely on slugs and snails to augment their diet in midsummer (when worms may be in short supply) and in late winter (when berry crops become depleted), the increased use of pesticides (particularly molluscicides) by farmers, horticulturalists and gardeners may be implicated (Marchant *et al* 1990).

Using national CBC data for 1989, the New Atlas method indicates a Hampshire population of around 30,000 pairs and a national total of 990,000 pairs.

There is clear evidence of passage and immigration in autumn. Between late September and mid-November, small numbers are seen moving, calls are heard at night and influxes are noted. At Fleet Pond, regular daily watching between 1987 and 1992 produced a total of 983 moving (mostly in directions between south and north-west) with a peak count of 54 on Oct. 1st 1989. Elsewhere, day totals have not exceeded 34 apart from that of 200 coasting west with Redwings at Titchfield Haven on Oct. 12th 1980. Song Thrushes are less frequently heard at night than Redwings, but records such as 40+ calling over Farlington Marshes on Nov. 4th 1986 suggest that heavy movements do occur. Increases indicative of overnight falls are recorded at coastal and inland localities, especially in the first half of October. In many cases, observers merely noted an increase, but examples of counts include 100 at Winchester College water meadows on Oct. 4th 1985, 70 at Old Winchester Hill on Oct. 20th 1985 and 65 at Sinah and Sandy Point (Hayling Island) on Oct. 12th 1986. A massive gathering, attracted to yew berries at Butser Hill, peaked at 700 on Oct. 24th 1964. Several hundred remained through November but all had gone by Dec. 13th.

In hard winter weather, a few may be detected during passerine movements, e.g. ten flying west at Titchfield Haven on Dec. 12th 1981. Loose flocks are sometimes noted in severe conditions, e.g. 43 at Langstone on Dec. 19th 1981 and 60+ in a field at Hamble on Jan. 5th 1985.

Evidence for the immigration of continental Song Thrushes is also provided by ringing returns. Two ringed as pulli in the Netherlands and one in Belgium were recovered in Hampshire in the following winter. Three ringed in Hampshire in winter were found in March or April in the Netherlands (2) and Belgium, indicating the return movement. A proportion of the Hampshire population, probably mostly juveniles, disperses in a south to south-west direction after the breeding season. Two ringed as pulli were recovered in their first winter in northern Spain and south-west France, while others ringed in summer were found in winter in France and Devon (3 each) and Spain (1). Cold weather movement is illustrated by one ringed at Fordingbridge on Dec. 22nd 1962 and found dead in Manche, France, 141 km south, on Jan. 17th 1963.

# Redwing                                              *Turdus iliacus*

A numerous to abundant winter visitor and passage migrant.

The first Redwings are usually seen in late September, often a few days earlier than Fieldfares. During 1970-91, the average arrival date was Sep. 27th,

with the earliest at Enham Alamein on Sep. 12th 1975. Heavy passage, both diurnal and nocturnal, may take place during October and November. Movement is principally to the west, although at the coast large flocks may arrive from the sea and move inland in directions between north-west and north-east. On the morning of Oct. 12th 1972, 4500 moved north or north-west off the sea at Hordle Cliff. Many were heard moving off west from nearby Keyhaven Marsh at dusk, and migration continued throughout the night and on the following day, when 1000 flew north-east over Woolmer. On Oct. 12th 1980, passage was recorded on a broad front across the county, with at least 7000 seen moving west, including 1800 over Fleet Pond in 2¾ hours. In most years, the heaviest movement is typically rather later and largely inland, e.g. 3834 moved west over Camp Farm (Aldershot) in 17 hours watching between Oct. 22nd and Nov. 13th 1983 with peaks of 1793 on Oct. 22nd and 1576 on Oct. 30th, and 10,022 were logged at Tunworth in 66.45 hours watching between Sep. 27th and Nov. 20th 1986, with the largest day total of 6190 west in three hours on Nov. 3rd. At Fleet Pond, regular watching between 1987 and 1992 produced a total of 17,182 on dates between Sep. 24th and Dec. 13th with a peak in late October. Most of these occurred in 1989 (5617) and 1992 (5925), with a maximum day total of 1335 mostly west on Oct. 27th 1992. Most heavy movements occurred in clear, anticyclonic conditions with light winds coming from directions between south-east and north-east.

As with Fieldfare, numbers on the ground are usually low in autumn. Gatherings such as 900 at Old Winchester Hill on Oct. 17th 1974 and 800 at North Stoneham on Nov. 1st 1973 were high for the time of year, but at Cheesefoot Head an estimated 10,000 were present on Nov. 10th 1974, when a continuous stream arrived from the north all afternoon. Numbers usually increase from late November onwards, although Redwings are usually outnumbered by Fieldfares, flock size rarely exceeding 500. Roosts form in a variety of woodland scrub, the largest recorded being at Fletchwood Lane (Ashurst), where over 2000 flew in at dusk on Feb. 16th 1977.

Hard weather may result in large numbers passing through the county. Most movements in excess of 1000 involve birds coasting westwards, e.g. on Dec. 12th 1981, when 2075 were logged at Titchfield Haven and at least 2500 at Warsash. However, the two heaviest movements witnessed both involved passage in the opposite direction. On Dec. 30th 1961, an estimated 30,000 moved ESE at Gilkicker Point, and on Feb. 6th 1986, 9669 flew east at Hill Head in six hours and 14,000 did likewise at Milford-on-Sea. Large influxes are also noted, e.g. 1200 at Crondall on Jan. 4th 1982 and 5000 in the Avon valley between Bickton and Sopley on Feb. 10th 1985, but these usually move on quickly. When lying snow or frost prevents access to open ground, the numbers of Redwings feeding among leaf litter in woodlands increase. On Feb. 18th and 19th 1978, an estimated 1000 were near Purbrook feeding under oaks, hollies and yews. Concentrations of 100-200 are also found in other frost-free areas such as sewage farms and watercress beds.

In mild winters, numbers are usually lower, but from late February until late March heavy nocturnal passage to the north-east is frequently recorded, e.g. on the night of Mar. 8th/9th 1981, hundreds moved over Titchfield Haven in strong winds and misty rain. Also at this time, flocks may swell to their highest level of the winter for a few days before declining, e.g. 1220 at Empshott on Mar. 17th 1984 and 1550 at Queen's Parade (Aldershot) four days later. These gatherings presumably include passage birds which have wintered further south or west. The departure is rapid; double-figure counts are occasionally made in the first week of April but in some years only a handful is recorded in that month. The last are normally seen in mid or late April, the average date during 1971-92 being Apr. 24th. In five of these years, birds lingered into May, the latest being a sick individual at South Warnborough on 12th in 1981. In addition, one found dead at Dunley (Whitchurch) on May 27th 1985 had been ringed at Malmohus, Sweden on Oct. 24th 1982.

There is one record of a presumed summering individual, at Southampton Common from May 17th-June 3rd 1965.

Ringing data indicate that birds occurring in Hampshire originate from Fenno-Scandia and that they may winter in different countries from one winter to the next. Hampshire-ringed birds have been recovered during the breeding season in Finland (2) and in subsequent winters in France (3), Italy (1) and Portugal (1). Seven foreign-ringed birds have been found dead in Hampshire, from Sweden (3), Belgium (2), Finland (1) and the Netherlands (1). Two short distance recoveries illustrate cold weather movements; one ringed at Tring on Jan. 8th 1979 had moved to Titchfield Haven by Jan. 24th of that year, and another trapped at Sevenoaks on Jan. 8th 1985 was found at Sway on Feb. 4th 1985.


# Mistle Thrush                                    *Turdus viscivorus*

A numerous resident and passage migrant.

The Mistle Thrush is widely distributed throughout the county. During the Atlas Survey, it was located in 994 (96%) tetrads, with breeding confirmed in 727, probable in 221 and possible in 46. Its apparent absence from most of the remainder was probably due to inadequate coverage. Its habitat preferences are similar to those of the other common thrushes, although it nests in trees rather than bushes and is generally found in more open country with less undergrowth (Simms 1978). It has adapted well to urban and suburban areas, where it finds ample nests sites in parks and gardens and sufficient food on lawns and playing fields.

Following recovery from the very hard winters of 1961/62 and 1962/63, the national population grew slowly until the 1981/82 winter reversed the trend. Further hard winters in 1984/85 and 1985/86 caused a continuing decline. Based on limited but consistent data from eight Hampshire CBC plots, the county population appears to have been less affected, remaining substantially constant throughout the 1980s. Using national CBC data for 1989, the New Atlas method indicates a Hampshire population of about 7500 pairs and a national total of 230,000 pairs.

After the breeding season, family parties join together to form large flocks, which may be found feeding on the ground or in berry-bearing shrubs, especially yews. The latter also provide a favoured roosting site. Large gatherings recorded include those of 200+ in yews at Stratfield Saye on Nov. 12th 1972, 100+ at Hampton Ridge on Oct. 1st 1976, 140+ at Marsh Court on July 5th 1977 and 171 at Warsash on Aug. 3rd 1977. Flocks normally break up from October onwards. National ringing data show that a proportion of first-winter birds moves south to France at this time. Adults, usually singly or in pairs, defend fruit-bearing shrubs or trees, especially hollies, throughout the winter months. In mild weather, however, they may join first-winters in flocks of other thrushes feeding on earthworms (Winter Atlas).

In late summer, flocks of up to 70 are recorded flying in various directions at inland sites and probably refer to local dispersal. From late September to early December, there is evidence of light passage. Almost daily coverage at Fleet Pond in autumn from 1987-92 produced a total of 437 moving (mostly in directions between south-east and west) on dates between Sep. 14th and Dec. 5th, with a peak day total of 11 west on Sep. 21st 1987. At Titchfield Haven, there have been fewer observations although the day totals were larger than at Fleet Pond. Between 1975 and 1987, 211 were noted coasting westwards on dates between Oct. 3rd and Dec. 5th. This included a flock of 100 on Nov. 2nd 1975; the next highest count was of 18 on Oct. 23rd 1987. Small numbers are occasionally noted during cold weather movements of other thrushes, e.g. 18 flew west at Titchfield Haven between Dec. 9th and 14th 1981.

The proportion of continental immigrants involved in these movements is probably very small. There has been no recovery of a continental-ringed bird anywhere in Britain, although small numbers are seen making landfall at east coast observatories (Winter Atlas). The bulk of the north European population winters in Belgium, France and Spain (BWP). The Hampshire ringing data is inconclusive. Of 38 recoveries, 29 were within Hampshire, and only four of these were during the autumn passage period. The only long distance movements were of one trapped at Minstead in April 1951 and found dead at Winchelsea, East Sussex the following January, and another trapped at East Cosham during cold weather in January 1982 and found dead at Colchester, Essex in February 1985.

# Cetti's Warbler
*Cettia cetti*

A scarce but increasing resident which first bred in 1979.

The first Cetti's Warbler to be recorded in Britain was at Titchfield Haven from Mar. 4th-Apr. 10th 1961 (Suffern & Ferguson-Lees 1964). At the time, much controversy surrounded the occurrence. Initially, it was considered possibly to be a Moustached Warbler and characteristics of that species were "seen" by some observers. On Mar. 19th, it was trapped, enabling its identity to be confirmed. Subsequently, several heated letters discussing the events were published (*Brit. Birds* 58: 225-227, 516-520).

The next were not until the autumn of 1972, when single birds were trapped at Farlington Marshes on Oct. 25th and Timsbury three days later. Between 1973 and 1976, ten individuals were recorded at various coastal and inland localities, including singing males at Keyhaven from Mar. 24th-Apr. 21st 1974 and Alresford Pond from May 5th-June 30th of the same year. In spring 1977, single males held territory in the Itchen valley near Winchester and in the Avon valley at Hale. In the autumn of that year, a small influx occurred, with 13 recorded, including five in the Itchen valley and six at Titchfield Haven which arrived between Oct. 14th and 19th.

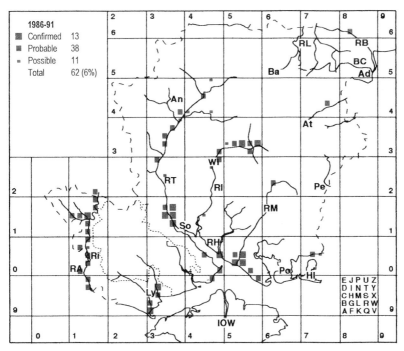

In 1978, at least four singing males were present in the Avon valley, and in the following year breeding was confirmed there for the first time. The breeding population in the county increased steadily during the 1980s, despite several cold winters. A full breeding survey in 1990 revealed 125-127 singing males. The Atlas Map shows the distribution recorded during 1986-91; of the 62 tetrads with registrations, 13 were apparently not occupied during the 1990 survey. Severe weather in February 1991 caused a marked fall in numbers in the following season, most notably at Titchfield Haven, but some recovery occurred in 1992 (table 67).

| | 78 | 79 | 80 | 81 | 82 | 83 | 84 | 85 | 86 | 87 | 88 | 89 | 90 | 91 | 92 |
|---|---|---|---|---|---|---|---|---|---|---|---|---|---|---|---|
| *Inland sites* | | | | | | | | | | | | | | | |
| Avon valley | 4 | 5 | 6 | 8* | 9 | 14* | 15 | 13 | 15* | 15* | 18* | 22* | 28 | 12* | 15* |
| Test valley | 0 | 0 | 0 | 1 | 1 | 3 | 1 | 1 | 3 | 5* | 10* | 14 | 11 | 6* | 8* |
| Itchen valley | 1 | 0 | 1 | 1 | 4 | 4 | 0 | 2 | 4 | 4 | 3 | 8 | 7 | 5 | 5* |
| Alresford Pond | 0 | 2 | 3 | 1 | 2 | 3 | 1 | 2 | 4 | 2 | 4 | 7 | 7 | 5 | 6 |
| Meon valley | 0 | 0 | 0 | 0 | 0 | 0 | 0 | 0 | 0 | 1 | 1 | 1 | 1 | 0 | 0 |
| North-east | 0 | 0 | 0 | 0 | 0 | 0 | 0 | 0 | 0 | 0 | 1 | 0 | 1 | 0 | 0 |
| *Coastal sites* | | | | | | | | | | | | | | | |
| Titchfield Haven | 0 | 0 | 0 | 2 | 3 | 1 | 3 | 6 | 7 | 13 | 15 | 36 | 40 | 16 | 24 |
| Warsash | 0 | 0 | 0 | 0 | 0 | 0 | 0 | 2 | 0 | 2 | 3 | 3 | 4 | 3 | 3 |
| Lower Test | 0 | 0 | 0 | 1 | 1 | 1 | 3 | 7 | 7 | 12 | 12 | 12 | 17 | 9 | 10 |
| Lymington/Hurst | 0 | 0 | 0 | 0 | 1 | 2 | 8 | 5 | 2 | 5 | 4 | 4 | 8 | 4* | 5 |
| Elsewhere | 0 | 0 | 0 | 0 | 1 | 0 | 2 | 1 | 1 | 1 | 2 | 3 | 1 | 1 | 0 |
| Totals | 5 | 7 | 10 | 15 | 22 | 28 | 33 | 39 | 43 | 60 | 73 | 110 | 125 | 61 | 76 |

* estimated total due to poor observer coverage

*Table 67. Annual totals of singing male Cetti's Warblers, 1978-92.*

In the peak year of 1990, the national population was estimated at 450 pairs (New Atlas), of which Hampshire held 28%.

Song occurs virtually throughout the year although there is a clear increase in activity in March and April, as singing males try to establish breeding territories. This results in local spring movements as wandering males occupy potential sites for a few days or weeks, and then move on again. There is evidence from ringing that such movements also involve females; one such individual ringed at Titchfield Haven in early April 1980 was found three weeks later at a Dorset breeding site, while another ringed in Windsor Great Park, Berkshire in April 1992 had moved to Alresford Pond by July 11th 1992 and bred there in 1993. On the other hand, established breeding birds appear to remain faithful to their territories throughout the year. It seems likely that dispersal movements involve mainly young birds, e.g. a juvenile female ringed at Fordingbridge in June 1990 was found breeding the following spring in the Itchen valley and remained there to breed again in 1992.

In autumn, dispersal of young birds is not well understood but some undoubtedly remain on or close to their natal sites. There has been a total of nine Hampshire movements of ringed Cetti's Warblers over 6 km between 1980 and 1991, and these clearly demonstrate an east-west pattern. Three individuals have moved to or from Dorset, and there have been two separate movements between the Avon and Itchen valleys. It may be significant that six of these movements concerned females (although in two cases the same individual was involved), and although it is not entirely clear when these movements occurred, such a degree of mobility is presumably of great importance to the Cetti's Warbler in its colonisation of new sites.

At Titchfield Haven, marked influxes suggesting immigration have been recorded in October and November since 1977, prior to the first breeding there in 1981. In recent years, such influxes have been masked by the growing

resident population and their offspring. That they still occur was shown by the recovery in October 1988 of one which had been ringed as a juvenile at Lower Test Marshes in the previous summer.

In winter, Cetti's Warblers occur in similar habitats to those occupied in the breeding season, although there may be a greater tendency to utilise pure reed stands as part of enlarged feeding territories. The species is rather inconspicuous in winter, and easily overlooked except for its diagnostic calls and the songs of territorial males, most frequently heard at dawn and dusk.

## Lanceolated Warbler                    *Locustella lanceolata*

One record. A first-year was caught and ringed at Damerham on Sep. 23rd 1979. This is the only record of this species for southern England.

The Lanceolated Warbler breeds in much of the Eastern Palearctic and winters in south-east Asia.

## Grasshopper Warbler                    *Locustella naevia*

A scarce summer visitor which has declined considerably since 1970.

The Grasshopper Warbler breeds in a variety of habitats, including open marsh and fen in river valleys, young conifer plantations, clear-felled woodland with naturally regenerating scrub, and heathlands, commons and downland. Most sites have an extensive impenetrable field layer of sedges, long grasses, nettles, willow herb and so forth, usually with scattered small shrubs, particularly brambles and gorse.

Numbers peaked between 1965 and 1970, when the species was widely recorded in the county except on the high chalk and in built-up areas. Large concentrations were present in several young conifer plantations, e.g. at Lordswood (14 singing males in 1967), West Wood (13 in 1967) and West Walk (12 in 1968). At this time, the population probably approached 200 pairs. Since then, there has been a steady decline. By the late 1980s, despite regular requests for all records to be submitted, less than 20 pairs or singing males were reported annually. As the Atlas Map shows, there were registrations in only 80

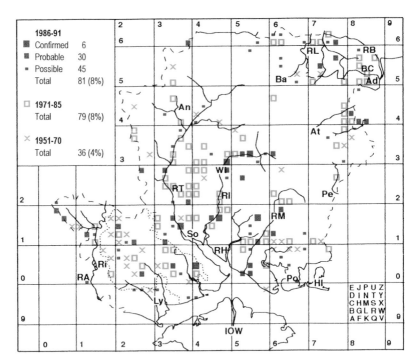

tetrads during the six year survey (45 of which related to possible breeding and may have involved passage birds), but the species was recorded in a further 120 between 1951 and 1985. Table 68 shows an analysis of the records for 1965-90 by habitat type, taking the maximum count for each site during each five year period.

|  | 1966-70 | 1971-75 | 1976-80 | 1981-85 | 1986-90 |
|---|---|---|---|---|---|
| Marsh/Fen | 24 | 34 | 42 | 32 | 21 |
| Woodland | 75 | 41 | 34 | 21 | 7 |
| Heaths/Commons/Downs | 40 | 38 | 27 | 18 | 24 |
| Total | 139 | 113 | 103 | 71 | 52 |

*Table 68. Cumulative totals of singing male Grasshopper Warblers in various habitat types in five year periods, 1965-90.*

The decrease is almost certainly greater than that shown in Table 68, since observer effort increased during the period and yet progressively fewer sites with suitable habitat held the species in successive years. During the Atlas Survey, Titchfield Haven was the only locality where Grasshopper Warblers were recorded annually, with six singing males in 1989 and one to three in other years. At Bentley Wood, Bishops Waltham Moors and Lower Test Marshes the species was recorded in three years, but in the 29 other tetrads where breeding was confirmed or probable, there were records in one or two years only. The available information suggests that there may now be fewer than 40 pairs breeding in the county (and even this may be an overestimate, given the species' tendency to sing when on spring passage). The British population in 1988-91 was estimated at 10,500 pairs (New Atlas).

384

Reasons for the decrease are not fully understood. The pattern mirrors the national picture, which showed a fivefold decrease during 1972-74, a modest improvement from 1979-81 and then a further steep decline (Marchant *et al* 1990). In Hampshire, although the conifer plantations occupied in the 1960s and 1970s are now unsuitable, other similar habitat created since then is largely unoccupied. Sites in river valleys and on heaths, commons and downs still appear suitable, and so it would seem that habitat availability is not a limiting factor. More likely, the fluctuations and underlying decline since 1970 are attributable to droughts in the wintering quarters in the Sahel region of West Africa.

The first usually arrive in mid-April, although the earliest were at Kingsley on Apr. 4th 1967 and Hocombe Plantation on the same date in 1973. In other years during 1971-92, first arrivals were noted between Apr. 4th and 24th with the average Apr. 15th. The main influx occurs in late April and early May with passage continuing until late May.

In autumn, few are detected and in some years there have been no records after Aug. 1st. However, ringing activities and other sightings indicate that most depart in August and early September. Between 1971 and 1992, there were records after Sep. 15th in 13 years with the latest at Hamble Common on Oct. 3rd 1982. Relatively few Grasshopper Warblers are ringed, and there has been only one recovery involving a Hampshire bird: one trapped on Hayling Island on May 15th 1976 and controlled at Portland Bill, Dorset on July 1st 1977.

## Savi's Warbler                    *Locustella luscinioides*

A rare summer visitor.

The first for the county was a male which held territory at Titchfield Haven from May 11th-June 21st 1969 but apparently did not attract a mate. Another singing male was there from May 27th-June 5th 1976. A pair possibly bred in 1977, and in the following year six singing males held territory with one pair confirmed breeding. Between 1979 and 1983, there were respectively two, three, one, two and one singing males with breeding confirmed in 1979 and 1982. More recently, an unmated male was present in late April and early May 1987 (Duffin 1991). The earliest arrival date was Apr. 13th 1981; in other years, first birds were noted on dates up to May 5th with the average Apr. 23rd. The latest was on July 13th 1978 (B S Duffin pers. comm.).

The only other records were of singing males at Farlington Marshes from June 14th-17th 1973 and May 27th-June 1st 1974, one caught there on Aug. 21st 1977 and a singing male at Keyhaven on May 6th 1989.

The known British breeding population fluctuated between ten and 20 pairs in 1981-90 (Spencer *et al* 1993).

## Moustached Warbler                 *Acrocephalus melanopogon*

One record. Two were watched for a total of about three hours at Eling Great Marsh on Aug. 13th 1951 (Wooldridge & Ballantyne 1952).

The Moustached Warbler is a resident and partial migrant which breeds from Iberia discontinuously east to Kazakhstan.

# Aquatic Warbler                    *Acrocephalus paludicola*

A rare autumn passage migrant.

One was procured at Farlington Marshes in September 1897 (K & M). Between 1956 and 1992, there were records in 20 years (fig. 70), with most in the 1970s in line with the national picture (Dymond *et al* 1989).

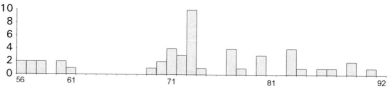

*Figure 70. Annual totals of Aquatic Warblers, 1956-92.*

Of 48 recorded, 33 were at Farlington Marshes, including 27 which were trapped during ringing activities. Only two of these were adults, including one caught on Aug. 11th 1973 with two juveniles. Three further juveniles were caught the next day and three more up to Sep. 10th. Others occurred at Keyhaven/Pennington Marshes (5), Titchfield Haven (4), and Ashlett Marshes, Latchmore Bottom, Lower Test Marshes, Paulsgrove Reclamation, Shepherds Spring and Tournerbury (1 each). There was a clear peak in mid-August (with 23 between Aug. 11th and 23rd), but the extreme dates were July 24th (1977, Shepherds Spring) and Oct. 3rd (1960, Titchfield Haven and 1971, Tournerbury). Most were recorded on one date only, but one individual, ringed at Farlington Marshes on Sep. 9th 1973, was retrapped a week later.

The number recorded each autumn must be influenced by the intensity of ringing activity (which has accounted for 60.4% of all records) and the incidence of favourable winds to drift migrants from their breeding grounds in eastern Europe. However, the apparent decline in the 1980s may be linked to a reduction in some breeding populations (BWP). It is interesting to note the monopoly of records from Farlington Marshes despite similar levels of ringing activity at other suitable sites such as Titchfield Haven and Lower Test Marshes.

# Sedge Warbler                    *Acrocephalus schoenobaenus*

A common summer visitor and passage migrant.

The Sedge Warbler breeds in open scrubland near streams and rivers and on the fringes of most wetland areas and marshes. It requires low, dense vegetation, typically sedges, nettles, umbellifers, willow-herb and meadowsweet, with scattered small bushes of hawthorn, sallows and bramble; vegetation structure is generally thought to be more important than plant species (Thomas 1984). It can also be found breeding in the drier margins of reed beds, especially where *Phragmites* growth is poor and where there is an invasion of a more diverse flora.

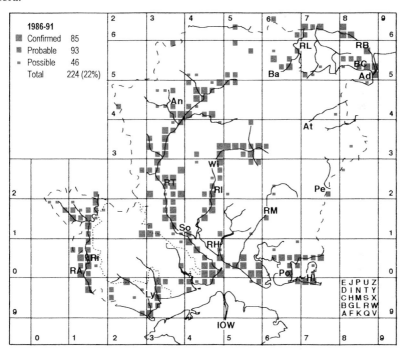

| 1986-91 | |
|---|---|
| ▦ Confirmed | 85 |
| ▦ Probable | 93 |
| ▪ Possible | 46 |
| Total | 224 (22%) |

Not surprisingly, the Atlas Map shows a distribution which closely corresponds with the river valleys and coastal wetlands. Overgrown wet meadows in many parts of the Itchen, Test and Avon valleys support considerable numbers, but the species is not easy to census without special effort (Bell *et al* 1968). Ringing studies in 1976-77 indicated that there may have been at least 100 pairs within a 2 km radius of the centre of Winchester and probably more than 1000 pairs in the Itchen valley upstream of Twyford. Similarly, a survey of part of the Test valley in 1978 suggested 500+ pairs along an 18 km length of the valley, and a survey in 1979 showed similar densities in the Avon valley. Assuming at least 500 pairs in parts of the river valleys not covered and *c.* 500 pairs in coastal marshlands and scrub and at other sites, there were 3000-4000 pairs breeding in Hampshire in the late 1970s. The available data indicate a decline in the county since then, and this has mirrored the national pattern. The British population crashed in 1969, and after recovering somewhat to 1977, then declined to only 30% of the 1968 level by 1985. In that year, the Hampshire population may have been as low as 1000-1500 pairs. The available records generally suggest that this may have been the case. On a part of Winnall Moors, there were 40 pairs compared with 100 in 1983, and in the Itchen valley near Bishopstoke only 18 pairs compared with 72 in 1981. On two CBC plots at Titchfield Haven, totalling 108 ha, the number of territories fell from 62 in 1981 to 30 in 1985 and then rose to 83 in 1989. Since 1985, the species has recovered slightly (Marchant *et al* 1990), so the Hampshire population may have been 2000-3000 pairs at the end of the Atlas Survey. The national total was estimated at 250,000 pairs in 1988-91 (New Atlas).

The first usually arrive by mid-April. In 1971-92, earliest dates were between Mar. 29th and Apr. 22nd with the average Apr. 9th. Earlier records before that period included those for Titchfield Haven on Mar. 21st 1957 and Stratfield Saye on Mar. 17th 1963. Arrivals at breeding sites usually peak in early May, but birds continue to arrive until late in the month.

Ringing has shown that short distance dispersal of young birds occurs by the beginning of July, with juveniles often moving several kilometres to congregate in optimal feeding areas, e.g. 53 juveniles were mist-netted on July 4th 1976 in one small area near Winchester. Longer distance dispersal may also take place during July, but true migration apparently does not commence until late July, with the main departure of locally-bred birds in the first half of August.

In autumn, high numbers occur in coastal reed beds and can be mist-netted for ringing, e.g. at Farlington Marshes 153 were caught on Aug. 8th 1971, 122 on Aug. 12th 1979 and 107 on Aug. 9th 1986. Large catches may coincide with high populations of the plum-reed aphid *Ilyalopterus pruni*, although those in 1979 and 1986 were the results of overnight falls. Certainly in the latter year, few aphids were present (P M Potts *in litt*).

Movement continues through September with the last birds usually recorded at the beginning of October. During 1971-92, latest dates were between Sep. 26th and Nov. 7th with the average Oct. 11th. The latest ever was one caught and ringed at Winchester on Nov. 9th 1963.

Ringing evidence shows that birds originating from all parts of Britain and Ireland pass through in autumn, but as yet there have not been any controls of foreign-ringed birds. There are numerous recoveries of Hampshire-ringed birds which confirm their migration routes and wintering grounds. 24 were recovered in France (mostly in the west), two each in Portugal and Spain, one in Morocco and six in West Africa, in Senegal and Mali (2 each), and Ghana and Sierra Leone (1 each).

## Marsh Warbler                         *Acrocephalus palustris*

A rare summer visitor and passage migrant.

There are several early records of breeding: a nest with eggs found at Alresford Pond in 1863 (K & M), one or two pairs regularly at Mottisfont in the 1890s (Meinertzhagen in Cohen) and two pairs said to have bred in the south-east of the county in 1907 (Cohen). The only other record in the first half of this century was of a singing male at Keyhaven on May 19th 1935 (*South Eastern Bird Report*).

The next was a male in song in the Avon valley on June 2nd 1963. There were no further records until 1979, when a male, apparently unmated, held territory near Bickton from June 5th-25th.

More recently, singing males were recorded in 1983 (1), 1986 (2), 1987 (2), 1989 (2), 1990 (1), 1991 (1) and 1992 (2). Those at Nursling on May 21st 1983 and Sinah Common on June 13th 1989 were almost certainly migrants, but the remainder were in suitable breeding habitat and some held territory for up to two weeks. No evidence has been submitted to suggest that any of them attracted a mate.

The only other records were of single birds at Keyhaven on Oct. 1st 1989 and Aug. 31st 1992.

## Reed Warbler                    *Acrocephalus scirpaceus*

A common but local summer visitor and passage migrant.

Most Reed Warblers nest in extensive reed beds, but they also occur along reed-filled ditches, riversides and wetland margins. The species is semi-colonial and even more difficult to census than the Sedge Warbler (Bell *et al* 1968). However, some guide to population levels is provided by ringing studies in large areas of reeds, and by conventional surveys of linear habitats. Large colonies include those at Titchfield Haven (max. 89 pairs on the CBC plot in 1988, and over 100 pairs estimated to be on the whole reserve), Fleet Pond (80 pairs in 1981, but no more than 40 since 1987 due to shrinkage of the reed beds),

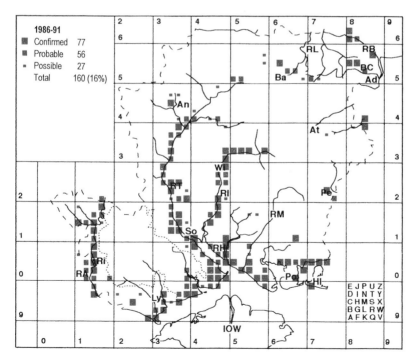

Alresford Pond (50 pairs, 1977), Needs Ore (44 pairs, 1992), Great Salterns Lake (30 pairs, 1977) and Calshot Reclamation (22 pairs, 1985). Considerable numbers also occur along the three main river valleys. Estimates have included *c.* 200 pairs in the Itchen valley (based largely on studies in 1976-77), 270 pairs between Nursling and Fullerton on the Test (1978 survey) and 240 pairs between Ringwood and Downton on the Avon (1979 survey). Assuming an additional 200-250 pairs in parts of the river valleys not covered, 250-300 pairs at other coastal sites and 50 pairs around other inland lakes and ponds, there must be at least 1500 pairs breeding in the county. In 1988-91, the British population was estimated at 40,000-80,000 pairs (New Atlas). With counting difficult, and ringing results dependent on variations in effort and weather, it is uncertain whether or not there have been any significant changes in numbers during the period. More than likely, the Hampshire population has followed the national pattern, which has shown no significant change during the last 20 years other than perhaps a slight upward trend (Marchant *et al* 1990).

The earliest ever were at Titchfield Haven on Apr. 4th in both 1983 and 1985. In other years during 1971-92, first arrivals were between Apr. 4th and 26th with the average Apr. 17th. The spring arrival is protracted, with its peak in the second half of May and movement continuing until mid-June. Ringing has shown that many adult birds are faithful to their breeding sites, and often return to the same patch of reeds in subsequent years. There is, nevertheless, some interchange between colonies, especially among younger birds, and there are numerous recoveries demonstrating relatively short-distance movements between colonies in Hampshire and surrounding counties.

Post-breeding dispersal commences in mid-July and most vacate inland breeding sites in late July and early August, e.g. an adult female ringed in Winchester on July 13th 1990 and retrapped three days later clearly departed quite soon after, as it was controlled in Mauritania, 3896 km SSW, on Aug. 2nd of the same year.

Passage takes place throughout August and September, with no pronounced peak. A few are usually still present at the beginning of October. During 1971-92, latest dates were between Oct. 5th and Nov. 13th, apart from a particularly late bird at Lower Test Marshes on Dec. 2nd 1984. The average latest date was Oct. 19th. There is ringing evidence that birds from the Midlands, northern England and Wales pass through, and some continental birds occur, at least on the coast. This is shown by three same-season movements: one ringed in the Netherlands on July 21st 1984 and controlled at Eastney, 469 km WSW, on Aug. 26th 1984, another ringed at Oxelosund, Sweden on Sep. 17th 1987 and controlled at Lower Test Marshes, 1466 km south-west, on Oct. 12th 1987 and a third, trapped at Oorderen, Belgium on Aug. 18th 1990 and controlled at Southampton Docks, 409 km west, on Sep. 2nd 1990.

There have also been 27 recoveries which show movements between Hampshire and Portugal, Spain and Morocco; many of these confirmed the established pattern of late summer movement down the west coast of Europe to Iberia, where the species apparently fuels up for its Saharan crossing.

British Reed Warblers winter in central West Africa, usually further south than the Sedge Warbler. Its population has therefore apparently not been affected by the drought in the Sahel zone (*cf.* Sedge Warbler, Whitethroat,

Redstart). As well as the Mauritanian bird already noted, one other Hampshire recovery confirms the African winter quarters: one ringed in Senegal on Mar. 18th 1989 and controlled at Fordingbridge, 4050 km NNE, on July 23rd 1989.

## Great Reed Warbler    *Acrocephalus arundinaceus*

Four records. The first was a male holding territory at Titchfield Haven from May 18th-24th 1960. The three other records all involved males holding territory in the same reed bed at Fleet Pond: on May 24th 1970, from May 20th-June 1st 1975 and from May 26th-June 3rd 1980.

The nearest breeding grounds of the Great Reed Warbler are in north-eastern France and the Low Countries, but it is decreasing in these areas. Birds from western Europe winter largely in tropical West Africa.

## Icterine Warbler    *Hippolais icterina*

A rare autumn passage migrant. There have been five records, as follows:

1981:      adult, Warsash, Aug. 8th;
1983:      probable adult, trapped, Sway, Aug. 22nd;
1985:      New Milton, July 4th;
1987:      Farlington Marshes, Aug. 30th;
1992:      juvenile, Sandy Point, Sep. 16th-19th.

The Icterine Warbler is a trans-equatorial migrant, breeding from north-eastern France, the Netherlands and Norway to western Russia and wintering in southern Africa.

## Melodious Warbler    *Hippolais polyglotta*

A rare autumn passage migrant, also recorded twice in spring. A total of 11 has been recorded, as follows:

1961:      Keyhaven, Sep. 2nd and 3rd;
1963:      Titchfield Haven, Sep. 2nd;
1964:      Needs Ore, Oct. 17th;
1965:      Hurst Castle, Sep. 25th and 26th;
1968:      Farlington Marshes, Sep. 14th;
1975:      Culverley, New Forest, June 8th;
1978:      Titchfield Haven, Aug. 12th;
1983:      Farlington Marshes, Sep. 24th and 25th;
1985:      singing male, Ludshott Common, June 10th;
1987:      Farlington Marshes, Sep. 29th;
1992:      Farlington Marshes, Sep. 12th-27th.

In addition, *Hippolais* warblers seen at Church Crookham on June 24th 1961 and Farlington Marshes on Sep. 3rd 1963 were almost certainly of this species.

The Melodious Warbler breeds chiefly in France, Spain, Italy and north-west Africa and winters in tropical West Africa.

## Dartford Warbler    *Sylvia undata*

A moderately common resident on the heaths of the New Forest and north-east.

Numbers of Dartford Warblers are subject to much fluctuation and may be reduced considerably following severe winter weather. There is some movement away from breeding areas in autumn, mostly by juveniles.

K & M described the Dartford Warbler as "a very local resident .... most numerous in parts of the New Forest". It was said to be numerous on the commons around Woolmer Forest in 1872, and also bred on Hayling Island in 1894 (D Johnson per B Campbell).

Little quantitative information is available for the first half of the century. In the New Forest, numbers were at a high level between 1925 and 1938 (Cohen), but a series of three cold winters between 1938/39 and 1941/42 virtually eliminated the species. The recovery had hardly started when the long cold spell in early 1947 resulted in a further reduction. Two active observers at the time, Cohen and K B Rooke, found only one pair between them in the summer of that year. Recovery was swift, however, because in 1951 it was described by Cohen as "by no means uncommon in suitable areas in the New Forest".

Since the mid-1950s, the New Forest Dartford Warbler population has been surveyed at regular intervals. Most of the population estimates were based on the assumption that suitable areas not examined carried birds at a similar density to those which were, but two of the most recent surveys in 1984 and 1988 achieved complete coverage.

From 1955 onwards, there was a steady rise in the population. The severe weather in February 1956 and the loss of much suitable habitat to a series of heath fires in late 1959 and early 1960 apparently had little deleterious effect. In 1961, 229 pairs were located and an estimated 350 pairs were present in the whole forest. Following severe weather in early 1962, numbers crashed. In that year, 36 pairs were located in 60% of the suitable habitat, leading to an overall estimate of 60 pairs (Tubbs 1963). However, worse was to follow. The prolonged spell of freezing weather between late December 1962 and early March 1963 almost exterminated the Dartford Warbler in England. Although over half the suitable habitat in the New Forest was searched, only six pairs were found (Tubbs 1967b). In 1964 and 1965, a slow recovery was evident, but there was a further severe reduction in 1966 which was attributed to a late and very heavy snowfall which occurred overnight on Apr. 13th/14th and throughout the following day. An estimated 80% of the available habitat (including all the 1963-65 breeding sites) was examined, often repeatedly, but birds were located in only one locality. There, three males and two females were present in early May but subsequently only one pair was present which reared one brood later in the season. Subsequently, it became known that a further pair had bred successfully in another area which had not been covered in any year since 1962 (Tubbs 1967b).

A series of mild winters thereafter facilitated recovery, but this was very slow at first. Only ten pairs were known in 1970, but two years later there were an estimated 100 pairs. In 1974, a survey carried out as part of a national census located 203 pairs in 80% of the suitable habitat, which indicated a total population of about 250 pairs (Bibby & Tubbs 1975). The next survey, in 1978, revealed a minimum of 71 occupied territories in approximately 60% of the suitable habitat, suggesting a total population of 118 pairs. In 11 blocks of heathland for which the 1974 and 1978 surveys were directly comparable, there was a 60% reduction from 140 to 55 territories. The decline was largely attributed to a spell of severe weather in February 1978, although some reduction may have already occurred in 1977. The winter of 1978/79, which was the coldest since 1962/63, resulted in a further reduction with probably no more than 70 pairs present in the following summer. In 1980, there were 53 pairs in 30-40% of the suitable habitat, suggesting a total of about 130 pairs. After another cold winter in 1981/82, a total of 56 pairs was located and the total population was estimated at 250 pairs. However, a complete survey in 1984 following two mild winters produced 203 pairs (Robins & Bibby 1985), so the 1982 figure may well be too high. In 1985, sample counts indicated a 4% increase despite the severe weather in February of that year, and in 1986 numbers were believed to be at about the same level despite further spells of sub-zero temperatures during the intervening winter.

Another full survey in 1988 produced the astonishing total of 454 pairs or singing males, a record total since modern recording began. A repeat survey in 1989 located 375 pairs, although some areas holding a total of 24 pairs in 1988 were not covered. This indicated a total of *c.* 400 pairs, although several observers felt that the birds were far more secretive than in the previous year, which suggests that some may have been missed. In subsequent years, sample surveys have shown that numbers have held up despite a week of snow and freezing temperatures in February 1991. In 1992, the population was believed to be in excess of 500 pairs (C R Tubbs pers. comm.).

The population in north-east Hampshire forms part of that which extends on to the heathlands of west Surrey. This has been subject to periodic extermination following severe winters. As in the New Forest, the population was at a high level during the 1930s. In 1933, there were at least 90 pairs on commons in the Haslemere district, some of which are in Hampshire, and in 1934 several pairs were recorded in the Basingstoke and Church Crookham areas. The species continued to prosper until 1938, when extensive heath fires resulted in most commons in north Hampshire being burnt out. This setback was exacerbated by severe weather in the following winter, such that the species was said to be almost extinct in 1939 (*South Eastern Bird Reports*).

The series of harsh winters in the 1940s certainly exterminated the Dartford Warbler in the area, and it was not until 1952 that it was again recorded, a male being seen at Broxhead Common on Apr. 19th. Nesting was not recorded until 1955, when a single pair was located at Ludshott Common. In 1961, at least ten pairs were present in east Hampshire although sites in the north-east were not covered. During the following winter, a spell of severe weather almost exterminated the population. In 1962, single pairs summered at two sites, with breeding confirmed at one. However, none survived the 1962/63 winter.

There were no further records until 1974, when a single pair bred at Weavers Down. In 1977, 20 pairs bred at six sites, and in the following year, 19 pairs at five sites. Between 1979 and 1987, there were records from eight sites with a maximum total of 12 pairs in 1980 and a minimum of two in 1987. Numbers remained low during this period as a result of five cold winters and several serious heath fires, with no single site being continuously occupied. Three consecutive mild winters thereafter permitted considerable expansion. Numbers peaked in 1990, when there were 31 pairs at five sites. The severe weather in February 1991 again decimated the population. Only eight pairs were located in 1991 although by 1993 there had been a rapid recovery, with 59 pairs or singing males at seven sites.

There have been occasional breeding records outside the two main areas. In 1959, a pair was found in gorse at Martin Down and in the following two years, young were raised (N W Orr *in litt*). Between 1976 and 1990, pairs were located in gorse and bramble at five coastal sites, as shown below.

|                | 1976 | 1977 | 1980 | 1983 | 1984 | 1985 | 1986 | 1987 | 1988 | 1989 | 1990 |
|----------------|------|------|------|------|------|------|------|------|------|------|------|
| Sites recorded | 1    | 1    | 1    | 2    | 3    | 3    | 3    | 2    | 2    | 2    | 2    |
| Pairs breeding | 1    | 1    | 1    | 2    | 5    | 5    | 3/4  | 3    | 2    | 2    | 2    |

Breeding was not confirmed on the coast in 1991 or 1992, but in 1993 birds were present in at least three localities, one of which had not been occupied before. During the Atlas Survey, breeding was also confirmed on four heaths just outside the New Forest boundary. In 1992, five pairs were found at one of these sites, and in 1993, at least five pairs were present in another area where the species had not previously been found. On the Atlas Map, some registrations have been moved by up to two tetrads for security reasons.

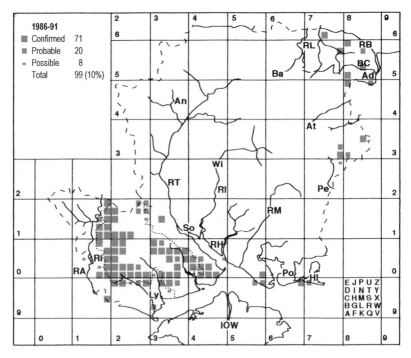

Between 1988 and 1991, the total Hampshire population probably peaked at around 500 pairs, but by 1993 it may have been as high as 600. The national total was at least 1040 pairs in 1992.

Recent surveys in the New Forest have provided precise details of the species' requirements. Optimum habitat consists of heather 30 cm or more high with clumps or scattered bushes of gorse, or gorse thickets ("brakes") interspersed with old heather. In 1988, there were 1830.6 ha of this vegetation supporting 406 pairs (89.4%) of the Dartford Warblers found (22.2 pairs/km$^2$) (Westerhoff & Tubbs 1991). This is subject to periodic burning in early spring to maintain the grazing for livestock in the forest. Until the early 1960s, this usually involved the firing of a small number of large areas of heath, with the result that all the pairs in a burnt area would be some distance from suitable habitat. Since the mid-1960s, the annual burning programme has been agreed in consultation with the Nature Conservancy Council (latterly English Nature) and, since 1986, the Hampshire Wildlife Trust. The policy has been to burn many small, rather than a few large, areas in order to create a mosaic of different age heath, thus minimising the need for displaced birds to move far. The burning rotation varies between ten and 30 years, which is also the age range of vegetation occupied by breeding Dartford Warblers. Hence Westerhoff and Tubbs (1991) concluded that the current regime is most favourable to the species, since the maximum area of optimum habitat is produced when the length of rotation is similar to its maximum age, as it is now.

The remaining 48 pairs (10.6%) were found at much lower densities in gorse brakes on acid grassland (28), mature heather without gorse (12), wet heath with gorse clumps on dry "islands" (5), a re-seeded gravel pit with gorse (2) and a Corsican pine plantation with tall heather (1). Further details are given by Westerhoff and Tubbs (1991). Forestry plantations were an important habitat in 1974, when 29 pairs (11.6% of the total population) were located in them, but by 1984 they were too old and none were found.

On the north-east heaths (where there is no grazing by livestock), birch and pine invasion is a major problem. A scattering of small trees is tolerated, but once they become too dense or tall the habitat becomes unsuitable. Fires, either accidental or deliberately started by arsonists, provide the main way of preventing succession to woodland. Unfortunately, they often occur in the middle of the breeding season, as at Ludshott Common in May 1980, and many birds and other animals must perish. They are also random, with the result that some heaths have been burnt repeatedly whereas others have been untouched for several decades. Most of the remaining suitable habitat is owned by the Ministry of Defence, National Trust or Hampshire County Council. Appropriate management has been undertaken at some sites; it is to be hoped that sufficient funds and manpower will become available for the necessary work to be carried out elsewhere.

The Dartford Warbler is one of the characteristic species of lowland heath. As the area of this unique habitat has become reduced and fragmented in southern England by lack of management, reclamation for agriculture and forestry, urban and industrial development and mineral extraction, so the importance of the New Forest, which has been safe from such pressures apart from some conifer planting in the 1960s, has increased. Between 1974 and 1992, the proportion of the British population found there has varied between 44% and 72%. Thus the Forest is clearly important as a reservoir from which other areas can be recolonised following severe winters. This is especially true in view of the loss of heathland in Dorset, the area of which fell from 10,000 ha in 1960 to 5512 ha in 1984, with most of the losses in the north-east of the county (Robins & Bibby 1985). In 1984, the north and west of the New Forest, where suitable habitat is locally distributed, held only 68 pairs (34%) of those found, and Robins and Bibby (1985) expressed concern about the isolation of the Dorset population from the area of the New Forest with the highest densities, i.e. the south and east. In 1988, due to careful planning of the burning programme, numbers in the north and west had increased to 212 pairs (47%) of those found, thus minimising the problems of possible recolonisation in Dorset (Westerhoff 1989).

Experience of the last 30 years has shown that the wintry conditions which decimate the population can be very localized. Several days of sub-zero temperatures can be tolerated, provided that there is some sunshine during the day. However, glazing or snow-lie of more than two days, both of which prevent access to invertebrates on the gorse, can prove devastating. The cold winters of the 1980s did not do too much damage in the New Forest, but in the north-east they caused repeated setbacks, especially at sites in the Bordon area which suffered heavy snowfalls.

Adult Dartford Warblers are generally faithful to their territories throughout the year, even in the event of snow or fire. However, the young have a high tendency to move in their first autumn (Bibby 1979). This no doubt accounts for the records from non-breeding coastal and inland localities, especially at times of high population levels. The cumulative monthly totals of such records for 1971-92 are shown below.

|        | Jun | Jul | Aug | Sep | Oct | Nov | Dec | Jan | Feb | Mar | Apr | May |
|--------|-----|-----|-----|-----|-----|-----|-----|-----|-----|-----|-----|-----|
| Coast  | 2   | 7   | 19  | 39  | 86  | 76  | 35  | 20  | 14  | 9   | 4   | 0   |
| Inland | 0   | 1   | 1   | 1   | 2   | 1   | 2   | 2   | 3   | 2   | 0   | 0   |

Most were in gorse brakes or brambles but other records have included singles in reeds at Calshot Reclamation, sea aster at Dibden Bay, a frozen rape field at Newlands Farm (Stubbington) and a dock bed near Bentley Sewage Farm. High counts included four at Keyhaven on Nov. 5th 1978, eight at Warsash on Oct. 27th 1983 and five there on Nov. 28th 1985. The table shows a clear autumn peak and suggests that most birds move on thereafter. The small numbers wintering have no doubt led to breeding in subsequent summers.

Ringing has provided details of post-breeding dispersal by juveniles. A chick ringed in the New Forest on June 1st 1975 was killed by a cat at Barn Elms, London, on Nov. 1st 1975, while another, colour-ringed at Frensham, Surrey on June 30th 1985 was seen near Fawley on Aug. 11th of that year. A third, colour-ringed in the New Forest on May 29th 1988, was seen on High Down, Isle of Wight, on Oct. 1st 1988 and finally a male from a 1989 north-east Hampshire nest was found breeding at a Surrey site on Apr. 14th 1990. Unfortunately, there have not been any foreign recoveries to lend support to the theory that some move south for the winter, although one was seen on a tramp steamer north of the Cherbourg Peninsula on Nov. 4th 1974 (Bibby 1979). There has been some evidence indicating return passage, e.g. single singing males at Warsash on Apr. 3rd 1973 and Apr. 2nd 1982 which were believed to have arrived off the sea, and one moving through a Portswood garden on Mar. 27th 1984.

## Subalpine Warbler                                          *Sylvia cantillans*

One record. A singing male was located along West Hayling shore on May 23rd 1984.

The Subalpine Warbler is a summer visitor to southern Europe; it winters in Africa, chiefly along the southern edge of the Sahara (BWP).

# Barred Warbler                                          *Sylvia nisoria*

Three records. Single juveniles were at Farlington Marshes on Oct. 16th 1965 and Aug. 22nd 1986, and Keyhaven on Oct. 7th 1990.

There is also a record of one which was ringed near Venice, Italy on July 24th 1943 and captured at Mansbridge in October of that year. However, reservations have been expressed about this recovery because autumn adults are so rare in Britain and the ring was not available for inspection.

The Barred Warbler breeds from central Europe east to Kazakhstan and winters chiefly in Kenya and Sudan. Small numbers (mostly juveniles) occur annually in autumn in Britain, particularly along the east coast.

# Lesser Whitethroat                                      *Sylvia curruca*

A common summer visitor and passage migrant.

The Lesser Whitethroat favours overgrown scrub and mature hedgerows. It can therefore most commonly be found in downland scrub, along bridleways and disused railway lines, and in orchards and mature gardens around villages and farms. It is fairly widespread, being largely absent only from heavily-wooded areas, heathlands and towns and cities. Although everywhere at quite low density, it is more scarce in arable farmland with large fields and low hedges than in areas with smallholdings, grazing paddocks and tall hedgerows.

The song is quite distinctive, but the song period is fairly short and not all observers are thoroughly familiar with it. Thus, during the Atlas Survey, birds

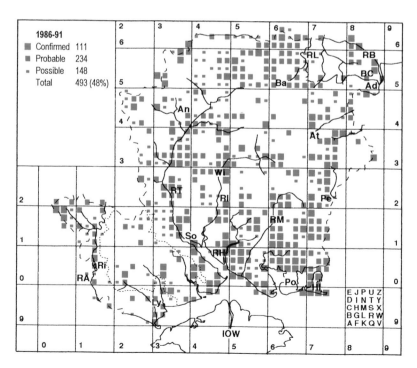

may have been overlooked in some tetrads or detected on one date only (and assumed to be passage migrants or only recorded as possibly breeding).

Using national CBC data for 1989, the New Atlas method indicates a county population of around 3500 pairs. However, it is felt that this overestimates the density on the large areas of arable farmland, and thus a range of 2500-3000 pairs is felt to be more appropriate. The British total in 1989 was estimated to be 80,000 pairs (New Atlas). Nationally, population levels have shown marked fluctuations but no long-term change (Marchant *et al* 1990); local data are insufficient to draw any conclusions about changes.

Lesser Whitethroats usually arrive from mid-April onwards, although the earliest ever was at West Lane (Hayling) on Apr. 1st 1989. In other years during 1971-92, first dates were between April 6th and May 4th, with the average Apr. 18th. Spring arrival normally peaks in early May, although passage continues throughout the month.

Post-breeding dispersal commences in mid-July, but records indicate that the main movement takes place in the second half of August and early September. Concentrations recorded include 19 at Sandy Point on Aug. 26th 1984, 23 at Sinah on Aug. 18th 1985 and 18 at Old Winchester Hill on Aug. 6th 1989. During 1971-92, latest dates were between Sep. 25th and Oct. 31st with the average Oct. 3rd.

There have also been four winter records. Single birds were at Swaythling on Mar. 7th 1971, Bishopstoke on Dec. 19th 1979, Farlington Marshes on Dec. 2nd and 17th 1986 and Highfield (Southampton) from Jan. 29th-Apr. 19th 1987.

The Lesser Whitethroat winters in north-east Africa, and movements are therefore oriented to the south-east. All three ringing recoveries/controls from Hampshire demonstrate this classic south-easterly movement: one ringed at Sway on July 5th 1967 and recovered at Bergamo, Italy, 1026 km south-east, on Sep. 10th 1968; another ringed at Bridgwater, Somerset on July 7th 1979 and controlled at Lymington on Aug. 29th of that year; and a third ringed at Havant on July 8th 1985 and controlled at Dungeness, Kent on Aug. 30th 1985. There is no indication that birds of continental origin occur in Hampshire, but the control at Lymington shows that birds from further west do pass through.

# Whitethroat                                     *Sylvia communis*

A numerous summer visitor and passage migrant.

The Whitethroat favours low hedges and scrub, with adjacent dense herbage of nettles, umbellifers etc. It is therefore typically found along roadside verges, in downland and coastal scrub, on some farmlands and on any rough waste spaces and margins. Densities are particularly high on heathlands with mature gorse and invading birch, e.g. at Ludshott Common and Bricksbury Hill in the north-east, but it is scarce in the New Forest, where the grazing regime prevents the development of similar habitat.

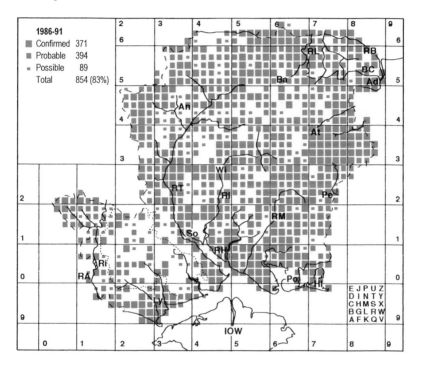

Although the species is relatively common, it is not nearly so numerous as in former years; the British population was drastically reduced after 1968, this being attributed to severe drought in the Sahel wintering area (Winstanley *et al* 1974). Since then, there has been a slight recovery, but numbers recorded in Hampshire are still well down on pre-1969 levels. There are relatively few quantitative data to illustrate the 1969 crash locally, but the three-fold decrease was so dramatic and widespread that nearly all observers remarked upon it. Since then, subjective assessments and casual records suggest that local fluctuations have roughly matched the national population indices for the species, with numbers high in 1977, relatively low in 1984-85 and then recovering subsequently. Using national CBC data for 1989, the New Atlas method gives a county population of around 17,500 pairs. However, as with the previous species, this is believed to overestimate numbers in intensively-farmed arable areas, and so a figure in the range 10,000-15,000 pairs is probably more appropriate. The national total was calculated to be 660,000 pairs (New Atlas).

The first usually arrive in mid-April. During 1971-92, earliest dates were between Mar. 27th and Apr. 28th, with the average Apr. 14th. Earlier records prior to that period include those for Gilkicker Point on Mar. 22nd 1957 and Farlington Marshes on Mar. 17th 1968. Spring arrivals peak in early May, although several observers have commented that birds now appear to be arriving later than in former years.

Post-breeding dispersal commences in mid-July, but emigration does not peak until the end of August and first week of September. High counts recorded include 25 at Sandy Point on Aug. 27th 1984, 30 at Dibden Bay on Aug. 17th 1986 and 30 at Old Winchester Hill on Aug. 6th 1989. Latest dates during 1971-92 were between Sep. 6th and Oct. 27th, with the average Oct. 3rd, apart from a late individual at Warsash on Nov. 10th 1990. Single birds at Basingstoke Old Sewage Farm on Dec. 15th 1959, Eastleigh Sewage Farm on Dec. 11th 1979 and Southampton Docks on Jan. 20th 1990 were presumably wintering.

Passage birds controlled in Hampshire have included individuals ringed in Warwickshire, Lincolnshire, Cleveland and Anglesey, but there has been no evidence of continental birds occurring. The only foreign recovery of a Hampshire-ringed bird involved one ringed at Ringwood on July 16th 1977 and recovered at Zamora, Spain, 1077 km SSW, on Sep. 25th 1981. West European Whitethroats winter in the Sahel region of West Africa.

## Garden Warbler                                    *Sylvia borin*

A common summer visitor and passage migrant.

The Garden Warbler is widespread, occurring in dense scrub, often in open broadleaved woodland and along woodland edges. It is typically found in thorn and bramble thickets, sallow scrub and woodlands with hazel coppice, overgrown clearings or young mixed plantations. Habitat structure seems more important than scrub composition; it seems to require very dense scrub, usually intermixed or adjacent to some taller shrubs or small trees.

The species is best located by song, but many observers have difficulty differentiating it from the Blackcap, and this may have led to some under-recording during the Atlas Survey. In any event, the Garden Warbler is generally less common than the Blackcap, although it can outnumber that species in particularly suitable habitat, e.g. in 1976 a ratio of 12:5 was reported along the Basingstoke Canal between Fleet and Aldershot and 7:2 at Yateley Gravel Pit. In both localities, Garden Warblers appeared to be nesting in dense brambles. In most areas it is encountered in small numbers; more than ten breeding pairs have only ever been recorded from seven sites: the Basingstoke Canal, Beacon Hill (Warnford), woodland near Bentworth, Ellingham and Ivy Lakes, Goose Green Inclosure (Alice Holt), Roydon Woods and Yateley Gravel Pit. In the New Forest, it is much less common than the Blackcap, with the total population in 1982 estimated to be less than 200 pairs. Using national CBC data for 1989, the New Atlas method indicates a county population of around 9000 pairs. Local experience suggests that this may be too high; if every tetrad where it was recorded during the Atlas Survey held five pairs, there would be 3600 in

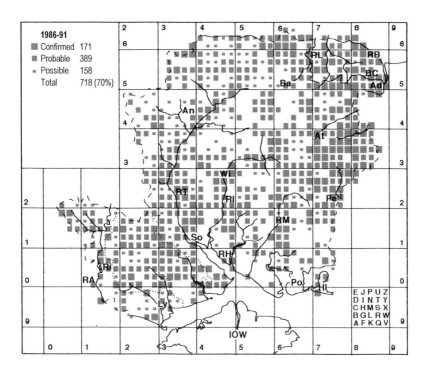

all. Allowing for under-recording and higher densities in some areas, a range of 4000-6000 pairs is considered appropriate. The national population was estimated at 200,000 pairs. Local data are insufficient to show whether there have been any significant changes in numbers; nationally, numbers reached a low-point in the mid-1970s but have increased steadily since (Marchant *et al* 1990).

Garden Warblers usually arrive in mid-April. During 1971-92, earliest dates were between Apr. 3rd and 29th with the average Apr. 13th. Additionally, a particularly early bird was heard and seen at Old Winchester Hill on Mar. 17th 1974. Arrivals peak in early and mid-May with some stragglers not taking up territory until the end of that month.

Post-breeding dispersal commences in mid-July, with migration proper in August, continuing into September. From 1971-92, latest dates were between Aug. 31st and Oct. 21st with the average Sep. 29th. In addition, single late birds were recorded at Widley on Nov. 6th 1981 and Plaitford Green on Nov. 29th 1987 (the latter mist-netted in a pear orchard). There has also been one winter record, of a bird at Bitterne Park from Nov. 27th 1988-Jan. 22nd 1989.

The Garden Warbler winters well to the south of the Sahara. Evidence for this is provided by two recoveries: one ringed at Hamble on Aug. 12th 1982 and found dead at Obagie, Nigeria, 4978 km south, on Dec. 25th 1986, and another ringed at Sway on May 11th 1988 and killed by a catapult in Brong-Ahafo Region, Ghana, 4760 km south, on Sep. 28th 1992. The only other foreign recovery of a Hampshire-ringed bird involved one caught at Winchester on July

8th 1981 and found dead at Guadalajara, Spain, 1124 km south, on Aug. 15th 1982. An interesting instance of apparent "reverse migration" is provided by a juvenile ringed at Winchester on July 9th 1988 and recovered in Edinburgh, 553 km north, on Aug. 21st 1988. The remaining 16 recoveries or controls all involved movements of less than 200 km apart from one ringed at Benacre, Norfolk on Aug. 31st 1966 and found dead at Chandler's Ford on Sep. 13th 1966.

## Blackcap                                             *Sylvia atricapilla*

A numerous summer visitor and passage migrant; small numbers winter.

In the breeding season, the Blackcap requires broadleaved woodland with a substantial shrub layer. It occurs wherever there is a small fragment of woodland, and may inhabit parkland and large gardens, and small copses and shelter belts on farmland. During the Atlas Survey, it was found in 982 (95%) tetrads, with breeding confirmed in 416, probable in 513 and possible in 53. It was absent from a few urban tetrads in the Portsmouth and Southampton areas and a scattering elsewhere, where it may have been missed through poor coverage.

In most areas, the Blackcap considerably outnumbers the Garden Warbler, e.g. a survey of mixed farmland and small woods north and west of Romsey in 1985 found 74 and 20 singing males respectively. In the New Forest, it is common in some areas, particularly where rhododendron has become established in broadleaved inclosures (D E Glue *in litt*). In 1982, the total population was estimated to be more than 1000 pairs, with densities of up to 20 pairs per km$^2$ in some areas (G C Evans *in litt*). Using national CBC data for 1989, the New Atlas method indicates a county population approaching 30,000 pairs. As with other warbler species, this is possibly an overestimate, and a range of 20,000-30,000 is considered more appropriate. Local data suggest that the population is increasing; this is in line with the national trend, which shows that numbers have increased steadily, especially on farmland, since the CBC was started in 1963 (Marchant *et al* 1990). The national population in 1989 was estimated to be 580,000 pairs (New Atlas).

Breeding Blackcaps apparently arrive in Hampshire from late March onwards but the presence of wintering birds (see below) makes it impossible to comment on or analyse earliest arrival dates. Singing males are usually widespread in breeding sites by late April, but arrivals peak in early May.

Some dispersal, probably of young birds, takes place in late July and through August, but the main departure of breeding birds is not until September. Peak movement is usually around the middle of that month, but in some years there is a secondary peak in early October. This often coincides with passage on the east coast of England, and suggests that continental birds may be involved. Evidence for this is provided by the control of a bird at Southampton Docks in October 1986 which had been ringed in Belgium on Sep. 6th of that year.

There have been 14 foreign recoveries of Hampshire-ringed birds. One of these involved a bird ringed at Cowplain on Sep. 28th 1975 and found dead 3525 km ESE in Lebanon on Nov. 3rd 1976. The remainder were found in Morocco (7), Spain (4) and Algeria and Sardinia (1 each). This agrees with the national picture, which indicates that most British breeding birds winter in the western Mediterranean basin, with only a small proportion crossing the Sahara to central West Africa.

The first recorded wintering bird appears to have been at Portchester from Dec. 31st 1897 into January 1898 (K & M). Between 1959/60 and 1972/73, the total recorded per winter did not exceed ten, but since then there has been a marked increase (fig. 71).

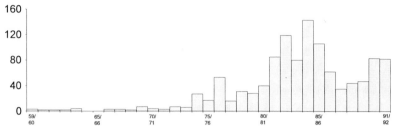

*Figure 71. Totals of wintering Blackcaps, 1959/60-91/92.*

Most records refer to one or two birds seen in birdwatchers' gardens during the course of a winter, often being attracted to food provided at bird tables. In calculating the winter totals, the maximum counts for each site on any one day during the winter (arbitrarily defined as Nov. 12th-Mar. 11th) have been used. However, garden ringing has shown that many more individuals may be involved. For example, at least eight were recorded in an East Cosham garden in 1984/85 and seven were mist-netted in a Chilbolton garden in 1990/91. The numbers recorded can therefore only represent a small proportion of the total present.

Wintering birds arrive from late October onwards and remain until March or the first half of April. Most records are for later in the winter, but this may be due to birds not resorting to gardens until natural food supplies have been exhausted. Recorded numbers are particularly high in severe weather, e.g. in February 1985, when 52 were noted at 28 sites. Wintering birds occur in all parts of the county, but there has been a preponderance of records in the Portsmouth-Southampton coastal plain and in the Itchen valley up to Winchester. This probably reflects the distribution of observers, although there are perhaps fewer records than might be expected from the north-east.

Leach (1981) investigated to what extent the wintering of Blackcaps in southern England was a recent phenomenon. On balance, he concluded that the increase was genuine and not just due to improved observer coverage. The Hampshire records support this view, but also suggest that numbers peaked during the period 1981/82-85/86. However, the recent apparent decline may be due to less rigorous recording.

National ringing data indicate that wintering birds originate from countries such as Norway, the Netherlands, Germany and Austria. The only Hampshire recoveries have been of two individuals ringed in Belgium in December 1981 and controlled in East Cosham during the 1983/84 winter.

## Pallas's Warbler                    *Phylloscopus proregulus*

Two records. Single birds were at Milford-on-Sea on Nov. 23rd 1974 and Thatcher's Copse (Brownwich) from Oct. 26th-28th 1988.

Nationally, records of this Siberian species have increased substantially in autumn during the last 20 years, presumably due to the greater prevalence of easterly winds in October and the ever-expanding army of observers.

## Yellow-browed Warbler                    *Phylloscopus inornatus*

A rare autumn passage migrant, with 13 records as follows:

| | |
|---|---|
| 1959: | Avington, Nov. 30th; |
| 1967: | East Boldre, Oct. 10th (trapped); |
| 1978: | Titchfield Haven, Dec. 1st-Jan. 1st 1979; |
| 1981: | Fleet Pond, Oct. 19th and 20th; |
| 1984: | Alresford Pond, Oct. 9th; |
| | Sinah Warren, Oct. 27th; |
| 1986: | Wellington Country Park, Nov. 30th and Dec. 1st; |
| 1988: | Bitterne Park, Sep. 25th (trapped); |
| | Sway, Oct. 3rd (trapped); |
| 1989: | Sinah Gravel Pit, Oct. 1st; |
| | Fleet Pond, Oct. 24th; |
| 1990: | Sinah Warren, Oct. 7th; |
| 1993: | Lordshill (Southampton), Sep. 25th and 28th. |

The increasing number of records of this Siberian breeder in Hampshire has mirrored the national trend; greater observer activity and favourable weather conditions have no doubt contributed.

## Wood Warbler                    *Phylloscopus sibilatrix*

A moderately common but local summer visitor and passage migrant.

The Wood Warbler requires mature broadleaved woodland, preferably oak, with limited understorey and an impoverished field layer. Its main stronghold is in the New Forest, where intensive survey work in 1980-83 provided information on densities, distribution and breeding biology. There were less than 4 singing males per $km^2$ in most areas, but 5-10 per $km^2$ in mature woodland in the north of the forest and more than 10 per $km^2$ in several parts of the

Bramshaw Wood, Salisbury Trench and Islands Thorns areas. The maximum density recorded was 18 singing males in the 1 km square SU2515 (Black Bush and Raven's Nest Inclosure) on May 30th 1982. Overall, it was estimated that there were around 450 territorial males in the whole of the New Forest. Territories were mostly in broadleaved woodland with a proportion of oak, and most nest-sites were among woodland debris, leaf litter, bilberries, or similar, invariably on the edges of small clearings or openings in the understorey. These situations appeared to offer considerable shelter from the elements, and also the gradual step-by-step approach to the nest which the adults apparently require when feeding young. This study showed that the majority of young fledged in mid-June, and that last nests were vacated by mid-July (Evans & Prater unpub.).

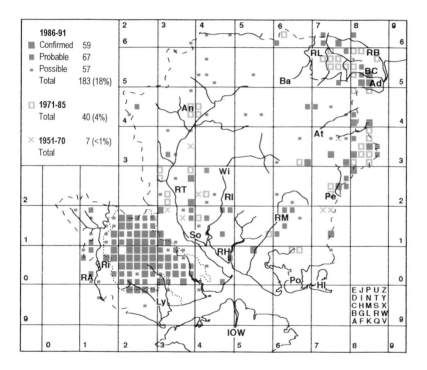

As the Atlas Map shows, Wood Warblers have been widely recorded elsewhere in the county. Since 1951, there have been reports from some 150 sites, but few of these have been regularly occupied. Even the distribution shown for 1986-91 probably exaggerates the true position, since many tetrads, especially in the centre of the county, held birds in only one year of the Atlas Survey.

Most are now recorded in the north-east, where the principal site is in mature beech, oak and birch woodland around Waggoners Wells. This area has been occupied annually since at least 1971 with a maximum of nine territorial males in 1988. In recent years, the only other locality with annual records has been Bourley Common, where up to four singing males have been present since 1986.

In other areas, the available records suggest a decline. In the period from

405

1968-76, counts of four to eight singing males were made at Cranbury Park, Harewood Forest, Mortimer West End, Nightingale Wood, Southampton Common and Southleigh Woods, but since then the only similar counts have been of four singing males at Burnt Grove (Romsey) and Lordswood in 1984.

The apparent decline away from the New Forest is not in line with the national trend, which since 1970 has shown sizeable annual fluctuations with a suggestion of a slight increase (Marchant *et al* 1990). However, Hampshire is on the eastern edge of the species' British range. Parslow (1973) suggested that it had become scarcer in peripheral areas; today, it is clear that most sites are occupied only sporadically. Thorough coverage of several suitable sites over a number of years would be necessary to determine whether the population is in decline or fluctuating. Even the New Forest population seems to fluctuate considerably from one year to another. In quite small, favoured areas numbers may decline to a low level for a year or so, and then increase again.

If it is assumed that the New Forest population is still at the level of the early 1980s, then the county total in the early 1990s approaches 500 males. This compares with the most recent estimate for Britain of 17,200 males in 1984-85 (Bibby 1989). While 500 males may not seem a relatively large proportion of the total, the New Forest is especially important in holding the only significant concentration away from the west and north of Britain. Note that all estimates are in terms of territorial males, since some are invariably unmated (Simms 1985) and others are polygynous (Temrin 1984).

First arrivals usually occur in the second half of April, and are often noted at breeding sites rather than on the coast. The earliest ever was at Horsebridge on Apr. 9th 1988. In other years during 1971-92, earliest dates were in the period up to May 9th with the average Apr. 22nd. Records from coastal and non-breeding inland sites shows that immigration extends until mid-May with the peak arrival in the first week of that month. Numbers, however, are low, with four on Hayling Island on May 10th 1985 and Apr. 29th 1989 the highest counts recorded.

Ringing evidence has shown that movement may commence almost as soon as young birds become independent, e.g. one ringed at Eyeworth Wood on June 13th 1981 (and therefore fledged about June 19th) was controlled at Horsham, West Sussex, on July 27th 1981 and another ringed near Aldershot on June 17th 1989 was recovered at Cuckfield, West Sussex, on July 30th 1989.

Few are detected after the breeding season, but the available records suggest that emigration is protracted, with sightings at non-breeding localities fairly evenly spread over the period between late July and early September. During 1971-92, latest dates were between July 24th and Sep. 13th with the average Aug. 23rd. However, the latest ever was one at Winchester Sewage Farm on Sep. 29th 1964. Like the Lesser Whitethroat, the Wood Warbler migrates to the south-east, and one Hampshire ringing recovery provides evidence for both the direction of departure and the comparatively early date of migration. This involved one ringed as a pullus at Lyndhurst on June 15th 1956 and recovered in Padova, Italy, 1160 km ESE, on Aug. 15th 1956. British Wood Warblers are believed to winter mostly in the forest and wooded savanna belt in the northern Afrotropics, and probably make direct flights from countries such as Italy to the southern edge of the Sahara (BWP).

Other ringing records of note include one trapped at Titchfield Haven on Aug. 6th 1988 and controlled at Cwmystwyth, Dyfed, on May 18th 1989, which shows that birds from elsewhere in Britain may occur on the Hampshire coast, and one ringed as a pullus in Islands Thorns Inclosure on June 13th 1980 and controlled at Goring Heath, Berkshire, on May 25th 1981, which shows that there is some interchange between the New Forest population and other sites.

## Chiffchaff                                        *Phylloscopus collybita*

A numerous summer visitor, which also winters in small numbers.

The Chiffchaff breeds in broadleaved woodland, and, provided there is adequate undergrowth, it will nest in farmland copses, shelter belts and large gardens, along hedgerows with mature trees as well as in more extensive woodlands. During the Atlas Survey, it was shown to be widely distributed, being found in 972 (94%) tetrads, with breeding confirmed in 379, probable in 522 and possible in 71. It was absent from a scattering of tetrads including several in urban areas of Portsmouth, Gosport and Southampton, which lack suitable breeding habitat. Using national CBC data for 1989, the New Atlas method indicates a county population approaching 30,000 pairs. However, local experience suggests that this overestimates densities in both woodland and farmland habitats, and that a range of 10,000-15,000 pairs is appropriate. The national total for 1989 was estimated at 640,000 pairs (New Atlas). Local data is insufficient to identify population trends, although nationally numbers declined (with fluctuations) between 1970 and 1984 but have since recovered (Marchant *et al* 1990).

The presence of wintering birds makes any analysis of arrival dates all but meaningless. However, judging by records away from favoured wintering sites, the first migrants typically arrive in mid-March, with a general and widespread influx usually in the fourth week of that month. Further evidence for at least some mid-March birds being migrants is provided by one ringing recovery, a first-year ringed in Portugal on Jan. 4th 1990 and controlled at Southampton Common, 1632 km NNE, on Mar. 22nd 1990. Arrivals peak in the second week of April, with birds continuing to take up territory through to the end of the month.

Some local movement of Chiffchaffs probably takes place in August, but passage is most evident in September and early October and may continue until early November. In 1982-90, 468 were caught at Southampton Docks on dates between Aug. 27th and Nov. 4th with 377 in the period Sep. 10th-Oct. 7th (B Dudley *in litt*). Concentrations recorded at well-watched sites include 59 at Beacon Hill (Warnford) on Sep. 7th 1986, 69 at Old Winchester Hill on Sep. 17th 1989 and 55 at Needs Ore on Sep. 24th 1989.

National ringing data indicate that most British birds winter in the Mediterranean basin and the Sahel region of West Africa. Recoveries and controls of Hampshire-ringed birds include two in Spain in October, one in Portugal in November and two in Africa. The latter two birds had been ringed at Emer Bog on Aug. 18th 1989 and East Cosham on Sep. 25th 1990 and were controlled at Djoudj, Senegal on Jan. 28th 1990 and Dec. 4th 1991 respectively.

The first wintering record was of one at Titchfield Common in late January and early February 1952. Since 1959/60, there have been records in every winter. Up to 1972/73, winter totals did not exceed ten, but subsequently there was an enormous increase (fig. 72), believed to be largely due to increased observer coverage and awareness. The apparent decline in recent winters is probably due to under-recording.

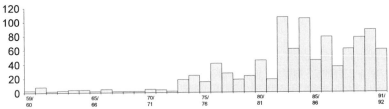

*Figure 72. Totals of wintering Chiffchaffs, 1959/60-91/92.*

The data in fig. 72 are based on maximum counts at each site on any one day during the winter (arbitrarily defined as Nov. 12th-Mar. 4th).

Most wintering birds are found close to water, in scrub around lakes, ponds and gravel pits, along river margins and in particular in the vicinity of sewage farms, where an abundance of insect food is available. In very cold weather, they seem to disappear altogether, either moving elsewhere, or perhaps perishing. Most records have been from the coastal strip between Hayling Island and Lower Test Marshes, the main river valleys and the north-east of the county. At favoured localities, parties of up to eight are sometimes noted, but ringing has shown that many more may actually be present. For example, at least 26 were at Budds Farm Sewage Works between Nov. 16th and Dec. 31st 1984, and a minimum of 20 was at Eastleigh Sewage Farm between Dec. 12th and 27th 1986.

Analysis of the records suggests that most wintering birds arrive in the second half of November. Recorded numbers peak in late December and early January (probably due to greater observer effort at this time), and then remaining steady until mid-March, when migrants start to arrive. Since 1981, there have been at least 20 records of birds showing the characteristics of the races *P.c. abietinus* or *P.c. tristis*, which breed in Fenno-Scandia and Russia. Most, however, appear to be typical *P.c. collybita*. Ringing evidence is limited, but one ringed in Belgium on Oct. 24th 1982 and controlled at Eastleigh, 472 km west, on Jan. 2nd 1983 indicates that at least some wintering birds are of continental origin. Others have been retrapped in subsequent winters, but none have been recovered or controlled in summer.

## Willow Warbler                              *Phylloscopus trochilus*

An abundant summer visitor and passage migrant.

The Willow Warbler breeds on woodland edges and in all kinds of scrub habitats. In Hampshire, high breeding densities are found in downland thorn scrub, young plantations and the birch scrub fringing commons and heaths. Since the decline of the Whitethroat in 1969, it has easily become our commonest warbler. During the Atlas Survey, it was found in 993 (96%) tetrads, with breeding confirmed in 495, probable in 456 and possible in 42. Those from which it was apparently absent were scattered throughout the county; apart from one or two urban and coastal squares which perhaps lack suitable habitat, it was presumably missed due to inadequate coverage. Using national CBC data for 1989, the New Atlas method indicates a county population of around 60,000 pairs. This possibly overestimates the total, especially in intensively-farmed areas, and a range of 40,000-60,000 is considered more appropriate. The British total was estimated at 2.3 million pairs (New Atlas).

The earliest ever was at Warsash on Mar. 17th 1992. In other years during 1971-92, first arrivals were recorded on dates in the period up to Apr. 4th with the average Mar. 26th. Spring arrivals normally peak in the third or fourth week of April, when large "falls" of up to 100 birds are not unusual; as many as 117 were at Sandy Point on Apr. 18th 1987. Migrants continue to arrive during the first half of May, e.g. at least 100 came in off the sea at Hurst Beach on May 3rd 1980.

There is some movement, probably of young birds dispersing, in July. The main emigration takes place in August, when peak counts at well-watched localities may exceed 100, e.g. 111 at Sinah on Aug. 17th 1985, 105 at Beacon Hill (Warnford) on Aug. 10th 1986 and 149 there on Aug. 25th 1990. Passage continues in the first half of September but by the end of the month few remain. During 1971-92, latest dates were between Sep. 21st and Oct. 29th with the average Oct. 12th. Additionally, a late bird was at Sinah Gravel Pit on Dec. 1st 1990.

Ringing has shown the passage of birds from further afield, with 12 from northern England, three from Scotland, three from Wales and four from Ireland. Continental birds almost certainly occur as well, especially in east or south-easterly winds, though there have not been any ringing recoveries to confirm this. However, there are a few records of birds showing the characteristics of the race *P.t. acredula*, which breeds in Scandinavia and eastern Europe. British Willow Warblers winter south of the Sahara in tropical Africa. There have been no ringing recoveries from the winter quarters, but three, ringed between July 15th and 31st, were recovered in Spain, Morocco and Portugal within seven weeks, while one ringed at Fordingbridge on Aug. 2nd 1988 was recovered in Morocco, 2122 km south, on Mar. 19th 1989.

# Goldcrest                                                    *Regulus regulus*

A numerous resident, passage migrant and winter visitor.

The Goldcrest is one of the most characteristic species of coniferous woodland. When the population is at a high level following a series of mild winters, territories are occupied in broadleaved woodlands and in gardens and churchyards with ornamental conifers and yews. The Hampshire CBC indices for 1981-91 illustrate the effects of severe winter weather. In 1987, following three hard winters, the index had fallen from the 1981 level of 100 to 44. By 1990, it had risen to 159, and many Goldcrests were found in the marginal habitats described above. This accounts for the wide distribution shown by the Atlas Map. It shows several gaps along the coast, especially along the western shore of Southampton Water and around Gosport and Portsmouth; these are all heavily built-up or industrialised areas where suitable habitat is lacking. The distribution is also patchy on the chalk in the south-east and especially in the

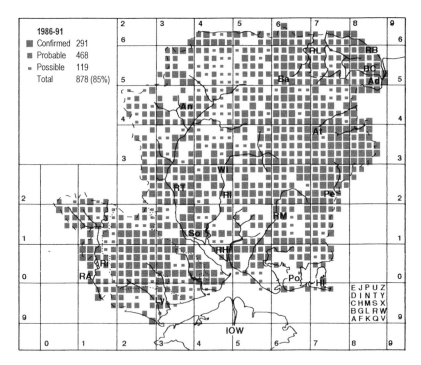

north-west of the county. Again, some tetrads in these areas lack the necessary woodland, although in the north-west especially the species was probably overlooked to a certain degree. A further cold spell in early 1991 clearly decimated the population, as the index fell back to 55 in that year, but since then recovery has again taken place.

Using national CBC data for 1989, the New Atlas method indicates a county population of around 20,000 pairs and a national total of 560,000 pairs. Clearly, both these figures would be appreciably lower after a severe winter.

Between late September and late November, influxes are regularly recorded at coastal and inland localities. Such "falls" usually involve counts of 30-60 birds, often concentrated in very small areas of atypical habitat such as coastal gorse scrub. Recent records of larger numbers include 100 at Thatcher's Copse (Brownwich) on Oct. 28th 1988, 75 at Old Winchester Hill and 69 at nearby Beacon Hill on Oct. 1st 1989 and 200 at Yateley Heath Wood on Nov. 25th 1990. There is occasionally evidence of passage in spring, often coinciding with arrivals of Chiffchaffs (Duffin 1991); e.g., in 1982, a small influx was noted at Titchfield Haven on Mar. 14th and at least six were at North Hayling on Mar. 27th.

Although national ringing data show that some continental birds occur in autumn, Hampshire information does not confirm this. Of 18 ringed in the county and recovered, only three had moved further than 100 km. These involved two ringed at Crookham Sewage Farm on consecutive days in December 1987 and controlled at the Calf of Man on Apr. 12th 1988 and Mar. 28th 1989, and one ringed at Oakhanger on Oct. 28th 1983 and found at

Sheffield on Apr. 13th 1984. 11 ringed elsewhere in Britain have been found in Hampshire. Three of these originated over 100 km to the north or north-west, including a juvenile ringed in Gwynedd on Aug. 17th 1981 and recovered at Ellisfield on Mar. 3rd 1984. Additionally, one ringed as a juvenile in County Down, Ireland, on Oct. 8th 1986 was controlled at Southampton Docks, 499 km SSE, on Oct. 12th 1987. Perhaps of greater interest were two birds trapped at Dungeness and Beachy Head in autumn and found in Hampshire within seven days of ringing. These may well have been of continental origin.

## Firecrest *Regulus ignicapillus*

A scarce breeder, passage migrant and winter visitor.

Prior to 1961, the Firecrest was a rare visitor, mostly recorded in early spring, but in that year up to four, including three singing males, were in one area of the New Forest between May 9th and June 25th. In the following year, six singing males were present and three family groups were seen. Between 1963 and 1966, up to eight singing males were located; in 1965 an occupied nest was found and the adults were later observed feeding three young. During this period, one or two singing males were found at four other sites although the only suggestion of breeding concerned a pair watched apparently carrying nesting material in 1964. The observations of 1962 and 1965 were the first fully authenticated records of breeding in Britain (Adams 1966).

Subsequently, Firecrests have continued to breed in the New Forest although there are evidently large fluctuations in the population from year to year. Between 1967 and 1984, the peak years were 1969, with 27 pairs or singing males in eight areas, 1981, with 17 in four areas including 14 at the original site, and 1983, with 24 in 15 areas including five at the original site. From 1973-79, no more than three singing males were reported per year. Although the fluctuations may be due partly to the vagaries of observer coverage, that they may be real was indicated by the work of one census worker, who found a total of eight singing males in 1983 in areas which held only one in the previous year.

Elsewhere in the county, Firecrests were first recorded during the breeding season in 1971, when at least three singing males were found in a plantation to the north of Whitchurch. Unfortunately, part of the site was obliterated soon afterwards by major road widening works. In 1974, a pair bred near Old Winchester Hill and another singing male was present. One or two males held territory there in five years up to 1984 and four were heard singing on May 29th 1983. Single pairs bred successfully in 1975 and 1979. In 1983, two males and a female were located in Alice Holt Forest and a year later one was observed carrying food in a different inclosure. Also in 1983, two males and a female were located at Ewshot. One pair returned the following year but breeding could not be confirmed.

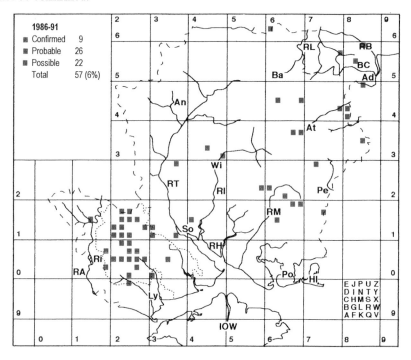

The Atlas Map shows the distribution recorded during the period 1986-91, with all records shown at the same level for security reasons. In the New Forest, there were registrations in 29 tetrads, but only in a few of these were Firecrests found in every year. The peak years were 1987, with at least 33 pairs or singing males (including 13 at the original site), 1989 with 37 and 1990 with 47 (including eight at the original site). It is difficult to estimate the population; some tetrads held five or more pairs or singing males on a regular basis while others may have been occupied by a single male in one year only. It seems likely that 50 or more pairs or singing males may be present in "good" years but in others the total is considerably lower.

In the rest of the county, there were registrations in 26 tetrads. In 20 of these, Firecrests were recorded in one year only and in the other six in two years, despite the fact that several were well-watched. Most tetrads held only one or two pairs or singing males, but at Yateley Heath Wood five pairs and two further males were present in a Norway spruce plantation in 1987. None returned in 1988 and by 1991 the area had been clear-felled. At another site, watched throughout the Atlas period, five singing males were present in 1990, but in the following year only one pair was located. In all, a total of 43 pairs or singing males was recorded with a maximum of 14 at eight sites in 1987. Firecrests are clearly overlooked to an unknown degree in Hampshire, but even in "good" years the total population, including the New Forest, seems unlikely to exceed 100 pairs or singing males. In 1988-91, the British population was estimated to be in the range 80-250 pairs (New Atlas), so clearly Hampshire, and the New Forest in particular, holds a major proportion of the national total.

Firecrests occur in a variety of habitats. Most are found in conifer plantations, especially of Norway spruce or Douglas fir, or in mature mixed woodland where these conifer species dominate. They also favour broadleaved woodland with a mixture of oak, beech, holly and sometimes ivy. In 1979, a pair bred in a yew copse at Old Winchester Hill.

Outside the breeding season, Firecrests have been recorded with increasing frequency since the 1970s (fig. 73).

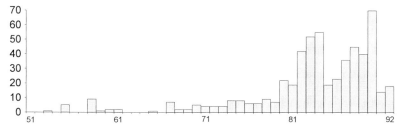

*Figure 73. Annual totals of Firecrests (excluding breeding birds), 1951-92.*

Between 1951 and 1970, most were recorded in spring between late March and early April. Records were all of one or two birds apart from six at Fareham on Apr. 9th 1958.

During the 1970s, autumn and winter occurrences became more frequent. There was a large influx in 1982 which commenced in late October. In the period up to mid-March 1983, 45 were reported. 14 wintered at three sites on Hayling Island (which was carefully searched), four at Titchfield Haven and a total of eight at four other coastal sites. Other records mostly involved singles on one date only. At the start of the influx, only three were any distance from the coast; subsequently, ten were found inland including nine in February and March. Since then the pattern has varied (perhaps reflecting differences in observer coverage as much as occurrences of Firecrests), although a trend to greater numbers wintering inland is evident. On Hayling Island, high counts have included eight at Sinah Warren on Nov. 4th 1984, six at Sandy Point on Dec. 6th 1986 and four there on Nov. 18th 1988, but the number recorded wintering has not approached the 1982/83 level. Notable inland records include those of four at Pitts Wood Inclosure on Jan. 3rd 1987, three trapped at Sway between Jan. 4th and 13th 1990, up to four at Fleet Pond between Jan. 16th and Mar. 17th 1990, five at Southampton Common on Nov. 11th 1990 and four at

Highbridge on Dec. 25th 1990. The cumulative monthly totals for 1951-92 (excluding breeding birds) are shown below.

| Jan | Feb | Mar | Apr | May | Jun | Jul | Aug | Sep | Oct | Nov | Dec |
|-----|-----|-----|-----|-----|-----|-----|-----|-----|-----|-----|-----|
| 76 | 70 | 106 | 57 | 9 | 3 | 0 | 2 | 24 | 78 | 113 | 109 |

Wintering and passage Firecrests occur in a wide variety of wooded habitats, including coastal scrub and those close to fresh water. Some are found with roving parties of tits and Goldcrests while others apparently take up winter territories.

In the absence of any ringing recoveries, the movements undertaken by Hampshire birds can only be guessed. Breeding birds appear to be summer visitors, arriving in late April or early May (but as much as a month earlier at established localities) and dispersing by late July or early August. The increasing number of winter records, especially in the New Forest, indicates that they may not move far, but, on the other hand, some of the high breeding season numbers have followed springs with favourable southerly winds. It has been suggested that those occurring in autumn and winter are of continental origin (Winter Atlas).

## Spotted Flycatcher                                    *Muscicapa striata*

A common summer visitor and passage migrant.

The preferred habitats of the Spotted Flycatcher include large rural and suburban gardens, parkland, churchyards, open broadleaved woodland and farmland spinneys, often in the vicinity of water where insect life is abundant. It is widely distributed but with gaps near the coast, especially around the shores of Southampton Water and east to Hayling Island, and on the chalk. This species can be unobtrusive, so it was undoubtedly overlooked in some tetrads during the Atlas Survey. However, coverage was good along the coast, which suggests a genuine scarcity there. During the last 20 years, many observers have reported local declines, which reflects the national picture provided by CBC monitoring (Marchant *et al* 1990). Unfortunately, too few pairs occur on Hampshire CBCs to provide a reliable comparison. Using national CBC data for 1989, the New Atlas method indicates a county population of around 3500 pairs. However, this clearly underestimates numbers in towns and villages and the true figure is probably in the range 4000-6000 pairs. The national total was estimated to be 120,000 pairs (New Atlas).

The earliest ever was at Fleet Pond on Apr. 19th 1983; in other years during the period 1971-92, first arrivals were recorded between Apr. 20th and May 11th with the average Apr. 30th. The main influx is normally in mid or late May. Numbers recorded on passage are usually low, counts of 25 at Hayling Island on May 25th 1985 and 75 there on May 15th 1988 being exceptional.

The main autumn movement is in the second half of August, when loose gatherings of 10-30 are frequently recorded, especially at inland localities. Higher counts include 60+ at Shepherds Spring on Aug. 16th 1978, and 53 at Old Winchester Hill and 51 at Beacon Hill (Warnford) on Aug. 20th 1989. Moderate numbers are still present in early September but counts have not exceeded 20 in that month. The last are normally recorded in late September or early October. During 1971-92, latest dates were between Sep. 25th and Oct.

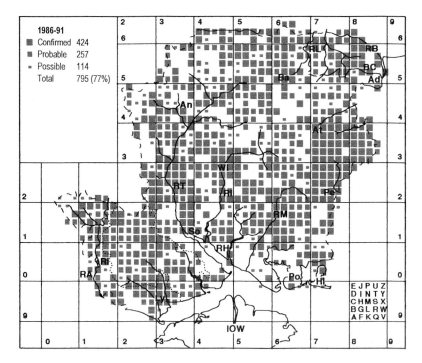

| 1986-91 | | |
|---|---|---|
| ■ Confirmed | 424 | |
| ■ Probable | 257 | |
| ▪ Possible | 114 | |
| Total | 795 (77%) | |

15th with the average Oct. 3rd. There are two later records, of two at Portsdown Hill on Oct. 16th 1965 and one at Longdown (New Forest) on Oct. 29th 1961.

There are only eight ringing recoveries of Hampshire birds. Six were local, but the other two involved birds ringed at different sites in Hampshire on Aug. 1st and 3rd 1968 and both recovered in the Spanish province of Jaen on Sep. 15th 1968 and Sep. 15th 1970 respectively. British birds winter in sub-Saharan Africa, mostly south of the equator.

# Red-breasted Flycatcher *Ficedula parva*

415

Four records. A male was at Southsea on May 1st 1944, a male and two females or first-winters were in a Farlington garden on Sep. 14th 1953, and single females or first-winters were at Broadlands Lake on Oct. 13th 1976 and Sinah Warren on Oct. 3rd 1989.

The Red-breasted Flycatcher breeds from central Europe to Kamchatka and winters in the Indian sub-continent and south-east Asia.

## Pied Flycatcher                                    *Ficedula hypoleuca*

A scarce passage migrant; rarely breeds.

The numbers of Pied Flycatchers recorded on migration have increased steadily since the early 1950s (fig. 74). This can be largely attributed to improved observer coverage. Fluctuations during the 1980s and early 1990s probably reflect variations in the numbers of birds occurring as much as observer effort; in the record autumn of 1984 the excellent coverage of one favoured area clearly coincided with a strong passage of the species (see below).

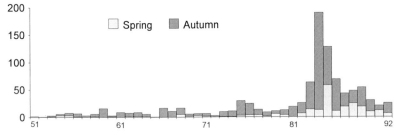

*Figure 74. Spring and autumn totals of Pied Flycatchers, 1951-92.*

In 1985, exceptionally early birds were recorded at West Lane (Hayling Island) on Apr. 4th and Fritham Plain four days later. In other years during 1971-92, first arrivals were recorded between Apr. 11th and 27th with the average Apr. 18th. Spring passage peaks in the last ten days of April and early May (fig. 75). Few are seen after about May 10th but stragglers, often lone males holding territory, occur up to the end of that month. Totals in spring have varied between none and 25 except in 1985, when 58 were recorded (fig. 74). As with several other migrant passerines (e.g. Black Redstart and Ring Ouzel), more are recorded at inland localities than on the coast. Most sightings involve one to three birds, but four were at Crab Wood on Apr. 28th 1985, Beacon Hill (Warnford) on May 2nd 1988 and Sinah on Apr. 23rd and 29th 1989. Birds are frequently grounded following drizzly, overcast nights, e.g. 28 were found at 19 widespread localities on Apr. 27th and 28th 1985.

In summer, pairs or unmated males are occasionally found in ancient and ornamental woodland in the New Forest. Breeding was confirmed at Pinnick Wood in 1954, Queen's Bower in 1968, Brook Wood in 1984 and near Fritham in 1992. Pairs or apparently unmated males were also recorded in June in 1956, 1975, 1982 and 1983 (2). Elsewhere, a male held territory around a nest box at Mislingford from Apr. 18th-June 10th 1987 but failed to attract a mate, and a pair was found entering a nest box at Hale on May 15th 1988 but it is not known if breeding was attempted.

In autumn, returning migrants normally occur from late July onwards (earliest date July 8th). Most are usually recorded in the second half of August, but in some years there is a secondary peak in early or mid September (fig. 75). Numbers are invariably higher than in spring, with a greater proportion recorded at coastal sites than inland. Between 1951 and 1979, when coverage was poor, autumn totals varied between none and 27, but in the 1980s between 34 and 70 were recorded in four years and at least 213 passed through in 1984 (fig. 74). Many of these were found on Hayling Island, where exceptionally good coverage of the area coincided with a large influx of the species. Counts peaked at 24 on Aug. 18th and 34, including 15 at Sandy Point, on Aug. 26th. Coverage was also good in 1983, 1985 and 1986, but in those years the maximum counts were between nine and 12. Elsewhere, notable counts have included five at Enham Alamein on Aug. 18th 1975, five at Old Winchester Hill on Aug. 17th 1975 and Aug. 20th 1989 and seven at Southampton Common on Aug. 16th 1984. Passage continues until late September or early October, but very few have been recorded after this time. Two particularly late birds were at Gosport on Oct. 21st 1967 and West Hill School (Titchfield) on Oct. 22nd 1977. In other years during 1971-92, latest dates were between Sep. 8th and Oct. 16th with the average Sep. 28th.

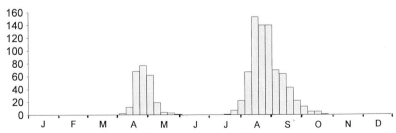

*Figure 75. Cumulative weekly totals of Pied Flycatchers (excluding breeding and summering birds), 1951-92.*

Several recoveries and controls suggest the origin of birds passing through Hampshire. Four ringed as pulli in Dyfed, Gloucestershire, Gwent and Powys were recovered on dates between Aug. 7th and 14th. Two other movements

involved a juvenile ringed in Finland on Aug. 26th 1966 and controlled at East
Boldre on Sep. 18th 1966, and another juvenile ringed at Sandwich Bay, Kent
on Aug. 11th 1983 and found dead at Woolston four days later. National ringing
data indicate that some British birds move first south-east within England and
then re-orientate south or south-west, often making a direct flight to Iberia
(Hope-Jones *et al* 1977). Thus, those occurring in Hampshire in mid-August are
probably mostly British-bred birds while those in September include some of
continental origin. Three further birds ringed as pulli in Gwent and Powys (2)
were recovered or controlled between Apr. 30th and May 6th in the following
spring. One of these, a female controlled at Widley on May 1st 1983, was killed
by a cat at Penrith, Cumbria on June 22nd of that year. The only recovery of a
Hampshire-ringed bird involved one trapped at Keyhaven on Aug. 10th 1969
and found in Morocco about May 2nd 1970. Pied Flycatchers winter south of
the Sahara between Guinea and the Central African Republic.

## Bearded Tit                                    *Panurus biarmicus*

A very scarce breeder; scarce passage migrant and winter visitor.

K & M described the Bearded Tit as "an accidental visitor", but gave two
records of breeding, one undated and the other in 1902; neither of them is
particularly convincing. Prior to 1964, there were very few records this century.
Single birds were at Titchfield Haven on July 3rd 1911 and Feb. 1st 1922 and
St. Cross from Nov. 3rd-5th 1956, up to three were at Titchfield Haven from
Jan. 15th-Apr. 3rd 1960 and two were at Fleet Pond from Dec. 9th 1961-Mar.
10th 1962.

The situation changed in the winter of 1964/65, when 20 were recorded,
including flocks of five at Nursling Gravel Pit on Oct. 24th, Titchfield Haven on
Oct. 31st and Farlington Marshes on Nov. 1st. In the following winter, 62 were
seen including flocks of 16 flying west at Lower Test Marshes on Oct. 10th and
17 there on Nov. 2nd; up to ten wintered at Titchfield Haven and Farlington
Marshes. Since then, the species has established a small breeding population and
become a regular winter visitor in variable numbers (fig. 76).

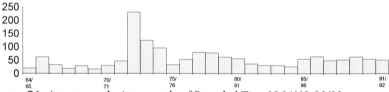

*Figure 76. Autumn and winter totals of Bearded Tits, 1964/65-91/92.*

The influxes into the county in the mid-1960s coincided with a major population
expansion in the Netherlands, where the Ijsselmeer land reclamation scheme
provided ideal breeding conditions (Mead & Pearson 1974). Also, following the
hard winter of 1962/63, a series of milder seasons allowed the breeding colonies
in East Anglia and Kent to flourish. Post-breeding dispersal from these sites
resulted in an increasing number of autumn immigrants reaching Hampshire.
This is confirmed by a series of ringing returns for 1966-71 which show regular
interchange between breeding colonies in East Anglia and the wintering site at

Farlington Marshes. Additionally, two ringed in Kent in September 1968 and July 1970 were controlled at Farlington in December 1969 and August 1971 respectively, while two ringed in the Netherlands in September and October 1971 were controlled there on Dec. 7th of that year.

The eruptive behaviour was the prelude to further range expansion as small colonies were established at suitable sites around the English east and south coasts (68-72 Atlas). In Hampshire, a single pair bred at Titchfield Haven in 1966 and then annually until 1975 except in 1968. At Farlington Marshes, single pairs were present for a day or two in 1971 and 1973 and summered in 1974. Subsequent breeding records are shown in table 69.

| | 76 | 77 | 78 | 79 | 80 | 81 | 82 | 83 | 84 | 85 | 86 | 87 | 88 | 89 | 90 | 91 | 92 |
|---|---|---|---|---|---|---|---|---|---|---|---|---|---|---|---|---|---|
| T Haven | 2 | 5/6 | 3 | 4/5 | 5 | 3 | 2 | 0 | 0 | 1 | 3 | 0 | 3 | 4 | 6 | 5 | 5 |
| F Marshes | 0 | 0 | 0 | 0 | 0 | 1 | 0 | 0 | 3* | 4* | 3* | 2* | 1 | 3* | 0 | 0 | 1 |
| Keyhaven | 0 | 0 | 0 | 0 | 0 | 0 | 0 | 0 | 0 | 0 | 0 | 0 | 0 | 1 | 2 | 2 | 2 |
| Lymington | 0 | 0 | 0 | 0 | 0 | 0 | 0 | 0 | 0 | 0 | 0 | 0 | 0 | - | - | - | 6 |
| Totals | 2 | 5/6 | 3 | 4/5 | 5 | 4 | 2 | 0 | 3 | 4 | 6 | 2 | 4 | 8 | 8 | 7 | 14 |

* number of females breeding; no more than two males were present except in 1987, when there were four.

*Table 69. Annual totals of breeding pairs of Bearded Tits, 1976-92.*

The 1989 breeding season was particularly productive, with at least 42 young raised, but in previous years fledging success was often poor due to cold, wet weather. Birds have also occasionally been seen in summer at Warsash and Lower Test Marshes but with no indication of breeding. Although the Hampshire total of 4-14 pairs in 1988-92 is insignificant compared with the estimated British population of 400 pairs (New Atlas), the potential for further expansion is great.

Post-breeding eruptive behaviour occurs in late September and October, when flocks may be seen departing from breeding sites. Ringing data confirm that some locally-bred birds leave their natal areas in winter, e.g. two ringed as juveniles at Farlington Marshes on July 13th 1985 (and still present there on Sep. 14th 1985) were controlled together at Budleigh Salterton, Devon on Nov. 3rd 1985. Some may not return; individuals nesting at Titchfield Haven have been found breeding in subsequent years at Farlington Marshes and in Dorset, Kent and Somerset (Duffin 1991).

October is the peak month for movement into and through the county, though there have been records from non-breeding sites as early as July. In 1972, some 230 were recorded in autumn, including 40 at Keyhaven and 20 at Alresford Pond on Oct. 15th, ten flying north-east over Woolmer on Oct. 18th, 12 at Needs Ore on Oct. 22nd and 31st, 30 at Fleet Pond on Oct. 31st, 30 at Farlington Marshes on Nov. 1st, 38 at Warsash on Nov. 5th and 23 at Great Salterns Lake on Nov. 26th. Totals in other years have been lower. Maximum counts at the main localities have been 30 at Keyhaven on Oct. 13th 1974, 37 at Titchfield Haven in October 1977 and 23 at Farlington Marshes in November 1985. Double-figure counts have also been made at Warsash (max. 16), Lower Test Marshes (max. 12) and Fleet Pond and Great Salterns Lake (max. 10). Other records, involving up to seven birds, have come from the coast at Calshot Reclamation, Gilkicker Point, IBM Lake, Lepe, Sinah Gravel Pit and Wildgrounds, and inland at Alresford Pond, Heath Pond, Marsh Court, Shepherds Spring and Twyford, all between Oct. 6th and Nov. 8th.

Numbers remaining for the winter are considerably lower (fig. 76). Following the influx in October 1972, some 79 wintered, including 24 at Great Salterns Lake, 20 at Warsash and 16 at Fleet Pond. Since then, numbers have been lower, with a maximum of 43 in 1980/81. Regularly used coastal sites include Farlington Marshes (max. 24), Great Salterns Lake (max. 15), Keyhaven (max. 15), Lower Test Marshes (max. 18) and Titchfield Haven (max. 10). Inland records have come from Alresford Pond (eight in December 1985 and two in January 1991) and Fleet Pond (up to ten wintered from 1970/71-78/79, but since then there have been records in only three winters with a maximum of three in 1985/86).

Most wintering birds leave by late March or early April. There is also evidence of passage at this time, e.g. 28 were at Titchfield Haven on Apr. 5th 1974 (many of which flew high to the north up the Meon valley) and three were inland at Bishopstoke from Apr. 2nd-4th 1987. The cumulative monthly totals (excluding breeding birds) for 1964/65-91/92 are shown below.

| Jul | Aug | Sep | Oct | Nov | Dec | Jan | Feb | Mar | Apr | May |
|-----|-----|-----|-----|-----|-----|-----|-----|-----|-----|-----|
| 10  | 12  | 64  | 895 | 755 | 339 | 454 | 329 | 282 | 165 | 5   |

Ringing data confirm that not all immigrants winter in the county; some pass through to sites in Dorset, Devon and other western counties. It has also been shown that, following the establishment of breeding colonies in Dorset, some autumn visitors arrive from the west, e.g. two ringed at Radipole Lake, Dorset on Sep. 3rd and 4th 1977 were controlled at Great Salterns Lake on Oct. 28th 1978 and one ringed at Lodmoor, Dorset on Sep. 12th 1982 was controlled at Farlington Marshes on Nov. 2nd 1982.

## Long-tailed Tit                                  *Aegithalos caudatus*

A numerous resident.

The Long-tailed Tit occupies a variety of habitats typified by scrub or bushy undergrowth and including broadleaved and mixed woodland, farmland (particularly with thick hedgerows), heathland and downland scrub and large gardens.

As the Atlas Map shows, it occurs throughout the county. Some of the apparent gaps in its distribution may be due to inadequate coverage, but it is, nevertheless, relatively scarce on some parts of the chalk, e.g. north-west of Winchester, as well as in urban areas such as Portsmouth. The national

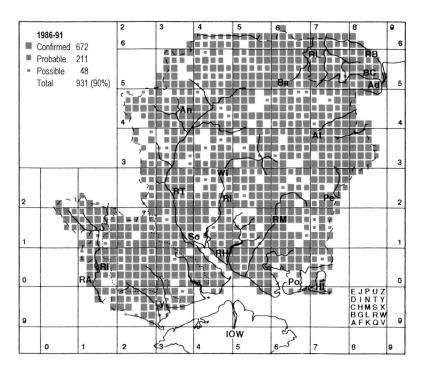

population shows large fluctuations caused by high mortality in severe winters (Marchant *et al* 1990) but overall, numbers have been stable throughout the 1980s. A similar pattern is evident from Hampshire CBC data although these are based on relatively small numbers of birds. Using national CBC data for 1989, the New Atlas method indicates a county population of around 9000 pairs. However, this underestimates densities in villages and towns and so a range of 9000-12,000 is considered more appropriate. This would drop substantially after a severe winter. The British total was estimated to be 210,000 pairs (New Atlas).

Outside the breeding season, the species is usually encountered in small parties, often accompanied by other tits. Parties of 20 or more are not uncommon but numbers seldom exceed 60. There were 60+ at Timsbury on Oct. 14th 1973, 69 at Hartley Wintney on Jan. 21st 1974, 72 at Elvetham on Jan. 1st 1975 and 69 at Marwell Zoological Park on Dec. 29th 1981. 100+ were counted at Warsash on Oct. 30th 1987 but this was the total of several parties.

Most remain close to their breeding territories throughout the year but occasional records of small parties at non-breeding sites in autumn show that some post-breeding dispersal does take place. This is confirmed by ringing studies. There have been ten recoveries of Hampshire-ringed birds at distances greater than 10 km from the ringing sites. Five ringed at Hamble in August 1983 were controlled at Kingswood, Surrey between December 1983 and February 1984, presumably having moved as a flock. Two movements in the opposite direction involved one ringed at Egham, Surrey on Oct. 9th 1971 and controlled at Cosham on Dec. 22nd 1971 and another ringed at Morden, Surrey on Dec. 28th 1973 and found dead at Froxfield on Dec. 7th 1974.

# Marsh Tit                                          *Parus palustris*

A common resident.

The Marsh Tit occurs in most types of broadleaved woodland. The Atlas Survey has shown it to be widespread in the eastern half of the county and in the New Forest, but local elsewhere. It is virtually absent from the well-watched coastal strip extending from Hayling and Portsea Islands around Southampton Water to Calshot.

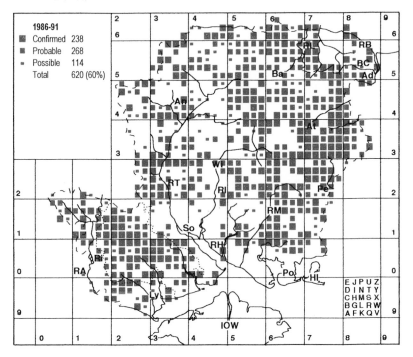

National CBC data indicate that numbers declined slowly in the 1970s and 1980s, for reasons which are not fully understood. In Hampshire, the limited quantitative information suggests that the population has suffered a similar fate. In 1982, seven CBC plots held a total of 17 pairs, but in 1990, following a period of relatively mild winters, the same plots held only 11 pairs. Estimation of the Hampshire population is difficult because of the wide variation in breeding densities in different parts of the county. In 1981, three CBC plots with a total area of 71.8 ha in ancient and ornamental woodland in the New Forest held 15 pairs, equivalent to about 21 pairs/km². In 1985, a 21.5 ha CBC plot in Crab Wood held ten pairs, equivalent to 46 pairs/km². However, such densities are clearly unrepresentative for the county as a whole. Using national CBC data for 1989, the New Atlas method indicates totals of around 4000 pairs for the county and 60,000 pairs for Britain.

After the breeding season, family parties generally remain in, or close to, the nesting territory, so that records from non-breeding sites are unusual. At Titchfield Haven, there were only eight occurrences between 1972 and 1990, while at Farlington Marshes there have only been three records, all between 1957 and 1962. Ringing information confirms that Marsh Tits are essentially sedentary. Of five recoveries of birds ringed in Hampshire, only one was distant from the ringing site: one ringed as a pullus at Hamble on May 26th 1978 and recovered at Eastleigh, 13 km north, on Dec. 12th 1979.

## Willow Tit                                                    *Parus montanus*

A moderately common but local resident.

The Willow Tit's preferred habitat is generally described as damp mixed woodland, often containing birch, willow, elder or alder (with an abundance of rotten stumps or boughs for the excavation of its nest chamber) and usually close to water. This preference holds true in Hampshire, particularly in the north and north-east where nest sites are typically found around gravel pits, lakes and along rivers and streams. It also occurs in drier situations, e.g. dense hawthorn scrub on the chalk, farmland copses and thick hedgerows, and occasionally young conifer plantations. In some places, its occurs with the Marsh Tit; there is no clear habitat distinction other than that the Marsh Tit tends to occur in larger tracts of more mature woodland.

The species was not known to K & M; the first mention that Cohen could trace was for 1936, when it was said to be "widely distributed in the north-east but not very numerous" and "by no means common in the New Forest but with a pair or two here and there among birches". C & T, with the results of the 68-72 Atlas available, considered it to be well distributed in the river valleys, on the chalk and in the north of the county, thin on the ground in the New Forest and south-east, and probably missing from the coastal strip.

20 years later, the range is broadly similar. During the Atlas Survey, breeding was confirmed in six 10 km squares where the species was not found in 1968-72, but this was probably due to under-recording in the earlier survey. Rather surprisingly, breeding was not confirmed in the New Forest, despite the availability of apparently suitable habitat. Records from the north-east indicate that Willow Tits are less common today than in the 1970s. This is consistent with the national picture which, based on CBC data, shows that the population

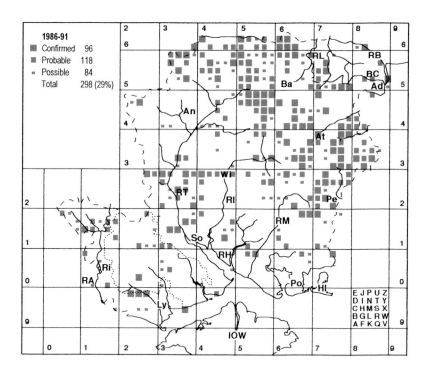

| 1986-91 | |
| --- | --- |
| ■ Confirmed | 96 |
| ■ Probable | 118 |
| ▪ Possible | 84 |
| Total | 298 (29%) |

declined slowly from the mid-1970s to the mid-1980s but has been stable since (Marchant *et al* 1990).

Estimation of the county population is difficult because the distribution is patchy and there is little quantitative information available. Using national CBC data for 1989, the New Atlas method indicates a Hampshire total of 1250 pairs. This may be a little high; if a density of 2-3 pairs per occupied tetrad is assumed and some allowance made for under-recording, a range of 700-1000 pairs is obtained. The British population was estimated to be 25,000 pairs in 1989 (New Atlas).

Willow Tits are essentially sedentary, usually wintering within, or close to, their breeding territories. Some dispersal does take place, however, since birds occasionally appear at non-breeding locations, often in mixed tit flocks. They are rare at well-watched sites on the coast. There were two at Dibden Bay in January and February 1975 and at least two at the Wildgrounds (Gosport) from July 26th-Oct. 3rd 1985. At Farlington Marshes, there have been only four records, the most recent being of one there from July 1st 1987-Apr. 3rd 1988.

## Coal Tit                                                      *Parus ater*

A numerous resident.

The Coal Tit is most numerous in coniferous woodlands. It also occurs, albeit at lower densities, in broadleaved and mixed woodland, heathland scrub, and in parks, large gardens, churchyards and farmland shelter belts, particularly where there are conifers.

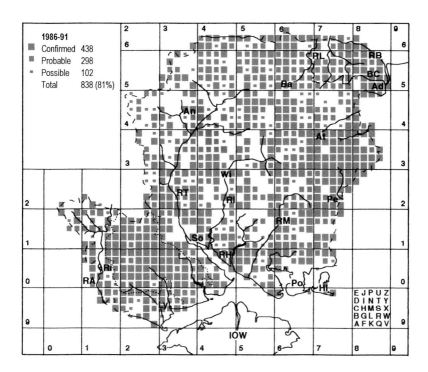

At the Atlas Map shows, it is widely distributed but occurs more densely in the north and east and New Forest than on the chalk. It is apparently scarce or absent in the urban centres of Portsmouth, Southampton and Totton and along the industrialised western shore of Southampton Water. CBC data show that the national population has remained fairly stable throughout the last 20 years. Local data show a similar position from 1981-91 but with troughs, which were quickly recovered, after the hard winters of 1981/82 and 1985/86. Using national CBC data for 1989, the New Atlas method indicates a county population of around 23,000 pairs and a British total of 610,000 pairs.

In autumn and winter, Coal Tits flock, sometimes with other tit species, and usually remain close to their breeding sites. Usually no more than 20 are recorded together, though as many as 40 were at Tweseldown on Sep. 8th 1977. Ringing studies, however, provide some evidence of dispersal. Of 36 recoveries of birds ringed in Hampshire, 31 were within 9 km of the ringing sites and none exceeded 30 km. Four ringed elsewhere have been recovered in Hampshire, the longest movement involving one ringed at Westbury, Wiltshire, on Nov. 19th 1983 and found dead at Whitchurch on Apr. 9th 1983. Dispersal is also indicated by autumn records from non-breeding coastal sites, e.g. six at Warsash on Oct. 27th 1973 and 17 overflying Titchfield Haven between Oct. 3rd and 10th 1977. Similar records from inland sites include those of a party of 27 at Shepherds Spring on Oct. 9th 1977 (the only record for the year there) and three flying high to the north-east over Fleet Pond on Nov. 5th 1989.

425

# Blue Tit                                    *Parus caeruleus*

An abundant resident and passage migrant.

The Blue Tit is principally a bird of broadleaved woodland (particularly oak) but is also found in many other habitats including mixed and coniferous woodland, heathland scrub and farmland. Its ready acceptance of nest boxes and other man-made nest sites enables it to penetrate deep into urban areas where it feeds in parks and gardens and on waste ground. During the Atlas Survey, it was located in 1021 (99%) tetrads with breeding confirmed in 947, probable in 69 and possible in five.

Hampshire CBC data indicate that numbers remained relatively stable throughout the 1980s, mirroring the national picture (Marchant *et al* 1990) Using national CBC data for 1989, the New Atlas method indicates a county population of 105,000 pairs. However, this underestimates numbers in towns and villages, and so an upper limit of 125,000 pairs is considered appropriate. The British total was estimated to be 3.3 million pairs (New Atlas).

Blue Tits are usually the most numerous species in post-breeding tit flocks. Mixed parties containing 50-100 Blue Tits with Long-tailed Tits, Great Tits and other species are not unusual, and occasionally larger numbers occur, e.g. 300 in a mixed flock at Tweseldown on Sep. 8th 1977, 120 at Blackmoor Golf Course on Aug. 11th 1985 and 150 at Fleet Pond on Aug. 23rd 1988.

The breeding population is mainly sedentary, but ringing studies provide evidence of dispersal, particularly by juveniles. There have been 846 recoveries of Hampshire-ringed birds, 783 within the county and the remaining 63 in southern England. The most distant recovery involved one ringed as a pullus at Woolton Hill on May 30th 1971 and controlled at Sandwich Bay, Kent on Feb. 16th 1973. Of almost 1100 ringed at Titchfield Haven, only one has been recovered further than 20 km away: a bird ringed on Sep. 29th 1974 and controlled at Portland Bill, Dorset on Dec. 4th 1975.

Recoveries in Hampshire of birds ringed elsewhere show a similar pattern of mainly local movements, the longest being by one ringed in Devon on Aug. 2nd 1973 and recovered at Longparish on Oct. 25th 1975. However, there has been evidence of passage through and immigration into the county in autumn, most notably in 1957, when unusually large numbers occurred between mid-September and early November (Cramp *et al* 1960). On Sep. 15th 1957, 250 were counted between early morning and early afternoon moving north-west up Southampton Water. Over the following days, numerous parties were seen on the coast moving mainly between north-east and north-west with a peak in mid-October. 120 were in a Gosport garden from Sep. 28th-Oct. 15th. At Southampton University, trapped birds were identified as belonging to the continental race *P.c. caeruleus*.

Although not on the scale of the 1957 irruption, it is possible that influxes occur in most autumns. There were 80+ at Warsash on Sep. 14th 1974, 147 at Dibden Bay on Sep. 26th 1981, 100 at Warsash on Oct. 12th 1981 and 100+ at Pennington Marsh on Oct. 30th 1983. Observations of movement at Titchfield Haven include 40 west on Oct. 30th 1977, 26 west on Oct. 6th 1981 and 37 west on Oct. 28th 1983. However, the lack of long distance recoveries (despite the thousands ringed) suggests that local dispersal is involved.

# Great Tit                                          *Parus ater*

An abundant resident.

The Great Tit occurs at its highest densities in broadleaved woodland, but it can be found in almost any habitat provided there are trees or large bushes for feeding and suitable holes and cavities as potential nest sites. It readily accepts both food and nest sites provided by man, thereby enabling it to occur throughout urban areas. During the Atlas Survey, it was located in 1018 (99%) tetrads, with breeding confirmed in 875, probable in 135 and possible in seven.

The national population has increased steadily from a low point caused by the severe weather in 1962/63 (Marchant *et al* 1990) but may have reached a plateau by the mid 1980s. In Hampshire, CBC indices through the 1980s present a confusing picture. Overall, the index fell from 100 in 1981 to 86 in 1991, but there were increases following severe winters in 1984/85 and 1990/91 and decreases after the mild winter of 1988/89. Fluctuations in breeding populations have been linked to reduced food supply and high mortality during the preceding winter following a failure of beech and other trees to produce a good seed crop (Perrins 1979). Using national CBC data for 1989, the New Atlas method indicates a county population of around 60,000 pairs. As with the Blue Tit, this underestimates numbers in suburban areas and so the true figure may be as high as 75,000 pairs. The British total was estimated to be 1.6 million pairs (New Atlas).

After the breeding season, parties of up to 30 are frequently encountered, often in mixed tit flocks, but numbers in excess of 100 are unusual. There were 134 at Old Winchester Hill on Feb. 14th 1982 and 144 at the same site on Feb. 12th 1984. 100 were feeding under beeches at West Wood on Jan. 7th 1983.

Great Tits are mainly sedentary. Of 234 recoveries of birds ringed in Hampshire, 220 were within the county and only one had moved more than 100 km: an adult ringed at Southampton on Feb. 20th 1982 and controlled at Thanet, Kent on Apr. 4th 1983. There is little evidence of movement into and through the county in autumn. Small numbers were noted during the Blue Tit irruption of 1957, e.g. eight flying high to the north-east over Titchfield Haven on Oct. 12th, though since then only 12 overflying birds have been seen there in October. Elsewhere, six flew high to the north over Calshot on Oct. 11th 1983 and two flew high overhead at Lepe on Nov. 6th 1986. Although continental birds may occur, ringing data suggest that most immigrants are of local origin. Of 16 recoveries in Hampshire of birds ringed elsewhere, all had moved less than 100 km apart from one ringed at Donnington Hall, Leicestershire on Dec. 7th 1985 and controlled at Tidworth on Mar. 21st 1987.

# Nuthatch                                          *Sitta europaea*

A numerous resident.

The Nuthatch relies principally on mature broadleaved trees for both feeding and nest sites, occurring in woodland or where there are suitable trees in parks, gardens and on farmland. During the Atlas Survey, the Nuthatch was found to be widespread and common in the north-east and New Forest, but patchily distributed on the chalk and absent from Hayling and Portsea Islands and the Gosport area.

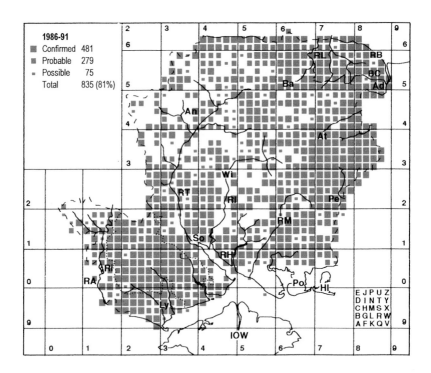

In Britain, the Nuthatch has been increasing and spreading slowly throughout the 1970s and 1980s (Marchant *et al* 1990). The reasons for the expansion are not clear but it is possible that the spread of Dutch elm disease during the period could have contributed by providing a ready food supply and improved nesting opportunities in decaying timber (Osborne 1982). On the basis of limited information from local CBC plots, the Hampshire population has remained relatively stable through the 1980s. Using national CBC data for 1989, the New Atlas method indicates a county population of around 7000 pairs. However, densities are higher than the national average in mature oak woodland; e.g. on three New Forest CBC plots there were 25 pairs/km$^2$ throughout the 1980s. Allowing for this, a range of 7000-9000 pairs is probably appropriate. The British population was estimated to be 130,000 pairs (New Atlas).

Nuthatches are largely sedentary, only dispersing short distances from their natal areas. All 25 recoveries of Hampshire-ringed birds have been within 10 km of the ringing site. They are occasionally recorded at non-breeding sites such as Chilling, Fort Purbrook, Titchfield Haven and Widley in late summer and autumn.

## Treecreeper                                          *Certhia familiaris*

A numerous resident.

The Treecreeper occurs mainly in broadleaved woodland but also in conifers, wooded parkland, timbered gardens, hedgerows with standards and

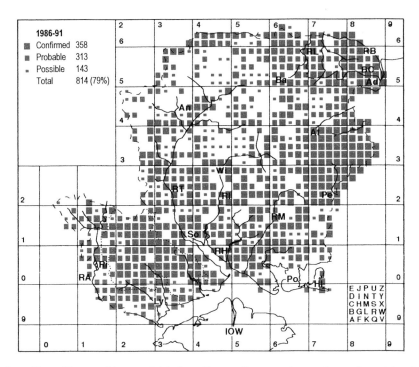

riverside willows, alders and birches. It usually nests in cracks and cavities in mature trees, but will also use artificial sites.

The Atlas Survey showed it to be widespread and common in the north-east and New Forest, but thinly spread on the chalk in the centre and north-west. However, the Treecreeper can be inconspicuous and is likely to have been overlooked in some tetrads.

From a low point after the 1962/63 winter, the national population increased slowly through the 1970s and 1980s, apart from a significant setback during the 1978/79 winter which was caused by the widespread glazing of ice over tree trunks (Marchant *et al* 1990). The limited information available for Hampshire suggests that the local population has stayed approximately constant through the 1980s. Using national CBC data for 1989, the New Atlas method indicates a county total of around 9000 pairs. As with the Nuthatch, this may underestimate the numbers in optimum woodland habitats, and so a range of 9000-11,000 pairs is proposed. The British total was estimated at 200,000 pairs (New Atlas).

Treecreepers are normally sedentary. This is illustrated by the three Hampshire ringing recoveries, all of which were local to the ringing site. For example, one ringed at East Worldham on Sep. 9th 1979 was recovered at the same place eight years later on Sep. 27th 1987. There is, nevertheless, some evidence of dispersal. In 1987, single birds were trapped at Southampton Docks on Aug. 9th and 11th and a third was seen there on Sep. 13th. These were the first records for the site since ringing began there in 1981. At Farlington Marshes, there have been only three sightings: in December 1954, July 1973 and September 1980.

# Penduline Tit
## *Remiz pendulinus*

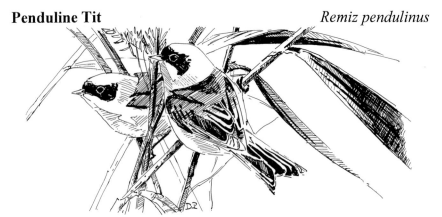

Four records. Two flew high to the west over Titchfield Haven on Oct. 28th 1989, one was trapped there on Nov. 9th of that year and a party of five were there on Oct. 23rd 1990†. Finally, two males were at Farlington Marshes from Jan. 23rd-Mar. 23rd 1991.

The Penduline Tit breeds from Spain to Manchuria. It has been recorded with increasing frequency in Britain since the 1980s; this parallels an expansion of its breeding range into the Netherlands, Denmark and Germany.

# Golden Oriole
## *Oriolus oriolus*

A very scarce passage migrant; occasionally breeds.

The first breeding record for the county appears to be from Mottisfont, where Meinertzhagen recorded a pair between mid-May and Aug. 21st 1897 and saw three juveniles at the end of July. In about 1920, a pair nested unsuccessfully near Owslebury (Cohen). The next record was not until 1969, when a pair nested successfully at Wickham. A male returned to the nest site on May 22nd in the following year but did not stay. In 1975, a pair probably bred in Frame Wood and a year later, a pair was suspected of breeding at Fletchers Thorns Inclosure. Also in 1976, up to three were at Chilland from July 12th-Aug. 3rd, which suggests local breeding, but in 1977 the only record from there was of one heard on July 7th. In 1984, a pair nested at Longwood Warren, raising two young, and in 1985, a juvenile was seen there on July 3rd.

During the Atlas Survey, breeding was confirmed in one area. In 1986, Golden Orioles were present in a wood from May 27th-Aug. 25th. Two males, two females and one other bird were seen on May 31st, though only one pair bred, raising three young. In the following year, a male was first heard on May 25th and a pair was seen on May 30th. Subsequently, two juveniles fledged and the last record was on Aug. 29th. In a nearby wood, an unmated male was present during June. In 1988, the only records were of one heard in the first wood on May 10th, a female or immature male there from May 30th-June 3rd and an adult male at the second wood on July 5th. Many trees were uprooted during the great storm of October 1987, and this, combined with disturbance caused by the removal of those trees during the 1988 breeding season, probably discouraged the orioles from nesting. None have been recorded in the area since.

In Hampshire, territorial Golden Orioles have been found in a variety of broadleaved woodlands. Those nests for which the tree was recorded were in oaks. Only at Chilland were the birds present in poplar, which is the preferred breeding habitat in East Anglia, the main stronghold of the species in Britain. The national population was estimated at 41-48 pairs in 1988-89 (New Atlas).

Other records show that the species is principally an overshooting spring migrant, with only a few seen in autumn. Between 1951 and 1992, a total of 46 was recorded, with annual sightings since 1973. 37 were at inland localities, including ten in the New Forest, and nine were at coastal sites. The cumulative monthly totals are shown below.

| Apr | May | Jun | Jul | Aug | Sep |
|-----|-----|-----|-----|-----|-----|
| 6 | 19 | 13 | 3 | 3 | 2 |

In 1957, two early birds were seen: near Holmsley on Apr. 5th and at Eyeworth Wood about the same time. Otherwise, the earliest was a male found dead at Woodmill (Southampton) on Apr. 19th 1970. Most of the records are concentrated in the period between mid-May and early June, and usually refer to males which hold territory for a day or two before moving on. Only five were seen after July 8th, late records being of males at Ellisfield on Sep. 10th 1975 and Heckfield on Sep. 29th 1979.

Prior to 1951, there were three sightings outside the extreme dates given: one at Avington in December 1897 (K & M), a male at Milford-on-Sea on Mar. 19th 1901 (Kelsall & Coles 1913) and a male at Highclere on Dec. 1st 1947 (*Brit. Birds* 42: 53).

The Golden Oriole winters in Africa, mainly south of the equator.

# Red-backed Shrike                                   *Lanius collurio*

A rare passage migrant. Formerly a moderately common but local summer visitor; last nested in 1984.

K & M described the Red-backed Shrike as "found in most parts of the county, but usually not very plentifully .... of late years, its range has greatly extended". Its subsequent decline as a breeding species in Britain has been well documented (Peakall 1962, Bibby 1973). However, 40 years ago the New Forest was one of its last strongholds in the country and it was widely, if thinly, spread through the rest of the county. The map below shows all known breeding sites since 1950.

In the New Forest, the species was first surveyed in 1957, when 68 pairs were found, but some large tracts of suitable habitat were incompletely surveyed. In the national census in 1960, 253 pairs were located in England, of which 61 (24.1%) were in the New Forest (Peakall 1962). By this time, they had gone from several heaths, especially in the south-east. These areas held 29 pairs in 1957, which suggests a mid-1950s population of around 100 pairs (Tubbs 1986a). A further survey in 1961 showed little change, with 57 pairs located in the Forest, but by 1966 there had been a decline to 31 pairs (Ash 1970), largely concentrated in the north-west. The final national census in 1971 produced 81 pairs in England, of which only seven were in the New Forest (Bibby 1973). In subsequent years, pairs were found nesting at 12 sites. In the north-west, where they were much disturbed, they bred annually until 1978. From 1979-81, one or two unmated males were present, and in 1982, two pairs reared young. The last pair was found there in 1983 but unfortunately its nest was robbed by egg collectors. Elsewhere in the Forest, at least two pairs were found in 1980, one pair in 1981 and three pairs and an unmated male in 1982. A single male returned to one of the 1982 sites in the following year. A thorough search of all known territories in 1984 failed to locate any shrikes (M R Campbell, P P Jennings, N W Orr, C G Packham *in litt*).

During the studies of the New Forest population in the 1950s and 1960s, at least 705 shrikes (82 adults, 26 juveniles and 597 pulli) were ringed (Ash 1970). The only foreign recovery was of one ringed as a pullus on June 17th 1960 and

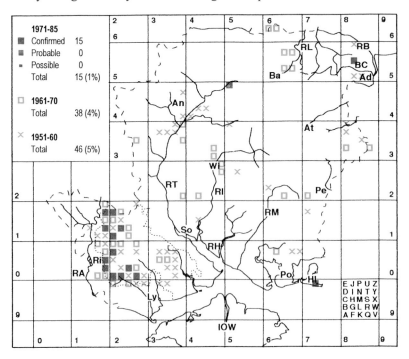

432

found mummified in an alpine pass in Bavaria, Germany, 973 km ESE, on Nov. 6th 1960. The only other distant recovery involved one ringed as a pullus on June 14th 1959 and found dead at Aldbourne, Wiltshire, on July 29th 1959. Details of retraps in subsequent years are given by Ash (1970). There is an earlier recovery of one ringed as a pullus in the New Forest on June 22nd 1948 and found dead at Winchelsea, East Sussex on July 30th 1948.

In the New Forest, Red-backed Shrikes were typically found breeding in three main habitat types: open heathland, usually with gorse and scattered pines and/or holly; stream margins with fairly dense growths of blackthorn, hawthorn, sallow etc, intermingled with tangles of wild rose, bramble and so on; and, much less often, young conifer or hardwood plantations, usually with a dense field layer of bramble or gorse (Ash 1970).

Elsewhere in the county, similar habitats were utilised, particularly the heaths of the north-east and thorn scrub on the chalk. As the map shows, breeding is known to have occurred in 42 tetrads since 1951, but 20 of these were deserted by 1960, 11 more by 1965 and a further eight by 1970. In the Winchester area, eight pairs were found in 1949 (Cohen) but this had declined to three pairs in 1962, after which none were seen. Another favoured area was the Test valley and nearby downland in the vicinity of Stockbridge. In 1960, four pairs were found around Barton Stacey camp and in 1965, there were two pairs on Broughton Down and one on Stockbridge Down. However, they were last known to breed in the following year, when one pair was at Broughton and another at West Down (Chilbolton). The north-east heaths were poorly watched in the early 1950s when they may have held a substantial population. Shrikes last bred at Ludshott Common in 1957, Bramshott Common in 1964, Woolmer in 1966 and Silchester in 1968. Two other pairs bred in 1968, at Sherfield-on-Loddon and Old Winchester Hill, and in 1971, a pair was found near Fleet Pond, two young being raised. At several of these last sites, unmated birds, usually males, appeared up to three years after the final successful breeding. A male was at Bramley Camp on July 12th 1979 but this sighting was not followed up. Two further records have recently come to light. Single pairs nested at Tournerbury (Hayling Island) in 1982 (D Johnson pers. comm.) and near Overton in 1984, the latter raising two young (C G Packham *in litt*).

The reasons for the accelerated decline of the breeding population are not fully understood. It has been linked to climatic change, resulting in a reduction in the availability of large flying insects which form the bulk of the diet (Tubbs 1986a), but other factors such as pesticides and scrub clearance may have been significant in some areas. In the New Forest, the species was heavily persecuted by egg collectors; there seems little doubt that such activity hastened its disappearance from that area.

Apart from breeding birds, 46 presumed passage migrants were recorded between 1957 and 1992. The cumulative monthly totals are shown below.

| Apr | May | Jun | Jul | Aug | Sep | Oct |
|-----|-----|-----|-----|-----|-----|-----|
| 4 | 12 | 5 | 0 | 8 | 12 | 7 |

The earliest was at Romsey on Apr. 23rd 1961, although there were earlier records for the New Forest on Apr. 19th 1965, Apr. 4th 1968 and Apr. 5th 1971. Spring records spanned the period up to June 10th and involved 14 birds at inland sites and seven at the coast. Those inland were mostly at old breeding sites, and were presumably unmated birds which moved on after failing to attract a mate. Since 1983, only nine have been seen, all between May 19th and June 8th. Of these, four were on New Forest heaths, two at Farlington Marshes and one each at Kingsworthy, Needs Ore and Normandy Marsh.

In autumn, all occurred between Aug. 1st and Oct. 9th apart from a late bird at Farlington Marshes on Oct. 22nd 1967. Ten were seen at inland sites and 14 at the coast. Those recorded in August were probably local breeders dispersing, because since 1972, only one has occurred in that month. Since 1975, 12 have occurred, nine of them between 1987 and 1992. Three were in the Pennington/Keyhaven area and at Farlington Marshes, and one each at Bishopstoke, Calshot Reclamation, Itchen Valley Country Park, Needs Oar, Sinah Warren and on a New Forest heath. Most were seen on one date only, but four stayed for about a week including two together at Farlington Marshes from Sep. 10th-15th 1987, and single birds remained at Pennington Marsh from Sep. 17th-Oct. 2nd 1983 and from Sep. 20th-Oct. 3rd 1992.

Most of those seen in recent years probably belong to the Fenno-Scandian breeding population and were displaced by easterly winds. Spring passage birds now occur so infrequently that, even if one establishes a territory, the chances of it attracting a mate are extremely low. The Red-backed Shrike breeds from western Europe to Kazakhstan and winters in eastern tropical and southern Africa, largely from Zambia and Malawi southwards.

## Lesser Grey Shrike                                  *Lanius minor*

Two records. One was found dead at Holt Pound (Alice Holt) on May 16th 1967 and another was at Portsdown Hill on July 15th 1973.

The Lesser Grey Shrike breeds from north-eastern Spain to Kazakhstan and winters in southern Africa. It has decreased markedly in France, Germany and Poland since 1920.

## Great Grey Shrike                                  *Lanius excubitor*

A very scarce winter visitor and passage migrant.

In the last 30 years, between two and 14 Great Grey Shrikes have been recorded each winter. Additionally, up to eight short-staying individuals, presumed to be passage migrants, were seen in October/November or March/April (fig. 77). Most were found in the New Forest, where nine areas of heathland have regularly held birds, but there have also been records from all parts of the county, including coastal marshes and scrub, downland, river valleys and the commons of the north-east.

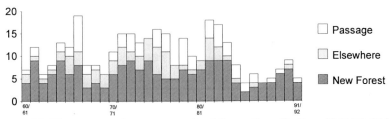

*Figure 77. Wintering and passage totals of Great Grey Shrikes, 1960/61-91/92.*

434

Yearly fluctuations may be due to a combination of several factors, e.g. autumn weather conditions, variations in observer effort and annual differences in breeding performance and summer survival. However, the records suggest an underlying downward trend. This was first noted in the 1970s, with the disappearance of birds from non-heathland sites, e.g. on downland in the north of the county near Whitchurch, Vernham Dean and Beacon Hill, around the lakes at Shepherds Spring and on the coast in the Lymington/Keyhaven area. In the Winchester area, a single bird was present in the Itchen water meadows or on nearby downland during every winter but one from 1970/71-1977/78, but none have been recorded since. On the heaths in the Fleet/Bricksbury area, one was present in every winter from 1972/73-77/78 (with two in 1975/76), but there were no further records until 1981.

There was a slight recovery in the early 1980s, with birds appearing in new areas – Leckford, Ludshott Common, Martin Down, Yateley Common/Blackbushe Airfield and Warren Heath – and returning to Bricksbury Hill, but only at Leckford did one reappear in the following winter. Numbers reached a low point in 1985/86, with only two in the New Forest and none located anywhere else. Even at Woolmer Forest, where one or two had wintered every year since watching began there in the early 1960s, none was seen after 1984/85. There was some sign of recovery in the New Forest by 1990/91, but elsewhere the only recent wintering records were from the Hillside/Greywell area in early 1987, Porton Down in 1989/90 and Ludshott Common in early 1991.

Most records are of lone individuals, with occasionally two or three together. Multiple occurrences tend to be in autumn or spring, indicating passage, e.g. two at Woolmer on Mar. 14th 1971 and Bricksbury Hill on Apr. 4th 1976 and three at Ashley Walk on Nov. 11th 1973 and Nov. 9th 1982.

Great Grey Shrikes normally arrive in October. Birds have been recorded in the first week of that month in four years with the earliest on Oct. 4th at Picket Post in 1972 and Farlington Marshes in 1978. In other years between 1960 and 1992, first dates fell in the period up to Nov. 3rd with the average Oct. 17th. Last dates were between Mar. 28th and Apr. 28th apart from two late birds at Ashley Walk on May 5th 1979 and Bishops Dyke on May 8th 1983. The average departure date was Apr. 11th.

Birds wintering in Britain probably originate from Fenno-Scandia; two ringed in Norway have been recovered in Britain (BWP).

## Woodchat Shrike                    *Lanius senator*

Three records. One was at Widden Bottom (New Forest) on May 19th and 20th 1955, a male was at Farlington Marshes on June 11th and 12th of that year and another was at Dibden Bay on June 14th 1981.

The Woodchat Shrike breeds from Spain and Morocco to Iran and winters in the northern Afrotropics.

## Jay                              *Garrulus glandarius*

A numerous resident and passage migrant.

The Jay is found predominantly in broadleaved woodland, especially oak, but it also occurs in conifer plantations, orchards, parks and large gardens.

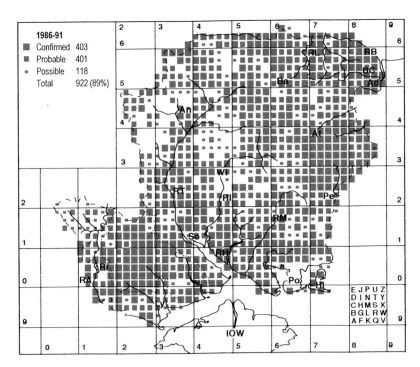

During the Atlas Survey, it was found to be widespread and common in the north-east and south-west, but rather patchily distributed on the sparsely-wooded chalk.

The national population has been fairly stable since the mid-1960s (Marchant *et al* 1990) and there is no evidence to suggest a different picture in Hampshire. Although it is has most probably benefited from a number of factors, including reduced levels of persecution, less damaging pesticides and increased urban tree planting, it has not increased in Hampshire to anything like the same extent as some of the other crows, particularly the Magpie. Using national CBC data for 1989, the New Atlas method indicates a county population of around 8000 pairs and a national total of 160,000 pairs.

The local breeding population is essentially sedentary, 31 out of 35 recoveries of Hampshire-ringed birds being within 9 km of the ringing sites. However, two were at distances greater than 100 km, both involving birds ringed as pulli in the same nest at Old Netley, Southampton on June 4th 1986 and shot at Downton Castle, Shropshire on Dec. 13th 1986 and at Potterspury, Northamptonshire five days later.

In most autumns, there is evidence of immigration into the county, with records of birds in unusual numbers and from unusual locations. In October 1983, an unprecedented influx coincided with the almost complete failure of the acorn crop in England and on the near continent. The movement, which was noted along the length of the English south coast, took place between mid-September and the end of October (John & Roskell 1985). In Hampshire, the peak occurred in early October, when several flocks in excess of 100 were recorded moving west or north-west along the coast with a maximum of *c.* 500 over Weston on Oct. 5th. Large movements recorded in other years include 150 east over Hill Head on Oct. 5th 1975, 114 north-east over Tunworth on Oct. 3rd 1986 and a total of 355 overflying Fleet Pond between Sep. 18th and Nov. 1st 1988 with a peak day total of 37 north on Oct. 13th.

Evidence of return movement was first noted in 1982, when a total of 36 was recorded between Apr. 25th and May 23rd at three coastal and two inland sites, mostly flying in directions between north and south-east. In 1984, following the influx of the previous autumn, there were numerous reports including those of 85 moving east over Calshot Spit on Apr. 26th and 42 at Calshot Reclamation on May 20th.

There is little ringing evidence to shed light on the origins of immigrants. The most distant of four recoveries from outside the county involved a bird ringed at East Grinstead, West Sussex on Aug. 22nd 1983 and shot at Dunley on May 5th 1984.

# Magpie                                            *Pica pica*

A numerous resident.

The Magpie is found in almost any habitat where there are suitable trees for nesting. It is probably most numerous in suburban areas, while it is least common in the intensively-farmed cereal-growing areas on the chalk, where persecution by gamekeepers is probably quite widespread. During the Atlas Survey, there were registrations in 1015 (98%) tetrads, with breeding confirmed in 766, probable in 218 and possible in 31. It was absent from only one inner city tetrad (in Portsmouth) and four on the chalk.

National CBC data indicate that numbers in Britain have expanded steadily since the early 1970s, especially in southern England (Marchant *et al* 1990). Information from Hampshire CBCs suggests an overall rise between 1980 and 1991, with the county index increasing from 100 to 130 in that period. However, numbers may have peaked in the mid-1980s, with the index at 146 in 1985 and

143 in 1987. Several factors could have contributed to the expansion including reduced persecution, restrictions on organochlorine pesticides and increased tree planting in cities and suburbs (Tatner 1982). Using national CBC data for 1989, the New Atlas method indicates a county population of around 20,000 pairs and a British total of 590,000.

Outside the breeding season, feeding and pre-roosting flocks of 20-30 are frequently reported with occasional counts in excess of 40. Roosting numbers generally build up to a maximum in mid-winter. A roost in alders at Fleet Pond, which has been monitored regularly since the late 1970s, has shown a steady increase, which reflects the increasing population in the north-east. Counts first reached three figures in March 1982 and peaked at 277 in December 1987. Elsewhere, the largest number reported has been of 135 in a pre-roost gathering near Highwood Reservoir on Jan. 1st 1989.

The Magpie is a highly sedentary species. This is confirmed by ringing data, which show that 31 out of a total of 35 recoveries of Hampshire-ringed birds were within 9 km of the ringing site and none were outside the county. However, there are occasional reports of high flying flocks, e.g. 21 west over Warsash and five east over Titchfield Haven during a heavy passerine movement on Oct. 20th 1983 and 13 west over Blackbushe Airfield on Oct. 31st 1992.

## Nutcracker                                          *Nucifraga caryocatactes*

Four records. One was at Exbury on Feb. 6th 1886 (K & M). More recently, one was at Fordingbridge from Dec. 6th-28th 1968 (when it was found dead), another was at Hurstbourne Tarrant and Stoke from late September to Nov. 24th 1969 (when it was killed by a cat) and a third was at Copythorne Common from Oct. 22nd-26th 1991.

Nutcrackers occurring in Britain are of the slender-billed race *N.c. macrorhynchus*, which breeds in north-east Russia and Siberia and erupts westwards when high population levels coincide with a failure of its favoured conifer seed crop.

## Chough                                              *Pyrrhocorax pyrrhocorax*

One record. Cohen gives details of one which stayed for two or three weeks at Cheesefoot Head about 1941; it was seen by a shepherd and a farm bailiff and used to stay around the sheep pen.

The Chough formerly bred on cliffs in several southern English counties, including the Isle of Wight, but is now confined in the British Isles to Wales, Ireland and western Scotland.

## Jackdaw                                             *Corvus monedula*

A numerous resident.

The Jackdaw occurs in both agricultural and suburban habitats; it is an adaptable species able to breed wherever there are suitable cavities for nest sites and adequate food supplies. During the Atlas Survey, the main gaps in its distribution proved to be along the coast, especially in Portsmouth and around the mouth of Southampton Water between Gosport and the Beaulieu River. This

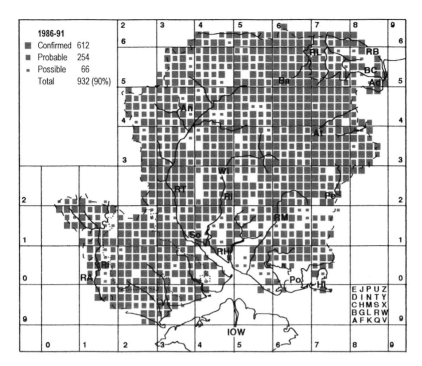

| 1986-91 | | |
|---|---|---|
| ■ | Confirmed | 612 |
| ▪ | Probable | 254 |
| ▫ | Possible | 66 |
| | Total | 932 (90%) |

probably reflects a shortage of food in urban areas and the relative lack of suitable trees elsewhere.

National CBC data show that there has been a general increase through the 1970s and 1980s although the upward trend was less in the second half of the period (Marchant *et al* 1990). There is insufficient evidence to confirm a similar pattern locally. Using national CBC data for 1989, the New Atlas method indicates a county population of around 9000 pairs. However, this is thought to underestimate numbers in parkland, well-wooded farmland and suburbia, and so a range of 12,000-15,000 pairs is perhaps more appropriate. The British total was put at 390,000 pairs (New Atlas).

Ringing data suggest that Hampshire birds only undertake local movements; of 50 recoveries, 42 were within 9 km of the ringing site and only one was outside the county. Diurnal movement, usually in a south-westerly direction, is noted in most years between mid-September and late November at both coastal and inland sites. Numbers are generally low, involving day totals of less than 50, but in 1983, 1820 were counted at four inland and two coastal sites between Oct. 17th and 23rd with peaks of 628 west at Warsash and 524 west at Sinah Common on Oct. 20th. High counts in other years include 223 west in three hours at South Hayling on Oct. 23rd 1982 and 200 west at Sinah Common on Oct. 27th 1984. The possible origin of these birds is suggested by the recovery of one ringed as a pullus at Canterbury, Kent in May 1935 and found dead at Stockbridge on Feb. 6th 1936. Return passage in spring is less noticeable, e.g. 93 flew over Fleet Pond between Mar. 9th and May 11th 1989 with a maximum of 27 north on Mar. 21st.

In winter, large gatherings occur on stubble and pasture and at rubbish tips. Such flocks sometimes exceed 1000 and occasionally much higher numbers are recorded, e.g. 5000 were feeding at Crondall on Nov. 30th 1981, 3500 at Caesar's Belt on Jan. 2nd 1987 and 3000 at Pittleworth Farm (Mottisfont) on Mar. 15th 1990. Roost flight lines are not well recorded but there is a daily cross-Solent movement outside the breeding season (*cf.* Rook), e.g. 1300 flew south over Lepe to the Isle of Wight at dusk on Jan. 2nd 1989. Few roosts have been counted, but that at Park Corner Farm (Odiham) held at least 10,000 birds in February 1982.

# Rook                                                    *Corvus frugilegus*

A numerous resident and probable winter visitor.

K & M described the Rook as "a common resident everywhere", but today, as the Atlas Map shows, there are some substantial areas where it is scarce or absent. It has probably never been common in the New Forest, where the mix of woodland and heath is unsuitable (see below). Comparison of the Atlas records with those from a survey carried out in 1975/76 shows that they have vacated much of the broad coastal strip from Hayling Island to Southampton and several tetrads in the extreme north-east. They are also relatively scarce in the north central and north-west sections of the county.

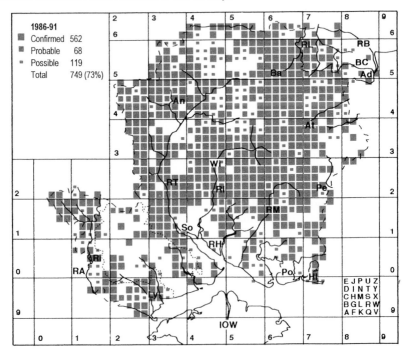

The first national Rook Investigation was carried out in 1944-46, when the number of nests in Britain was estimated to be 1,413,000 and the trend was upwards. The growth continued until the late 1950s (Parslow 1973), but a second survey in 1975-76 estimated only 800,000 nests, a 43% fall relative to 1944-46 (Sage & Vernon 1978). In 1980, a further survey based on randomly selected 10 km squares confirmed that the trend was still downwards in south central and south-east England although substantial increases had taken place in other parts of Britain. The estimated national population had increased slightly to 850,000-860,000 pairs (Sage & Whittington 1985).

The available data for Hampshire mirror the national and regional trends (table 70). The population fell by 40% between 1944/46 and 1975/76 and was still declining in 1980, but there is only limited information to show how it has fared since. A local survey of an area around Broughton showed that between 1985 and 1991 the number of rookeries increased from 13 to 19 and the number of nests by 40% (N R Fuggles-Couchman *in litt*). Based on the 1975 and 1980 survey results, and allowing for some recovery over the past decade, the county population is estimated at 17,000-22,000 pairs.

| Year* | Occupied nests | Number of rookeries | Average nests per rookery | Reference |
|---|---|---|---|---|
| 1944/46 | 32,711 | 550-820 | 40-60 | Fisher 1947 |
| 1975/76 | 19,363 | 832 | 23 | Sage & Vernon 1978 |
| 1975/76 | 19,164 | 826 | 23 | Sage & Vernon 1978 |
| 1975+ | 4614 | 201 | 23 | |
| 1980+ | 4422 | 183 | 24 | Sage & Whittington 1985 |

\* Surveys above line refer to pre-1974 boundary; those below to post-1974 boundary.
+ 1980 sample survey of eight 10 km squares and comparable 1975 data.

*Table 70. Results of surveys of Rooks in Hampshire, 1944-80.*

The decrease in the Rook population between 1944-45 and 1975-76 was apparently accompanied by a corresponding reduction in the average size of rookeries (table 70), although because of the way in which the 1944/46 survey was carried out, the number of rookeries at that time is uncertain. At some sites this trend has continued. For example, a 1991 sample survey of 25 Hampshire sites where large rookeries were recorded in 1975 and 1980 showed that many were greatly reduced (P J Puckering *in litt*). One at Enham Alamein, which held 310 nests in 1975 and 345 in 1980, held only 133, while another at Phoenix Green had declined from 160 nests in 1975 to only 50. However, since new colonies are being established, some of which contain quite high numbers of nests, there is insufficient evidence to establish any overall trend.

The reasons for the changes in total population, distribution and size of rookeries are not clear but are almost certainly linked to changes in farming practices, particularly their impact on the size and quality of available feeding areas. Rooks seem to do best in areas of mixed farming where food is available throughout the year (Brenchley 1984). In Hampshire, historical declines may have been caused by a switch from grassland to cereal farming, in which case the more recent increase in sheep farming may result in an upturn in the population. Other factors such as increased use of pesticides, greater mechanisation and reduction in spring tillage may all have contributed to the decline. The loss of trees, caused for example by Dutch elm disease, is not thought to have had a major impact (Tapper 1981; Sage & Whittington 1985), but locally, tree loss can lead to rookeries being abandoned or force birds to move to less ideal nest sites. In the Froxfield area, storm damage resulted in birds nesting in hedgerows in 1982 and low hazel coppice in 1992. At Porton Down, there is a well-established rookery in hawthorn scrub. Nests have also been recorded occasionally on electricity pylons.

Outside the breeding season, birds from several rookeries form communal roosts which are often shared with Jackdaws and Carrion Crows. Some traditional roosts are very large, e.g. one at Park Corner Farm (Odiham) held up to 15,000 in autumn 1981 and another at Belmore House (Upham) held around 12,000 in December 1971. Groups of 50-500 have been watched leaving the coast between Keyhaven and Lepe at dusk, apparently to roost on the Isle of Wight (cf. Jackdaw). Pre-roost and feeding flocks of up to 2000 are also seen, the latter often at rubbish tips such as Bramshill and Paulsgrove.

It is generally accepted that our winter population is increased by immigrants from north-western Europe, although firm evidence is lacking. In autumn, small numbers are recorded moving between late September and early December, e.g. 128 south over Titchfield Haven between Sep. 29th and Nov. 22nd 1982. At Park Corner Farm, 275 moving high to the west on Dec. 13th 1981 were possibly cold weather immigrants. Occasional groups of birds have been observed leaving the coast but no Hampshire-ringed bird has been recovered abroad and no continental ring has been controlled in the county. Most recoveries of Hampshire-ringed Rooks have been within 9 km of the ringing site and all were under 100 km distant.

## Carrion Crow                                      *Corvus corone*

A numerous resident.

The Carrion Crow breeds wherever suitable nesting trees are available in woodland, farmland and built-up areas. K & M described it as "sparingly distributed in all districts". By 1972, it was common except in heavily keepered areas on the chalk to the north of Winchester (C & T). The Atlas Survey has indicated that it remains rather thinly spread in the centre and north-west of the county. While some of the gaps on the Atlas Map may be due to under-recording, it is probable that persecution by farmers and gamekeepers continues to depress numbers in those areas (cf. Magpie).

The progressive reduction in persecution has helped the national population to increase dramatically. Between 1962 and 1988, there was a threefold increase in both the woodland and farmland national CBC indices (Marchant *et al* 1990). Using national CBC data for 1989, the New Atlas method indicates a Hampshire population of around 18,000 pairs. However, given the patchy distribution in the north-west, this probably overestimates the density on farmland and a figure of 15,000 pairs is considered more appropriate. The British total was estimated to be 790,000 pairs (New Atlas).

Outside the breeding season, Carrion Crows form communal roosts. The largest on record is of 700 in a beech wood at Old Winchester Hill on Aug. 31st 1972; the same roost held 500+ on July 16th 1973. Sizeable flocks are also recorded in pre-roost gatherings and scavenging at rubbish tips or along the shoreline. There were 300+ feeding at Lane End Down on Jan. 19th 1975, 191

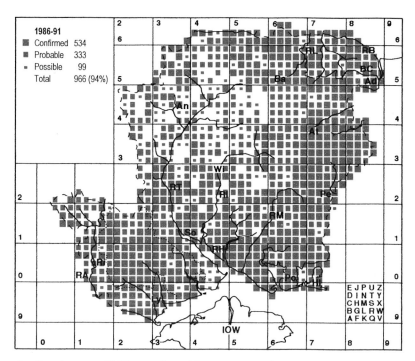

| | | 2 | 3 | 4 | 5 | 6 | 7 | 8 | 9 | |
|---|---|---|---|---|---|---|---|---|---|---|

**1986-91**
■ Confirmed 534
■ Probable 333
▪ Possible 99
  Total 966 (94%)

```
E J P U Z
D I N T Y
C H M S X
B G L R W
A F K Q V
```

IOW

on the foreshore at Chilling at low tide on Nov. 13th 1990 and 220 at Selborne on Dec. 26th 1990. Flocks of 100-145 have been recorded at ten other sites, including the Weston Shore/Newtown Rubbish Tip area, where three-figure counts were made in four winters between 1985/86 and 1989/90 with a maximum of 130 on Oct. 31st 1989.

There is little evidence to indicate that local birds disperse very far. One ringed as a pullus at Fleet Sewage Farm on May 15th 1979 was controlled at Sway on July 15th 1979. Three other recoveries involved movements of 13-24 km but the remaining five did not exceed 6 km. Sight records suggesting passage in spring or autumn are few. At Sinah Common, 58 were counted moving west between Oct. 6th and 29th 1983, a period of exceptionally heavy crow movement (*cf.* Jay and Jackdaw). 25 moved east at Hayling Bay on Apr. 26th 1984, 49 north-west over Camp Farm (Aldershot) on Oct. 14th 1984 and 37 west and north-west over Fleet Pond on Oct. 12th 1991.

The Hooded Crow *C.c. corone* is a rare winter visitor to the county, which has occurred less frequently in recent years. K & M described it as "of regular and fairly common occurrence on all our coasts but only sparingly and occasionally in some inland localities". Since 1951, there have been records in 22 years, with a total of 38 recorded, 11 in 1951-60, eight in 1961-70, 15 in 1971-80 and four in 1981-92. All records were of single birds on dates between Oct. 17th and May 26th. The cumulative monthly totals for 1951-92 are shown below.

| Oct | Nov | Dec | Jan | Feb | Mar | Apr | May |
|-----|-----|-----|-----|-----|-----|-----|-----|
| 4 | 4 | 3 | 8 | 9 | 12 | 6 | 1 |

Although 19 out of 38 were at localities at or adjacent to the coast, records have been for all parts of the county, with rubbish tips being especially favoured. Most were seen on one date only but stays of a month or longer have occurred.

## Raven                                             *Corvus corax*

A rare visitor which formerly bred.

K & M described the decline of the Raven as a breeding species in Hampshire. They listed the New Forest, Old Basing, Wickham, Tangley Clump (Hurstbourne Tarrant), Whitsbury, Longwood Warren, Avington and South Tidworth as 19th century nesting sites, so evidently Ravens were quite widespread 150 years ago. Persecution was cited as the main cause of the decline, with the last recorded nesting in 1887. However, the progressive switch from sheep husbandry to cereal cultivation must also have contributed (D E Glue *in litt*).

There are few records for the first half of this century, when observer coverage was poor. Since 1951, there have been records in 22 years, with a total of 33 recorded, 11 in 1951-60, six in 1961-70, eight in 1971-80 and eight in 1981-92. Apart from one at Wherwell on July 22nd 1956, all records have been from the coast, New Forest, Avon valley and Damerham/Martin area. Since 1962, only single birds have been seen at any one time, apart from two in the north-west of the New Forest between Jan. 10th and late March 1971. The only other long staying individuals were at Godshill Wood from Aug. 26th-Sep. 13th 1967 and Martin Down from July 26th-Aug. 7th 1981. The most recent record was of one flying west over Pilley on Sep. 10th 1992. The cumulative monthly totals for 1951-92 are shown below.

| Jan | Feb | Mar | Apr | May | Jun | Jul | Aug | Sep | Oct | Nov | Dec |
|-----|-----|-----|-----|-----|-----|-----|-----|-----|-----|-----|-----|
| 2   | 5   | 6   | 6   | 4   | 0   | 4   | 5   | 2   | 1   | 0   | 4   |

Most Hampshire records probably involve individuals dispersing from breeding sites in Dorset and the Isle of Wight.

## Starling                                         *Sturnus vulgaris*

An abundant resident, passage migrant and winter visitor.

The Starling is a familiar bird around our homes and gardens and occurs in many other habitats ranging from farmland to the inner cities. Originally a tree hole nester, it now breeds in almost any suitable cavity, particularly in recesses and crevices in buildings and other man-made sites. It is absent only where such sites are not available; for example on open heathland or saltmarsh. During the Atlas Survey, it was encountered in 1005 (97%) tetrads, with breeding confirmed in 926, probable in 59 and possible in 20.

For such an adaptable and opportunistic species, it is surprising to find that the national CBC indices for woodland and farmland have both declined markedly since peaking in the mid-1960s (Marchant *et al* 1990). This trend may be linked to the use of pesticides and other changes in farming practices (O'Connor & Shrubb 1986). These have reduced the availability of grassland invertebrates which are the main food supply during the breeding season. CBCs do not monitor urban and suburban habitats, however, so the overall population trend is uncertain. Using national CBC data for 1989, the New Atlas method indicates a county population of around 25,000 pairs. This appears to considerably underestimate the densities in suburban and urban areas, and therefore an upper limit of 50,000 pairs is considered appropriate. The national total was estimated at 1.1 million pairs (New Atlas).

Post-breeding roosts, initially consisting largely of juveniles, build up from late May onwards. Gatherings of up to 5000 have been noted in a variety of locations (particularly reed beds), while larger counts have included 29,000 at Cheesefoot Head in July 1972, 20,000 at Fleet Pond in July and August 1957 and 14,000 there in July 1971. Numbers at the latter site have been much reduced in recent years, with no count exceeding 4000 since 1974.

Conspicuous diurnal movement is noted in most years between late September and late November at both coastal and inland localities. The heaviest passage usually occurs on frosty mornings in late October and the first half of November. Examples include 6753 west over Hayling Island between Oct. 16th and Nov. 13th 1982 with a peak count of 1201 in two hours on Oct. 25th, 14,408 mostly moving west over Tunworth between Sep. 30th and Nov. 20th 1986 with a maximum day total of 8825 west in three hours on Nov. 3rd (*cf.* Redwing) and 3707 west at Sinah Common in five and a half hours on Oct. 31st 1992. At Fleet Pond, regular daily watching in 1987-92 produced a total of 36,599 between Sep. 22nd and Nov. 30th. Annual totals varied between 1307 and 13,271 (in 1990); high counts included 4437 west on Nov. 2nd 1990 and 3400 west on Oct. 27th 1992.

In winter, large roosts form, most frequently in urban areas. Particularly high numbers have been reported in the Portsmouth area. Until 1966, a roost numbering several hundreds of thousands was at Fort Brockhurst (Gosport), but this was abandoned following scrub clearance. Later records include possibly 100,000 at three roosts in the city in January and February 1984, 40,000 at Portsmouth Golf Course in November 1985 and 60,000 in Portsmouth City Park in February 1987. Similar gatherings reported elsewhere include "hundreds of thousands" at Dean (Winchester) in late 1971 and 110,000 at Cheesefoot Head in November 1973. Feeding flocks of up to 10,000 are occasionally reported but the most astounding record is of an estimated 1 million at East Worldham on Dec. 9th 1956, which flew off west at 1530 hrs to an unknown roost site. The method by which the observer arrived at this figure is described in Cohen.

Hard weather may result in considerable movement, especially along the coast. Large day totals recorded include 20,000 east at Gilkicker Point on Dec. 31st 1961, 145,000 west there the next day and 40,000 west over Farlington Marshes in one hour on Dec. 9th 1967. Despite the increased frequency of hard winters since the late 1970s, less movement has been detected; 22,000 west at Titchfield Haven in three hours on Dec. 31st 1978 has been the only total to reach five figures.

Spring passage is indicated in March and early April by light diurnal movements and increases at roosts. At West Park (Damerham), a roost which held "tens of thousands" during the winter of 1956/57 increased to "hundreds of thousands" on Mar. 7th 1957 but most had moved on within a week. Another roost at North Farnborough Cemetery peaked at 10,000 on Mar. 30th 1986.

An extensive series of ringing recoveries indicates that migrants originate from as far afield as Kazakhstan, Russia, Lithuania, Latvia, Poland, Finland and

Sweden as well as from the near continent. There are two interesting records of birds ringed in Hampshire in winter and recovered in the following winter in Greece and Italy, which shows that Starlings can vary their migration route and wintering area from year to year.

## Rose-coloured Starling                        *Sturnus roseus*

Seven records. Of eight recorded by K & M, two were within the present day county boundary – at Fordingbridge in July 1876 and Greatham on May 4th 1896. More recently, single adults were at Rockbourne on June 27th 1954, Pilmore Gate Heath (New Forest) on Mar. 14th 1959, in a Fleet garden from June 12th-23rd 1968 and at Fareham on Apr. 24th 1972. Finally, a first-year regularly visited a garden in Portsmouth between Mar. 26th and Apr. 24th 1985.

The Rose-coloured Starling breeds from south-eastern Europe to Kazakhstan and Iran and winters largely in the Indian sub-continent. British records are accounted for by westward eruptive movements in summer.

## House Sparrow                        *Passer domesticus*

An abundant resident.

The House Sparrow is found wherever people are living, whether in city centres or isolated farms. It nests in suitable cavities in buildings and feeds and roosts communally in parks and gardens. During the Atlas Survey, there were registrations in 972 (94%) tetrads, with breeding confirmed in 856, probable in 98 and possible in 18. It was absent only from parts of the New Forest, some sparsely populated areas on the chalk and coastal tetrads containing saltmarsh.

The Common Bird Census, which is not ideally suited to monitoring urban and semi-colonial species like the House Sparrow, and the BTO Garden Bird Survey suggest that the national population may be falling (Marchant *et al* 1990). Changing agricultural practices, such as increased use of insecticides and herbicides and the earlier removal of stubble for autumn sowing of cereals, might be reducing feeding opportunities, particularly in late summer and autumn. Even so, the Hampshire population is clearly large, although there is no information about numbers or population trends in the county. Using national CBC data for 1989, the New Atlas method indicates a population of around 15,000 pairs. However, this clearly underestimates numbers in built-up areas; the true figure may be in the range 40,000-60,000 pairs. The British population in 1988-91 was estimated at 2.6-4.6 million pairs (New Atlas).

From late summer, some House Sparrows leave their breeding sites in search of food. Post-breeding flocks can be found feeding in ripening cereal crops, in stubble fields, around farmyards or on saltmarsh. Flocks of a few hundred are occasionally recorded, e.g. 500 were at West Hayling between July and September 1984 and 450 were at Crow in October of the same year. Winter feeding flocks are smaller, with 300+ in kale at Dogmersfield on Jan. 18th 1976 the largest recorded in recent years.

The Hampshire population is essentially sedentary. There have been 136 recoveries of Hampshire-ringed birds and all but four have been within 10 km of the ringing site. Some limited autumn dispersal does take place, however. There have been two recoveries in Hampshire of birds ringed outside the county: one ringed at Maidstone, Kent on Aug. 24th 1961 and recovered at Fareham on Oct. 14th 1961 and another ringed at Kidlington, Oxfordshire on Oct. 23rd 1966 and recovered at Southampton on Nov. 17th 1966. There is also limited evidence of diurnal movement in October and November from coastal sites, e.g. 56 flew west at Titchfield Haven between Oct. 6th and 22nd 1981. No movement has been detected at inland sites.

# Tree Sparrow                                *Passer montanus*

A scarce resident; passage migrant and winter visitor in variable numbers. A considerable decline has occurred in the last 15 years.

The Tree Sparrow is one of the county's most enigmatic species. The resident population is now small and elusive, even though there is no shortage of apparently suitable habitat. As a winter visitor, it is subject to periodic fluctuations with its status ranging from common in peak years to rare in others.

In Hampshire, Tree Sparrows nest singly or in small colonies, usually in holes provided by mature hedgerows and scattered trees (such as oak, elm and willow) on parkland, farmland and wasteland. They also use nest boxes, and have bred in abandoned buildings and machinery at gravel pits.

K & M wrote: "as a breeding species, it is distinctly rare, and even unknown in many parts (of the county)". This was evidently the position throughout the first half of the century; Cohen, reviewing the period 1905-57, described reports as "extremely sparse and mostly of one or two birds". He knew of only two regular breeding haunts in the 1950s – at Fyfield and Purbrook. The Tree Sparrow was undoubtedly scarce during this period, although many suitable areas in the north of the county were never visited by birdwatchers.

From 1959 onwards, there was a remarkable change in status. Large autumn movements and winter flocks began to be recorded, although numbers varied greatly from year to year. The breeding population also increased, particularly in the north-east, where the species became quite widespread.

Since the mid-1980s, the position has reversed, with few recorded in autumn and winter, and a marked reduction in breeding numbers. In 1976, there was a total of at least 20 pairs breeding at Eversley, Frimley, Ash Vale and North Camp Gravel Pits, Bramshill, Elvetham Park and Dogmersfield Park. Ten years later, at the start of the Atlas Survey, all these sites had been abandoned. In 1982, when the decline was probably already underway, 25 pairs were located in the Odiham/Crondall/Bentley area including small colonies of five to six pairs at Lower Swanthorpe Farm and Coldrey Park. By 1991, breeding was only known at one site in that area. The desertion of apparently thriving colonies is characteristic of the species.

The Atlas Map incorporates all the known breeding records for 1951-85. The population peaked between the late 1960s and mid-1970s, and probably exceeded 500 pairs during that period. The distribution shown for 1986-91 exaggerates the current position, because the species has disappeared from several tetrads where it was found early in the Atlas fieldwork. The county population may now not exceed 50 pairs. The Tree Sparrow's fluctuating fortunes in Hampshire have mirrored the national trend. Summers-Smith (1989), reviewing regional bird literature, estimated that the British population fell from

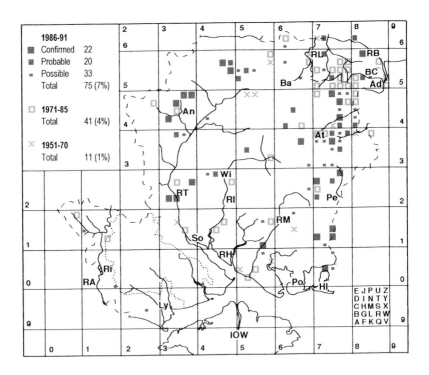

over 850,000 pairs in the mid-1960s to 285,000 in 1985. By 1989, it had declined further to an estimated 110,000 pairs (New Atlas).

Various reasons have been put forward for the fluctuations in the British population. Summers-Smith (1989) concluded that the expansion in the 1960s was the result of autumn immigration following population expansion in continental Europe. Such influxes were much reduced in the 1980s, but the recent decline is shared with other farmland seed-eating species, such as the Linnet and Corn Bunting. Thus the widespread use of herbicides for weed control, leading to a reduction in supplies of the favoured fat hen, and the lack of winter stubble may be implicated. The decline in Hampshire may have been particularly marked because the species is on the south-western edge of its British range. Locally, the felling of trees used by some colonies may have had an effect.

The first major autumn influx to Hampshire was in 1959. The largest movement recorded was of 125 flying WNW at Weston Shore on Nov. 1st; subsequently, wintering flocks were located at 11 sites with a maximum of 500 at Basingstoke Old Sewage Farm in March 1960. An even larger influx occurred in 1961. Recorded movements totalled 2556 between Oct. 14th and Nov. 5th; most were moving west but the largest day total was of 1000 east at Gilkicker Point on Oct. 14th. Wintering flocks totalled 2600 at ten sites, mostly in kale with fat hen, with a maximum of 750 at Titchfield Haven in February 1962. The pattern of autumn influxes followed by wintering flocks continued through the 1960s although in reduced numbers. Day totals of birds moving did not exceed

65 while the largest of only four three-figure flocks recorded was of 450 at Winchester Sewage Farm in February 1965.

Analysis of the records for the 22 "winters" from 1970/71-91/92 (table 71) shows that movement peaks in mid-October and is more prominent at the coast than inland. Winter numbers are relatively constant from December-February but dispersal takes place rapidly from mid-March onwards.

| | Aug | Sep | Oct | Nov | Dec | Jan | Feb | Mar | Apr | May |
|---|---|---|---|---|---|---|---|---|---|---|
| Flocks | 80 | 45 | 1960 | 2130 | 5276 | 5228 | 4953 | 1632 | 628 | 65 |
| Movements | 0 | 11 | 2281 | 25 | 7 | 0 | 0 | 0 | 0 | 0 |

*Table 71. Cumulative monthly totals of flocks and movements of Tree Sparrows, 1970/71-91/92.*

During this period, both autumn and winter numbers continued to fluctuate, but there was an underlying downward trend (fig. 78). In 1976, the peak year for movement, most were recorded at Hill Head, where 290 flew east on Oct. 10th, 400 west on Oct. 16th and 158 east on Oct. 25th. At Fleet Pond, a total of 315 (mostly moving west) was recorded between Oct. 9th and Nov. 4th. This movement presaged unprecedented winter numbers, with flocks of 100 or more at 19 sites, including maxima of 500 at Marsh Court in November, 900 at Tundry Pond in December and 400 at Easton in February 1977. Since then, autumn movement has been light except in 1983, when 551 flying west at Warsash on Oct. 22nd accounted for the relatively high number recorded in that year. The following winter was the last in which three-figure flocks were recorded, with up to 180 at Hook Rubbish Tip and 120 at Timsbury during January 1984. The number wintering has now dropped to a very low level.

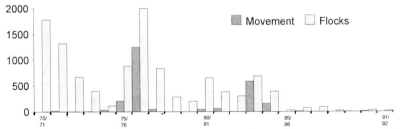

*Figure 78. Autumn movements and winter flocks of Tree Sparrows, 1970/71-91/92.*

The origins of winter immigrants remain uncertain. There have been seven recoveries of birds ringed in Hampshire during the 1976/77 winter, in Berkshire (2), Buckinghamshire, Northamptonshire, Kent, Sussex and Wiltshire. Five were found during the following breeding season, which suggests that at least some of the visitors have fairly local origins. It remains to be established that continental birds do reach Hampshire.

# Chaffinch                                     *Fringilla coelebs*

An abundant resident, passage migrant and winter visitor.

The Chaffinch occurs wherever there are trees and bushes, especially in broadleaved woodland, hedgerows, heathland scrub, urban parks and gardens. It

449

is also found, albeit at lower densities, in conifers. During the Atlas Survey, there were registrations in 1016 (99%) tetrads, with breeding confirmed in 806, probable in 200 and possible in ten; it was absent only from a few along the coast which contained saltmarsh.

Despite its vulnerability to agricultural chemicals, the national population has grown slowly since the start of CBC indexing in 1962 (Marchant *et al* 1990). This may reflect a recovery from an earlier fall thought to have been caused by the widespread use of organochlorine insecticides as seed dressings. In Hampshire, CBC data indicate that the population has been stable through the 1980s. Using national CBC data for 1989, the New Atlas method indicates a county total of around 130,000 pairs. However, this considerably underestimates numbers in suburban areas and so the true figure is probably at least 150,000 pairs. The British population was estimated at 5.4 million pairs in 1989 (New Atlas).

In autumn, there is usually a conspicuous diurnal movement over the county, largely in directions between south-west and north-west, which peaks between the second week of October and early November. The largest day totals have been recorded on the coast at Titchfield Haven: 1560 west in two hours on Oct. 11th 1980 and 683 west on Oct. 17th 1983. However, systematic watching at inland sites has shown that the movement takes place over a broad front. At Tunworth, a total of 2096 flew over in 60 hours observation between Sep. 26th and Nov. 20th 1986 with a peak of 305 moving mostly west in two hours on Oct. 31st. At Fleet Pond, regular daily watching from 1987-92 produced a total of 12,791 mostly moving in directions between south-west and north-west on dates between Sep. 11th and Nov. 30th. Annual totals varied between 1441 and 2849 (in 1990) with peak day totals of 410 west and south-west on Nov. 1st 1990 and 384 south-west on Oct. 28th 1992.

During the winter months, small flocks are widespread in a variety of habitats where suitable seeds are available. Larger gatherings of several hundred are especially attracted to beech woods when there is a good mast crop. Those to reach four figures were of 2000 at Red Rice (Andover) on Mar. 13th 1977, 1000 at Houghton on Dec. 24th 1989, 1600 at Long Beech (New Forest) on Jan. 20th 1991 and 1000+ at Denny Wood two days later. Apart from the Houghton flock, which was in weedy fields, all were under beeches. This and other finch species are rarely noted in cold weather movements although a total of 12,000 flew east at Gilkicker Point on Dec. 31st 1961 and Jan. 1st 1962.

Analysis of the records for the 22 "winters" from 1970/71-91/92 illustrates the pattern described above (table 72).

|  | Jul | Aug | Sep | Oct | Nov | Dec | Jan | Feb | Mar | Apr |
|---|---|---|---|---|---|---|---|---|---|---|
| Flocks | 100 | 150 | 980 | 2650 | 8615 | 15935 | 21170 | 16480 | 10230 | 1410 |
| Movements | 0 | 0 | 996 | 17374 | 5725 | 19 | 0 | 0 | 35 | 0 |

*Table 72. Cumulative monthly totals of flocks of 100+ and movements of Chaffinches, 1970/71-91/92.*

The recovery of six foreign-ringed birds in Hampshire between November and March confirms that some wintering birds are of continental origin. Four were ringed in Belgium and one in the Netherlands in autumn, and the other was ringed in Denmark the previous winter. There have also been 15 foreign recoveries of birds ringed in Hampshire in winter: one each in western Germany, the Netherlands and Sweden in spring, two in Sweden and one in eastern Germany in summer, five in Belgium and one each in Norway and Sweden in autumn, and two in Belgium in winter. Movements within Britain have been of less than 100 km, apart from one found in Cornwall two winters later.

# Brambling                                   *Fringilla montifringilla*

A moderately common winter visitor and passage migrant.

Bramblings occur in variable numbers each winter. In the 22 winters from 1970/71-91/92, recorded totals varied between 50 (in 1976/77) and 2400 (in 1975/76). The trend appears to be downwards. In the first half of that period, six totals were in excess of 1000 and the average was 950 per winter. In the second half, only two totals reached four figures and the average was 535, despite the increased number of birdwatchers. The winter distribution in Europe is primarily dictated by the availability of beech mast (Winter Atlas). In Hampshire, there has been some correlation of good and bad mast years with high and low Brambling numbers but most large flocks have been found in fields containing stubble or weeds. In hard weather, small groups of up to 20 may become widespread in gardens where food is provided. The largest gathering reported was attracted to kale stubble and maize put out for cattle at Winchfield in early 1976; this peaked at 1250 on Feb. 24th. Between 1959 and 1992, there were 22 reports of flocks of 200 or more, including 500 near Preshaw on Nov. 19th 1970, 600 at Wonston on Mar. 30th 1974, 400+ at Gritnam Inclosure and 750+ at Faccombe on Nov. 30th 1991. Only eight of these have been since 1980, despite the greatly increased observer activity. As with other finches, the increased use of herbicides and the autumn ploughing of stubbles may account for the apparent decline of the Brambling in Hampshire.

The first are usually seen in the second week of October, although the earliest ever was one flying south over Fleet Pond on Sep. 29th 1988. In other years during 1970-91, earliest dates were between Oct. 2nd and 30th with the average Oct. 9th. Diurnal movements are usually light and peak in late October or early November. At the coast, the maximum day total recorded was of 75 NNW over Weston Shore on Nov. 1st 1959, but in other years counts have rarely exceeded 20. Inland, regular watching at Fleet Pond during 1987-92 produced a total of 510 moving in directions between south-west and north-west on dates between Sep. 29th and Dec. 14th. Annual totals did not exceed 48 except in 1992, when 383 were recorded with peaks of 185 west on Oct. 27th and 70 west on Dec. 14th. The only other comparable movement recorded was at Tunworth, where a total of 113 was noted between Oct. 3rd and Nov. 17th 1986 with a peak of 30 on Nov. 2nd.

Only a handful have been involved in recent cold weather movements but in the severe winters of the early 1960s there were three records of day totals in the range 27-50.

Numbers tend to peak late in the winter, possibly being swelled by further arrivals from the continent or returning migrants. Light diurnal movements are sometimes noted in spring, e.g. 23 north-west over Enham Alamein on Apr. 1st 1976, but on Mar. 4th 1965 there was an unprecedented passage of 745 east at Gilkicker Point. Departures are normally complete by mid-April. During 1971-92, latest dates were between Mar. 27th and Apr. 27th with the average Apr. 18th, apart from a male which remained at Mark Ash Wood (New Forest) until May 13th in 1983 and another male which summered in 1978. The latter had been ringed in a Totton garden in early April and was last seen on May 2nd. However, a ringed Brambling was again present on July 17th in close association with a female Chaffinch. The next day three juveniles were seen which showed characteristics of both species and may well have been hybrids.

Analysis of the records for the 22 "winters" from 1970/71-91/92 illustrates the pattern described above (table 73).

| | Sep | Oct | Nov | Dec | Jan | Feb | Mar | Apr |
|---|---|---|---|---|---|---|---|---|
| Flocks | 0 | 142 | 1981 | 2267 | 4826 | 5304 | 6341 | 1014 |
| Movements | 1 | 370 | 263 | 10 | 14 | 4 | 8 | 59 |

*Table 73. Cumulative monthly totals of flocks of 10+ and movements of Bramblings, 1970/71-91/92.*

Bramblings wintering in Britain originate from Fenno-Scandia and further east to the Urals (Winter Atlas). There has been one Hampshire recovery of a Norwegian-ringed bird: one ringed as a juvenile at Kaldholelva, on the western seaboard, on Sep. 8th 1968 and controlled at Swanmore, 1280 km SSW, on Jan. 2nd 1970. Other recoveries, all in subsequent winters, involved movements to or from western Germany and the Netherlands (2 each) and Belgium (1), which illustrates the fact that birds seldom spend successive winters in the same place. Two ringed in Hampshire in winter were recovered in spring in Marlborough, Wiltshire and High Wycombe, Buckinghamshire, when they were presumably on their return migration.

## Serin                                                  *Serinus serinus*

A rare visitor. The first for Britain was procured at Eastney in April 1852 but there were no further records in the county until 1961, when one was at Farlington Marshes on Nov. 4th. Since then, there have been ten records, as follows:

1965:     1 male and 2 females, Culverley Farm (Beaulieu), Mar. 7th;
1967:     1, Farlington Marshes, Oct. 30th;

| 1973: | 3 flying south, Fleet Pond, Sep. 17th; |
|---|---|
| 1974: | 1 male, Old Winchester Hill, Sep. 16th; |
| 1977: | 1 male, Beaulieu Abbey, Mar. 18th and 19th; |
| 1985: | 1 singing male, Twyford, May 20th; |
| | 1 flying south, calling, Tadley, July 9th; |
| 1987: | 1 male flying south-west, Farlington Marshes, May 9th; |
| 1988: | 1 male, Needs Ore Point, Apr. 6th; |
| 1991: | 1 singing male, Keyhaven, May 2nd, left east. |

The Serin is a summer visitor to its nearest breeding grounds in northern France and the Low Countries. It regularly occurs in spring in neighbouring south coast counties and so it is surprising that it has not been recorded more frequently in Hampshire. Several other claims have, however, not been accepted by the *BBRC* or the *HOSRP*.

# Greenfinch                            *Carduelis chloris*

A numerous resident, passage migrant and winter visitor.

The Greenfinch breeds in scrub, farmland hedgerows, orchards and woodland edge but reaches its highest densities in gardens, parks and churchyards in villages and towns. It is particularly attracted to sites with ornamental evergreens and may outnumber the Chaffinch in such habitat. During the Atlas Survey, it was found in 991 (96%) tetrads, with breeding confirmed in 559, probable in 402 and possible in 30. The only significant area from which the species is absent is the ancient and ornamental woodland and surrounding open heathland of the New Forest. Greenfinches have a varied diet which, in woodland, includes weed seeds and the fruits of various trees and bushes. Their absence from parts of the New Forest has been attributed to the lack of such food in the limited shrub layer and poor ground flora resulting from intense grazing by livestock (Glue 1973, Irvine 1977).

The national population has been remarkably steady for the past two decades (Marchant *et al* 1990). This is despite various negative influences on breeding success and winter survival, such as reduced stubble and fallows and the greater use of herbicides, which has reduced the availability of weed seeds and caused noticeable reductions in numbers of some other finches. One explanation for their resilience may be that they have learned to exploit the food provided at garden bird tables. In the hard winter of 1963, Newton (1972) found that several hundred, trapped in roosts near Oxford, had been feeding almost exclusively on peanuts. Using national CBC data for 1989, the New Atlas method indicates a county population of 15,000 pairs. However, this includes only 1000 pairs in habitats other than farmland and woodland. Since they undoubtedly reach their highest density in suburban habitats, a range of 20,000-30,000 pairs seems appropriate. The national population was estimated at 530,000 pairs (New Atlas).

Autumn movements, which peak in the second half of October, are mostly to the west and more prominent at the coast than inland localities. High day totals have included 636 west at Weston Shore on Oct. 12th 1960, 567 west at Titchfield Haven on Oct. 28th 1961, 674 north at Warsash on Oct. 21st 1981, 400 west at Sinah on Oct. 20th 1983 and 301 west at Warsash on Nov. 20th 1986. Inland, the only significant numbers have been recorded at Fleet Pond.

During 1987-92, a total of 2224 flew over in directions between south and north-west between Sep. 17th and Nov. 30th. Annual totals varied between 221 and 539 (in 1989) with a peak of 105 south and west on Oct. 30th 1989. Like other finches, few have been involved in recent cold weather passerine movements, but in the severe winter of 1961/62, heavy passage was reported at Gilkicker Point, with 2000 ESE on Dec. 31st and 3000 east the next day, and Needs Ore, with 850 west on Dec. 31st.

Flocks of locally-bred birds may be seen from July onwards but they become more widespread and increase in size after the arrival of autumn immigrants. Between 1966 and 1981, there were 15 reports of flocks of 500 or more, those to reach four figures being of 1500 at Timsbury on Jan. 16th 1971, 1500 at Cheesefoot Head on Feb. 6th 1972, 1500+ at Beacon Hill (Warnford) on Jan. 21st 1973 and 3000 at Hancombe Bottom (Morestead) in late February 1974. Most were in fields of kale or maize where they fed on the seeds of weeds such as fat hen. The apparent absence of similarly-sized flocks in recent years presumably reflects the increased use of herbicides in agriculture. Wintering flocks gradually break up in February and March, possibly due to dispersal to garden feeders. Ringing has shown that there is a considerable turnover in gardens; up to 300 birds have been caught during a winter although only a few are present at any one time. Winter visitors apparently depart in late March or early April although local breeding birds may continue to feed on peanuts until early May.

Analysis of the records for the 22 "winters" from 1970/71-91/92 illustrates the pattern described above (table 74).

| | Jul | Aug | Sep | Oct | Nov | Dec | Jan | Feb | Mar | Apr |
|---|---|---|---|---|---|---|---|---|---|---|
| Flocks | 300 | 1710 | 1720 | 1685 | 5125 | 10055 | 13375 | 9125 | 3545 | 960 |
| Movements | 0 | 0 | 108 | 4601 | 1509 | 61 | 24 | 0 | 20 | 0 |

*Table 74. Cumulative monthly totals of flocks of 100+ and movements of Greenfinches, 1970/71-91/92.*

Ringing of this species, which is easily caught at garden feeding stations, has shown that many of our wintering birds originate from counties to the north-east, in a corridor from Surrey and Buckinghamshire to Lincolnshire, Norfolk and Suffolk. There have been 1057 recoveries and controls involving Hampshire birds. 613 were within the county, 442 to or from other English counties, one to Guernsey and one to the channel coast of France. The last two both involved birds ringed in Hampshire in winter and recovered in the following winter. National ringing data show that only a very small proportion of British Greenfinches winters abroad (Winter Atlas).

# Goldfinch                                          *Carduelis carduelis*

Present throughout the year. A numerous breeder and passage migrant, but numbers are much reduced in winter.

As the Atlas Map shows, the Goldfinch breeds in most parts of Hampshire but is generally thinly spread. It occurs in large gardens, parks and churchyards in villages and towns and penetrates heavily built-up areas along railway lines and on waste ground. It is also found in farmland, parkland, orchards, scrub and woodland edge provided that weeds (particularly composites such as dandelions

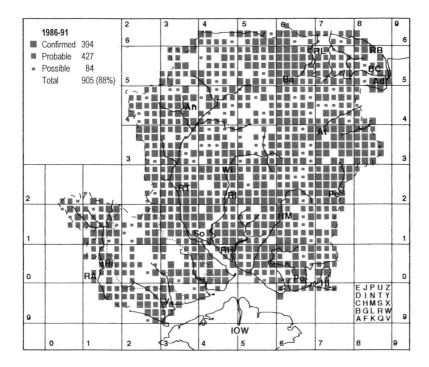

| | | 2 | 3 | 4 | 5 | 6 | 7 | 8 | 9 | |
| 1986-91 | | 6 | | | | | | | 6 |
| ■ Confirmed | 394 | | | | | | RL | RB | |
| ■ Probable | 427 | | | | | | | BC | |
| ■ Possible | 84 | 5 | | | | Ba | | Ad | 5 |
| Total | 905 (88%) | | | | | | | | |

and thistles) are available nearby. It is absent from some intensively farmed areas on the chalk and also the woodlands and heaths of the New Forest.

Its popularity as a cage bird ensured that the British population was low until restrictions on trapping allowed numbers to rise. The upward trend continued through the first half of this century and into the period monitored by the Common Birds Census. The national CBC index peaked in 1977 and subsequently went into decline, most markedly in woodland and special habitats (Marchant *et al* 1990). As with other seed-eaters, the Goldfinch is susceptible to changes in agricultural practices, particularly the increasing use of herbicides. It is influenced less by winter food availability in this country than most other finches, however, because most of the population winters in France, Spain and Portugal. Using national CBC data for 1989, the New Atlas method indicates a county population of around 6000 pairs. As with several other species, this makes insufficient allowance for densities in villages and towns, and thus a range of 7000-10,000 pairs is considered appropriate. The British population was estimated at 220,000 pairs (New Atlas).

In late summer and autumn, flocks form and are especially attracted to fields and waste ground with an abundance of thistles and other composites. Such gatherings regularly reach three figures and there have been eight reports of 300 or more on dates between Aug. 9th and Oct. 21st, with the highest being of 460 at Waltham Chase meadows on Aug. 13th 1984.

Diurnal movement is noted in most years and peaks in late September and October. It is most prominent at coastal sites, where it is usually in an easterly direction. Particularly heavy movement was recorded in 1969, when 2250 were logged at Gilkicker Point between Oct. 5th and 19th with peaks of 900 south-east on 5th and 800 south on 19th, and in 1992, when 2245 flew east at Needs Ore in 35 hours watching between Sep. 26th and Oct. 13th with a peak of 723 in seven hours on Sep. 27th. Other records include 525 east at Hordle Cliff on Oct. 13th 1972, 450 east at Normandy Marsh in one hour on Oct. 17th 1988 and 684 east at Needs Ore on Oct. 19th 1991. Systematic watching at Fleet Pond has shown that passage is usually light at inland sites. During 1987-92, a total of 1573 was recorded moving in directions between south and north-west on dates between Sep. 17th and Nov. 30th. Annual totals varied between 121 and 478 (in 1990) with a peak of 51 west on Oct. 19th 1987.

During the winter months, flocks are usually much smaller than in autumn, anything in excess of 100 being noteworthy. Between November and March, there have been 16 records of flocks in the range 100-156, including three each from Fleet Pond and Winchester Sewage Farm. On six occasions there was a build-up to a peak in late March, indicating spring passage. Three much larger gatherings, of 500+ at Harbridge on Feb. 17th 1972, 600+ at East Worldham on Feb. 25th 1973 and 1000 at Titchfield Abbey on Mar. 5th 1977 are difficult to explain. Goldfinches continue to feed on thistle seeds during the winter months if they are available but make increasing use of birch and alder. They are rarely involved in cold weather movements. Only two birds have been recorded moving in recent years but in the 1961/62 winter, 100 flew west at Needs Ore on Dec. 31st and 500 moved east at Gilkicker the next day.

Spring passage extends from late March until mid-May and is usually in a northerly direction, most records being of small flocks arriving off the sea and continuing inland. Counts are usually in single or double figures but two larger day totals have been recorded: 120 flying north at Hurst Beach on Apr. 19th 1976 and 146 moving north at Hill Head on May 3rd 1980.

Analysis of the records for the 22 "winters" from 1970/71-91/92 illustrates the pattern described above (table 75).

|           | Jun | Jul | Aug  | Sep  | Oct  | Nov | Dec  | Jan  | Feb  | Mar  | Apr  | May |
|-----------|-----|-----|------|------|------|-----|------|------|------|------|------|-----|
| Flocks    | 100 | 350 | 4370 | 9630 | 5655 | 880 | 1715 | 2020 | 3010 | 2720 | 1160 | 225 |
| Movements | 0   | 19  | 67   | 210  | 6503 | 675 | 0    | 0    | 2    | 10   | 1266 | 386 |

*Table 75. Cumulative monthly totals of flocks of 50+ and movements of Goldfinches, 1970/71-91/92.*

Hampshire ringing studies confirm the winter quarters of some of our breeders and those which pass through in autumn. Of 29 birds ringed in the county and recovered, 16 were found in Spain and two in France. The remainder had moved less than 100 km. One, ringed as a juvenile at East Boldre on Aug. 11th 1964, was controlled at Fuenterrabia, Spain on May 1st 1965 and subsequently found dead in Les Landes, France on Nov. 8th 1965. The only recovery of a foreign-ringed bird involved one ringed in Les Landes on Nov. 25th 1976 and found dead at Lee-on-the-Solent on Oct. 24th 1978.

# Siskin

*Carduelis spinus*

Present throughout the year. A moderately common breeder (largely confined to the New Forest), common passage migrant and winter visitor.

K & M described the Siskin as "a winter visitor, never occurring in any numbers". During the 1950s, it started to breed in maturing conifer plantations in many parts of England (Marchant *et al* 1990), including the New Forest where the first nest was found in South Oakley Inclosure in 1953. There has also been a considerable increase in the wintering population, part of which has been shown by ringing to originate from eastern Europe.

The breeding population in the New Forest increased slowly during the 1950s, and in 1960 a total of about ten pairs was found in five inclosures. Numbers remained at this level or lower until the mid-1970s, when there was a sudden spread to most inclosures with mature conifers. In 1982, the population was estimated to be in excess of 100 pairs, while in 1985 "loose breeding colonies" were found in more than 30 localities by two observers. The Atlas Survey has revealed that Siskins remain widespread in the New Forest, although there was a crash in the population in 1987. Numbers have since recovered but they have probably not returned to the level of the early 1980s (C R Tubbs *in litt*). Breeding was confirmed or probable in 50 tetrads; assuming a density of three to five pairs per occupied tetrad in "good" years suggests a population in the range 150-250 pairs.

The Atlas Map shows registrations in over 70 tetrads outside the New Forest, but many of these probably referred to lingering wintering birds rather than breeders. Since 1978, occasional birds or pairs have been recorded in summer in several localities, but it was not until 1987 that breeding was confirmed. At Yateley Heath Wood, two or three pairs were present and a flock of 16, including several recently-fledged juveniles, was seen on June 13th. Since then, breeding has also occurred at Bramshill and Bricksbury Hill, but in many other areas with suitable habitat, such as Ringwood Forest and the Woolmer/ Longmoor area, it has yet to be confirmed. It is doubtful if the population away from the New Forest exceeded 20 pairs in 1991.

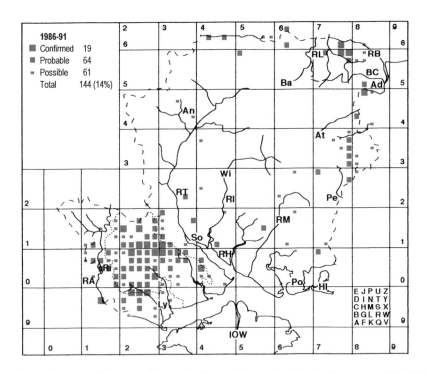

The total Hampshire population is thus estimated to be in the range 170-270 pairs, although it can be expected to increase in the future as the species strengthens its foothold in areas away from the New Forest. In 1988-91, the British population was estimated at 300,000 pairs (New Atlas).

Outside the breeding season, flocks of Siskins are most frequently encountered feeding in alders, often near water, but as the winter advances birch, larch and pine may be utilised and they also visit garden peanut feeders. During the 1950s and 1960s, the species was scarce in winter – only five three-figure flocks were reported with a maximum count of 150. Numbers showed an overall increase in the 1970s although in the 1976/77 winter fewer than 100 were recorded. During that decade, ten flocks reached 200, with maxima of 400 at Warwick Slade Inclosure (New Forest) on Feb. 3rd 1976, 350 at Minley on Feb. 26th 1976 and 350 at Frensham Outlet Pond on Dec. 10th 1977. Between 1980/81 and 1991/92, there were 33 flocks of 200 or more. At Fleet Pond, the wintering flock peaked at over 400 in six winters with a maximum of 700 on Jan. 9th 1982 and Dec. 20th 1990, but elsewhere the largest gathering was of 350 at Broadlands Lake on Jan. 20th 1986. These data indicate that the wintering population has continued to increase, although this could be attributed to greater observer activity. Analysis of the records for Fleet Pond, which has been consistently watched throughout the 22 year period, shows an average winter peak of 140 in the first decade and 380 thereafter, which suggests that the increase is real.

During the 1970s, Siskins were rarely encountered in any numbers before mid-October. Since then, they have been increasingly recorded in September, most notably in 1985 when about 1200 were recorded in that month. Autumn movement is usually more evident at inland than coastal sites. During 1987-92, a total of 3365 was recorded at Fleet Pond, mostly moving in directions between south and west, between Sep. 1st and Nov. 30th. Annual totals varied between 91 and 1012 (in 1991) with a peak day total of 109 south-west and west on Nov. 2nd. As with other finch species, the direction of coastal movement is variable, usually into the wind. The largest total recorded was at Hayling Island in 1985, when 712 were logged between Sep. 10th and Oct. 8th with peaks of 117 west on Sep. 20th, 198 east on Sep. 28th and 100 north on Oct. 5th. Since then, the only day total in excess of 100 has been of 120 east at Normandy Marsh on Oct. 17th 1988.

Numbers of wintering birds apparently decline from February onwards, although initially this may be explained by dispersal into gardens to feed on peanuts, which become an increasingly important food supply as natural crops are exhausted. Ringing has shown that several hundred may occur in a garden in the course of one winter. Most have left by mid-April, although birds occasionally linger into early May, and in recent years some have continued to visit peanut feeders until this time. Unlike Linnets and Redpolls, there is little evidence of spring passage. Analysis of the records for the 22 "winters" from 1970/71-91/92 (table 76) illustrates the pattern described above.

|           | Jul | Aug | Sep  | Oct  | Nov  | Dec   | Jan   | Feb  | Mar  | Apr  | May |
|-----------|-----|-----|------|------|------|-------|-------|------|------|------|-----|
| Flocks    | 60  | 29  | 710  | 3385 | 7210 | 14460 | 16765 | 8825 | 4815 | 1820 | 20  |
| Movements | 31  | 39  | 2134 | 3387 | 653  | 50    | 7     | 26   | 31   | 93   | 4   |

*Table 76. Cumulative monthly totals of flocks of 20+ and movements of Siskins, 1970/71-91/92.*

Ringing activities have produced a total of 208 recoveries or controls involving Hampshire birds. 97 were found within 100 km of the ringing site and a further 78 moved greater distances within the United Kingdom, including three to or from Northern Ireland and 43 to or from Scotland. This indicates that Scottish breeders form a substantial part of our wintering population. Of 33 movements to or from continental Europe, 24 involved birds ringed or recovered in March/April or September-November in Belgium (9), Germany (7), the Netherlands (3), Norway (2) and Denmark, France and Sweden (1 each), which suggests they were on migration at the time. Three ringed in Hampshire were found in Belgium, Czechoslovakia and France in subsequent winters, while one ringed in the Netherlands in winter was controlled in Hampshire a year later, thus showing birds vary their wintering areas from one year to the next. The likely origins of some of these birds are suggested by the recovery during the breeding season of two in Norway and one in the Baltic States, and the control of two in Hampshire which had been ringed in summer in the Baltic States and Russia. The latter was the greatest distance moved, and involved an adult ringed near Leningrad on June 29th 1983 and controlled at Totton, 2415 km WSW, on Feb. 12th 1984.

There have been two recoveries involving Hampshire breeding birds. An adult ringed in Totton in March 1980 was controlled at Emery Down in July of that year, and one ringed as a juvenile at Emery Down on July 16th 1980 was controlled at Sevenoaks on Feb. 25th 1984. We have as yet insufficient data to draw any conclusions about the wintering areas of our breeding birds.

# Linnet                                           *Carduelis cannabina*

Present throughout the year. A numerous breeder and passage migrant, but numbers are usually much reduced in winter.

The Linnet is a bird of open country which, as the Atlas Map shows, is widely, but thinly, distributed throughout the county. The highest densities are found in scrub, especially gorse, on heathland, downland and waste ground and along the coast. It also occurs in farmland hedgerows and young conifer plantations.

Like the Goldfinch, the Linnet was a sought-after cage bird until the turn of the century. The restrictions on trapping followed by the agricultural recession between the wars allowed the population to grow. It peaked in the mid-1960s but has fallen markedly since (Marchant *et al* 1990). Once again, it is the widespread use of herbicides for weed control that appears to be implicated. More than any other finch, the Linnet depends on weeds of cultivation, such as chickweed and fat hen. Their relative scarcity under modern farm management practices would seem to be the key factor in the species' decline (O'Connor & Shrubb 1986).

In Hampshire, where there is much arable land, the increased intensity of modern weed control in crops particularly favoured by Linnets must have taken its toll. It is probable that the county population has fallen sharply over the past 30 years. During the 1980s, local CBC data show major fluctuations, but overall a downward trend. For example, a 33.2 ha CBC plot on Farlington Marshes held up to 17 pairs (51 pairs/km$^2$) in the early 1980s but only six pairs in 1990 (18 pairs/km$^2$), and a 54 ha plot at Martin Down held 10 pairs (18.5 pairs/km$^2$) in 1980 but only four pairs (7.4 pairs/km$^2$) in 1991.

There is less quantitative information available for heathlands. In the New Forest, very high densities averaging 139 pairs/km$^2$ were recorded on three plots totalling 54 ha of suitable habitat in 1972 (Jackson & Long 1973), but numbers appear to be lower today (C R Tubbs *in litt*). Their decline in habitats that should have been unaffected by herbicides suggests that breeding birds may be suffering the effects of agricultural management on their wintering grounds in France, Portugal and Spain. It will be interesting to see whether the increasing availability of oil-seed rape can compensate for the reduction in agricultural weeds. Linnets will feed on rape seeds as soon as they are available in June and this may help to improve chick survival rates.

Using national CBC data for 1989, the New Atlas method indicates a county population of 12,000 pairs. This certainly overestimate densities in intensively-farmed areas and so a range of 6000-10,000 pairs is suggested. The British total was estimated to be 520,000 pairs (New Atlas).

Post-breeding flocks build up from July onwards and reach their highest level in October, when large numbers of migrants are present. Such gatherings usually number a few hundred, but those to reach four figures have been of 3000 near Old Winchester Hill on Oct. 14th 1973, 1700 at Droxford on Sep. 14th 1974, 1750 in the Calshot/Fawley area on Oct. 3rd 1976 and 1000 at Dibden Bay on Sep. 20th 1981. The latter flock was feeding on the seeds of sea-aster, but most are reported from arable farmlands and wastelands where other weeds provide food.

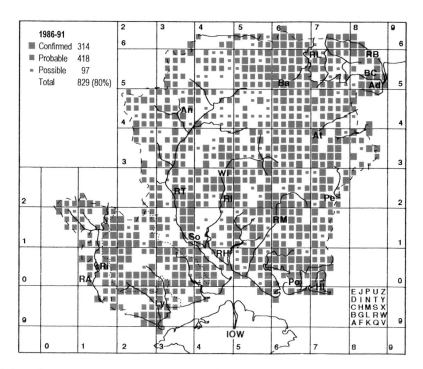

Diurnal movements usually peak in mid-October. As with most *Carduelis* finch species, passage is more noticeable at the coast than inland. The heaviest movements usually involve birds coasting east or south-east, but movements to the west or south out to sea also occur. Between 1959 and 1976, there were nine day totals in excess of 1000 including 2790 south-east at Gilkicker Point on Oct. 19th 1963, 2600 east and south-east there on Oct. 19th 1969, 2250 east at Hordle Cliff on Oct. 12th 1972 and 3000 east at Needs Ore on Oct. 14th 1973. Since then, the only count to exceed 500 was of 975 flying west at Hook on Oct. 20th 1983. In 1992, movement was well recorded at Needs Ore, with 835 moving west in 16½ hours watching between Sep. 13th and 26th, and 1218 east in 17 hours watching between Sep. 27th and Oct. 7th. At inland localities, movement is usually to the south or south-west. Systematic watching at Fleet Pond during 1987-92 produced a total of 2629 moving over on dates between Sep. 6th and Nov. 28th. Annual totals varied between 251 and 644 (in 1991) with a peak on 150 west and south on Oct. 4th 1991.

Winter flocks usually number a few hundred at most, but severe weather has sometimes produced massive gatherings, especially where kale with fat hen has been available. In 1960, a flock estimated at 7000 was at Martin on Jan. 17th, only a few days after a heavy cold weather movement had been witnessed at Farlington Marshes and Titchfield Haven. Between 1967 and 1980, there were 11 reports of four-figure flocks, including 3000+ at Cheesefoot Head on Dec. 28th 1971 and 2000 at Hancombe Bottom (Morestead) in February and early March 1974. Since then, only seven counts have reached 500 with a maximum of 800 on the coast at Redbridge during cold weather on Jan. 12th 1987.

Few have been noted in cold weather passerine movements in recent years, but in the early 1960s, several massive day totals were recorded, including 2000 west at Needs Ore and 15,000 ESE at Gilkicker Point on Dec. 31st 1961, 10,000 east at Gilkicker the next day and 9800 east there on Dec. 31st 1962.

There is a clear spring passage between late March and early May, when flocks appear in areas where none have wintered and a noticeable northerly movement takes place. Spring flocks rarely exceed 150 but in 1985 a gathering on Hayling Island peaked at 400 on Apr. 20th and 400 were grounded at Sway during thundery weather on May 12th. Diurnal movements normally involve small flocks moving north or coasting eastwards. High day totals have included 1200 north at Gilkicker on Apr. 17th 1971, 252 north at Hurst Beach on Apr. 23rd 1973 and 341 north-east there on Apr. 19th 1976, but no recent counts have reached three figures. Inland, the movement is on a broad front and so the numbers recorded at individual sites are fairly low. At Fleet Pond, which is covered almost daily, the highest total recorded was in 1990, when 233 moved north and north-west between Mar. 17th and May 3rd with a peak of 48 on Apr. 13th.

Analysis of the records for the 22 "winters" from 1970/71-91/92 illustrates the pattern described above (Table 77).

| | Jul | Aug | Sep | Oct | Nov | Dec | Jan | Feb | Mar | Apr | May |
|---|---|---|---|---|---|---|---|---|---|---|---|
| Flocks | 900 | 6750 | 11690 | 24865 | 8845 | 17965 | 18770 | 11180 | 5395 | 4355 | 550 |
| Movements | 8 | 276 | 214 | 18513 | 553 | 200 | 0 | 104 | 392 | 4603 | 114 |

*Table 77. Cumulative monthly totals of flocks of 50+ and movements of Linnets, 1970/71-91/92.*

A full analysis of Linnet ringing recoveries was unavailable at the time of writing. However, at least seven birds ringed in Hampshire in autumn or as pulli have been recovered in south-west France, which is a major wintering area for British-bred Linnets (Newton 1972). Another, ringed at Sway during cold weather on Jan. 24th 1979, was found dead at Royston, Hertfordshire, on July 8th 1979. This indicates the possible origin of some of the birds which arrive in the county during hard winters.

# Twite                                                        *Carduelis flavirostris*

A scarce winter visitor and passage migrant which declined during the 1980s.

The favoured habitats of Twites are coastal saltmarshes, fields and reclaimed land where they feed on small seeds, often in association with Linnets. They are easily overlooked in mixed flocks unless the call note is well known, and even then a careful observer will probably underestimate the number present.

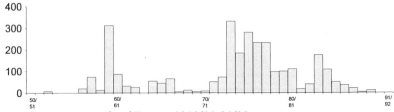

*Figure 79. Winter totals of Twites, 1950/51-91/92.*

The first for the county were eight or nine at Farlington Marshes on Dec. 22nd 1952. No more were seen until November 1956, but since then there have been records in every winter except two (fig. 79).

In the late 1950s, Farlington Marshes was the main locality, although numbers there usually showed an autumn peak and were much reduced after the turn of the year. In 1959/60, when numbers were high, flocks were discovered around Southampton Water and at Pennington Marsh. After the mid-1960s, Twites became scarce and irregular at Farlington Marshes, but during the 1970s sites further west held substantial flocks. In the late 1980s, numbers were at a very low level, despite the availability of some suitable habitat. Counts at the principal localities are summarised in table 78.

| Locality | Range of winters with counts of 10+ | No. of winters with counts of 10+ | Average max. counts for those years | Peak counts | |
|---|---|---|---|---|---|
| Farlington Marshes | 1956-66 | 9 | 45 | 150, | 24/10/59 |
| Eling Great Marsh/ Southampton Docks | 1976-90 | 11 | 39 | 84, | 6/12/79 |
| Dibden Bay | 1959-83 | 14 | 78 | 200, | 3/12/75 |
| | | | | 200, | 27/11/77 |
| Fawley/Calshot | 1972-75 | 3 | 30 | 46, | 24/2/74 |
| Normandy/Pennington | 1959-84 | 8 | 32 | 60, | 9/1/74 |

*Table 78. Summary of counts of Twite at principal localities, 1956/57-91/92.*

Other double figure counts have been made at Needs Ore (23, Jan. 27th 1960), Warsash (22, Jan. 5th 1972; 29, Dec. 22nd 1973; 30, Oct. 15th 1980), Paulsgrove Reclamation (70, Feb. 23rd 1974) and Tournerbury (15, Dec. 12th 1981).

Twites normally arrive between mid-October and early November. Earlier records include those of single birds at Farlington Marshes on Oct. 3rd 1971 and Titchfield Haven on Sep. 30th 1973. There is evidence of through passage in autumn, with flocks building up and then declining (as at Farlington Marshes) or staying for one or two days (as at Warsash in 1980). A few have been detected in diurnal passerine movements, e.g. four flying west at Gilkicker Point on Nov. 2nd 1962 and six moving west at Warsash on Oct. 20th 1983. Peak counts of wintering flocks are usually recorded in December or January, with numbers falling from February onwards and the last normally leaving by late March or early April. Later records include those of two at Normandy Marsh on Apr. 9th 1974 and seven at Dibden Bay on Apr. 13th 1975.

There have been nine inland records, mostly of one to three but including flocks of six at Woolmer on Nov. 24th 1962, flying south-west over Ashley Walk on Nov. 15th 1975 and flying north up the Test valley at Romsey on Feb. 18th 1982, and four at Athelstan Road allotments (Southampton) on Jan. 18th 1987.

The cumulative monthly totals of all records for 1952-92 are shown below.

| Sep | Oct | Nov | Dec | Jan | Feb | Mar | Apr |
|---|---|---|---|---|---|---|---|
| 1 | 456 | 1194 | 1436 | 1138 | 956 | 599 | 57 |

No Twites have been ringed in Hampshire. Data from Essex suggest that birds wintering there are from the Pennines breeding population (Winter Atlas) and this may be true of those in Hampshire.

# Redpoll                                           *Carduelis flammea*

Present throughout the year. A moderately common breeder, common passage migrant and winter visitor.

K & M described the Redpoll as "a winter visitor to all parts, sometimes fairly plentiful, particularly at the times of autumn and spring migration". They also stated that "a few remain to nest", but gave only one record.

What few records there are for the first half of this century suggest that Redpolls were very scarce in winter, only occurring in small flocks. There are no confirmed breeding records for the period, which agrees with Parslow (1973), who described a marked increase in many lowland counties from about 1900-10 followed by a complete disappearance in the 1920s.

From about 1950, there was an increase in many parts of England, and this coincided with the first breeding record from the New Forest in 1956, when a pair with three juveniles was seen near Picket Post on July 7th. From the late 1950s, Redpolls bred at up to six sites there, although numbers stayed at a fairly low level. Starting in the mid-1970s, there was a rapid expansion, and by 1987 Redpolls were common and widespread in the New Forest, mainly nesting in old gorse brakes sheltering emergent birch (C R Tubbs *in litt*). In that year, at least 50 pairs were reported at 20 sites but the population was no doubt considerably higher than this. In 1988, there was a decline, and since then numbers have not recovered to the previous high level. The Atlas Map shows that breeding was confirmed or probable in about 50 tetrads in or adjacent to the New Forest. Assuming a density in the range 3-5 pairs per occupied tetrad before the decline suggests a population of 150-250 pairs. In 1991, it is doubtful if the population exceeded 100 pairs and it may have been considerably lower.

The only other area where Redpolls breed regularly is the north-east, where they are found on heathlands with invasive birch and pine and also in young conifer plantations. In 1971, a survey of all the heathlands failed to produce any, but in 1977 numbers had increased such that in excess of 35 pairs or singing males were present at seven sites including small colonies at Bricksbury Hill, Longmoor Inclosure and Ludshott Common. In subsequent years, numbers fluctuated although no particular search was made. In 1987, 30 pairs were found at ten localities. The Atlas Map shows confirmed or probable breeding in 45 tetrads. Some of these will only have held a single pair, although others held birds at a similar density to the New Forest. The population in the north-east probably peaked at between 50 and 100 pairs during the Atlas Survey period.

In other areas of the county the Redpoll remains a rare breeder. Prior to the Atlas Survey, there were occasional summer records but the only reports of confirmed breeding were in 1982, when three pairs bred at Baddesley Common/Emer Bog and at least one at Squabb Wood (Romsey). During the survey, breeding was confirmed in only two tetrads, in suburban areas of Fareham and Southampton. Both registrations referred to fledged young so it is possible that they were reared elsewhere.

Despite the increase and spread of the Redpoll in the last 20 years, numbers continue to fluctuate, probably in response to the availability of food such as birch seed. At the start of the Atlas Survey in 1986, the county population was possibly as high as 350 pairs but in 1991 it may have been no more than 100

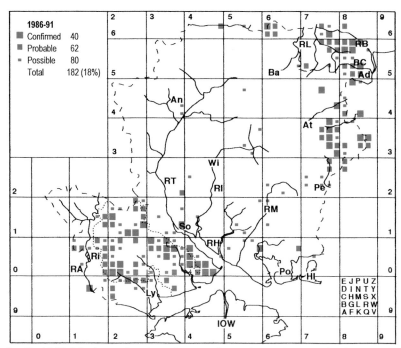

| 1986-91 | | |
|---|---|---|
| ■ Confirmed | 40 | |
| ■ Probable | 62 | |
| ▪ Possible | 80 | |
| Total | 182 (18%) | |

pairs. In 1988-91, the national total was estimated at 160,000 pairs (New Atlas).

Outside the breeding season, very few were recorded until the late 1950s. In the winter of 1959/60, flocks of 100-150 were found at three sites, the first time such numbers had been recorded. Subsequently, no further flocks of this magnitude were recorded until 1972 apart from one of 200 at Crookham on Mar. 22nd 1961. During the last 20 years, the pattern has been one of fluctuating numbers but generally at a higher level than before.

In some years, there is a considerable autumn influx, characterised by large flocks, such as 250 at Fawley Refinery on Oct. 14th 1973 and 500 at Fleet Pond on Oct. 19th 1975, and conspicuous diurnal movement. At coastal localities, this is usually into the wind, as with other finches. A movement of 230 east at Needs Ore on Oct. 12th 1975 was exceptional; in other years, autumn totals have failed to reach this level, 205 (mostly moving west) at Hayling Island between Sep. 20th and Oct. 27th 1985 being the maximum. More may be recorded at inland sites, where movement is primarily in directions between south and north-west. During 1987-92, 2697 were logged at Fleet Pond on dates between Sep. 15th and Nov. 28th. Annual totals varied between 254 and 840 (in 1991). The peak day total was of 209 west and south-west on Nov. 9th 1991 but other counts did not exceed 76.

In other years, autumn passage is light and the main influx occurs in December. Small wintering flocks, often mixed with Siskins, occur on heaths and in river valleys throughout the county, especially where alder seed is available. Of 20 flocks of 200 or more recorded between 1970/71 and 1991/92, 15 were in the north-east of the county. The well-watched Fleet Pond was prominent, with peaks of 200-350 in seven winters and a maximum of 600 on

Nov. 25th 1987. Numbers also reached 200 at Yateley Gravel Pit in three winters with a maximum of 400 on Jan. 11th 1977. Elsewhere, the highest numbers were recorded in the 1975/76 winter, when 400 were at Enham Alamein on Dec. 6th, 350 at Bishops Dyke on Dec. 30th and the same number at Bassett on Jan. 10th. Since then, the only flock of comparable size to be reported was of 350 at Emer Bog on Nov. 7th 1987. As the winter progresses, the diet may change to birch or pine seeds, sallow catkins and fat hen. 300 were feeding on fat hen seeds on farmland near Eversley Church on Jan. 24th 1981.

Dispersal of winter flocks usually occurs in February and early March but in some years numbers increase again in spring, e.g. 500 at Fleet Pond on Mar. 29th 1976. Passage is also indicated by the appearance of flocks in areas where they have not wintered, e.g. 270 in birches at Half Moon Common on Apr. 9th 1985, 300 in Scots pine at Yateley Heath Wood on Apr. 10th 1991 and 300 at Long Valley on Apr. 26th 1992. Small northward movements are also detected at this time at both coastal and inland localities, e.g. 227 moving in directions between north-east and north-west over Fleet Pond between Mar. 28th and Apr. 26th 1990. Passage sometimes continues into early May.

Analysis of the records for the 22 "winters" from 1970/71-91/92 illustrates the pattern described above (Table 79).

|  | Jul | Aug | Sep | Oct | Nov | Dec | Jan | Feb | Mar | Apr | May |
|---|---|---|---|---|---|---|---|---|---|---|---|
| Flocks | 0 | 70 | 398 | 5220 | 5600 | 6990 | 7335 | 4815 | 4160 | 5950 | 280 |
| Movements | 16 | 4 | 548 | 3035 | 1397 | 48 | 4 | 4 | 172 | 518 | 99 |

*Table 79. Cumulative monthly totals of flocks of 20+ and movements of Redpolls, 1970/71-91/92.*

The limited Hampshire ringing data suggest that our passage and wintering birds originate from further north in Britain. Of 20 movements within Britain, 16 were of more than 100 km, including two birds ringed in Hampshire in winter and found on Merseyside in May and in Strathclyde in June. Three others ringed in Hampshire were found on the continent (two in France and one in Belgium) in later winters, which suggests that birds change their wintering areas from year to year, presumably in response to available food supplies. The only recovery of a Redpoll which may have been locally-bred involved an adult ringed at Church Crookham in July 1984 and found at nearby Crondall in March 1989.

Birds showing the characteristics of the continental race, the Mealy Redpoll *C.f. flammea*, have been reported occasionally in winter but are doubtless overlooked.

# Two-barred Crossbill                                      *Loxia leucoptera*

Two records. A male was with Crossbills at Slufters Inclosure from Mar. 14th-Apr. 28th 1984 and another male was at Rhinefield Inclosure from Nov. 2nd-6th 1990†.

Small numbers of Two-barred Crossbills occasionally reach Britain following eruptions from their breeding grounds in the taiga zone of Finland and Russia.

# Crossbill                                        *Loxia curvirostra*

A scarce resident whose numbers are periodically augmented by westward eruptions from the boreal forests of northern Europe. These occur when a high population level coincides with a failure of the spruce crop, which is the preferred food.

During the 19th century, Crossbills were occasionally recorded breeding in the New Forest and at other sites such as Alice Holt Forest and Southampton Cemetery, usually following irruptions the previous summer (K & M). Since 1910, the species has probably nested annually, but in highly variable numbers, in the New Forest but has remained a sporadic breeder in other parts of the county.

In the last 40 years, there were irruptions in seven years between 1953 and 1966, in 1972, in 1979 and then in five years between 1983 and 1990. These varied greatly in size, the largest being in 1958, 1962, 1966 and 1990. Such invasions normally start in late June or July, when parties of Crossbills, often detected by their loud "chip, chip, chip" contact calls, are seen moving overhead or appear in areas where spruce or pine cones are available. In some years, most have apparently moved on by September, but a further, smaller wave of immigrants may occur in October. During the winter months, groups may become established in areas with a plentiful food supply, but movement largely ceases at this time. There is some evidence of a return in March, although this is not generally to be expected with an irruptive species.

Analysis of the records for 1959/60-91/92, excluding those in the New Forest and other sites where resident birds may have been established, illustrates the pattern described above (Table 80).

| | Jun | Jul | Aug | Sep | Oct | Nov | Dec | Jan | Feb | Mar | Apr | May |
|---|---|---|---|---|---|---|---|---|---|---|---|---|
| Flocks | 97 | 246 | 65 | 51 | 98 | 101 | 33 | 7 | 0 | 6 | 31 | 7 |
| Movements | 124 | 241 | 206 | 99 | 208 | 59 | 6 | 15 | 2 | 58 | 7 | 8 |
| Average direction of movement | WSW | WNW | WNW | W | NNW | WSW | | | | NNE | | |

*Table 80. Cumulative monthly totals of Crossbills (excluding "resident" birds), 1959/80-91/92.*

Most records of birds moving have involved parties of fewer than ten, but larger groups have included 12 flying east at Keyhaven on July 17th 1972, 12 west at Titchfield Haven on Aug. 21st 1988, 20 west over Allbrook on June 16th 1990, 25 south-west over Bishopstoke on Aug. 29th 1990, 14 NNW over Mattingley Green on Aug. 15th 1991 and 25 south at Fleet Pond on Nov. 12th 1991.

In the springs following large arrivals, flocks, often containing many singing males, occur in suitable breeding habitat. However, the numbers of pairs attempting breeding is usually low. Nesting may be more widespread in the

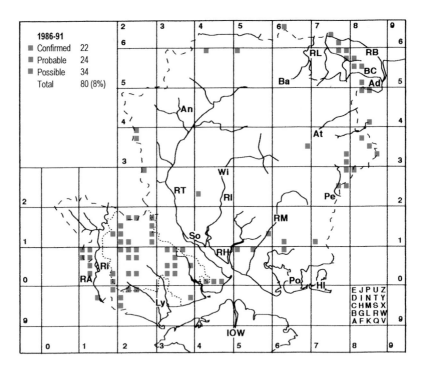

second spring after an irruption, especially if numbers have been augmented by a supplementary arrival in the intervening year.

In the New Forest, following invasions in two successive years, the population reached a high level in 1960, when at least 100 pairs bred (C R Tubbs *in litt*). Since then, numbers have fluctuated around a lower level. During 1975-92, three observers found between zero and 12 nests annually. They estimated that the total Forest population in that period varied between zero and 30 pairs (M & P Combridge, P Toye *in litt*). After the large irruption in 1990, an estimated 300 Crossbills were wintering in the inclosures, but only a few pairs bred in 1991. In some non-invasion years, the species appears to desert the Forest after the breeding season, possibly due to the local failure of the cone crop, only to reappear early in the following spring.

Elsewhere in the county, most breeding records have come from the heaths and conifer plantations of the north-east. One observer found 16 nests in that area in 1936, although since then no more than five pairs have been proved breeding in a single season. In some years very few are seen, e.g. only one in 1978, which indicates that Crossbills are not permanently established in the area. Large numbers were present in spring 1991: in three areas near Fleet flocks peaked at 30+ on Mar. 30th, 55+ on Apr. 21st and 80 on June 3rd respectively, while there were 48 at Weston Common on Feb. 25th and 35+ at Woolmer on Apr. 13th. However, only two pairs are known to have bred.

The Atlas Map shows all records for 1986-91, which are shown at the same level for security reasons. It clearly exaggerates the distribution for any one year.

# Scarlet Rosefinch                    *Carpodacus erythrinus*

One record. A male was at Titchfield on Aug. 13th 1913.

The Scarlet Rosefinch breeds from Sweden and Germany to Kamchatka and central China and winters in the Indian sub-continent and south-east Asia. It is extending its breeding range westwards and bred in England for the first time in 1992.

# Bullfinch                    *Pyrrhula pyrrhula*

A numerous resident.

The Bullfinch breeds in thick scrub and undergrowth in woodlands, thickets, hedgerows and garden shrubberies. Suitable habitat is found throughout the county and the species is widespread but nowhere abundant. Although it is inconspicuous and may easily have been under-recorded, the Atlas Map probably gives an accurate pattern of its distribution. It is missing from the heavily urban centres of Portsmouth and Southampton but is quite common in the suburbs, in parks, gardens and horticultural districts. It is particularly thin on the ground in some of the intensively-farmed cereal-growing areas on the chalk, e.g. to the east of Winchester and in the Martin area. In the New Forest, the absence of a shrub layer from much of the woodland limits nesting and/or feeding opportunities and it is most frequently found in holly thickets and young plantations.

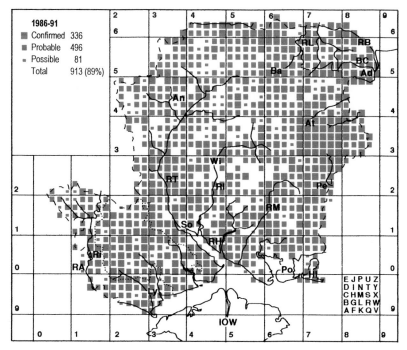

The British population increased during the 1940s and 1950s (Parslow 1973). National CBC data show that numbers continued to grow in the early

469

1960s (despite the severe winter of 1962/63) and peaked in the mid-1970s. Since then, there has been a substantial decline in both farmland and woodland habitats. Suggested reasons for the decrease include hedgerow removal, the increase in intensive arable farming and the recovery of the Sparrowhawk (Marchant *et al* 1990). Hampshire CBC data are insufficient to ascertain to what extent local numbers have followed the national trend. Using national CBC data for 1989, the New Atlas method indicates a county population of 9000 pairs and a national total of 190,000 pairs.

Outside the breeding season, Bullfinches normally occur in pairs or small flocks but gatherings of 20 or more are sometimes recorded, especially in freezing conditions. The largest in recent years was of 30 at Stockbridge Down on Dec. 26th 1980. Hampshire ringing data indicate that local birds do not move far; of 56 ringed and recovered, 53 were found within the county and only three of these had moved more than 10 km. Four recoveries suggest that Hampshire may receive birds from elsewhere in England in winter. These involved birds ringed in Dorset in March, Essex in April and August, and Kent in August, and all found in Hampshire in the following winter. The most distant movement involved one ringed at Farlington Marshes in January 1977 and killed in Herefordshire in February 1978. Autumn migration watches have also produced evidence which suggests movement into or through the county. Between 1971 and 1992, a total of 170 was recorded moving between Sep. 23rd and Nov. 15th, with most in the middle two weeks of October. At inland sites, movement was mostly to the south-west, west and north, while at the coast 24 moved west and 31 east. Double-figure day totals were of ten moving south or south-west at Camp Farm on Oct. 11th 1986 and 18 east at Lepe on Oct. 23rd 1987.

# Hawfinch                          *Coccothraustes coccothraustes*

A resident, moderately common in the New Forest but thinly distributed and elusive elsewhere.

Hawfinches are found in broadleaved woodland, parkland and large gardens, particularly where trees such as hornbeam, cherry, holly, yew and beech are available.

All breeding records since 1951 are incorporated into the Atlas Map, which shows that the greatest concentration is in the New Forest and adjoining woodlands. The available records suggest that the population in the Forest was at a high level in the early 1960s but possibly declined subsequently. Since the mid-1970s, the numbers reported in both summer and winter have shown an overall increase. Greater observer activity is no doubt partially responsible for this, though it is uncertain whether or not there has been a genuine expansion of the population. The species is semi-colonial, several pairs often nesting in close proximity. At such sites, displaying birds are often conspicuous in early spring, although later in the season they are more difficult to find. Such concentrations have been reported from several areas with densities up to 5 pairs per km$^2$. During the Atlas Survey, there were registrations in 51 tetrads. Assuming a range of 3-5 pairs per occupied tetrad indicates a total for the New Forest of 150-250 pairs.

Away from the New Forest, Hawfinches are infrequently encountered, and

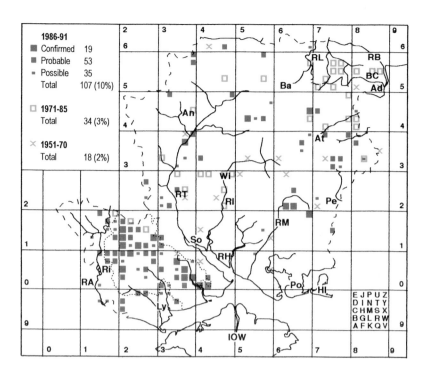

even at their known haunts can be extremely elusive. Although small "colonies" have occasionally been recorded, e.g. in Harewood Forest and the Woodmancott/Dummer area, the Atlas Survey has demonstrated that they are very thinly distributed across the county and virtually absent from the south-east. Registrations were obtained in only 39 tetrads during 1986-91, while records have been traced for a further 46 squares for 1951-85. Assuming that each of these is still occupied at a density of 1-2 pairs per tetrad, and that they were undiscovered in a further 30 tetrads, suggests a total in the range 125-250 pairs. Thus the population for the whole county is estimated to be 275-500 pairs. In 1988-91, the British total was estimated to be in the range 3000-6500 pairs (New Atlas).

Outside the breeding season, most observations are of small numbers but occasionally larger gatherings are discovered, usually feeding on yew berries or wild cherries in late summer or hornbeam seeds in winter and spring. Between 1977 and 1992, double-figure flocks were recorded in the New Forest in every year except one. They are most frequent in late winter and early spring (table 81).

| | Jun | Jul | Aug | Sep | Oct | Nov | Dec | Jan | Feb | Mar | Apr |
|---|---|---|---|---|---|---|---|---|---|---|---|
| Flocks of 10+ | 1 | 3 | 0 | 0 | 0 | 3 | 3 | 6 | 15 | 10 | 8 |
| Average size | 14 | 15 | 0 | 0 | 0 | 20 | 22 | 18 | 19 | 16 | 18 |

*Table 81. Summary of Hawfinch flocks in the New Forest, 1977-92.*

Seven reports were of 20 or more, including 33 on Feb. 1st 1991 and 40 on Nov. 13th 1992.

Elsewhere, such numbers are far more unusual. Between 1953 and 1966, there were single date records of flocks of 13-17 at Harewood Forest, Pilot Hill, Liss and East Meon, while in 1964 up to 14 were at Farlington Marshes from Feb. 9th-Mar. 27th with two staying until Apr. 25th. Subsequently, favoured areas have included Moyles Court (max. 30 in February 1975), Embley Park, Romsey (max. 27 roosting on Feb. 27th 1982), Greywell (max. 30+ on Dec. 28th 1988), Chilbolton (max. 16 on Mar. 18th 1989) and Bordon (19 on Feb. 19th and Mar. 20th 1989). However, the numbers quoted are exceptional for the areas involved and normally less than ten are present, if any can be found at all.

Since 1973, there have been several records of birds in flight over coastal sites and non-breeding inland localities which suggest passage. In autumn 1988, eight were recorded during diurnal passerine movements including five flying south over Meonstoke on Oct. 16th. The following winter was exceptional for the species with abnormally high counts at several sites in Hampshire (see above) and other counties in southern England. This may indicate an influx from elsewhere, possibly where the hornbeam crop had failed. Otherwise, all records were of one to three birds apart from those of eight flying off north-east from Mayfield Park (Sholing) on Mar. 14th 1980 and six moving north over Little London (Andover) on Mar. 19th 1989.

There have been no ringing recoveries involving Hampshire birds.

## American Redstart                          *Setophaga ruticilla*

One record. A first-winter male was at Winchester College water meadows from Oct. 4th-6th 1985.

The American Redstart breeds in Canada and the eastern USA and winters in Central America, the West Indies and northern South America.

## White-throated Sparrow                     *Zonotrichia albicollis*

One record. One briefly glimpsed at Needs Ore Point on May 5th 1961 and identified on May 19th of that year may have been the bird which was on board the RMS Queen Elizabeth before it docked at Southampton on May 2nd (Sharrock 1961; Durand 1961). This was the second for Britain and Ireland but since then a further 17 have occurred.

The White-throated Sparrow breeds mainly in central and eastern Canada and winters in the south-eastern USA.

See also Appendix 1.

## Dark-eyed Junco                            *Junco hyemalis*

One record. A first-summer male held territory near Church Crookham from May 30th into July 1987. It was seen again in the same area on May 20th 1988 and in a nearby garden on Feb. 9th 1989. In the following winter it was present around the same garden from Dec. 27th-Mar. 9th. This was the 14th for Britain and Ireland; subsequently, a further two have been recorded.

The Dark-eyed Junco breeds in Alaska, Canada and the north-eastern USA and winters through most of the USA.

See also Appendix 1.

# Lapland Bunting

*Calcarius lapponicus*

A rare autumn passage migrant and winter visitor.

The first Lapland Bunting for the county was recorded by Meinertzhagen on plough at Mottisfont on Jan. 4th 1898, but the next was not until 1953, when a male was at Black Point on Dec. 23rd. Since then, 57 have been seen, with a maximum of six in the winters of 1962/63 and 1970/71 (fig. 80).

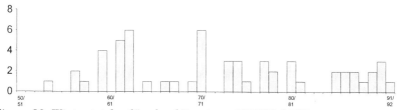

*Figure 80. Winter totals of Lapland Buntings, 1950/51-91/92.*

Virtually all occurred on the coast, with the majority in the Lymington/Hurst area (19) and at Farlington Marshes/Langstone Harbour (13). Others were seen at Warsash (6), Dibden Bay (5, including 3 on Sep. 16th 1970), Needs Ore Point (4, including 3 on Jan. 27th 1960), Gilkicker Point and Titchfield Haven (2 each), and Sandy Point and Redbridge (1 each). Inland, one flew north-west over Damerham on Sep. 18th 1956, another was at Hazeley Heath on Dec. 13th 1980 and single birds flew over Godshill on Nov. 3rd 1989 and Picket Post on Nov. 24th 1991. The cumulative monthly totals for 1950/51-91/92 are shown below.

| Sep | Oct | Nov | Dec | Jan | Feb | Mar |
|-----|-----|-----|-----|-----|-----|-----|
| 11 | 11 | 7 | 11 | 20 | 5 | 3 |

The earliest was at Pennington Marsh from Sep. 9th-15th 1970. Records typically involved one or two birds which were seen briefly or stayed for a few days. Those in winter often appeared during hard weather. Longer stays included one at Farlington Marshes from Oct. 30th 1959-Jan. 2nd 1960, one or two at Pennington Marsh from Jan. 6th-27th 1963 and another there on Dec. 13th 1975 which stayed until Mar. 14th 1976, the latest date on record.

It has been suggested that Lapland Buntings wintering in Britain originate from Scandinavia, with occasional influxes from Greenland (Winter Atlas).

## Snow Bunting                                    *Plectrophenax nivalis*

A very scarce autumn passage migrant and winter visitor.

During 1951/52-91/92, Snow Buntings were recorded in every winter except three. Numbers reached their highest level during the late 1950s and early 1960s, but subsequently the total per winter has only three times exceeded ten (fig. 81).

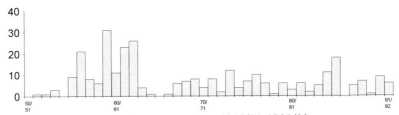

*Figure 81. Winter totals of Snow Buntings, 1950/51-1991/92.*

In all, 321 were recorded during that period, with the favoured areas being Lymington/Hurst (72 birds), Farlington Marshes and the shores of Langstone Harbour (55), Gilkicker/Warsash (49), Dibden Bay/Calshot (33) and Sinah/Black Point (29).

In the 1950s, most sightings were of one or two birds, but in 1956 five were at Brownwich on Feb. 21st and a flock of 20 was at Southampton Docks on Oct. 27th. The first definite wintering occurred in 1959/60, when up to 11 were at Dibden Bay and four at Farlington Marshes. There was also a flock of 15+ at Needs Ore on Jan. 27th. In 1961/62, up to seven wintered at Dibden Bay while in early 1963, up to 12 were at Farlington Marshes in hard weather from Jan. 5th-Feb. 24th. Other notable flocks at this time were of seven at Warsash on Nov. 19th 1961, five flying north at nearby Brownwich on Nov. 27th 1961 and six at Black Point on Jan. 25th 1963.

After the early 1960s, the species became much scarcer; most records were in autumn and of only one or two birds which rarely stayed for more than a few days. The only instances of wintering involved up to three at Hurst Beach in 1971/72, up to three at Pennington Marsh in 1975/76, one at Calshot in early 1977 and one or two at Farlington Marshes in 1977/78. Larger numbers recorded involved six flying south over Rowner (Gosport) on Nov. 26th 1969, five at Sinah Golf Course on Dec. 26th 1984, a flock of 14 flying north-east over Sturt Pond on Feb. 23rd 1986, four at Langstone Harbour on Dec. 4th and 5th 1990 and four at Eastoke car park (Hayling) on Jan. 5th 1991.

There have been 21 inland records involving 25 individuals. All occurred during the years 1956-84 and were confined to the periods between Oct. 9th and Dec. 31st and Feb. 2nd and Mar. 24th. They were from all over the county but particularly on the chalk (13 birds) and the heaths of the New Forest (4) and north-east (2). All were seen on a single date only apart from one at Cheesefoot Head on Oct. 9th 1976 which was joined by another bird the following day.

The cumulative monthly totals for 1950/51-91/92 are shown below.

|  | Oct | Nov | Dec | Jan | Feb | Mar |
|---|---|---|---|---|---|---|
| Coast | 45 | 96 | 80 | 79 | 47 | 8 |
| Inland | 4 | 8 | 5 | 0 | 4 | 3 |

The earliest recorded sightings were of single birds at Pennington Marsh on Oct. 3rd 1975 and Fawley on the same date a year later, while the latest was at Calshot on Mar. 25th 1977.

The Snow Bunting has a circumpolar distribution. Those occurring in southern England may originate from Iceland or Greenland, although in severe winters birds from Scandinavia may also occur (Winter Atlas).

# Yellowhammer                                     *Emberiza citrinella*

A numerous resident.

The Yellowhammer prefers well-drained, open countryside, breeding in farmland hedgerows (particularly in arable areas), woodland edges, heathland and downland scrub and young conifer plantations. During the Atlas Survey, it was apparently absent from an area around Southampton, including the lower Itchen and Test valleys. The agricultural land there is better suited to cattle rearing and market gardening than to cereal growing. Such factors apparently combine to make it unsuitable for the species. It was also absent from densely built up zones and well-wooded areas such as the heart of the New Forest.

The national population, as monitored by the CBC, has remained remarkably constant for the past 30 years (Marchant *et al* 1990). Hampshire data indicate a recent decline, with the local CBC index falling from 100 in 1981 to 59 in 1991. However, the sample provided by CBCs is small and it is uncertain whether such a reduction has occurred across the county. Densities in some areas are high, e.g. on three chalkland CBC plots at Martin Down, Oxenbourne Down and Old Winchester Hill, there were 28, 31 and 42 pairs/km$^2$ respectively in 1990. A survey of all the north-east heaths in 1971 produced 131 pairs while a partial survey in 1980/81 showed numbers little changed. Using national CBC data for 1989, the New Atlas method indicates a county population of 30,000 pairs. However, this overestimates densities in some intensively-farmed areas and so

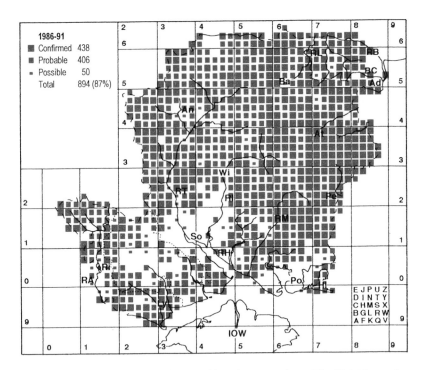

an upper limit of 25,000 pairs is considered appropriate. The British total was estimated at 1.2 million pairs (New Atlas).

Outside the breeding season, Yellowhammers normally occur in small flocks, often mixed with other buntings, finches and Meadow Pipits. Larger gatherings of 100 or more may form, especially in hard weather. They are particularly attracted to strawstacks or where straw has been spread out as food for farm animals. High counts have included 200 at Shepherds Spring, which appeared after snow on Dec. 31st 1978, and 250 at Roke Farm (Odiham) in severe weather on Feb. 7th 1982. Several roosts have been discovered in scrub and low bushes, particularly bramble, but they are usually small, holding 30-70 birds.

National ringing results reveal that about 70% of adults winter within 5 km of their breeding territories (Winter Atlas). The limited Hampshire data support this – of 12 recoveries all but one involved movements of less than 10 km. However, small numbers are sometimes noted during diurnal passerine movements in autumn. Between 1980 and 1987, a total of 67 moved west or north-west on dates between Oct. 11th and Nov. 30th (only five in November), with maximum day totals of ten west at Warsash on Oct. 20th 1983 and ten north-west (in one flock) over Camp Farm (Aldershot) on Oct. 13th 1984. Despite the large flocks which form in severe winters, none have been detected in recent hard weather movements, which suggests that local birds are involved. However, on Dec. 31st 1961 and Jan. 1st 1962, 53 flew east at Gilkicker Point and 83 south at Farlington Marshes; this was quite exceptional and clearly caused by the extreme weather conditions.

# Cirl Bunting                                    *Emberiza cirlus*

Formerly a moderately common but locally distributed resident; now extinct as a breeder and not recorded since 1985.

The Cirl Bunting may not have colonised England until the late 18th century, for it was not until 1800 that it was first discovered by Montagu in Devon. It was unknown to White, who lived at Selborne until his death in 1793. However, Blyth, writing in the second volume of the *Naturalist* in 1837, described the Cirl as "nowhere more plentiful than in the vicinity of Alton, whence it is strange that Gilbert White should have overlooked it". K & M described it as "a local resident .... highly characteristic of the southern parts of the county .... and also found commonly in most inland localities, but not in all".

Favoured habitats included the sides of river valleys and along the droves which led from them up on to the middle levels of the surrounding chalk downlands, and the coastal strip, especially behind the low cliffs between Highcliffe and Milford-on-Sea and Warsash and Hill Head. It was a far more suburban species than the Yellowhammer, frequently being found in villages, around farms and in open parkland, as on Southampton Common. On the downs, it was usually associated with extensive hedgerows with a certain amount of high timber, especially ash and elm.

Numbers were possibly at their highest level during the first half of this century, but unfortunately only anecdotal evidence is available for that period. The map below shows the distribution of all breeding records since the late 1930s. Cirl Buntings were absent from most of the New Forest (although occasionally occurring along its fringes), the high chalk and the extreme north of the county between Woolton Hill and Tadley. However, in many suitable areas on the chalk in the north and east coverage was virtually non-existent. There is no reason to doubt that it occurred throughout this region, especially since it was found along the length of the Hog's Back over the county boundary in Surrey. The map shows presence in 160 tetrads; allowing for those where it was not recorded and for known densities of up to seven pairs per tetrad it seems likely that the population in the 1940s approached or even exceeded 1000 pairs.

The selection of records which follows gives some idea of the decline, which accelerated through the 1950s and 1960s until very few remained by the late 1970s. During severe weather in January 1954, over 50 were at Micheldever, and eight to ten pairs bred there in that year. Also in 1954, 30 singing males were located within 12 km of Andover (E L Jones *in litt*). In 1955, four pairs bred near Fawley, and in 1957 there were "many" breeding pairs around Damerham, 18 in the Andover area (found with no special search), seven on Southampton Common and six to eight around Hill Head. In the following winter, a flock of 50 (mostly males) was found with a few Greenfinches and Yellowhammers at Kingsworthy on Dec. 24th and 15 were still there on Feb. 21st. In 1959, there were still at least six pairs on Southampton Common, and in the Havant area five pairs were located where there had been 13 in 1939 (N W Orr *in litt*).

It had disappeared from Martin Down by the early 1960s, but hung on until the 1970s in some surrounding districts on the chalk (N W Orr *in litt*). Other strongholds were along the coastal strip between Highcliffe and Milford-on-Sea

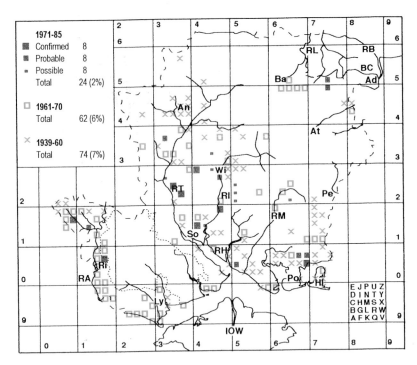

1971-85
▨ Confirmed 8
▪ Probable 8
▫ Possible 8
Total 24 (2%)

□ 1961-70
Total 62 (6%)

× 1939-60
Total 74 (7%)

and in the Avon valley. Orr found 15 pairs between the western edge of the New Forest and the Dorset border in 1961 and 14 in 1963. It last bred in the Hill Head area in 1961 but survived at nearby Hook until 1971. In the early 1960s, breeding pairs were known from ten sites in the Basing/Mapledurwell area (J A Lucas *in litt*). At Houghton in the Test valley only one pair was found in 1965 where there had been four in 1962.

Cirl Buntings still survived in the Portsdown area in the late 1960s, e.g. in 1968, two or three pairs bred between Fort Widley and Purbrook, one at Farlington Marshes and one at Northney on Hayling Island. One pair bred annually at Farlington Marshes until 1973, while on Portsdown itself single pairs were found in 1972 and 1974 and the last was a singing male in 1975. On Southampton Common there were still five pairs in 1969; thereafter only one pair was reported annually, with the last in 1974 apart from single birds on one date only in 1976 and 1978. In the early 1970s, pairs were also found at Droxford Mill, Compton Down and Timsbury.

In 1978, Orr only located three pairs in its former stronghold in the south-west; at Rockford, the species continued to breed until 1982 and probably did so in 1983. Elsewhere, between 1977 and 1982 the only breeding season records came from the Morestead/Owslebury area (1977-79), near Odiham (1979/80), Martin Down (1979), Farley Mount (1980), near Danebury (1982) and near Mottisfont (1982). Apart from two instances of pairs seen, the records all referred to lone singing males, and in no case was breeding confirmed.

Since then, the only records have been of a male with Yellowhammers at Hayling Oyster Beds on Oct. 25th 1983, at least two at Pennington Marsh on

Sep. 23rd 1984 and a male among 15 Yellowhammers at Shepherds Spring on Jan. 27th 1985.

Unfortunately, coverage of most areas where the Cirl Bunting was known to occur was poor, e.g. around Andover during the 1960s. Thus we will never know the full picture of its disappearance, but the population was probably well below 50 pairs at the time of the 68-72 Atlas, when it was recorded in 16 10 km squares. There are several factors which may have contributed to its decline in Hampshire and most other English counties. In coastal areas especially, much habitat was destroyed by house building. Climatic deterioration is also thought to have contributed, since the species has now withdrawn to the sheltered valleys of south Devon, where the summers are warm and the winters mild. The use of herbicides and insecticides reduces summer survival and breeding success, while the autumn ploughing of stubbles affects winter food supplies. In the early 1990s, stubble has been left through the winter in several areas of Devon and the breeding population has increased.

## Ortolan Bunting                                   *Emberiza hortulana*

A rare vagrant. The first was an adult male obtained at Mottisfont on Apr. 7th 1897. Since then, there have been five records, as follows:

1956:   2, Damerham, Sep. 17th;
1961:   Needs Ore Point, Oct. 15th;
1983:   Warsash, Sep. 22nd;
1984:   Sandy Point, Sep. 2nd;
1992:   Keyhaven, Aug. 31st.

The Ortolan Bunting breeds from Spain and Scandinavia to Iran and Mongolia and winters in the Sahel region of Africa and south Arabia.

## Little Bunting                                      *Emberiza pusilla*

Two records. A male was trapped at Winnall Moors as it flew in at dusk with Reed Buntings on Mar. 18th 1986†. It was roosted overnight and released the next morning. A female was trapped at Titchfield Haven on Feb. 16th 1992 and remained in the area until Apr. 17th 1992†.

The Little Bunting breeds from Fenno-Scandia to eastern Siberia and winters largely in south-east Asia. An increasing number of British records in recent years suggests that there is a very small, but regular, wintering population.

## Reed Bunting                                     *Emberiza schoeniclus*

A common resident, passage migrant and winter visitor.

The Reed Bunting breeds wherever there are suitable wetland habitats. The highest concentrations occur in the main river valleys and on coastal marshes, particularly where there are stands of reeds or other rank vegetation with scattered bushes. It also occurs on heathlands with scattered bushes and small trees, most frequently in damp areas but also in drier situations. Other dry habitats utilised, especially when population levels are high, include young conifer plantations and farmland hedgerows and scrub.

National CBC data show that the population increased following the hard winters of the early 1960s and remained at a high level until the mid-1970s. A

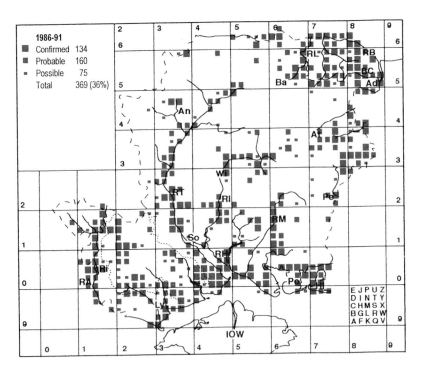

decline then began, which steepened through the adverse effect of the cold winters of 1978/79 and 1981/82. Since 1983, numbers have stabilised at a lower level (Marchant *et al* 1990). Information from Hampshire CBC plots shows a similar picture, with the county index showing little change during 1981-91 apart from short-term fluctuations due to increased mortality in cold winters. Densities were highest at Titchfield Haven, where the total number of territories recorded in 108 ha varied between 25 in 1982 and 63 in 1986, with a mean density of 38 pairs per km². Several breeding surveys carried out over the county's river systems have provided further information about breeding numbers and densities. In 1978, 112 pairs were located along 19 km of the Test valley between Totton and Fullerton at a density of 5.8 pairs per km, while in 1979, 51 territories were plotted along 28.6 km of the Avon valley between Ringwood and Downton at a density of 1.8 pairs per km. Various surveys in the Itchen valley have produced densities ranging between 2.2 and 5.0 pairs per km.

The county population is difficult to assess owing to wide variations in density. Using national CBC data for 1989, the New Atlas method gives a total of around 4000 pairs. This is possibly a little too high; assuming an average of five to ten pairs per occupied tetrad indicates a figure in the range 1850-3700 pairs. In 1988-91 the British population was estimated at 220,000 pairs (New Atlas).

In autumn, light movements, usually to the west, occur between late September and early November. At the coast, high counts have included 55 south at Warsash on Oct. 12th 1991 and 50 west at Titchfield Haven a week later, but usually day totals do not exceed 20. Inland, even fewer are recorded.

Regular watching at Fleet Pond during 1987-92 produced a total of 54, mostly moving west, between Sep. 26th and Nov. 25th. Annual totals varied between none and 31 (in 1991) with a peak day total of nine west on Oct. 16th 1991.

As a ground-feeding species, Reed Buntings are particularly vulnerable to hard winter weather and prolonged snow cover. This results in a movement of birds from northern and eastern areas of Britain to winter in the milder central and southern counties of England, including Hampshire. From October onwards, reed bed roosts build up, although it is apparent from ringing studies that these may be of a transient nature with a rapid turnover of individuals, particularly during the early winter. Large roosts recorded include 514 at Fleet Pond in December 1986 and 524 there in November 1989, 500+ at Winnall Moors in January 1958, 300 at Marsh Court in December 1976 and 300+ at Alresford Pond in January and February 1977. Roosts of over 100 have also been recorded at Greywell and Great Salterns Lake (Portsmouth).

The distribution of Reed Buntings in winter is not fully understood, but small flocks regularly appear at garden feeding stations, on farmland and along the coast. At Titchfield Haven, up to 40 per day have been attracted to millet provided in recent winters. Ringing has shown that 100-150 individuals are present in the course of a winter. Large flocks have been found in a variety of farmland crops, e.g. 175 in game cover at Stratfield Saye in December 1981, 200 in cabbages at Hamble in January 1987 and 200 in maize at Elvetham in February 1990. Heathland also appears to be attractive, e.g. up to 160 at Matley Bog in January and February 1972, 220 on a burnt area near Fleet Pond in December 1975 and 150 at Hamble Common in January 1981. However, the largest number ever recorded was a flock of 1500 at New Millersford Plantation (New Forest) on Jan. 8th 1967, declining to 750 by Jan. 15th.

Towards the end of winter, reed bed roosts decline, the timing depending on weather conditions. Males may begin to disperse in February, presumably in order to return to their breeding areas. Most have departed by the end of March except for the local breeding population.

Ringing studies have revealed much about the origin of Reed Buntings wintering in Hampshire. Birds ringed or recaptured in the county between October and March have produced 36 recoveries of over 50 km. Four involved birds ringed in Belgium (2) and the Netherlands and Norway (1 each) during August-November, while the remainder were to or from all parts of England. Evidence from ringing suggests that the Hampshire breeding population is mainly resident, although local movements regularly occur, for example, between the coast and the river valleys.

## Black-headed Bunting          *Emberiza melanocephala*

One record. A male was in a garden at Purbrook on May 28th 1993.

The Black-headed Bunting breeds from south-eastern Europe to Iran and winters in the Indian sub-continent.

## Corn Bunting          *Miliaria calandra*

A moderately common but declining resident.

In Hampshire, the Corn Bunting is most closely associated with arable farming on the chalk, especially favouring barley fields with hedgerows, fences or telephone or electricity wires, which can be used as song-posts. It also occurs on farmland in some coastal areas.

Little information on numbers in Hampshire is available for the first half of the century. Nationally, the CBC index shows a peak in the early 1970s, following a steady increase coinciding with the agricultural revival during and after the Second World War (Marchant *et al* 1990). Subsequently, the index fluctuated in the late 1970s and then fell sharply, so that in 1991 it was at one-third the level of the peak in 1973. In Hampshire, the species has disappeared from some areas; this is illustrated by the Atlas Map which incorporates breeding records for 1971-85 as well as those for the 1986-91 Atlas Survey period.

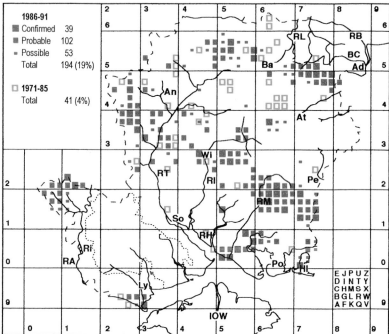

The available information shows that, at most sites where the species survives, there have been considerable declines. At Martin Down, up to ten singing males were present during the 1960s but no more than two were recorded between 1987 and 1991, and none in 1992. In the Bentworth/Lower Wield area, six to ten pairs were located in 1977; this was said to be a great reduction on previous years. During the Atlas Survey, none were found there. Between Lockerley and West Dean, Corn Buntings were common in the early 1970s, such that no counts were made, but in 1978 only one male was found and since then the species has been sporadic in its appearance; the only record in 1992 involved a singing bird on one date only. Between Hillside and Greywell, 34 singing males were counted in 1979, but in 1987 and 1988 there were 14 and 13 respectively, and a further reduction had taken place by 1992. A dense colony in the Crondall/Well area comprised at least 30 territorial males in 1981 and 24 in 1987, but only seven were found in 1992 although the search was not exhaustive. At the coast, numbers on a CBC plot at Castle Farm (Warblington) rose from five in 1981 to eight in 1984 but did not exceed two between 1987 and 1991. In the Brownwich/Chilling area, there were at least ten in territory in 1984, seven or eight in 1987, four in 1989 but only one in 1992.

In other areas, few counts have been made. Those to reach double figures have been of 12 singing males at Fawley Down in 1981, 40 in the Chalton/Blendworth area in 1982 and 38 between Corhampton and Clanfield in 1985. In the latter two areas, numbers had certainly declined by 1992 although no complete counts were available (J Rowe pers. comm.).

Like several other farmland species, the Corn Bunting has "slipped away" without its decline being fully documented. The distribution shown on the Atlas Map probably exaggerates the true position in 1992. Some tetrads have held ten or more territorial males, but assuming a range of three to five per tetrad in those where breeding was confirmed or probable and one in the rest equates to a county population of 450-750 singing males, but this may now be too high. In 1988-91, the British total was estimated at 160,000 pairs (New Atlas).

Outside the breeding season, Corn Buntings occur in small flocks with other buntings and finches. They are particularly attracted to straw stacks, fields where straw has been spread out for cattle, stubble turnips and permanent grass. In the last 20 years, large gatherings have included 200 at Cheesefoot Head on Nov. 2nd 1975, 100+ on cattle food at Lower Swanthorpe Farm (Crondall) on Feb. 24th and 25th 1980, 110 around a straw stack at Roke Farm (Odiham) on Dec. 12th 1981, 100+ in gardens at Greywell on Feb. 14th 1986, 80+ at West Hayling on Jan. 21st and Mar. 2nd 1990 and 65 at Longstock on Feb. 16th 1991. Most of these high counts were made in hard weather.

Communal roosts are most frequently found in reed beds. Those which have been regularly monitored over the last 20 years have declined, presumably reflecting the reduction in the breeding population. In the three winters from 1972-75, numbers at Winnall Moors peaked between 300 and 400. During 1981-86, maxima there were in the range 105-150 but since then the highest count has been of 45. A similar picture has emerged at Titchfield Haven, where flocks of up to 60 were regular in the 1960s and early 1970s with a maximum of 90 on Dec. 30th 1973. Roosting flocks became smaller and less frequent thereafter and by the late 1980s no longer occurred (Duffin 1991). Other sites where roosts have been recorded include Avington (100, March 1955), North Binness Island, Langstone Harbour (36 in brambles, December 1973), Alresford Pond (max. 50, February 1977), Easton (120, January 1978), Winchester water meadows (max. 80, February 1979), Chilbolton (60, January 1981), Greywell (max. 106, Jan. 31st 1981), Soberton Down (up to 60 in lucerne, September-November 1984), Itchen Stoke (100 in brambles, Dec. 27th 1984) and Itchen Abbas (54, Feb. 29th 1992). Many of these sites were only occupied irregularly. As with the feeding flocks, several of the highest counts were made in hard weather.

Although Corn Buntings are sometimes hard to find in their breeding areas in winter, there is little evidence to suggest that they move far. There has been only one recovery of this seldom-ringed species. It involved a bird trapped on Dec. 27th 1976 and found at the same place on June 24th 1978. Records of possible migrants include single birds at Gilkicker Point on Apr. 2nd 1985, flying in off the sea at Hurst Beach on May 9th 1988 and flying west at Sinah on May 12th 1990. Cold weather movements were occasionally reported in the 1960s, e.g. 20 west over Hampton Ridge on Jan. 3rd 1960, 40 west at Brownwich on Dec. 10th 1961 and 20 south at Fordingbridge on Jan. 11th 1966, but none have been detected since.

The decline in Hampshire may be linked to the effects of agricultural intensification on winter food supplies. The use of herbicides and the reduced extent of winter stubble combine to limit the availability of grain and weed seeds (Thompson *et al* 1992). Locally, the cessation of cultivation of stubble turnips, a favoured winter habitat in south-east Hampshire (J Rowe pers. comm.), may also have had a deleterious effect.

### Appendix One. Ship-assisted Birds.
The following records relate to North American landbirds which were on board trans-Atlantic liners when they docked at Southampton. Some possibly qualify for acceptance as Category A records, although none of them have ever been submitted to the *BBRC*.

## Northern Parula                                        *Parula americana*
One was found on the RMS Mauretania during an eastbound crossing of the North Atlantic on Sep. 19th 1962. It was kept in semi-captivity and fed on soft fruit, crumbs and water. It died after the ship docked in Southampton (Durand 1972).

## Blackpoll Warbler                                      *Dendroica striata*
One was present on the RMS Queen Elizabeth in Southampton on Oct. 12th 1961. Despite attempts to get it to fly ashore, it remained on board and subsequently died during the crossing to New York (Durand 1972).

## Song Sparrow                                          *Zonotrichia melodia*
One was on board the RMS Mauretania when it docked in Southampton on Oct. 14th 1962; it was still present the next day (Durand 1963).

## White-crowned Sparrow                              *Zonotrichia leucophrys*
One was found on the RMS Queen Elizabeth 2 on Sep. 21st 1988, soon after leaving New York. It was still on board as the ship arrived in Southampton on Sep. 26th, having fed on crumbs during the voyage (Frankland 1989).

## White-throated Sparrow                              *Zonotrichia albicollis*
Four which arrived in Southampton on a Cunard ship in October or November 1958 were placed in East Park aviary in the city, where the last died in January 1964 (Sharrock 1965). Two were on board the RMS Mauretania when it docked in Southampton on Oct. 14th 1962; both were still present on the following day but on 16th at least one was seen in a small park outside the dock gates (Durand 1963).

## Dark-eyed Junco                                          *Junco hyemalis*
One was on board the RMS Mauretania when it docked in Southampton on Oct. 14th 1962 and was still present the next day (Durand 1963).

# Appendix Two. Category D species and other exotics.

## Lesser White-fronted Goose
*Anser erythropus*

Two adults were in the Lymington/Hurst area in late August and early September 1985, one of which remained until Dec. 23rd 1985, one adult was at Blashford Lakes on Dec. 21st and 31st 1986, and another adult was seen at Portsmouth Harbour, Titchfield Haven and Needs Ore between December 1991 and May 1992.

## Bar-headed Goose
*Anser indicus*

Escapes from wildfowl collections have resulted in a small feral population of this Eastern Palearctic species gaining a foothold in the county. The first to be recorded appeared at several sites in the north-east during 1972. One was at Winnall Moors on Mar. 19th 1974, but there were no further sightings until 1980, when up to four were at Stratfield Saye. Since 1983, up to three pairs have bred there each year and the maximum count was of 25 on Sep. 17th 1983. Small numbers seen elsewhere in the north-east no doubt originate from this flock. In the upper Itchen valley, up to four have been present since 1983; these originated from a wildfowl collection at Headbourne Worthy from which the young were allowed to escape. From 1989-92, a pair has bred annually at Overton Lagoons in the upper Test valley, but their origin is not known. Occasional birds are now seen elsewhere, especially at coastal sites, usually consorting with Canada Geese. As many as nine were at Paulsgrove Reclamation on Oct. 3rd 1985.

## Wood Duck
*Aix sponsa*

Up to 12 have been reported in most years since the early 1970s in various parts of the county, but there has been no indication that breeding has occurred in the wild.

## Egyptian Vulture
*Neophron percnopterus*

Single adults were at Bishop's Dyke on June 16th 1968 and Farlington Marshes on Oct. 31st and Nov. 1st 1969. The latter bird was later caught in Sussex and showed signs of having had clipped primaries, thus denoting previous captivity.

## Demoiselle Crane
*Anthropoides virgo*

One was seen with three Spoonbills near Beaulieu from Oct. 23rd-25th 1927 and again on Nov. 9th 1927, when it was accompanied by two Spoonbills. Another was seen at Stoney Cross Airfield on Aug. 11th 1963. Records of this species are usually assumed to relate to escaped individuals although natural vagrancy is not impossible.

Other species recorded include White Pelican, Sacred Ibis, Greater Flamingo, Chilean Flamingo, Black Swan, Emperor Goose, Magellan Goose, Ruddy-headed Goose, Ashy-headed Goose, Cape Shelduck, Australian Shelduck, Chiloe Wigeon, Bahama Pintail, Cinnamon Teal, Ringed Teal, Marbled Teal, New Zealand Brown Duck, Rosybill, Harlequin, Barrow's Goldeneye, Hooded Merganser, Black Kite, Saker, Peacock, Silver Pheasant, Crowned Crane, Palm Dove, Budgerigar, Cockatiel, Quaker Parakeet, Peach-faced Lovebird, Eagle Owl, Chestnut-flanked White-eye, Superb Starling, Ashy-headed Starling, Golden Sparrow, Red-eared Waxbill, Black-headed Mannikin, Canary and Red-headed Bunting.

# Gazetteer

## *compiled by E J Wiseman*

| | | | |
|---|---|---|---|
| Abbots Ann | SU 3243 | Bishop's Dyke | SU 3405 |
| Abbotstone Down | SU 5836 | Bishopstoke | SU 4619 |
| Acres Down | SU 2709 | Bishops Sutton Watercress Beds | SU 6031 |
| Alice Holt Forest | SU 8042 | Bisterne | SU 1400 |
| Allbrook | SU 4521 | Bitterne (Southampton) | SU 4413 |
| Allington Lane Gravel Pit | SU 4717 | Bitterne Park (Southampton) | SU 4414 |
| Alresford Watercress Beds | SU 5833 | Black Bush | SU 2515 |
| Alresford Pond | SU 5933 | Blackbushe Airfield | SU 8059 |
| Amberwood Inclosure | SU 2013 | Black Dam (Basingstoke) | SU 6552 |
| Amery Farm Estate (Alton) | SU 7240 | Black Gutter Bottom | SU 2016 |
| Ampfield | SU 4023 | Blackmoor | SU 7733 |
| Andover Airfield | SU 3245 | Blackmoor Golf Course | SU 7734 |
| Anton valley | SU 3740 | Black Point (Hayling Island) | SZ 7599 |
| Arlebury Lake | SU 5732 | Blashford Lakes | SU 1507 |
| Ashlett Creek | SU 4603 | Blendworth | SU 7113 |
| Ashlett Mill Pond | SU 4603 | Bordon | SU 8035 |
| Ashley Farm (Stockbridge) | SU 3730 | Bossington | SU 3331 |
| Ashley Manor (Stockbridge) | SU 3830 | Botley Wood | SU 5410 |
| Ashley Walk | SU 2014 | Bourley Reservoir | SU 8250 |
| Ashley Warren | SU 4956 | Boveridge | SU 0714 |
| Ashmansworth | SU 4157 | Braishfield | SU 3725 |
| Ashurst | SU 3310 | Brambridge | SU 4622 |
| Ash Vale Gravel Pit | SU 8853 | Bramley Camp | SU 6559 |
| Avington | SU 5332 | Bramshaw Wood | SU 2516 |
| Avon Castle | SU 1303 | Bramshill (Warren Heath) | SU 7759 |
| Avon Causeway | SZ 1497 | Bramshill Common | SU 7562 |
| Avon Tyrrell | SZ 1499 | Bramshill Police College Lake | SU 7560 |
| Backley Plain | SU 2106 | Bramshill Rubbish Tip | SU 7561 |
| Baddesley Common | SU 3921 | Bramshott Common | SU 8633 |
| Badnam Creek (River Hamble) | SU 4808 | Bransbury Common | SU 4141 |
| Badshot Lea Gravel Pit | SU 8649 | Bratley | SU 2208 |
| Baffins Pond (Portsmouth) | SU 6601 | Bricksbury Hill | SU 8349 |
| Bartley | SU 3012 | Broadlands Estate | SU 3520 |
| Barton-on-Sea | SZ 2392 | Broadlands Lake | SU 3516 |
| Barton Stacey | SU 4340 | Brockenhurst | SU 3002 |
| Basingstoke Old Sewage Farm | SU 6452 | Brockley Warren | SU 4236 |
| Bassett (Southampton) | SU 4216 | Brook Wood | SU 2614 |
| Baughurst | SU 5860 | Broomy Plain | SU 2010 |
| Beacon Hill (Highclere) | SU 4557 | Broomy Walk | SU 2010 |
| Beacon Hill (Warnford) | SU 6022 | Broughton | SU 3132 |
| Beaulieu Abbey | SU 3802 | Broughton Down | SU 2932 |
| Beaulieu Estuary | SZ 4298 | Brown Candover | SU 5739 |
| Beaulieu Heath (East) | SU 4005 | Browndown | SZ 5899 |
| Beaulieu Heath (West) | SU 3500 | Browndown Rubbish Tip | SZ 5799 |
| Beaulieu Mill Pond | SU 3802 | Brownhill Inclosure | SZ 2399 |
| Bedhampton Rubbish Tip | SU 7005 | Brownwich | SU 5103 |
| Belmore House (Upham) | SU 5521 | Brownwich Cliffs | SU 5103 |
| Bentley | SU 7844 | Broxhead Common | SU 8037 |
| Bentworth | SU 6640 | Breamore | SU 1517 |
| Bere Mill | SU 4748 | Buckland (Portsmouth) | SU 6501 |
| Bickerley Common | SU 1404 | Bucklers Hard | SU 4100 |
| Bickton | SU 1412 | Budds Sewage Farm | SU 7005 |
| Bighton | SU 6134 | Bullington | SU 4641 |
| Bighton Lane Watercress Beds | SU 5933 | Burghclere | SU 4661 |

486

| | | | |
|---|---|---|---|
| Buriton Rubbish Tip | SU 7320 | Culverley Farm (Beaulieu) | SU 3604 |
| Burley Lawn | SU 2203 | Curbridge | SU 5211 |
| Burley Old Inclosure | SU 2404 | Cut Bridge (Milford-on-Sea) | SZ 2990 |
| Bury Marshes | SU 3811 | Damerham | SU 1016 |
| Butser Hill | SU 7120 | Danebury | SU 3237 |
| Cadland | SZ 4699 | Danes Stream (Milford-on-Sea) | SZ 2792 |
| Cadland Creek | SU 4505 | Darby Green | SU 8360 |
| Cadland Estate | SZ 4699 | Dean (Alresford) | SU 5833 |
| Cadnam | SU 2913 | Dean Hill | SU 2425 |
| Caesar's Belt | SU 4853 | Denmead | SU 6611 |
| Calshot | SU 4802 | Denny Lodge Inclosure | SU 3404 |
| Calshot Spit | SU 4802 | Denny Wood | SU 3305 |
| Camp Farm (Aldershot) | SU 8752 | Dibden Bay | SU 4008 |
| Canoe Lake (Portsmouth) | SZ 6498 | Dilton Farm (Brockenhurst) | SU 3300 |
| Carter's Clay | SU 3024 | Dogmersfield Lake | SU 7551 |
| Casbrook Common Rubbish Tip | SU 3525 | Dogmersfield Park | SU 7651 |
| Castle Farm (Warblington) | SU 7205 | Downton | SU 1821 |
| Cemetary Lake (Southampton) | SU 4114 | Drayton | SU 6705 |
| Chalton | SU 7316 | Droxford Mill | SU 6018 |
| Chandlers Ford | SU 4321 | Dummer | SU 5846 |
| Charity Down Farm (Longstock) | SU 3438 | Dunley (Whitchurch) | SU 4553 |
| Charlton Gravel Pit (Andover) | SU 3446 | Dur Hill Down | SU 1901 |
| Chawton | SU 7037 | Dur Wood | SU 5523 |
| Chawton Park | SU 7037 | East Aston | SU 4345 |
| Cheesefoot Head | SU 5327 | East Boldre | SU 3700 |
| Cheriton | SU 5828 | East Cosham | SU 6605 |
| Cherque (Gosport) | SU 5701 | East Hayling | SU 7302 |
| Chickenhall Sewage Farm | SU 4618 | Eastleigh | SU 4419 |
| Chidden Down | SU 6619 | Eastleigh Railway Yard | SU 4518 |
| Chilbolton | SU 3939 | Eastleigh Sewage Farm | SU 4618 |
| Chilcomb | SU 5028 | East Liss | SU 7827 |
| Chilland | SU 5232 | East Meon | SU 6722 |
| Chilton Candover | SU 5940 | Eastney | SZ 6799 |
| Chilworth Manor | SU 4018 | Eastney Point | SZ 6899 |
| Church Crookham | SU 8152 | Eastney Sewage Outfall | SZ 6899 |
| Clanfield | SU 6916 | Eastoke Car Park | SZ 7598 |
| Closewood Farm (Denmead) | SU 6610 | Easton | SU 5132 |
| Colbury | SU 3410 | East Tytherley | SU 2929 |
| Coldrey Park (Bentley) | SU 7743 | East Wellow | SU 3020 |
| Cole Henley | SU 4641 | East Winner Bank | SZ 6998 |
| Combe | SY 3960 | East Worldham | SU 7438 |
| Compton Down | SU 4525 | Ecchinswell | SU 5059 |
| Copythorne Common | SU 3015 | Efford Rubbish Tip | SZ 3192 |
| Corhampton | SU 6020 | Eling | SU 3612 |
| Cosham | SU 6505 | Eling Great Marsh | SU 3712 |
| Cowplain | SU 6911 | Eling Tide Mill | SU 3612 |
| Crab Wood | SU 4329 | Ellingham Lake (Blashford) | SU 1408 |
| Cracknore Hard | SU 4011 | Ellisfield | SU 6345 |
| Cranbury Park | SU 4423 | Elvetham Park | SU 7856 |
| Cranesmoor | SU 1902 | Emer Bog (North Baddesley) | SU 3921 |
| Cranmer Pond (Woolmer Forest) | SU 7932 | Embley Park | SU 3220 |
| Crawley | SU 4234 | Emery Down | SU 2808 |
| Creech Farm (Denmead) | SU 6310 | Empshott | SU 7531 |
| Crockford Bridge | SZ 3599 | Emsworth | SU 7406 |
| Crondall | SU 7948 | Emsworth Channel | SU 7402 |
| Crookham | SU 7952 | Enham Alamein | SU 3649 |
| Crookham Sewage Farm | SU 8252 | Enham Cross Roads | SU 3648 |
| Crow | SU 1603 | Eversley Church | SU 7760 |

| | | | |
|---|---|---|---|
| Eversley Gravel Pit | SU 7662 | Great Litchfield Down | SU 4755 |
| Ewhurst Pond | SU 5757 | Great Salterns Lake (Portsmouth) | SU 6701 |
| Ewshot | SU 8149 | Gritnam Wood | SU 2806 |
| Exbury | SU 4200 | Greywell | SU 7151 |
| Exton | SU 6120 | Hale | SU 1918 |
| Eyeworth Wood | SU 2215 | Half Moon Common | SU 2916 |
| Faccombe | SU 3958 | Hamble | SU 4807 |
| Fair Oak Sand Pit | SU 4918 | Hamble Airfield | SU 4707 |
| Fareham | SU 5706 | Hamble Common | SU 4806 |
| Fareham Creek | SU 5805 | Hamble Estuary | SU 4805 |
| Farley Mount | SU 4029 | Hamble Spit | SU 4805 |
| Farlington Marshes | SU 6804 | Hamer Warren Sand Pit | SU 1210 |
| Farnborough | SU 8754 | Hampton Ridge | SU 1913 |
| Farnborough Airfield | SU 8552 | Hancomb Bottom (Morestead) | SU 5125 |
| Farringdon | SU 7135 | Harbridge | SU 1410 |
| Fawley | SU 4503 | Hardway (Gosport) | SU 6101 |
| Fawley Down | SU 5126 | Harefield | SU 4613 |
| Fawley Pier | SU 4704 | Harewood Forest | SU 3943 |
| Fawley Power Station | SU 4603 | Harestock | SU 4631 |
| Fawley Reclamation | SU 4801 | Hartley Wespall | SU 6958 |
| Fawley Refinery | SU 4504 | Hartley Wintney | SU 7656 |
| Fawley Reservoir | SU 4405 | Harvest Slade Bottom | SU 2106 |
| Fernycroft | SU 3605 | Haslar Creek (Gosport) | SZ 6299 |
| Finkley | SU 3848 | Haslar Hospital (Gosport) | SZ 6298 |
| Fleet | SU 8154 | Hatchet Pond | SU 3601 |
| Fleet Pond | SU 8255 | Hatchet Moor | SU 3500 |
| Fletchers Thorns Inclosure | SU 2604 | Havant | SU 7106 |
| Fletchwood Lane (Ashurst) | SU 3311 | Havant Thicket | SU 7110 |
| Fordingbridge | SU 1414 | Hawkhill Inclosure | SU 3502 |
| Fort Brockhurst (Gosport) | SU 5902 | Hawkley | SU 7429 |
| Fort Elson (Gosport) | SU 6001 | Hawley Lake | SU 8357 |
| Fort Fareham Wood | SU 5704 | Hayling Bay | SZ 7298 |
| Fort Purbrook | SU 6706 | Hayling Island | SU 7101 |
| Fort Widley | SU 6506 | Hayling Oyster Beds | SU 7102 |
| Four Lanes End | SU 7248 | Hazel Down (Longstock) | SU 3639 |
| Four Marks | SU 6734 | Hazeley Down | SU 5025 |
| Frame Wood | SU 3503 | Hazeley Heath | SU 7558 |
| Freefolk Wood | SU 4944 | Headbourne Worthy Watercress Beds | SU 4832 |
| Frensham Great Pond | SU 8440 | Head Down (Buriton) | SU 7319 |
| Frensham Outlet Pond | SU 8340 | Headley | SU 5162 |
| Frimley Gravel Pit | SU 8856 | Heath Pond (Petersfield) | SU 7522 |
| Frith End | SU 8039 | Hedge End | SU 4912 |
| Fritham Plain | SU 2213 | Heckfield | SU 7260 |
| Froxfield | SU 7025 | Hen Wood (East Meon) | SU 6522 |
| Fullerton | SU 3739 | Hen Wood (Tunworth) | SU 6647 |
| Furzeley | SU 6510 | Highbridge | SU 4621 |
| Fyfield | SU 2946 | Highclere | SU 4360 |
| Gilkicker Point | SZ 6097 | Highfield (Southampton) | SU 4214 |
| Gilkicker Pond | SZ 6097 | Hightown (Ringwood) | SU 1705 |
| Godshill | SU 1714 | Highwood Reservoir | SU 4616 |
| Godshill Wood | SU 1716 | Hill Head | SU 5402 |
| Goleigh Wood | SU 7131 | Hillside Marsh | SU 7550 |
| Goodworth Clatford | SU 3642 | Hilsea Lines (Portsmouth) | SU 6604 |
| Goose Green Inclosure | SU 8040 | Hilsea Moat | SU 6604 |
| Gosport | SU 6000 | Hiltingbury | SU 4322 |
| Grange (Northington) | SU 5636 | Hinton Admiral | SZ 2095 |
| Grateley Station | SU 2641 | HMS Daedalus (Lee-on-the-Solent) | SU 5601 |
| Greatbridge (Romsey) | SU 3522 | HMS Dolphin (Gosport) | SZ 6298 |

| | | | |
|---|---|---|---|
| Hocombe Plantation | SU 4323 | Langstone Harbour | SU 6802 |
| Holmsley | SU 2200 | Langstone Mill Pond | SU 7105 |
| Holmsley Gravel Pit | SZ 2099 | Lasham Airfield | SU 6743 |
| Holt Pound (Alice Holt Forest) | SU 4481 | Latchmore Bottom | SU 1812 |
| Hook (Warsash) | SU 4905 | Laverstoke | SU 4948 |
| Hook Links (Warsash) | SU 4904 | Leckford | SU 3737 |
| Hook Rubbish Tip (Warsash) | SU 5105 | Le Court (Greatham) | SU 7631 |
| Hordle | SZ 2695 | Lee (Nursling) | SU 3617 |
| Hordle Beach | SZ 2791 | Lee-on-the Solent | SU 5500 |
| Hordle Cliff | SZ 2792 | Leigh Park | SU 7108 |
| Horndean | SU 7013 | Lepe | SZ 4598 |
| Horsea Island (Portsmouth Harbour) | SU 6304 | Linbrook Lake (Blashford) | SU 1506 |
| Horsebridge | SU 3430 | Linkenholt | SU 3558 |
| Houghton | SU 3432 | Liphook | SU 8431 |
| Hucklesbrook | SU 1509 | Lisle Court lagoon | SZ 3595 |
| Hucklesbrook Gravel Pit | SU 1510 | Liss | SU 7727 |
| Hunton | SU 4839 | Liss Forest | SU 7828 |
| Hursley | SU 4225 | Little London (Andover) | SU 3749 |
| Hurst Beach | SZ 3090 | Lodge Farm (Odiham) | SU 7452 |
| Hurstbourne Tarrant | SU 3853 | Lodge Farm (Southwick) | SU 6109 |
| Hurstbourne Priors | SU 4346 | Long Down (Hambledon) | SU 6619 |
| Hurst Castle | SZ 3189 | Longdown (New Forest) | SU 3508 |
| Hurst Narrows | SZ 3289 | Long Island (Langstone Harbour) | SU 7004 |
| Hythe Pier | SU 4208 | Longmoor | SU 7930 |
| IBM Lake (Cosham) | SU 6404 | Longparish | SU 4344 |
| Ibsley | SU 1409 | Longstock | SU 3636 |
| Ibsley Common | SU 1710 | Long Valley (Bricksbury Hill) | SU 8352 |
| Inchmery | SZ 4398 | Longwater Lawn (Lyndhurst) | SU 3208 |
| Inkpen | SU 3564 | Longwood Warren | SU 5226 |
| Islands Thorns Inclosure | SU 2115 | Lordswood | SU 3916 |
| Itchen Abbas | SU 5332 | Lower Bordean Farm | SU 6924 |
| Itchen Estuary | SU 4309 | Lower Brook (Mottisfont) | SU 3427 |
| Itchen Navigation | SU 4618 | Lower Pennington | SZ 3193 |
| Itchen Stoke | SU 5532 | Lower Swanthorpe Farm (Crondall) | SU 7747 |
| Ivy Lake (Blashford) | SU 1507 | Lower Test Marshes | SU 3614 |
| Janesmoor | SU 2413 | Lower Wield | SU 6340 |
| John O'Gaunt's Lake | SU 3530 | Lower Whitehill Farm (Overton) | SU 5146 |
| Kentford Lake | SU 3219 | Lower Woodcott Down | SU 4555 |
| Keyhaven Marsh | SZ 3192 | Low Hill Farm (Marwell Park) | SU 5020 |
| Keyhaven Saltings | SZ 3191 | Ludshott Common | SU 8535 |
| Kimbridge | SU 3225 | Lymington | SZ 3295 |
| Kingfisher Lake (Blashford) | SU 1506 | Lymington Estuary | SZ 3493 |
| Kingfisher Lake (Testwood) | SU 3514 | Lymington River | SZ 3494 |
| Kingsclere | SU 5258 | Lymore | SZ 2992 |
| Kingsley | SU 7838 | Lyndhurst | SU 2908 |
| Kingsley Sand Pit | SU 7637 | Manor Wood (Minstead) | SU 2710 |
| Kingston (Avon valley) | SU 1401 | Mansbridge (River Itchen) | SU 4415 |
| Kingston Common Pond | SU 1403 | Manydown Estate (Basingstoke) | SU 5852 |
| Kingston Great Common | SU 1802 | Mapledurwell Watercress Beds | SU 6851 |
| Kings Worthy | SU 4932 | Marchwood | SU 3909 |
| Knight's Enham | SU 3648 | Marchwood Power Station | SU 3911 |
| Knowle | SU 5509 | Mark Ash Wood | SU 2407 |
| Ladywell Lake | SU 5732 | Marsh Court (Stockbridge) | SU 3533 |
| Lainston | SU 4431 | Martin | SU 0619 |
| Lakeside (Eastleigh) | SU 4417 | Martin Down | SU 0419 |
| Lane End Down | SU 5525 | Martyr Worthy | SU 5732 |
| Langley (Fawley) | SU 4401 | Marwell Zoological Park | SU 5021 |
| Langstone Channel | SU 6901 | Matley Bog | SU 3307 |

| | | | |
|---|---|---|---|
| Mayfield Park (Southampton) | SU 4410 | Odiham | SU 7450 |
| Mayflower Park (Southampton) | SU 4111 | Old Alresford | SU 5834 |
| Mengham (Hayling Island) | SZ 7299 | Old Alresford Watercress Beds | SU 5933 |
| Meon | SU 5203 | Old Basing | SU 6652 |
| Meonstoke | SU 6119 | Old Netley | SU 4710 |
| Micheldever | SU 5139 | Old Portsmouth | SZ 6399 |
| Micheldever Station | SU 5142 | Old Winchester Hill | SU 6420 |
| Middle Wallop | SU 2937 | Oliver's Battery | SU 4527 |
| Middle Wallop Airfield | SU 3038 | Otterbourne | SU 4623 |
| Milford-on-Sea | SZ 2891 | Ovington | SU 5631 |
| Millbrook | SU 3813 | Overton | SU 5149 |
| Millersford Bottom | SU 1816 | Overton Lagoons | SU 5150 |
| Millersford Plantation | SU 2017 | Ower | SU 3216 |
| Mill Rythe | SU 7300 | Owslebury | SU 5123 |
| Milton Reclamation (Portsmouth) | SZ 6799 | Oxenbourne Down | SU 7118 |
| Minley | SU 8258 | Oxey Creek | SZ 3393 |
| Minley Rubbish Tip | SU 8156 | Park Corner Farm (Odiham) | SU 7748 |
| Minstead | SU 2811 | Park Gate | SU 5108 |
| Mislingford | SU 5814 | Park Prewett Hospital (Basingstoke) | SU 6153 |
| Mitchelland | SU 6210 | Passfield Pond | SU 8234 |
| Mockbeggar Lake (Blashford) | SU 1509 | Paulsgrove | SU 6306 |
| Moon Hill | SU 3502 | Paulsgrove Reclamation | SU 6305 |
| Moorcourt Farm (Nursling) | SU 3417 | Paulsgrove Rubbish Tip | SU 6305 |
| Moortown (Ringwood) | SU 1504 | Paultons Park | SU 3016 |
| Morestead | SU 5025 | Pennington Marsh | SZ 3292 |
| Morey's Lake (Blashford) | SU 1407 | Penton Mewsey | SU 3347 |
| Mortimer West End | SU 6363 | Perham | SU 2549 |
| Mottisfont | SU 3227 | Petersfield | SU 7423 |
| Moyles Court | SU 1608 | Pewit Island (Portsmouth Harbour) | SU 6003 |
| Needs Ore | SZ 4297 | Phoenix Green | SU 7555 |
| Nether Wallop | SU 3036 | Picket Post | SU 1906 |
| Netley | SU 4508 | Pigeon House Farm (Widley) | SU 6407 |
| Netley Marsh | SU 3313 | Pilley | SZ 3398 |
| Newlands Farm (Stubbington) | SU 5604 | Pilmore Gate Heath | SU 2708 |
| New Milton | SZ 2395 | Pilot Hill (Newbury) | SU 3959 |
| Newnham | SU 7053 | Pinglestone Watercress Beds | SU 5833 |
| Newton Valence | SU 7232 | Pinnick Wood | SU 1907 |
| Newtown Rubbish Tip (Weston) | SU 4510 | Pitt | SU 4528 |
| Noar Hill | SU 7431 | Pitt Down | SU 4129 |
| Nomansland | SU 2517 | Pittleworth Farm (Mottisfont) | SU 3229 |
| Normandy Marsh | SZ 3394 | Pitts Deep | SZ 3795 |
| North Baddesley | SU 3919 | Pitts Wood Inclosure | SU 1914 |
| North Binness Is. (Langstone Harbour) | SU 6904 | Plaitford Green | SU 2821 |
| North Boarhunt | SU 6010 | Plastow Green | SU 5361 |
| North Camp (Aldershot) | SU 8652 | Polhampton | SU 5250 |
| Northfields Farm (Twyford) | SU 4825 | Popham | SU 5643 |
| North Gorley | SU 1511 | Potbridge Fishery | SU 7454 |
| North Hayling | SU 7303 | Portchester | SU 6105 |
| Northington Lake | SU 5636 | Portchester Castle | SU 6204 |
| Northney (Hayling Island) | SU 7303 | Porton Down | SU 2135 |
| North Ripley | SZ 1699 | Ports Creek | SU 6703 |
| North Stoneham | SU 4317 | Portsdown Hill | SU 6406 |
| North Tidworth | SU 2449 | Portsmouth | SZ 6497 |
| North Waltham | SU 5646 | Portsmouth Airfield | SU 6603 |
| North Warnborough | SU 7351 | Portsmouth Dockyard | SU 6300 |
| Nursling Gravel Pit | SU 3515 | Portsmouth Harbour | SU 5902 |
| Oakhanger | SU 7735 | Port Solent Marina | SU 6305 |
| Ocknell Inclosure | SU 2411 | Portswood (Southampton) | SU 4314 |

490

| | | | |
|---|---|---|---|
| Posbrook | SU 5304 | Sherfield English | SU 2922 |
| Preshaw | SU 5722 | Shipton Bellinger | SU 2345 |
| Preshaw Down | SU 5822 | Shortheath Ponds | SU 7736 |
| Purbrook | SU 6708 | Silchester | SU 6362 |
| Purbrook Heath | SU 6607 | Sinah Common (Hayling Island) | SZ 6999 |
| Preston Candover | SU 6041 | Sinah Golf Course | SZ 6999 |
| Pyestock | SU 8353 | Sinah Gravel Pit | SZ 6999 |
| Pylewell (Lymington) | SZ 3595 | Sinah Warren | SZ 6999 |
| Quarley Hill | SU 2642 | Sleaford | SU 8038 |
| Queen Alexander Hospital (Cosham) | SU 6506 | Sleaford Reservoir | SU 8039 |
| Queen Bower | SU 2804 | Sloden Inclosure | SU 2113 |
| Queen Elizabeth Country Park | SU 7219 | Slufters Inclosure | SU 2210 |
| Queen's Parade (Aldershot) | SU 8652 | Snatchanger Farm (Odiham) | SU 4749 |
| Quidhampton Watercress Beds | SU 5250 | Soberton Down | SU 6116 |
| Ramridge Copse | SU 3148 | Solent Breezes | SU 5003 |
| Raven's Nest Inclosure | SU 2514 | Somerley Park | SU 1307 |
| Redbridge | SU 3713 | Somerley Rubbish Tip | SU 1207 |
| Red Rice (Andover) | SU 3441 | Sopley | SZ 1597 |
| Regents Park (Southampton) | SU 4013 | Southampton Airport (Eastleigh) | SU 4517 |
| Rhinefield | SU 2602 | Southampton Common | SU 4114 |
| Rhinefield Sandys Inclosure | SU 2504 | Southampton Eastern Docks | SU 4210 |
| Ridge | SU 3418 | Southampton University | SU 4215 |
| Ridley Plain | SU 2006 | Southampton Western Docks | SU 3812 |
| Ridley Wood | SU 2006 | South Gorley | SU 1610 |
| Ringwood Forest | SU 1108 | South Hayling | SZ 7198 |
| River Itchen | SU 4312 | Southleigh Woods | SU 7408 |
| Roche Court (Fareham) | SU 5808 | Southington Watercress Beds | SU 5049 |
| Rockbourne | SU 1118 | South Oakley Inclosure | SU 2205 |
| Rockford | SU 1708 | South Parade Pier (Portsmouth) | SZ 6598 |
| Roke Farm (Odiham) | SU 7649 | Southsea | SZ 6799 |
| Roman Road (Basingstoke) | SU 6052 | Southsea Castle | SZ 6498 |
| Romsey | SU 3521 | South Tidworth | SU 2347 |
| Rooksbury Mill (Andover) | SU 3544 | South Warnborough | SU 7247 |
| Ropley | SU 6431 | Southwick | SU 6208 |
| Round Copse (Sherfield) | SU 6855 | South Wonston Farm | SU 4636 |
| Rowbarrow Pond | SU 3504 | Sowley Farm | SZ 3796 |
| Rowland's Castle | SU 7310 | Sowley Pond | SZ 3796 |
| Rowner | SU 5801 | Sowley Marsh | SZ 3796 |
| Rownhams | SU 3817 | Sowley Shore | SZ 3795 |
| Royal Pier (Southampton) | SU 4110 | Sparsholt | SU 4331 |
| Roydon Woods (Brockenhurst) | SU 3100 | Spinnaker Lake (Blashford) | SU 1507 |
| Rushmore Down | SU 3454 | Spithead (The Solent) | SZ 6195 |
| Salisbury Trench | SU 2514 | Squabb Wood (Romsey) | SU 3321 |
| Salterns 8 acre Pond (Lymington) | SZ 3293 | Standford | SU 8134 |
| Salterns Marsh (Lymington) | SZ 3293 | Stanmore (Winchester) | SU 4628 |
| Salterns Rubbish Tip (Portsmouth) | SU 6701 | Stanswood Bay | SU 4700 |
| Sandy Point (Hayling Island) | SZ 7498 | St. Cross (Winchester) | SU 4728 |
| Selborne | SU 7433 | St. Deny's (Southampton) | SU 4314 |
| Selborne Common | SU 7333 | Stephens Copse (Froxfield) | SU 7026 |
| Set Thorns Inclosure | SZ 2699 | Steventon | SU 5447 |
| Shalden | SU 6941 | St Mary Bourne | SU 4250 |
| Shawford | SU 4724 | Stockbridge | SU 3535 |
| Shawford Down | SU 4624 | Stockbridge Common | SU 3534 |
| Sheepwash Farm (Purbrook) | SU 6509 | Stockbridge Down | SU 3734 |
| Sheet | SU 7524 | Stoke Fruit Farm (Hayling) | SU 7101 |
| Shepherds Spring | SU 3646 | Stoke | SU 4051 |
| Sherborne St John | SU 6255 | Stokes Bay | SZ 5898 |
| Sherfield-on-Loddon | SU 6757 | Stone Point (Lepe) | SZ 4598 |

| | | | |
|---|---|---|---|
| Stoney Cross | SU 2511 | Well | SU 7646 |
| Stubbington | SU 5503 | Wellington Country Park | SU 7161 |
| Stubbs Wood | SU 3603 | Wendleholme | SU 4907 |
| Sturt Pond (Milford-on-Sea) | SZ 2991 | West Dean | SU 2527 |
| Stratfield Saye | SU 7061 | West Down (Chilbolton) | SU 3838 |
| Sutton Scotney | SU 4639 | Western Court Watercress Beds | SU 6032 |
| Swanmore | SU 5715 | West Meon | SU 6424 |
| Sway | SZ 2798 | Weston | SU 4410 |
| Swaythling | SU 4415 | Weston Common | SU 6944 |
| Tadley | SU 6061 | Weston Shore | SU 4409 |
| Tadley Common | SU 6062 | West Park (Damerham) | SU 1117 |
| Tangley Clump | SU 3453 | West Tisted | SU 6529 |
| Tanners Creek (Lymington) | SZ 3695 | West Tytherley | SU 2629 |
| Tanners Lane (Lymington) | SZ 3695 | West Walk (Wickham) | SU 5912 |
| Tantany Wood | SU 3604 | West Wellow | SU 2818 |
| Teglease Down | SU 6519 | West Winner | SZ 6898 |
| Testwood | SU 3514 | West Wood | SU 4129 |
| Thatcher's Copse (Brownwich) | SU 5203 | Wherwell | SU 3941 |
| The Kench (Hayling Island) | SZ 6999 | Whitchurch | SU 4648 |
| Tichborne | SU 5730 | White Dell Farm (Fareham) | SU 5808 |
| Tidpit Down | SU 0617 | White Hill (Kingsclere) | SU 5156 |
| Timsbury | SU 3425 | Whitenap | SU 3720 |
| Timsbury Gravel Pit | SU 3421 | Whitsbury Down | SU 1121 |
| Titchfield | SU 5305 | Wickham | SU 5711 |
| Titchfield Abbey | SU 5406 | Wickham Sewage Farm | SU 5610 |
| Titchfield Haven | SU 5302 | Wicor (Portchester) | SU 5904 |
| Totton | SU 3513 | Widden Bottom | SZ 2899 |
| Tournerbury (Hayling Island) | SZ 7399 | Widley | SU 6506 |
| Town Quay (Southampton) | SU 4110 | Widley Farm (Portsdown) | SU 6607 |
| Trotts Wood | SU 3711 | Wield | SU 6238 |
| Tufton Warren Farm (Whitchurch) | SU 4744 | Wildgrounds (Gosport) | SU 5701 |
| Tundry Pond | SU 7752 | Wilverley Lodge | SU 2500 |
| Tunworth | SU 6748 | Wilverley Plain | SU 2501 |
| Tweseldown Racecourse | SU 8251 | Winchester College Water Meadows | SU 4828 |
| Twyford | SU 4824 | Winchester Sewage Farm | SU 4927 |
| Twyford Down | SU 4827 | Winchfield | SU 7654 |
| Upton | SU 3655 | Winnall Moors | SU 4830 |
| Upton Grey | SU 6948 | Winslade | SU 6548 |
| Vales Moor | SU 1804 | Wonston | SU 4739 |
| Vernham Dean | SU 3356 | Woodcott Down (Upper) | SU 4456 |
| Vernon's Farm (Southwick) | SU 6209 | Woodfidley | SU 3404 |
| Vinney Ridge | SU 2605 | Woodgreen | SU 1717 |
| Waggoners Wells | SU 8534 | Woodlands | SU 3211 |
| Wallington Valley (Fareham) | SU 5808 | Woodmancott | SU 5642 |
| Walpole Park (Gosport) | SZ 6199 | Woodmill (Southampton) | SU 4315 |
| Waltham Chase | SU 5615 | Woodside (Lymington) | SZ 3294 |
| Warblington | SU 7205 | Woolmer Forest | SU 8032 |
| Warnford | SU 6223 | Woolston | SU 4410 |
| Warnford Park | SU 6323 | Woolton Hill | SU 4261 |
| Warren Farm (Needs Ore) | SZ 4197 | Wootton St. Lawrence | SU 5953 |
| Warren Flats (Needs Ore) | SZ 4196 | Worthy Down | SU 4534 |
| Warren Heath (Bramshill) | SU 7759 | Yateley | SU 8160 |
| Warren Shore (Needs Ore) | SZ 4196 | Yateley Common | SU 8259 |
| Warsash | SU 4906 | Yateley Gravel Pit | SU 8261 |
| Warwick Slade | SU 2706 | Yateley Heath Wood | SU 8057 |
| Watership Down | SU 4957 | Yew Tree Bottom | SU 2500 |
| Watton's Ford | SU 1301 | Yew Tree Heath | SU 3606 |
| Weavers Down | SU 8030 | | |

# Hampshire Observers 1951-1992

* Participants in HOS Tetrad Atlas Breeding Bird Survey

Abbott P
Abbott S G*
Adamas K M
Adams M C
Adams P J
Adburrow D J
Addington J S
Agland P C
Aiken H
Airey A F
Aitken H
Akers P G
Albrecht J S M
Alexander G*
Alexander J
Alexander K
Allan A
Allday P S A
Allen A
Allen J*
Alley S L
Allison P*
Allison R
Allnutt D P
Amor R
Amphlett A
Anderson P
Anderton D A
Andrews B
Andrews E A L
Andrews J
Andrews R W
Angell B J
Angell D
Angell H
Angliss M
Ansell N B
Appleton S
Arkell K R
Armstrong G
Arnold M
Arnott M J
Arnott M S*
Asbridge R
Ash J S
Ashburn E A
Ashby C B
Asher I*
Ashmore A*
Ashton J M
Aslin J S
Aspinall S J
Atkin K
Atkins D
Atkins J D
Atkins S
Atrill D J
Atrill R
Atrill T
Attrill D T
Attrill J
Auld C
Austin T
Avery G
Axten D W
Baatsen R
Bacon A F L
Bacon H R
Bacon J C
Baigent J A

Bailey A
Bailey G
Bailey P*
Bailey T
Baird R D
Baker B G
Baker C
Baker E K
Baker M J*
Baker R
Baker V
Balch C C
Balch S
Baldock A J
Baldwin J*
Ball D*
Ball M W
Ballantyne C
Banks M B
Banks R
Banks S
Barden P J
Barlow G F
Barlow J H
Barker J
Barnes J R
Barnes P
Barnes R F
Barrell G*
Barrett A
Barrett D
Barrett G C
Barrett R*
Barston P
Barstow S F
Bartlett J
Bartlett M D
Bartlett T G*
Batchelar D M
Batchelor E
Bateman P
Bateup P H*
Batt E H
Baverstock D
Bayes D P
Bayliss J
Beale C R H
Bealey C G*
Beames I R
Beardshaw L*
Beazley J
Bell D A
Bell R*
Bellegueulle J
Bennett A B
Bennett J C*
Bennett M
Best S J
Betton K F*
Betts F
Betts T F G
Bevis A J
Bide W*
Bidmead H
Biggs D T
Bighton K
Bill D I*
Billett D F
Billett R A
Binstead N*

Birch A*
Birt R
Bishop D R
Bishop M S
Bishop R D J
Biss K*
Bizley S
Blackburn A R
Blackburn J E
Blair J M
Blakeley A
Blanchard A P
Bland D W
Blank T H
Blockey C
Bloss J
Bluett P
Blunt G
Blyth R O
Boalch K
Boarder W J
Bodkin G
Bogarde L
Bolger E
Bolton
Bond A J
Bonham P F
Bonner R
Booth R G
Boras W
Borland J C J
Borrow I*
Boshford R
Boswall J H
Boswell J
Boswell S*
Bottomley J B
Boulton C
Boutflower J C
Bower R
Bowers A R
Bowers D K
Bowers J K
Bowes I*
Bowles A
Bowley J J
Bowley T E
Bowman R P
Boyes J S W
Boyes S
Boyle C G
Boys J V
Brady P
Bramble F
Brame J*
Brandess G
Braunton H
Branford H
Brazier D
Bream R
Brent S
Brett E C
Brew P J
Brewer R
Brice T E
Briggs K B*
Bright D
Bright P
Bristow M
Britten N

Broadley D
Broadley J C
Bromage I
Bromhead J
Brooke D M
Brookes C
Brooks C
Broomfield L G*
Brotherton H
Brothwell D*
Brown C
Brown G*
Brown I G
Brown I H*
Brown J H F
Brown J M
Brown K
Brown P
Brown R
Brown W H D
Browning D
Browsey B W
Bruce M M
Brundell A*
Brunt R P M*
Brunton R J*
Bryan-Brown J W*
Bryant B
Bryant M*
Buchanan J
Buchette A
Buchette D
Buckett R H
Buckland S J
Buckler D J
Buckley J*
Buckshall J
Budd P A
Bulson P S
Bunce G J*
Bundy G
Bundy R
Burchall G
Burfitt R
Burges D J
Burnop M W
Burnett C*
Burns A P
Burns B
Burns K E
Burns P
Burt M J
Burt R
Burton B
Burton J L
Burwood R W
Bury C A
Bury S
Bushell A R
Butcher D A P
Butcher R D J
Butler A
Butler D J
Butler J
Butler K*
Butler R
Butterworth A M B*
Butterworth S
Button G A
Buxton J M

Buzzard G G*
Byers T
Cadbury C J
Cade M
Cadman W A
Calderwood I
Calvert A*
Cameron R McL
Campbell B E
Campbell C H*
Campbell M A
Campbell M R*
Campbell P
Campbell R
Campbell W R
Cannings G C
Cannings M C
Cantelo J
Cantle K
Carlos-Perkins D S
Carpenter J M
Carpenter R J*
Carpenter T F
Carr D
Carrell H
Carrington J
Carter A G*
Carter A V*
Carter C I*
Carter C J*
Carter G
Carter S H*
Carwardine M
Cass M
Case M*
Case S*
Castle P E
Cave J
Caws S
Cawsey J
Cawthorne R A
Cayme H M
Chadder P
Chadwick P J
Chamberlain J E
Chamberlain P G*
Chambers P
Champion M H
Champion N G S
Champion R S
Chandler R
Chapman D A
Chapman J
Chapman L
Chapman R A*
Chappell J A
Chappell R
Chappell P J*
Charles J C S
Charlton D
Chase D*
Chase J M
Chatters C
Cheke D J*
Cheke R A
Cheke Y C*
Chelmick D G
Chelnick D
Chennells B*
Chennells J

493

Chesbrough P S
Cheverton J M
Chilcott D J
Chilcott M
Chilcott R
Chipchase R M
Chittenden R H
Christmas S E
Christmas T J
Christie D A*
Christophersen H O
Church D
Churches E
Clabon T
Clafton B
Clafton F R
Clark A J*
Clark A P
Clark E*
Clark J A*
Clark J M*
Clark R F
Clark S
Clark T
Clarke C S
Clarke D M E
Clarke M*
Clarke S
Clarkson J G
Clase H J
Claxton A J
Clay F N*
Clay G H
Clay R
Clayden C N
Clayton I T
Cleal D
Cleave A J*
Clegg A L
Clegg C R A
Clegg J M
Clements R*
Clifford M J
Clifton J
Clifton P J R
Cliyatt T A
Cloutman J*
Cloyne J M*
Clulee D
Coates B*
Coates M
Cobb J
Cobb N
Cockburn C
Cocks J*
Cockshoot S
Codlin T D*
Coe C J
Coe K D
Cohen E
Cohen S H
Cole A*
Cole G
Cole R E
Coles R K
Coleman M
Coleman R J
Collard J H
Colley E W
Collin P N
Colin-Stokes R*
Collins A R
Collins B
Collins C B
Collins D R
Collins F B

Collins M
Collins M A
Collins P R
Colliver N
Collman J R*
Colston P
Combes R P
Combridge M C*
Combridge P L*
Compton A W
Conchie J
Condell G
Constantine D A T
Cook B*
Cook C
Cook D L
Cook G M*
Cook P F*
Cook R*
Cook R A*
Cooke R
Cooke R E*
Coomber R F
Cooper A E
Cooper C
Cooper D G
Cooper E F
Cooper J E
Cooper L R
Cooper P F
Cooper W F
Cope R F
Copeland P
Copley J
Coppin N
Corbet J
Corbett J S
Corke A T K*
Cornelius P F S
Corr D A S
Cort J S
Cortule J S
Coslett K M
Cottle N W*
Court-Smith D St J
Cousins J
Cowan F
Cowan J R*
Cowie N
Coyle R*
Cox A
Cox A J F
Cox L W R
Cox M A
Cozens J
Cram F
Craw W A
Crease A J*
Cremona R U
Crewe P R
Crisp K
Crocker N
Croker R
Cronan A J
Cronan D
Crook J
Crook N
Crookshank J K
Croom E
Cross E V
Cross J K
Crouch D*
Crouch L
Crowley P J
Crowley T L
Croxsam S

Cull J F
Culley I G
Cundall R J
Curber R M
Cuerel P*
Curry P
Curry R*
Curtis C R
Cuthbert C R*
Cutler H L*
Dagger J H K
Dale S
Dalton M
Daly P M
Damont D J
Dann M P
Darter C E
Dave R
Davey S R
Davey V G
Davidson D M
Davidson J O'C
Davies B H*
Davies E H R
Davies S*
Davis A M
Davis M
Davis N
Davis P G
Davis R B
Davis S
Davison R
Dawson A
Dawson C
Daly P M
Day P L
Dayton M
Dedman J*
Delany S
Dell C
Dell D H
Dell J
Dennis G J
Dennis R H
Denny J F
De Potier A*
De Vries P J*
Dickinson E C
Dicks D E J
Dickson A
Dickson H A
Dighton K
Dilke R
Dimmock D P
Dinsdale E P*
Dixon A
Dixon B
Dixon J
Dixon M
Dixon T G
Dobb R
Doble P F*
Dobson J
Dodds J
Dodgson J
Doe C
Doe E
Doggett D W R*
Donaghey H
Doran T M J
Dougall T W
Douglas H A
Douglas K S
Dowell S D*
Downing R
Downs S

Doyle M J
Doyle S
Draper C
Draper J C
Dudley A J
Dudley B*
Duffell P
Duffin B S*
Duffin I S
Duffin T M
Duffy M D
Dunn D N
Dunn R
Dunniece G*
Durell C F
Durnell P R
Durrell J
Dymott P
Eagle P
Eagles J M
Eagles J W
Eagling R J
Earl M
Earp W J
Earwicker G A
East M A
Easto R P*
Easto V J*
Eaton D*
Eaton N
Edgeller M L
Edmeades D
Edmund Rev
Edom C
Edom J H M
Edwards G R
Edwards H*
Edwards K
Edwards R D
Edwards S B
Edwards W G
Edwin T W*
Eldridge G*
Eley I J
Elford C B*
Elgood J
Elkins N
Ellcombe P
Ellery T*
Elliott D F
Elliott M B
Ellis J
Elmes P F
Elmes R*
Elms N E G
Emmett R E
Entwhistle M
Etheridge L*
Evans A W
Evans B R
Evans D G*
Evans G C*
Evans H
Evans J
Evans K*
Evans N
Evans P
Evans R D
Evans T
Everett J
Everett W G
Eyre J A*
Facer D
Faithfull J
Farmer J*
Farr G

Farren D
Farwell G*
Farwell I G
Fasham M R J
Faulkner W J M
Fawkes P F*
Felgate M L
Fellows B J
Fellows E J
Felstead H C
Fennel J
Ferguson W C
Ferns P N
Ffennell D W H
Field A
Field G
Field V
Fielder A
Fieldsend D C
Findley P
Firth K J*
Fisher A
Fisher D*
Fisher G H
Fisher M C
Fisher R E
Fletcher H M
Flint K
Flint P R
Flower G D
Folkes P*
Foad M
Follett J C
Follows S P
Foord F
Foord J
Foord M*
Foot D
Forbes G V
Ford J
Ford R E
Forge K
Forster G H
Forster I
Forster M J
Foster B T*
Foster Z
Fowler G C W
Fowler N H
Fox C J
Foxton A J
France D W
Frankcom J*
Frankum R G
Fraser M
Frazer D
Frazer O H
Freeborn K
Freeman D
Freshwater D V
Frost R K*
Fry C H
Fry D
Fry R M
Fuggles-Couchman N R*
Fullager P J
Fuller H W C*
Fuller R J
Furmage D B
Furness P M
Fussey C
Gale B
Gallagher J
Gallagher M*
Gallagher S D
Gallop P W

494

Gambi P
Gambrill D A*
Gammage P A
Gaskin I
Gauntlett F M
Gantlett S J M
Gardner L
Gardner N J
Gardner P M
Garnett R O B
Garr J J
Gaskell J
Gates M
Gatley H T
Gatley S J
Gatrall W
Geary S
Gee B D
Gent C R
Gibbons M F
Gibbons M J
Gilham B
Gill M F
Gipson P
Girdlestone H N
Gittens G
Gleason R
Glombek G M*
Glover C J
Gloyn J C
Gloyne J
Glue D E
Goater B
Gobbett D
Gobbett K*
Goddard D C*
Goddard D J
Goddard F J
Goddard J
Godden R J
Godfrey D J
Godfrey K M
Godfrey P
Godwin T
Goman J
Gomes R
Goodall L
Goodhart J
Goodhart M
Goodheart M
Goodliffe V H
Goodspeed J R
Goodyer B
Goodyer S M
Gordon R
Goris L H
Gough R
Gowrley R*
Grafton J
Graham A C
Graham K D
Grant K R
Grant P*
Grant P R
Grass H
Gravely L
Gray J
Gray I J
Gray S J
Greatorex G J*
Green A
Green C
Green D G
Green G P
Green N
Green R E

Greenhalf M R
Gregory A S
Gregory P A
Gregory P E
Gresham Cooke A
Griffiths C H M
Griffiths R
Grisewood F H
Grist D M
Grossert A
Grove E A
Grove P
Grove S J
Gulliver J*
Gulliver W*
Gumn D G*
Gumn M
Guningham J
Gunn J M
Gurney M A
Gutteridge A C*
Gutteridge H L
Gutteridge T
Guy L
Guy T J
Guyatt T A
Gwynn B S
Habard C A
Hack K M B
Hack P J
Hackston G*
Haggar K J*
Haig P
Haisell O*
Haisell P
Haken R W
Hale A P S*
Hale E
Hall A
Hall C
Hall D A L
Hall N J
Hall P J
Hall S
Halliday D
Hallowes R C
Halls J
Halsey M
Hanby A M
Hamlyn J
Hancock A P
Hancock J*
Hand R
Hardacre, A J
Hardy C M*
Hardy G
Hargreaves P M
Hargreaves R A*
Harkness R
Harley B H
Harrington A
Harrington J*
Harris C J
Harris G I
Harris H V
Harris P M
Harris R A*
Harris R E
Harrison J M
Harrison M
Harrison P
Hart P R
Harvey D A
Harvey H C
Harvey M I
Harvey S C

Hatfield H L
Hatherley P R
Haton O A
Hatton M
Hawkins D
Hawkins M J
Hay M J W*
Hay W A
Hayden A
Haynes D G
Haynes R
Hayward L W
Hayward R*
Heal C H
Headley M
Hearn A W P
Heath A
Heath B A
Heath R
Heath T
Heathcote M
Heathcote T G
Heather K
Heather S R
Heaton A J
Hebden F
Hedley B*
Hellard R J
Helyar W G
Henderson C
Henderson D
Henderson T W
Henley R A
Henry A J
Henty C J
Herlihy D J
Herlihy M V
Hesling A
Hett S
Hewett R
Hewitson D R
Hewitt A J*
Hewitt R J D
Hewson C
Hibberd J W*
Hibbs B
Hickman S J
Hicks G J*
Higgens J
Higson E R
Higson L E
Hiley I*
Hill A G
Hill B J
Hill C H J
Hill D
Hill H M
Hill J M
Hilton J I*
Hiscocks D A*
Hoad B
Hoad R S
Hoadley B*
Hobbs A*
Hobby P
Hobern D*
Hoblin R
Hockey R C A
Hodson P
Hogbin G L
Hoidge F A W
Hold A
Holden D W
Holland D G J
Holland M*
Holliday R

Hollins J R W*
Hollman
Hollocks J
Hollow D
Hollow P A
Holloway P
Holmes E J
Holmes F D
Holmes M R
Holmes P
Holroyd R
Holt C
Holt J
Holtom A C S
Holyhead J
Honnor F J
Hook O
Hooper S
Hopkins G R
Hopkins J R
Hopkins V F
Hopkinson G
Hopkinson H C
Hopkinson J H
Hore H H
Horn I M
Horner A J
Horton D
Horton N
Houghton I
Houseman C
Howard M*
Howarth S*
Howe R
Howell R
Howells B L
Howells M*
Howells R L
Hubble D W L
Hudson F E
Hudson J*
Hudson M J
Huggins G
Hughes A
Hughes D*
Hughes K D*
Hughes S W M
Hulbert F J
Hull C
Hull M J
Hullett M E
Humphrey P
Humphriss M J
Hunnybun D J
Hunt J
Hunt P R*
Hunt R
Hunter C
Hunter M
Hunter P J
Hurford C
Husband C I
Husband E M
Hustings D J
Hutchings A*
Hutchins P E*
Hutchinson M M
Hutchinson P
Huxford R W*
Huxley G H*
Hyde P
Ilsley K
Impey J M
Ingleby R A O
Ingram C
Ingram S

Inness P J
Insley H
Ironside E A
Irvine J
Irvine R F
Jackson D
Jackson J
Jackson K*
Jackson R
Jackson S
Jackson T A
Jacobs G W
Jacobs R*
James A R*
James C M
James T C
Janes F V
Jardine N
Jeffrey P A*
Jellicoe M R
Jenkins D
Jenkins J
Jennings F M*
Jennings P P
Jennings T J*
Jepson R H
Johnson A D
Johnson D*
Johnson G H
Johnson K
Johnson M
Joicey J*
Jollands A
Jolly C
Jones B M*
Jones C
Jones D
Jones E E H
Jones E L
Jones G
Jones H S
Jones J
Jones J A W*
Jones J M*
Jones M*
Jones M H*
Jones N R
Jones P
Jones R
Jones S A S*
Jorgensen T H
Joughin R W
Joynes C*
Judd G E
Judkins H A
Julian D H
Jupe T
Kay-Robinson H P
Keane K G
Keane P S*
Kearns K
Keen A L
Keen S G*
Kefford H K
Keith B*
Keith S
Kenchington K
Kendall J
Kendall N
Kennedy J
Kennedy L
Kennett D W
Kent P W
Kent R
Kerley A G
Kerr R G

Kerry T
Kerslake P J
Kesby J
Ketteringham J
Kiddier J
Kieser J
Kimber Y
King B A
King M
King R
King R J
King S S
King V A
Kingston A*
Kingston E A
Kingston S
Kinns G
Kinsey G
Kinsey N J
Kitchin C
Knight K*
Knight M
Knightley C
Knott A*
Knowles C
Knowlton D
Kopinski M
Lachlan C*
Lake P
Lakin G*
Lakin I*
Lakin W L*
Lamb E T
Lambert F R
Lambert G T
Lambert M P
Lance J
Landymore N
Lane R H S
Lang D C
Lang M
Lang P
Langley K
Langman M
Lansdown P
Latham J O*
Lathbury K
Laurence R
Lavender R A
Lawler S W
Lawman T A
Lawrence E S
Lawrence G J
Lawrence R A
Lawrence R H
Lawson J
Leach R A*
Leaney R M
Leather V M
Leathes J
Le Brocq P F
Leckie J*
Lee A V
Lee G
Lee L R
Lee P
Lee S L B
Legg J
Legg R D E
Legge W G D*
Lemare R S
Lemon E*
Lester G D*
Letford W A
Leverett R E
Levett R K*

Lewis D W*
Lewis G E
Lewis I
Lewis J
Lidstone-Scott R
Liford R G
Liley M J S
Lindsay J D
Lindsey N T
Line R J
Linington S
Linsey J D
Linsey N J
Little S J
Lister D J
Littleton R
Livett A J
Lloyd G C*
Lloyd G K
Lock B
Lock J M
Lockton D
Lodge P
Londsey N J
Lord J
Lord P*
Lord R E*
Lott H J
Lovett C*
Lovett J*
Low D M
Lowe G
Lowman M I
Lucas J A*
Lucas R G
Lucian D
Lundy S
Lushington R*
Lycett I G
Lyth B M
Maasz P
Maasz T*
Macafee T C H*
MacAlpine E A M
MacDonald C R
Machin R J
MacKarness P J
Mackinnon A J
Mackinnon P V
Maclean G M
Maclean K J H
Maclean N M
Macklin J
Macklin R N*
Mackworth Praed C W
MacManus T S
Maconochie R R
MacPhearson I
Maddox L M
Madgewick A
Major J E
Mallock D J
Mann P D
Manns D J
Mansfield J H O
Mantle P L J*
Marchant J H
Markwood W*
Marley R
Marr B A E
Marr M J
Marriott B
Marriott G
Marriott N H
Marsh E A
Marsh P

Marsh Z
Marston P C
Martin D*
Martin G*
Martin K P*
Martin M D
Martin S*
Martin T M*
Martins R
Maskell R
Maskrey J
Mason A
Masters B J
Masters E
Masters L H J
Mathias R E
Maton O A*
Matthews D
Matthews P
Maule J
Maule P W
Maundrell A*
May R H
Mayall R G
Maycock K W*
Mayhead C*
Mayhead L
Maynard P J*
Mays P
Mayes P
McAndrews P
McAndrews S
McCann N
McCann R J
McCarthy D
McCarthy J E
McCarthy M G
McCarthy P
McGregor I R
McHoal J M
McIntyre G E
McJanett T
McLeod N
McMillan A T
McPhail
McPherson I
McQuarrie A F
McQuillin J F
McQuillin I J
McQuitty J C
McVail M J
Mead E
Medhurst H
Meek E
Megeasy R
Melhuish M
Mellen K
Mercer B J
Merritt R
Merritt W
Michael T
Miles D
Miles J C
Miller E M
Miller J A d'E
Miller K I
Miller-Hallett J L
Millington R G
Millington S J
Mills D
Mills J G*
Milne J
Milsom T P*
Milward L
Minton C D T
Mitchell A F

Mitchell D*
Mitchell J
Mitchison D
Mockler M
Moir C M
Mole D C
Moll N G C
Money N
Montague L P
Montague R
Montgomery K*
Moody A
Moody E J*
Moody M P
Moore B
Moore H S
Moore J
Morgan B
Morgan J H*
Morgan V
Morris B
Morris C
Morris D J
Morris E
Morrison D M
Morrison P I*
Morrison S M*
Morton M
Moses S P
Moss J
Moss M
Mottram N
Mould J E M
Mould R B
Moule G H W
Moult C J*
Mowlem A
Mountfort G
Mullins J R
Mumford V J*
Mummery L*
Munday R A*
Munns D J
Murphy D J
Murphy G*
Murphy K G
Murphy M H
Murphy P
Murray J
Mutch J N
Myers G
Nash H*
Nash P*
Naylor E G
Nelson W
Nevitt R
Newell M A
Newell S M
Newman E
Mewman H
Newnham E M
Newport B
Newton M
Nicholl J D A
Nicholson D M
Nicoll C*
Nicoll E F*
Nicoll P J
Nicolson G A*
Nisbett I C T
Noakes J M*
Noble K
Nolan M E
Norris A Y*
Norris C W
Norris K A*

Norris T L
Norriss T J*
North A*
North A J
North M
Northcote-Wright D
Northeast J L
Northwood C J
Norton J A*
Norton R*
Norton W J E
Noyce P
Nurney D
Nurse M W*
Oades R D
Oakleaf D
Oakley L
Oakshatt J
O'Connell P
Oddie W E
Oliver A F
Onley D J
Opie M
Oram M A
Orchard P*
Orchard P H
O'Riordan P K
Orlebar J H R
Orr N W*
Orton J
Osborne L F
Osborne L W
Outlaw R*
Overton R
Owen P D
Owton W E
Oxley U F
Packer J J
Packham C G
Padfield S E
Page M J
Page P W K
Page S*
Pain J*
Painter M G*
Palmer E
Palmer K H
Palmer K W*
Palmer M E
Palmer M J
Palmer P
Palmer R J
Pankhurst M
Paradise D J*
Parfitt A*
Paris J C
Parker A
Parker D C
Parkin R
Parkin W R
Parr C*
Parrinder E
Parry M J
Parslow J L F
Parsons A J*
Parsons D J
Parsons R
Pateman T
Paton V S
Patrick C M C
Patrick K
Paul D H
Paulson-Ellis C W G
Paulson-Ellis M P E
Pavey J F
Pawling M E A*

Payn J
Payne A
Payne M
Peace N D*
Peall S M
Pearce E F
Pearce-Smith A
Pearce-Smith N
Pearson D J*
Pearson P W
Peart D E M
Peers M F
Pemberton B S
Pembroke J*
Penfold R
Penn G
Penrose F
Penrose M A M
Pepin C E
Peplar G R M
Pepperdine E E
Percy W
Percy D M
Perry A R
Perry P A
Perkins D C
Perkins R*
Peskett G L
Peters S P
Pettet A V
Petty D*
Petty N C
Philips M
Philpot M G
Philpott M
Pickess B P
Pickin M
Picknell A V
Pictor G D
Pidgeon E*
Pidgeon P G
Pierce G G
Pierce T G
Pilkington J L L
Pillow I
Pink A
Piper M L
Pitman D
Pitt M J
Pittam J*
Player J
Plowman S N
Plunkett J S L
Pollack R D
Pollinger B R*
Pomeroy D
Poole D
Pope A E
Pope C R
Popham C
Port M H
Porter R F
Pothecary J*
Potts A
Potts P M*
Potts W A
Pounds H E
Powell D*
Powell C M
Powell R
Powney M
Prater A J
Pratt E A
Pratt N H*
Preddle G
Prestt I

Price D
Price E
Price G H
Price G J
Price T D
Prince M G
Prior K*
Prior P N
Probyn J
Probyn M
Proctor B
Puckering P J*
Pugh P R
Pullan G M
Pullen N D
Pullin G
Pumfrett D
Purkiss A E
Puttick J H
Puttick N M
Pym A
Quick A K
Quin-Smith G W
Raban D
Rabbetts P L
Raby P N
Rackett B J
Radford D J
Radford F W P
Rae J
Rae R
Rafter M*
Ralph J D
Ralphs I L
Ramage R M
Rand N A
Randall C
Rawlence D A
Rayfield P A
Ranger R J*
Raymond V B*
Raynor E M*
Raynor P J*
Read M
Reader P
Ready P
Reaney J
Redmayne G B
Reed C
Reed M J
Reed P
Rees G H
Rees P J
Reese R A
Reeves C J
Reeves L
Reeves S A
Reeves W
Reid M
Reid P A
Renyard B W*
Reveley R
Rew G A M
Reynolds B
Reynolds F L
Rhodes A S
Rhodes C K
Riall A B
Riall J M L
Rich G
Richards D M
Richards E
Richards G A
Richards J R A
Richards M
Richards P

Richardson A
Riddell K D
Riddlestone D
Riddy M
Ridge H M
Ridge R
Riley D A
Ringrose M
Ritchie S*
Roach M K
Roberts A*
Roberts B S
Roberts D
Roberts E T*
Roberts G C M*
Roberts M T M
Robertson A W P
Robertson D B C
Robinson C C
Robinson G
Robinson P K*
Rodgers L F
Rogers A
Rogers C
Rogers M
Rogers M J
Rogers N R
Rollinson K M
Rollinson S J C
Rolls J C
Rooke K B
Rooke R
Roper E
Rose A
Rose P
Ross C
Rowe J*
Rowe S
Rowland G J S*
Rowlatt H F*
Rowlett R
Rozzel R
Rozzelli B
Rumis H
Ruscoe S R*
Russell A
Russell C
Russell D H
Russell E
Russell J
Russell R W*
Ruston R
Ruthen A R
Rutherford W
Rycroft D*
Rycroft R N
Ryden C
Rylands K
Ryves D
Sacree B R
Sainsbury V
Sampson A J
Samways M*
Sanderson R F
Sanger D G
Sapsed K
Sargeant D J*
Saundby R
Saunders R*
Saunders-Davies D A P
Savage A M
Savage B
Savage C*
Sawdy C E*
Sawle A C
Sawyer E L

Scaife D
Scammell R
Scapens P J
Scapens R J
Schmidt K
Schofield P*
Scott J G*
Scott K P
Scott M A*
Scott P
Scouller D
Scouller A
Seabroke M M
Seabroke R
Seago C
Searle A
Searle J D
Searle I
Sears B
Sears J H
Selwood J
Senior R J*
Seymour J C
Shackleton K
Shakespeare A A
Shakespeare W
Sharkey B
Sharland P
Sharland R E
Sharp G*
Sharp P
Sharrock J T R
Shave N
Shaw A G
Sheldon B C*
Shelly J A
Shelton D
Shepard W
Shepherd B
Shepherd H R
Shepherd M
Shepherd W
Shepperd M J
Shergold M J
Shergold R
Sherwood G R
Shillitoe I
Shillitoe J R D*
Shillitoe K V*
Ship R*
Short P
Short R
Shrubb M
Shrubsole M*
Sidaway D*
Silcocks A F
Silcocks T B
Silvers C O
Simcox W*
Simkin D J
Simpkins C D
Simmonds M D*
Simmonds P E L
Simms E
Simms J R*
Simonds J
Simonds M
Simons J
Simpson A
Simpson D O
Simpson I M
Simpson R N
Simson E C L
Sivell P*
Skarratt R J M
Skilleter L M

Slade C*
Slater B*
Slater P
Slater S*
Small B
Small R G
Smallbone A C*
Smallwood J
Smart A
Smart G
Smedley M J
Smeed A W G
Smith A
Smith B E
Smith C J
Smith D*
Smith H
Smith J
Smith L
Smith M D
Smith M H
Smith M P J
Smith N A
Smith P J S
Smith R E
Smith R G
Smith S J
Smith S W*
Smith T
Smout T C
Snelgrove R
Snellgrove B
Snook A M*
Snow L
Snow R A
Snoxell M J S
Snudden T
Southern L J C
Sparkes P
Sparrow J
Speak E M
Speak P W
Spicer S
Spokes G
Sporne I M
Sporne K
Sporne L
Sporne S H
Spreadborough A J
Spreadborough P
Spriggs J W
Spring-Smyth J*
Spring-Smyth T
Spurgin M J
Spurgin S J
Squires R
Stacey M J
Staffel T E
Stafford J
Stagg S*
Stainer D
Stallard C E
Standley P E
Standring K T
Stane K*
Stanham H G
Stanniforth W
Stansbury P B
Stanford W
Staples B
Staples J
Steadman J St J
Stenning J H*
Stent P
Stephens W
Stephenson G C*

497

Stephenson G H
Sterry P
Stevens C
Stevens D
Stevens M B
Steventon D J
Steward J K
Stewart A H
Stewart B G
Stewart G R S
Stewart M A
Stewart R A
Still R
Stoate C*
Stockwell J
Stockwell P
Stockwell T*
Stoddard G
Stokes J
Stone B
Stone M H
Stoneham W R
Stonehouse B
Stoney A D*
Stranack F*
Strangeman P J
Streatfield R A
Stroud A*
Styles A G
Sudbury A W
Suffern C
Sullivan A*
Summers G
Sutcliff K*
Sussex D
Sutton B
Sutton G A
Swan M
Swash A*
Swash G*
Sylvester J
Symonds V G
Talbot J R
Talbot K
Tanner D J
Tanner J S
Tarrant I B
Tatton Brown C E
Tatton Brown S
Taverner J H*
Taverson
Taylor B
Taylor C
Taylor D H*
Taylor J J
Taylor M
Taylor M J*
Taylor U B
Telfer M G
Temple J M*
Terry E F
Terry M G W
Terry M H

Tester C
Thackrah J R*
Tait A H*
Thearle D
Thelwell D A*
Theobald M
Thirlwell I*
Thomas J
Thomas K
Thomas L C
Thomas R
Thomas W J
Thompson D*
Thompson G
Thomson D*
Thomson P
Thorne J S
Thorpe R I
Threadgold J G
Thumwood I
Thurlow I
Thurston M H
Tidy G
Tilly W J
Toft R
Tompsett A J
Tooney J
Towne E
Townroe S O
Townsend M
Toynton P*
Tregear V W
Trengrove P
Troake P M*
Truckle P D
Truckle W H
Tubbs C R
Tubbs J M
Tuck B A
Tucker G W
Tucker J
Tucker M W*
Tucker P
Tuckley N
Tuersley N A
Tugendhat M
Tull S
Tunnah E*
Turner A*
Turner K A*
Turner R
Turton M H
Twine P*
Twist T F
Tyas C J*
Tyler M J*
Tyler M W
Tyler R J
Tyler S
Uloth T
Underhill G H
Underhill M
Unsworth C D

Unsworth D J*
Uphill N
Uridge H
Vardy C R
Vaux A M
Veall R M*
Veall M E
Venables C
Venner J
Venning D R
Venning F E W
Verrier C
Vickers E P
Vickers F P
Vigurs D W
Villiers N*
Vincer C D
Vine F W
Voysey F M*
Waddell T A
Wadlow D L
Waever B
Walker A
Walker F
Wall K T
Wallis D
Wallis S
Walmsley A P*
Walters J M*
Walters K
Walton J M
Walton L S
Walton F Z
Warburton H*
Ward B*
Ward H L H*
Warner J
Warner M
Warren B C H*
Warren P*
Warwick C
Warwick H
Waterman J R
Waters D*
Waters D K*
Waters W E*
Watkins J W
Watkins V I
Watson A B
Watson D
Watson R F
Watten D E
Watterson A E
Watts I R
Wear C H
Weare C G
Wearing M
Wearn G
Weatherly L F*
Weaver G
Webb J
Webb R C*
Webber M I

Webster B C
Weedon A F G
Weiler P M*
Welch A J
Welch P
Welchman D*
Welland E T
Weller J
Wellow E T
Wells D R
Wells E
Wells G A H
Wells J C K
Wells R
Welshman M D
West H H
West S
Westerhoff D V*
Westerhoff G B
Westlake L
Weston I
Westrup A W
Westwood D J
Wheatley N
Whichall J
Whiffen R M*
Whitaker J*
Whitbread J*
White C C
White D C
White I*
White J R J
White P
White R K
White R W
White S L
White T
White W P
Whitelock M
Whiteley J C
Whitfield S N D
Whiting D
Whittington P
Wichall J A
Wilas R
Wiley R L
Wilkes K
Wilkinson A
Wilkinson D*
Wilkinson R
Williams C I M
Williams D
Williams E
Williams P
Williams R
Williams T G*
Williams V A*
Williamson A N
Williamson D A J
Williamson I D
Williamson P
Willmott J
Willsman P

Wills K B*
Wilmshurst R J
Wilsdon H M*
Wilson D
Wilson G*
Wilson H M V
Wilson J
Wilson K M
Wilson M S
Wilson P*
Wilton I J*
Windebank W
Windiate M
Wingate M J
Winter N
Winter T G
Wise A J
Wiseman A
Wiseman D G*
Wiseman E J*
Wiseman W J
Witherick M E
Withey L
Witts B
Wood C
Wood J
Wood J K R*
Wood S*
Woodhead T
Woodley B*
Woodman R C
Woods H E
Woods J
Woodward D
Woodward S
Wooldridge H
Wooldridge G
Wooley S K*
Woollard S L
Worgan C
Wren L I
Wrenn A
Wright D*
Wright F W
Wright G W
Wright I*
Wright J
Wright S J
Wyatt N G
Wylie A E*
Yelland D*
Yeoman Walker R*
Youmans D*
Young E E*
Young H G
Young I*
Young J
Young L*
Young R A
Younghusband C
Youngman R
Ziegler D
Zimmer L J

# References

Adams, M C 1966. Firecrests breeding in Hampshire. *Brit. Birds* 59: 240-246.

Ash, J S 1960. Bird of prey numbers on a Hampshire game-preserve during 1952-59. *Brit. Birds* 53: 285-300.

Ash, J S 1970. Observations on a decreasing population of Red-backed Shrikes. *Brit. Birds* 63: 185-205; 225-239.

Aspinall, S & Tasker, M L 1992. *Birds of the Solent*. Joint Nature Conservation Committee. Aberdeen.

Aspinall, S J, Taverner, J H & Wiseman, E J 1993. History of Black-headed Gull colonies in Hampshire and neighbouring counties. *Brit. Birds* 86: 103-114.

Bainbridge, I P & Minton, C D T 1978. The migration and mortality of the Curlew in Britain and Ireland. *Bird Study* 25: 39-50.

Batten, L A 1973. Population Dynamics of Suburban Blackbirds. *Bird Study* 20: 251-258.

Batten, L A, Bibby, C J, Clement, P, Elliott, G D & Porter, R F 1990. *Red Data Birds in Britain*. Poyser. London.

Bell, B D, Catchpole, C K & Corbett, K J 1968. Problems of censusing Reed Buntings, Sedge Warblers and Reed Warblers. *Bird Study* 15: 16-21.

Berry, R & Bibby, C J 1981. A breeding study of Nightjars. *Brit. Birds* 74: 161-169.

Bibby, C J 1973. The Red-backed Shrike: A vanishing British species. *Bird Study* 20: 103-110.

Bibby, C J 1979. Foods of the Dartford Warbler *Sylvia undata* on Southern English heathland. *J. Zool. London.* 188: 557-576.

Bibby, C J 1981. Wintering Bitterns in Britain. *Brit. Birds* 74: 1-10.

Bibby, C J & Tubbs, C R 1975. Status, habitats and conservation of the Dartford Warbler in England. *Brit. Birds* 68: 177-195.

Biddle, M 1975. Excavations at Winchester 1971. *Antiq. J.* 55: 295-337, 326-328.

Bill, D I & Hollins, J R 1989. *Report on Portsmouth Harbour low water wader counts - winter 1988/89*. Unpub. MS.

Billett, D F 1966. Birds of prey numbers in the Langstone Harbour, Farlington Marshes and Portsmouth Area (PG Observation Area) 1953-62. *Hampshire Bird Report* 1965: 23-31.

Billett, D F & Grant, P J 1971. Frankin's Gull in Hampshire: a species new to Britain and Ireland. *Brit. Birds* 64: 310-313.

Blackwood, J W & Tubbs, C R 1970. A quantitative survey of chalk grassland in England. *Biol. Conserv.* 3: 1-5.

Blaker, G B 1933. The Barn Owl in England - Results of the Census. *Bird Notes & News* 15: 169-172, 207-211.

Blindell, R M 1977. The Numbers and Distribution of Nightingales *Luscinia megarhynchos* in Hampshire in 1976. *Hampshire Bird Report* 1977: 53-56.

Boyd, H 1954. The "wreck" of Leach's Petrels in the autumn of 1952. *Brit. Birds* 47: 137-163.

Branson, N J B A, Pointing, E D & Minton, C D T 1978. Turnstone migration in Britain and Europe. *Bird Study* 25: 181-187.

Brenchley, A 1984. The use of birds as indicators of change in agriculture. Pp. 123-128 in: Jenkins, D (ed), *Agriculture and the Environment. ITE symp. 13*. ITE/NERC. Cambridge

British Ornithologists' Union Records Committee (BOURC) 1986. Twelfth report. *Ibis* 128: 601-603.

British Ornithologists' Union Records Committee (BOURC) 1992. Sixteenth report. *Ibis* 134: 211-214.

Brown, R J B 1955. The migration of the Coot in relation to Britain. *Bird Study* 2: 135-142.

Burges, D 1991. RSPB New Forest Woodlark *Lullula arborea* Survey, 1990. *Hampshire Bird Report* 1990: 74-77.

Burton, J F 1956. Report on the National Census of Heronries, 1954. *Bird Study* 3: 42-73.

Campbell, B 1960. The Mute Swan survey in England and Wales, 1955-56. *Bird Study* 7: 208-223.

Campbell, B 1979. *A Birdwatcher at Large*. Dent. London.

Campbell, B, Pringle, J W S & Hasler, W J 1931. The Birds of Winchester. *Winchester College NHS Report* 1927-31: 22-42.

Catt, J A 1977. Loess and cover sands *in* Shotton, F W (ed). *British Quarternary Studies - Recent Advances*. Oxford University Press. Oxford.

Catt, J A 1978. The contributions of loess to soils in lowland Britain *in* Limbrey, S and Evans, J G (eds). *The Effect of Man on the Landscape: The Lowland Zone*. Council for British Archaeology Research Report 21.

Chalkley, W 1900. *Collection of Hampshire birds 1863-1900*. Warren & Son, Winchester.

Chandler, R J 1981. Influxes into Britain and Ireland of Red-necked Grebes and other waterbirds during winter 1978/79. *Brit. Birds* 74: 55-81.

Chapman, F 1933. *Autobiography of a Bird Lover*. Appleton-Century. London.

Chatwin, C P 1960. *British Regional Geology: The Hampshire Basin and Adjoining Areas*. HMSO. London.

Cheke, A S 1962. *Birds of the Winchester District*. P & G Wells. Winchester. Also cyclostyled Supplement, 1963. Unpub.

Christie, D A 1979. Large gathering of Cuckoos. *Brit. Birds* 72: 552.

Clark, J M 1979. The numbers and distribution of breeding Grebes and Wildfowl in Hampshire in 1978. *Hampshire Bird Report* 1978: 61-76.

Clark, J M 1984. *Birds of the Hants/Surrey Border*. Hobby Books. Fleet.

Clarke, M J 1987. *Past and Present Mire Communities of the New Forest and their Conservation*. PhD thesis. University of Southampton.

Clarke, R & Watson D 1990. The Hen Harrier *Circus cyaneus* Winter Roost Survey in Britain and Ireland. *Bird Study* 37: 84-100.

Cloyne, J M 1977. *Ornithological Survey of the Itchen Valley, Hampshire, 1976*. Unpub. MS.

Cocker, M 1989. *Richard Meinertzhagen, Soldier, Scientist, Spy*. Martin, Secker & Warburg.

Cohen, E 1963. *Birds of Hampshire and the Isle of Wight*. Oliver & Boyd. Edinburgh.

Cohen, E & Taverner, J H 1972. *A Revised list of Hampshire and Isle of Wight Birds*. Oxford Illustrated Press. Oxford.

Colebourn, P 1983. *Hampshire's Countryside Heritage. 2: Ancient Woodland*. Hampshire County Council. Winchester.

Combridge, P & Parr, C 1992. Influx of Little Egrets in Britain and Ireland in 1989. *Brit. Birds* 85: 16-21.

Coulson, J C, Butterfield, J, Duncan, N, Kearsey, S, Monaghan, P & Thomas, C 1984. Origin and behaviour of Great Black-backed Gulls wintering in north-east England. *Brit. Birds* 77: 1-11.

Cramp, S (Ed) 1977, 1980, 1983, 1985, 1988, 1992, 1993. *The Handbook of the Birds of Europe, The Middle East and North Africa. The Birds of the Western Palearctic.* Vols. 1-7. Oxford University Press. Oxford.

Cramp, S, Conder, P J & Ash, J S 1960-65. *Deaths of Birds and Mammals from toxic chemicals.* BTO/RSPB/GRA reports.

Cramp, S, Pettet, A & Sharrock, J T R 1960. The irruption of tits in autumn 1957. *Brit. Birds* 53: 49-77, 99-117, 176-192.

Cranswick, P A, Kirby, J S & Waters, R J 1992. *Wildfowl and Wader Counts 1991-92.* Wildfowl and Wetlands Trust. Slimbridge.

Crook, J H 1953. An observational study of the Gulls of Southampton Water. *Brit. Birds* 46: 385-397.

Davenport, D L 1982. Influxes into Britain of Hen Harriers, Long-eared Owls and Short-eared Owls in winter 1978/79. *Brit. Birds* 75: 309-316.

Davies, A K 1988. The distribution and status of the Mandarin Duck in Britain. *Bird Study* 35: 203-208.

Davies, S A 1904. *Catalogue of the S A Davies collection of eggs incorporated in the Winchester College general collection.* Unpub. MS.

Davis, P G 1982. Nightingales in Britain in 1980. *Bird Study* 29: 73-79.

Dewar, G 1899. *Wildlife in Hampshire Highlands.* Dent. London.

Dewar, G 1903. *The Birds in our Wood.* Lawrence and Bullen. London.

Dimbleby, G W 1967. *Plants and Archaeology.* Baker. London.

Dobinson, H M & Richards, A J 1964. The effects of the severe winter of 1962/63 on birds in Britain. *Brit. Birds* 57: 373-434.

Doody, P (ed). 1984. *Spartina anglica* in Great Britain. *Focus on Nature Conservation 5.* Nature Conservancy Council. Peterborough.

Duffin, B S 1991. *The Birds of Titchfield Haven.* Pekkari Books. Hill Head.

Durand, A L 1961. White-throated Sparrow and American Robin crossing Atlantic on board ship. *Brit. Birds* 54: 439-440.

Durand, A L 1963. A remarkable fall of American land-birds on the Mauretania, New York to Southampton, October 1962. *Brit. Birds* 56: 157-164.

Durand, A L 1972. Landbirds over the North Atlantic: unpublished records 1961-65 and thoughts a decade later. *Brit. Birds* 65: 428-442.

Dyer, K R 1975. The Buried Channels of the "Solent River", Southern England. *Proc. Geol. Ass.* 86: 239-245.

Dymond, N, Fraser, P A & Gantlett, S J M 1989. *Rare Birds in Britain and Ireland.* Poyser. London.

Edlin, H L 1952. The Changing Wildlife of Britain. Batsford. London.

Evans, G C 1981. A Survey of Wetland Breeding Birds in the Test Valley. *Hampshire Bird Report* 1980: 68-70.

Evans, L G R 1993. *Rare Birds in Britain 1992.* Private publication.

Everett, M & Prytherch, R 1991. News and Comment. *Brit. Birds* 84: 592.

Eyre, J A 1988. The 1987 BTO Lapwing Survey in Hampshire. *Hampshire Bird Report* 1987: 82-84.

Fiuczynski, D & Nethersole-Thompson, D 1980. Hobby studies in England and Germany. *Brit. Birds.* 73: 275-295.

Flegg, J J M & Glue, D E 1973. A Water Rail Study. *Bird Study* 20: 69-77.

Fox, A D 1987. The breeding status and September distribution of the Gadwall in Britain and Ireland. *Brit. Birds* 81: 51-66.

Fox, A D & Salmon, D G 1989. The winter status and distribution of Gadwall in Britain and Ireland. *Bird Study* 36: 37-44.

Frankland, J B 1989. North American landbirds on the QE2. *Brit. Birds* 82: 568-569.

Fuller, R J, Baker, J K, Morgan, R A, Scroggs, R & Wright, M 1985. Breeding populations of the Hobby *Falco subbuteo* on farmland in the southern midlands of England. *Ibis* 127: 510-516.

Fuller, R J & Lloyd, D 1981. The distribution and habitats of wintering Golden Plovers in Britain, 1977-1978. *Bird Study* 28: 169-185.

Gibbons, D W, Reid, J B & Chapman, R A 1993. *The New Atlas of Breeding Birds in Britain and Ireland: 1988-91.* Poyser. London.

Glue, D E 1972. Bird prey taken by British owls. *Bird Study* 19: 91-95.

Glue, D E 1973. The breeding birds of a New Forest valley. *Brit. Birds* 66: 461-472.

Glue, D E 1977. Feeding ecology of the Short-eared Owl in Britain and Ireland. *Bird Study* 24: 70-78, 192-194.

Grant, P J 1986. *Gulls: a guide to identification.* Second Edition. Poyser. Calton.

Gray, A J & Benham, P E M (eds). 1990. *Spartina anglica - A Research Review.* HMSO. London.

Gray, A J, Marshall, D F & Raybould, A F 1991. A century of evolution in *Spartina anglica. Advances in Ecological Research* 21: 1-62.

Green, F H W 1940. *The Land of Britain. Part 89. Hampshire with a section on water meadows in southern England.* Land Utilisation Survey of Britain. London.

Green, G P & Cade, M 1989. *Where to Watch Birds in Dorset, Hampshire and the Isle of Wight.* Christopher Helm. London.

Grey, E 1909. *Cottage Book, Itchen Abbas 1894-1905.* Chiswick Press. London.

Grey, E 1926. *The Falloden Papers.* Constable. London.

Grey, E 1927. *The Charm of Birds.* Hodder & Stoughton. London.

Harber, D D 1964. The influx of Cranes in October 1963. *Brit. Birds* 57: 502-508.

Harber, D D and the Rarities Committee 1966. Reports on rare birds in Great Britain in 1965. *Brit. Birds* 58: 280-305.

Harris, M P 1962. Recoveries of ringed Great Black-backed Gulls. *Bird Study* 9: 192-197.

Harrison, T H & Hollom, P A D 1932. The Great Crested Grebe enquiry, 1931. *Brit. Birds* 26: 62-92, 102-131, 142-155, 174-195.

Hawker, P 1814. *Instructions to young sportsmen in all that relates to guns and shooting.* Longman, Brown, Green, Longmans and Roberts. London.

Haynes, F N & Coulson, M 1982. The decline of *Spartina* in Langstone Harbour, Hampshire. *Proc. Hants Field Club Archaeol. Soc.* 38: 5-18.

Hazel, V 1983. *Hampshire's Countryside Heritage. 4: Heathlands.* Hampshire County Council. Winchester.

Heycock, C W 1939. Changes in birds in the Winchester District 1932-38. *Bird Notes & News* 18 (5): 111-115. Winchester College NHS.

Hinsley, S A 1986. *Blashford Lakes Feasibility Study. Breeding Birds Survey.* Report to Nicholas Pearson Associates.

Hirons, G 1980. The significance of roding by Woodcocks: an alternative explanation based on observations of marked birds. *Ibis* 122: 350-354.

Hirons, G 1982. Conclusion of the studies on Woodcock. *Game Conserv. Ann. Rev.* 13: 35-42.

Hodson, J M & West, I M 1972. The Holocene deposits at Fawley, Hampshire and the development of Southampton Water. *Proc. Geol. Ass.* 83: 421-444.

Hollom, P A D 1940. Report on the 1938 survey of Black-headed Gull colonies. *Brit. Birds* 33: 202-221, 230-244.

Hope Jones, P, Mead C J & Durman, R F 1977. The Migration of the Pied Flycatcher from and through Britain. *Bird Study* 24: 2-14.

Hotker, H 1989. Sex ratios and weights of Meadow Pipits *Anthus pratensis* in their winter quarters. *Ringing and Migration* 10: 124-131.

Hudson, A V, Stowe, T J & Aspinall, S J 1990. The status and distribution of Corncrakes in Britain in 1988. *Brit. Birds* 83: 173-187.

Hudson, R 1965a. Summary of foreign-ringed birds in Britain and Ireland during 1906-63. *Brit. Birds* 58: 87-96.

Hudson, R 1965b. The spread of the Collared Dove in Britain and Ireland. *Brit. Birds* 58: 105-139.

Hudson, R 1972. Collared Doves in Britain and Ireland during 1965-70. *Brit. Birds* 65: 139-155.

Hudson, R 1973. *Early and Late Dates for Summer Migrants*. British Trust for Ornithology. Tring.

Hudson, R & Marchant, J H 1984. *Population estimates for British breeding birds*. BTO Research Report 13.

Hudson, W H 1901. *A Summer's End on the Itchen*. Longmans Magazine 38: 17-30.

Hudson, W H 1903a. *Hampshire Days*. Longmans, London.

Hudson, W H 1903b. Last Hampshire Ravens. *Animal Life.* 1: 14-16.

Hudson, W H 1913. *Adventures among birds*. Hutchinson. London.

Hughes, S W M, Bacon, P, & Flegg, J J M 1979. The 1975 census of the Great Crested Grebe in Britain. *Bird Study* 26: 213-226.

Hutchinson, C D & Neath, B 1978. Little Gulls in Britain and Ireland. *Brit. Birds* 71: 563-581.

Insley, H & Boswell, R C 1978. The timing of arrivals of Reed and Sedge Warblers at South Coast Ringing sites during Autumn Passage. *Ringing and Migration* 2: 1-9.

Insley, H & Jackson, R V 1976. Warbler passage at Lower Test Marsh during autumn 1975. *Hampshire Bird Report* 1975: 49-54.

Insley, H & Young, L 1981. Autumn passage of Ringed Plovers through Southampton Water. *Ringing and Migration* 3: 157-164.

Irvine, J 1977. Breeding Birds in New Forest Broad-leaved Woodland. *Bird Study* 24: 105-111.

Jackson, R & Long, J 1973. Developing a long term population density study in the New Forest. *Hampshire Bird Report* 1972: 59-68.

John, A W G & Roskell, J 1985. Jay movements in autumn 1983. *Brit. Birds* 78: 611-637.

Johnson, I G 1966. Water Pipits wintering on watercress beds. *Brit. Birds* 59: 552-554.

Johnson, I G 1970. The Water Pipit as a winter visitor to the British Isles. *Bird Study* 17: 297-319.

Kear, J 1990. *Man and Wildfowl*. Poyser. London.

Keen, D H 1980. The environment of deposition of the south Hampshire plateau gravel. *Proc. Hants Field Club Archaeol. Soc.* 36: 15-24.

Kelsall, J E 1890. A briefly annotated list of the Birds of Hampshire and the Isle of Wight. *Proc. Hants Field Club Archaeol. Soc.* 1 (4): 90-122; supplemented in 1898.

Kelsall, J E & Coles, R E 1913. The Birds of Milford. *Milford-on-Sea Record Soc.* 1 (6): August.

Kelsall, J E & Munn, P W 1905. *The Birds of Hampshire and the Isle of Wight*. Witherby. London.

Kelso, J E H 1912. *Notes on Some Common & Rare British Birds*. Century Press. London.

Kingsley, C 1867. Charm of Birds. *Frazer's Magazine*. July issue.

Kirby, J S, Ferns, J R, Waters, R J & Prys-Jones, R P 1991. *Wildfowl and Wader Counts 1990-91*. Wildfowl and Wetlands Trust. Slimbridge.

Kirby, J S & Tubbs, C R 1989. Wader Populations in The Solent 1970/71 to 1987/88. *Hampshire Bird Report* 1988: 83-104.

Kirby, J S, Waters, R J & Prys-Jones, R P 1990. *Wildfowl and Wader Counts 1989-90*. Wildfowl and Wetlands Trust. Slimbridge.

Knox, A 1988. Taxonomy of the Rock/Water Pipit superspecies *Anthus petrosus, spinoletta and rubsecens. Brit. Birds* 81: 206-211.

Knox, A G 1993. Richard Meinertzhagen - a case of fraud examined. *Ibis* 135: 320-325.

Lack, P 1986. *The Atlas of Wntering Birds in Britain and Ireland*. Poyser. Calton.

Leach, I H 1981. Wintering Blackcaps in Britain and Ireland. *Bird Study* 28: 5-14.

Lloyd, C, Tasker, M L & Partridge, K 1991. *The Status of Seabirds in Britain and Ireland*. Poyser. London.

Longstaff, T G 1926. Local changes in Distribution. *Ibis* Ser. XII Vol. II: 637-656.

Marchant, J H, Hudson, R, Carter, S P & Whittington, P 1990. *Population Trends in British Breeding Birds*. British Trust for Ornithology. Tring.

Marchant, J H, Prater, A J & Hayman, P 1986. *Shorebirds: an identification guide to the waders of the world*. Helm. London

Marren, P 1990. *Woodland Heritage*. David & Charles. Newton Abbot.

Meade, C J & Pearson, D J 1974. Bearded Reedling Populations in England and Holland. *Bird Study* 21: 211-214.

Meade-Waldo, E G B 1900. *Victoria History of Hampshire*. 1: 208-238. Constable. London.

Meinertzhagen, R 1959. 19th Century Recollections. *Ibis* 101: 46-52.

Meinertzhagen, R 1964. *Diary of a Black Sheep*. Oliver & Boyd. London.

Mikkola, H 1983. *Owls of Europe*. Poyser. Calton.

Milne, B S 1959. Variation in a population of Yellow Wagtails. *Brit. Birds* 52: 281-295.

Moffat, A J & Cope, D W 1984. *The Hampshire chalklands. Soils of the Southampton District*. British Society of Soil Science.

Monk, J F 1963. The past and present status of the Wryneck in the British Isles. *Bird Study* 10: 112-132.

Moreau, R E 1951. The British status of the Quail and some problems of its biology. *Brit. Birds* 44: 257-276.

Morris, A 1993. The 1992 Nightjar Survey - a light at the end of the tunnel for this threatened species? *BTO News* 185: 8-9.

Munn, P W 1919. Notes on the Birds of Hampshire and the Isle of Wight. *Proc. Hants Field Club Archaeol. Soc.* 8 (3): 277-288.

Munn, P W 1920. Notes on the Birds of Hampshire and the Isle of Wight. *Proc. Hants Field Club Archaeol. Soc.* 9 (1): 23-36.

Murton, R K 1965. *The Woodpigeon*. Collins. London.

Murton, R K & Ridpath, M G 1962. The autumn movements of the Woodpigeon. *Bird Study* 9: 7-41.

Naish, M. 1960. *The Agricultural Landscape of the Hampshire Chalklands*. MA Thesis. University of London.

Newnham, J A 1985. Some aspects of Spring Migration observed from the Sussex Coast 1984. *Sussex Bird Report* 37: 61-64.

Newton, I 1972. *Finches*. Collins. London.

Newton, I 1986. *The Sparrowhawk*. Poyser. Calton.

Nicholson, E M 1929. Reports on the British Birds Census of Heronries, 1928. *Brit. Birds* 22: 269-323, 333-372.

O'Connor, R J & Mead, C J 1984. The Stock Dove in Britain, 1930-80. *Brit. Birds* 77: 181-201.

O'Connor, R J & Shrubb, M 1986. *Farming and Birds.* Cambridge University Press. Cambridge.

Ogilvie, M A 1978. *Wild Geese.* Poyser. Berkhamsted.

Ogilvie, M A 1981. The Mute Swan in Britain, 1978. *Bird Study* 28: 87-106.

Ogilvie, M A 1986. The Mute Swan in Britain, 1983. *Bird Study* 33: 121-137.

Osborne, P 1982. Some effects of Dutch elm disease on nesting farmland birds. *Bird Study* 29: 2-16.

Owen, M, Atkinson-Willes, G L, & Salmon, D G 1986. *Wildfowl in Great Britain.* 2nd Edition. Cambridge University Press. Cambridge.

Owen, M & Salmon, D G 1988. Feral Greylag Geese in Britain and Ireland, 1960-86. *Bird Study* 35: 37-45.

Pain, J 1981. The Distribution of Nightingales *Luscinia megarhynchos* in Hampshire in 1980. *Hampshire Bird Report* 1980: 61-63.

Pain, J 1990. Water Pipits *Anthus spinoletta* on Hampshire Watercress Beds. *Hampshire Bird Report* 1989: 84-86.

Pain, J & Steventon, D J 1979. Inland Wintering Waders and Water Pipit Survey, Winter 1978/79. *HOS Newsletter* No. 4, Autumn 1979.

Parr, S J 1985. The breeding ecology and diet of the Hobby *Falco subbuteo* in southern England. *Ibis* 127: 60-73.

Parslow, J L F 1973. *Breeding Birds of Britain and Ireland.* Poyser. Berkhampsted.

Payne-Gallwey, Sir R 1893. *The diary of Colonel Peter Hawker 1802-1853.* Longmans. London.

Peakall, D B 1962. The past and present status of the Red-backed Shrike in Great Britain. *Bird Study* 9: 198-216.

Pennington, W 1969. *The History of the British Vegetation.* English Universities Press. London.

Perrins, C 1979. *British Tits.* Collins. London.

Peterken, G F 1981. *Woodland Management and Conservation.* Chapman & Hall. London.

Piersma, T 1986. Breeding waders in Europe. A review of population size estimates and a bibliography of information sources. *Bull. Wader Study Group* 48, suppl.: 1-116.

Portsmouth Group 1991. *The Birds of Langstone Harbour and its environs 1952-86.* Unpub. MS.

Potts, G R 1980. The effects of modern agriculture, nest predation and game management on the population ecology of partridges (*Perdix perdix* and *Alectoris rufa*). *Advances in Ecological Research* 11: 1-82.

Potts, G R 1984. Grey partridges: how a computer model can help solve practical game managment questions. *Game Conserv. Ann. Rev.* 15: 56-59.

Prater, A J 1973. The wintering population of Ruffs in Britain and Ireland. *Bird Study* 20: 245-250.

Prater, A J 1975. The wintering population of the Black-tailed Godwit. *Bird Study* 22: 169-176.

Prater, A J 1981. *Estuary Birds of Britain and Ireland.* Poyser. Calton

Prater, A J 1989. Ringed Plover *Charadrius hiaticula* breeding population of the United Kingdom in 1984. *Bird Study* 36: 154-159.

Pratt, N H & Glue, D E 1968. The influence of reclamation on wader numbers at Dibden Bay 1950-67. *Hampshire Bird Report* 1967: 38-53.

Prendergast, E D V & Boys, J V 1983. *The Birds of Dorset.* David & Charles. Newton Abbot.

Prescott, R 1983. *Hampshire's Countryside Heritage. 6: Chalk Grassland.* Hampshire County Council. Winchester.

Presst, I 1965. An enquiry into the recent breeding status of some of the smaller birds of prey and crows in Britain. *Bird Study* 12: 196-221.

Rackham, O 1986. *The History of the Countryside.* Dent. London.

Ratcliffe, D. 1980. *The Peregrine Falcon.* Poyser. Calton.

Read, M 1985. *Ornithological Survey and Appraisal of the Blashford Lakes 10th November 1984-30th April 1985.* Report to Wessex Water.

Read, M 1986. *Ornithological Report for the Blashford Lakes 1st November 1985-31st October 1986.* Report to Wessex Water.

Read, M 1988. *Ornithological Report for the Blashford Lakes. December 1986-March 1987 and October 1987-March 1988.* Report to Wessex Water.

Reed, T 1985. Estimates of British breeding wader populations. *Bull. Wader Study Group* 45: 11-12.

Roberts, N 1989. *The Holocene.* Blackwell. Oxford.

Robertson, P A, Tapper, S C & Stoate, C 1989. *Estimating game densities in Britain from land use maps.* Game Conservancy Trust. Unpub. report.

Robins, M & Bibby, C J 1985. Dartford Warblers in 1984 Britain. *Brit. Birds* 78: 269-280.

Rogers, M J and the Rarities Committee 1988. Report on rare birds in Great Britain in 1987. *Brit. Birds* 81: 535-596.

Rogers, M J and the Rarities Committee 1991. Report on rare birds in Great Britain in 1990. *Brit. Birds* 84: 449-505.

Rowland, G J S 1993. Survey of Breeding Birds along the Basingstoke Canal, 1991. *Hampshire Bird Report* 1991: 81-84.

Sage, B L & Vernon, J D R 1978. The 1975 National Survey of Rookeries. *Bird Study* 25: 64-86.

Sage, B L & Whittington, P A 1985. The 1980 sample survey of rookeries. *Bird Study* 32: 77-81.

Salmon, D G, Prys-Jones, R P & Kirby, J S 1988. *Wildfowl and Wader Counts 1987-88.* Wildfowl and Wetlands Trust. Slimbridge.

Sargeant, D E 1952. Little Auks in Britain. 1948 to 1951. *Brit. Birds* 45: 122-133.

Sclater, P L 1897. *List of Hampshire Birds in Hants and Dorset Court Guide and Blue Book.* Deacon. London.

Scott, R E 1968. Rough-legged Buzzards in Britain in the winter of 1966/67. *Brit. Birds* 61: 449-455.

Scott, R E 1978. Rough-legged Buzzards in Britain in 1973/74 and 1974/75. *Brit. Birds* 71: 325-338.

Sharrock, J T R 1961. White-throated Sparrow in Hampshire. *Brit. Birds* 54: 366-367.

Sharrock, J T R 1965. White-throated Sparrows in Hampshire. *Brit. Birds* 58: 230.

Sharrock, J T R 1976. *The Atlas of Breeding Birds in Britain and Ireland.* British Trust for Ornithology. Tring.

Sharrock, J T R and the Rare Breeding Birds Panel 1980. Rare Breeding Birds in the United Kingdom in 1978. *Brit. Birds* 73: 5-26.

Shawyer, C R 1987. *The Barn Owl in the British Isles.* The Hawk Trust. London.

Sheail, J 1971. The formation and maintenance of water-meadows in Hampshire, England. *Biol. Conserv.* 3: 101-106.

Simms, E 1978. *British Thrushes*. Collins. London.

Simms, E 1985. *British Warblers*. Collins. London.

Sitters, H P 1986. Woodlarks in Britain 1968-83. *Brit. Birds* 79: 105-116.

Smallbone, A C 1984. Census of breeding and non-breeding Mute Swans in Hampshire. *Hampshire Bird Report* 1983: 67-69.

Smit, T & Piersma, T 1989. Numbers, midwinter distribution and migration of wader populations using the East Atlantic flyway *in* Boyd, H and Pirot, J-Y (Eds.) *Flyways and reserve networks for waterbirds*. IWRB Spec. Publ. 9. Slimbridge.

Smith, S 1950. *The Yellow Wagtail*. Collins. London.

Snow, B & Snow, D 1988. *Birds and Berries*. Poyser. Calton.

Spencer, R and the Rare Breeding Birds Panel 1991. Rare breeding birds in the United Kingdom in 1989. *Brit. Birds* 84: 349-370, 379-392.

Spencer, R and the Rare Breeding Birds Panel 1993. Rare breeding birds in the United Kingdom in 1990. *Brit. Birds* 86: 62-90.

Stanley, P L, Brough, T, Fletcher, M R, Horton N & Rochard J B A 1981. The origins of Herring Gulls wintering inland in Southeast England. *Bird Study* 28: 123-132.

Steventon, D J 1977. Dunlin in Portsmouth, Langstone and Chichester Harbours. *Ringing and Migration* 1: 141-147.

Steventon, D J 1981. Wintering Golden Plovers in Hampshire, 1976/77 and 1977/78. *Hampshire Bird Report* 1980: 64-67.

Steventon, D J 1983. The Ringed Plover *Charadrius hiaticula* in Hampshire. *Hampshire Bird Report* 1982: 84-88.

Steventon, D J 1984. Breeding Waders of Wet Meadows in Hampshire. *Hampshire Bird Report* 1983: 70-73.

Steventon, D J 1985. Breeding Ringed Plover Survey, 1984. *Hampshire Bird Report* 1984: 81-84.

Suffern, C 1920. *The log of a loblolly boy at sea 1915-17*. Unpub. MS in Suffern's collected papers, University of Southampton Library.

Suffern, C & Ferguson-Lees, I J 1964. Cetti's Warbler in Hampshire. *Brit. Birds* 57: 365-366.

Summers-Smith, J D 1950. A History of the Birds of the Newbury District. *Trans. Newbury District Field Club* 9: 59-86.

Summers-Smith, J D 1989. A history of the status of the Tree Sparrow *Passer montanus* in the British Isles. *Bird Study* 36: 23-31.

Tapper, S 1981. The effects of farming and Dutch elm disease on corvids. *Game Conserv. Ann. Rev.* 12: 98-101.

Tapper, S 1992. *Game Heritage*. Game Conservation Series. *Game Conservation Trust*.

Tatner, P 1978. A review of House Martins (*Delichon urbica*) in part of South Manchester, 1975. *Naturalist* 103: 59-68.

Tatner, P 1982. Factors influencing the distribution of Magpies *Pica pica* in an urban environment. *Bird Study* 29: 227-234.

Taverner, J H 1959. The spread of the Eider in Great Britain. *Brit. Birds* 52: 245-258.

Taverner, J H 1962. *Wildfowl in Hampshire*. Warren & Son, Winchester.

Taverner, J H 1963. Further notes on the spread of the Eider in Great Britain. *Brit. Birds* 56: 273-285.

Taverner, J H 1967. Wintering Eiders in England during 1960-65. *Brit. Birds* 60: 509-515.

Taverner, J H 1970. Mediterranean Gulls nesting in Hampshire. *Brit. Birds* 63: 67-79.

Taverner, J H 1972. Mediterranean Gulls in Hampshire 1970-71. *Brit. Birds* 65: 185-186.

Taverner, J H 1975. Water Pipits at Hampshire watercress beds. *Brit. Birds* 68: 47-48.

Taverner, J H 1980. *The Birds of the Gins and Needs Oar Point.* Unpub. MS.

Taylor, K, Hudson, R & Horne, G 1988. Buzzard breeding distribution and abundance in Britain and Northern Ireland in 1983. *Bird Study* 35: 109-118.

Temrin, H 1984. Why are some Wood Warbler (*Phylloscopus sibilatrix*) males polyterritorial? *Ann. Zool. Fennici.* 21: 243-247.

Thelwell, D A 1973. Grey Wagtail Breeding Survey 1972. *HFC Ornithological Section Newsletter* No.10. January 1973.

Thomas, D K 1984. Aspects of habitat selection in the Sedge Warbler *Acrocephalus schoenobaenus. Bird Study* 31: 187-194.

Thompson, D, Evans, A & Galbraith, C 1992. The Fat Bird of the Barley. *BTO News* 178: 8-9.

Thompson, P 1990. The Grey Partridge in Hampshire. *Hampshire Bird Report* 1989: 73-76.

Tubbs, C R 1963. The significance of the New Forest to the status of the Dartford Warbler in England. *Brit. Birds* 56: 41-48.

Tubbs, C R 1967a. Population study of buzzards in the New Forest during 1962-66. *Brit. Birds* 60: 381-95.

Tubbs, C R 1967b. Numbers of Dartford Warblers in England during 1962-66. *Brit. Birds* 60: 87-89.

Tubbs, C R 1968. *The New Forest: An ecological history.* David & Charles. Newton Abbot.

Tubbs, C R 1972. Analysis of nest record cards for the Buzzard. *Bird Study* 19: 96-104.

Tubbs, C R 1974a. *The Buzzard.* David & Charles. Newton Abbot.

Tubbs, C R 1974b. Woodlands: their History and Conservation *in* Warren, A & Goldsmith, F B, *Conservation in Practice.* Wiley. London.

Tubbs, C R 1977. Wildfowl and waders in Langstone Harbour. *Brit. Birds* 70: 177-199.

Tubbs, C R 1978. An ecological appraisal of the Itchen Valley flood plain. *Proc. Hants. Field Club Archaeol. Soc.* 34: 5-22.

Tubbs, C R 1980. Bird populations of The Solent 1951-77 in *The Solent Estuarine System. NERC publications Series C* 22: 92-100.

Tubbs, C R 1985. Buzzards *Buteo buteo* and Land Use in the New Forest, Hampshire, England. *Biol. Conserv.* 31: 41-65.

Tubbs, C R 1986a. *The New Forest.* Collins. London.

Tubbs, C R 1986b. The decline and present status of the English lowland heaths and their vertebrates. *Focus on Nature Conservation 11*: Nature Conservancy Council. Peterborough.

Tubbs, C R 1991a. *The Solent: A Changing Wildlife Heritage.* Hampshire and Isle of Wight Wildlife Trust. Romsey.

Tubbs, C R 1991b. The population history of Grey Plovers (*Pluvialis squatarola*) in the Solent, Southern England. *Bull. Wader Study Group* 61: 15-21 and erratum 63: 32.

Tubbs, C R 1992. The diaries of William Mudge, Wildfowler. *Bull. Wader Study Group* 65: 46-54.

Tubbs, C R in press. *The Solent: History, Ecology and Conservation.* Packard. Chichester.

Tubbs, C R & Tubbs, J M 1982. Brent Geese Branta bernicla bernicla and their food in The Solent, Southern England. *Biol. Conserv.* 23: 33-54.

Tubbs, C R & Tubbs, J M 1985. Buzzards (*Buteo buteo*) and land use in the New Forest, Hampshire, England. *Biol. Conserv.* 31: 141-165.

Tubbs, C R, Tubbs, J M & Kirby, J S 1992. Dunlin *Calidris alpina alpina* in The Solent, southern England. *Biol. Conserv.* 60: 15-24.

Tyler, S J 1970. Observations on the Grey Wagtail in the New Forest. *Hampshire Bird Report* 1969: 37-40.

Tyrvainen H 1975. The winter irruption of the Fieldfare *Turdus pilaris* and the supply of rowan-berries. *Orn. Fenn.* 52: 23-31.

Unsworth, D J 1991. 1990/91 low tide survey of Southampton Water. *Hampshire Bird Report* 1990: 77-93.

Vancouver, C 1810. *General View of the Agriculture of Hampshire*. Phillips. London.

Vesey-Fitzgerald, B 1942. *A Country Chronicle*. Chapman and Hall. London.

Voisin, C 1991. *The Herons of Europe*. Poyser. London.

Voous, K H 1973. List of Recent Holarctic Bird Species. Non-passerines. *Ibis* 115: 612-638.

Voous, K H 1977. List of Recent Holarctic Bird Species. Passerines. *Ibis* 119: 223-250, 376-406.

Waton, P 1982. Man's impact on the chalklands: some new pollen evidence *in* Limbrey, S and Bell, M (eds). *Archaeological Aspects of Woodland Ecology*. Symposia for the Association of Environmental Archaeology No. 2: BAR International Series 146.

Watson, D 1977. *The Hen Harrier*. Poyser. Berkhamsted.

Webb, N 1986. *Heathlands*. Collins. London.

West, I M 1980. Geology of The Solent estuarine system. *The Solent Estuarine System: An Assessment of Present Knowledge*. NERC publications Series C 22: 6-18.

Westerhoff, D 1989. Results of the 1988 survey of Dartford Warbler *Sylvia undata* in the New Forest. *Hampshire Bird Report* 1988: 77-78.

Westerhoff, D & Tubbs, C R 1991. Dartford Warblers *Sylvia undata*, Their Habitat and Conservation in the New Forest, Hampshire, England in 1988. *Biol. Conserv.* 56: 89-100.

Williamson, J 1861. The farming of Hampshire. *J. Roy. Agric. Soc. Eng.* 22: 239-346.

Williamson, K 1955. Migrational drift and the Yellow Wagtail complex. *Brit. Birds* 48: 382-403.

Williamson, K 1962. *Bird Migration* 2: 131-159.

Winstanley, D, Spencer, R & Williamson, K 1974. Where have all the Whitethroats gone? *Bird Study* 21: 1-14.

Wise, J R 1862. *The New Forest: its History and Scenery*. Sotheran. London.

Witherby, H F 1894. *Forest birds, their haunts and habits*. Kegan Paul, Trench, Trubner and Co. London.

Witherby, H F 1922. Western Mediterranean Shearwater in Hampshire. *Brit. Birds* 15: 243.

Witherby, H F, Jourdain, F C R, Ticehurst, N F & Tucker, B W 1938-41. *The Handbook of British Birds* Vols. 1-5. Witherby. London.

Wooldridge, G E & Ballantyne, C 1952. Moustached Warblers in Hampshire. *Brit. Birds*. 219-220.

Yonge, C 1892. *An Old Woman's Outlook in a Hampshire Village*. Macmillan. London.

Yonge, C 1898. *John Keble's Parishes*. Macmillan. London.

# Index

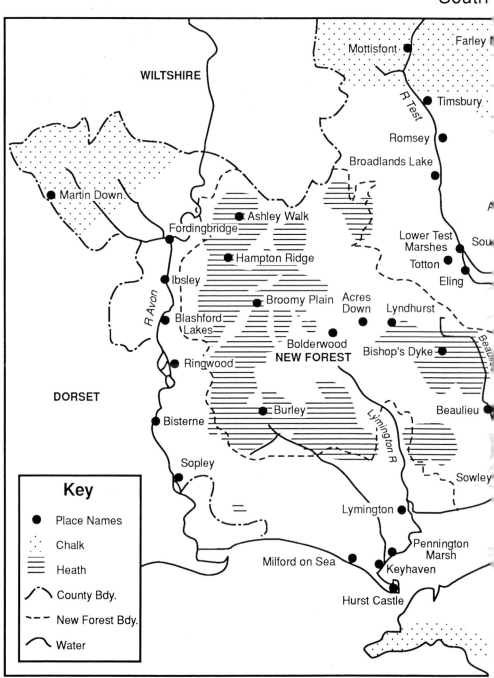

WILTSHIRE

Mottisfont

Farley

R Test

Timsbury

Romsey

Broadlands Lake

Martin Down

Ashley Walk

Lower Test
Marshes

Sou

Fordingbridge

Totton

Hampton Ridge

Eling

Ibsley

R Avon

Broomy Plain

Acres
Down

Lyndhurst

Blashford
Lakes

Bolderwood

Bishop's Dyke

Beau

NEW FOREST

Ringwood

DORSET

Beaulieu

Burley

Bisterne

Lymington R

Sopley

Sowley

Lymington

Milford on Sea

Pennington
Marsh

Keyhaven

Hurst Castle

## Key

- ● Place Names
- ⋮ Chalk
- ≡ Heath
- ⌢ County Bdy.
- - - New Forest Bdy.
- ⌐ Water